855

THEORY AND DESIGN OF
STEAM AND GAS TURBINES

THEORY AND DESIGN OF
STEAM AND GAS TURBINES

JOHN F. LEE

Associate Professor of Mechanical Engineering
North Carolina State College

NEW YORK   TORONTO   LONDON

McGRAW-HILL BOOK COMPANY, INC.

1954

THE MAPLE PRESS COMPANY, YORK, PA.

Dedicated to

WILLIAM F. RYAN

Friend and Inspiration
to Young Engineers

PREFACE

This book has been written to fulfill a need for a combined text on steam and gas turbines for the mechanical-engineering student. The increasing importance of the gas turbine as a prime mover has inspired the introduction of new courses in this field in most of the mechanical-engineering curricula offered in this country. However, this has been done with some misgivings in many instances because of an understandable reluctance to add another specialized course to an already overcrowded curriculum. Struck with the close similarity of the basic principles involved in a study of the modern steam turbine and the gas turbine, the author was impressed with the possibility of eliminating much needless repetition by incorporating gas turbines in an existing course in steam turbines. A study of these two prime movers offers an unusual opportunity to apply many of the basic principles learned in thermodynamics, fluid mechanics, and other fundamental courses, thus providing a powerful educational tool quite apart from the practical importance of steam and gas turbines. The author offered such a combined course for several years, on a one-semester basis, to senior and graduate mechanical-engineering students at the University of Maine and is convinced that such a treatment can be highly successful. The present book is an outgrowth of this combined course.

Another need which this book is intended to meet is that of the practicing engineer whose experience and training have been largely in the field of steam turbines but who now finds himself concerned with the design of gas turbines. It is hoped that this book will provide a useful link between the fundamentals of the steam turbine and the gas turbine, thus making the transition a little easier.

In writing a book such as this, one is always plagued with the question as to what should be omitted in order to keep the book within bounds. The answer can be found only in the ruthless elimination of all material not directly related to the fundamentals or essential to the development of the main theme. Even at that, much material is retained in order to satisfy a diversity of tastes in the course offering. Hence it will be found that the book is organized in such a way that sufficient material is offered for a more extensive course or a very brief course. In fact, the book may be used for separate courses in steam and gas turbines with the advantage of the continuity offered by a single book.

A special word is offered concerning Chaps. 3 and 6. Chapter 3 is offered to satisfy the demands of many teachers who find a brief review of thermodynamics essential when the students have had different backgrounds in this subject. A number of practicing engineers have expressed a need for a convenient and concise review of thermodynamics before undertaking a study of steam and gas turbines. Those who do not feel a need for Chap. 3 may omit it without any loss of continuity. Chapter 6 is introduced to provide a general background in gas dynamics for the undergraduate mechanical-engineering student who has not been introduced to this subject.

The author is indebted to many people who have contributed directly and indirectly to the writing of this book. Professors H. D. Watson, I. H. Prageman, and R. C. Hill of the University of Maine have each examined portions of the manuscript. Professor Watson has lent his encouragement and has given material assistance in many ways even to the extent of providing stenographic assistance. Credit is especially due H. D. Emmert and S. M. Osthagen of the Allis-Chalmers Manufacturing Company for technical assistance and advice. Many turbine manufacturers have provided illustrative material, and their names appear under the illustrations contributed. Miss Claire Sanders typed a major portion of the manuscript.

One is always indebted to the existing literature, and the author wishes to take cognizance of the books he used as a student or teacher: "Steam Turbines" by E. F. Church, "The Theory and Design of Gas Turbines and Jet Engines" by E. T. Vincent, and "Steam Turbine Theory and Practice" by W. J. Kearton. The literature references of which direct use has been made are included at the end of each chapter.

It is supposed that despite the careful checking of the manuscript by several people some errors will escape notice. The author invites correspondence relating to any discovered errors or suggestions for improving the presentation.

JOHN F. LEE

CONTENTS

Preface vii

1. Steam-turbine Types 1

   1-1. Introduction. 1-2. Nomenclature. 1-3. Classification of Turbines
   as to Flow Passages. 1-4. Classification of Turbines as to Flow Arrangement. 1-5. Classification as to Use and Operating Conditions. 1-6.
   Other Classifications. 1-7. Recapitulation of Classifications.

2. Gas-turbine Types 28

   2-1. Introduction. 2-2. Nomenclature. 2-3. Classifications. 2-4.
   Classification According to Application. 2-5. Classification According
   to Cycle. 2-6. Classification According to Arrangement. 2-7. Classification According to Combustion. 2-8. Classification According to Fuel.
   2-9. Some Advantages of the Gas Turbine.

3. Fundamentals of Thermodynamics 51

   3-1. Introduction. 3-2. Thermodynamics Systems. 3-3. Processes.
   3-4. Equations of State. 3-5. Equation of State of an Ideal Gas. 3-6.
   Some Other Equations of State. 3-7. Work. 3-8. The First Law of
   Thermodynamics. 3-9. Specific Heats. 3-10. Joule's Law. 3-11.
   Relationships between Specific Heats of Ideal Gases. 3-12. Adiabatic
   Processes. 3-13. Joule-Thomson Experiment. 3-14. Enthalpy. 3-15.
   Steady-flow Energy Equation. 3-16. Second Law of Thermodynamics.
   3-17. The Reversible Cycle. 3-18. Some Consequences of the Carnot
   Cycle. 3-19. Entropy. 3-20. Some Consequences of the First and
   Second Laws of Thermodynamics. 3-21. Thermodynamic Properties of
   Gases. 3-22. The Clausius-Clapeyron Equation.

4. Steam-turbine Cycles 83

   4-1. Introduction. 4-2. Carnot Cycle. 4-3. Rankine Cycle. 4-4.
   Reheat Cycle. 4-5. Regenerative Cycle. 4-6. Effect of Temperature
   and Pressure on Cycle Efficiency. 4-7. Thermal Efficiency. 4-8. Heat
   Rate and Steam Rate. 4-9. Mechanical Efficiency. 4-10. Engine
   Efficiency.

5. Gas-turbine Cycles 93

   5-1. Introduction. 5-2. Carnot Cycle. 5-3. Ideal Brayton or Joule
   Cycle. 5-4. Irreversible Brayton Cycle. 5-5. Ideal Brayton Cycle with
   Regeneration. 5-6. Irreversible Brayton Cycle with Regeneration. 5-7.
   Stirling Cycle. 5-8. Ideal Ericsson Cycle. 5-9. Theoretical Intercooling.
   5-10. Actual Intercooling. 5-11. Reheat. 5-12. Combined Effects of
   Intercooling, Reheating, and Regeneration. 5-13. Closed Cycles. 5-14.
   Operating Media Other than Air.

6. Elementary Gas Dynamics 116

6-1. Introduction. 6-2. Continuity Equation. 6-3. Isentropic Flow Relations. 6-4. Sonic Velocity and Mach Number. 6-5. Mach Waves. 6-6. Plane Normal Shock Waves. 6-7. Relationship of State Properties through Plane Normal Shock. 6-8. Inclined or Oblique Waves. 6-9. Strong Oblique Shock Waves. 6-10. Stagnation Temperature, Enthalpy, and Pressure. 6-11. Isentropic Flow in a Passage of Varying Cross-sectional Area. 6-12. Reynolds Number. 6-13. Adiabatic Flow with Friction in a Passage of Constant Cross-sectional Area. 6-14. Compressible Frictionless Flow with Heat Transfer in a Passage of Uniform Section. 6-15. Isentropic Flow in Nozzles. 6-16. Two-dimensional Concentric Circulatory Flow. 6-17. Elementary Airfoil Theory. 6-18. Induced Drag, Shock, and Compressibility Burble.

7. Design of Nozzles 161

7-1. Introduction. 7-2. Nozzle Construction. 7-3. Critical Pressure Ratios. 7-4. Nozzle Losses. 7-5. Divergence and Position Angles. 7-6. Wet Steam. 7-7. Supersaturated Steam. 7-8. Shock Waves in Nozzles. 7-9. Nozzle Discharge Coefficients. 7-10. Nozzle Calculations.

8. Energy Interchanges in Fluid Machinery. 181

8-1. Introduction.

The General Theory
8-2. Momentum Principles. 8-3. Streamline Theory. 8-4. Momentum and Circulation. 8-5. Energy Changes in the Fluid.

The Impulse Turbine
8-6. Introduction. 8-7. Impulse and Reaction Forces. 8-8. Relative Velocity. 8-9. Blade Velocity. 8-10. Blade Work and Efficiency— Ideal Impulse Blades. 8-11. Velocity Diagrams. 8-12. Theoretical Work and Efficiency of the Simple Impulse Stage. 8-13. Combined Nozzle and Blade Efficiency—Simple Impulse Stage. 8-14. Impulse Turbine Staging. 8-15. Curtis Staging. 8-16. Velocity Ratio for Optimum Efficiency—Curtis Staging. 8-17. Mixed Staging.

The Reaction Turbine
8-18. Introduction. 8-19. Velocity Diagrams. 8-20. Theoretical Work and Efficiency—Symmetrical Reaction Stage. 8-21. Comparison of Energy-absorbing Abilities of Various Stages.

The Axial-flow Compressor
8-22. Introduction. 8-23. Velocity Diagrams. 8-24. Energy Transfer from Rotor to Fluid.

9. Design of Turbine Flow Passages. 208

9-1. Introduction. 9-2. Isentropic Velocity Ratio. 9-3. Energy Distribution in Turbines. 9-4. Effect of Carry-over Velocity on Energy Distribution.

Impulse Turbine Flow Passages
9-5. Impulse Blade Profiles. 9-6. Blade Pitch and Width. 9-7. Blade Height. 9-8. Blade Entrance and Exit Angles. 9-9. Angle of Efflux. 9-10. Geometry of Impulse Blade Profiles. 9-11. Losses in Impulse Blade Passages.

Reaction Turbine Flow Passages
9-12. Reaction Blade Profiles. 9-13. Blade Angles, Gauging, and Pitch. 9-14. Blade Width and Height. 9-15. Losses in Reaction Blade Passages. *Flow Passages with Radial Equilibrium* 9-16. Free Vortex. 9-17. Forced Vortex. 9-18. Requirements for Radial Equilibrium. 9-19. Velocity Diagrams. 9-20. Elements of the Airfoil. 9-21. Single Airfoil Principle. 9-22. Limitations of the Single Airfoil Principle. 9-23. Cascade Principle. 9-24. Secondary Flow Losses. 9-25. Some General Comments on the Design of Turbine Flow Passages. 9-26. Relationships between the Velocity Ratios. 9-27. Design Calculations for Impulse Stage Flow Passages. 9-28. Design Calculations for Multistaged Turbine Flow Passages.

10. Mechanical Aspects of Turbine Design 271

10-1. Introduction.
Parasitic Losses
10-2. Disc Friction. 10-3. Windage Losses. 10-4. Leakage. 10-5. Preventive Measures to Reduce Leakage. 10-6. Labyrinth Seals. 10-7. Carbon-ring Seals. 10-8. Water, Steam, and Air Seals. 10-9. Special Sealing Devices. 10-10. Leakage Efficiency. 10-11. Bearing Losses. 10-12. Radiation Losses. 10-13. Miscellaneous Losses. 10-14. Stage Output and Efficiency. 10-15. Turbine Output.
The Turbine Rotor
10-16. Blade Stresses. 10-17. Centrifugal Stresses. 10-18. Bending Stresses. 10-19. Vibrations. 10-20. Disc Stresses. 10-21. Blade Fastenings. 10-22. Shrouding. 10-23. Lacing Wires. 10-24. Cooling of Gas-turbine Blades.
Metallurgical Considerations
10-25. Properties of Metals. 10-26. Creep. 10-27. Endurance. 10-28. Damping. 10-29. Corrosion; Oxidation. 10-30. Workability. 10-31. Characteristics and Properties of Some Alloys. 10-32. Materials Other than Steel.
Turbine Casing and Accessories
10-33. Steam-turbine Casing. 10-34. Gas-turbine Casings. 10-35. Joints.

11. Steam-turbine Control and Performance. 309

11-1 Introduction.
Control
11-2. Control and Supervisory Instruments. 11-3. Principles of Governing. 11-4. Direct-acting Speed-responsive Governors. 11-5. Characteristics of the Simple Speed-responsive Governor. 11-6. Speed-responsive Governors with Servomotors. 11-7. Hydraulic Speed-responsive Governor. 11-8. Pressure Regulators. 11-9. Speed Regulation and Parallel Operation. 11-10. Emergency Governors.
Performance
11-11. Introduction. 11-12. Effect of Throttle Governing. 11-13. Effect of Initial Pressure and Temperature Changes. 11-14. Effect of Nozzle

Governing. 11-15. Parsons Number and Quality Factor. 11-16. Performance of Automatic Extraction Turbines. 11-17. Performance of the Mixed-pressure Turbine. 11-18. A-C Generator. 11-19. AIEE-ASME Preferred Standard Turbine.

12. The Centrifugal Compressor 349

12-1. Introduction. 12-2. Description and Operation. 12-3. Energy Transfers and Relations. 12-4. Losses. 12-5. Adiabatic Efficiency. 12-6. Effect of Compressibility. 12-7. The Diffuser. 12-8. Prewhirl. 12-9. Performance Characteristics. 12-10. Pressure Coefficient and Slip Factor. 12-11. Surging. 12-12. Centrifugal Compressor Design Calculations.

13. The Axial-flow Compressor 371

13-1. Introduction. 13-2. Stage Characteristics. 13-3. Blading Efficiency. 13-4. Design Coefficients. 13-5. Blade Loading. 13-6. Lift Coefficient and Solidity. 13-7. Cascade Characteristics. 13-8. Blade Angles. 13-9. Mach Number and Reynolds Number. 13-10. Three-dimensional Flow Considerations. 13-11. Supersonic Axial-flow Air Compressor. 13-12. Performance Characteristics. 13-13. Axial-flow Compressor Computations.

14. Combustion 401

14-1. Introduction.
The Thermochemistry of Combustion
14-2. Combustion Equations. 14-3. Laws of Gas Mixtures. 14-4. Entropy of a Mixture of Ideal Gases. 14-5. Chemical Equilibrium. 14-6. Heat of Reaction. 14-7. The Le Châtelier Principle. 14-8. Reactions Involving Solids and Liquids. 14-9. Third Law of Thermodynamics. 14-10. Heats of Reaction and Heats of Combustion—The Reference State. 14-11. Flame Temperatures. 14-12. Dissociation.
The Mechanics of Combustion
14-13. Combustibles in Fuels. 14-14. Combustion Mechanisms. 14-15. Physical Characteristics of Combustion and Reactive Mixtures. 14-16. Pressure Losses.
The Combustor
14-17. Requirements of the Combustor. 14-18. Combustion Efficiency. 14-19. Fuel Injection and Atomization. 14-20. Combustion Chamber.

15. The Regenerator. 433

15-1. Introduction. 15-2. Heat Transfer. 15-3. Heat Transfer by Conduction and Convection. 15-4. Regenerator Types and Mean Temperature Difference. 15-5. Film Coefficient. 15-6. Pressure Losses. 15-7. Regenerator Effectiveness. 15-8. Some Economic Aspects of Regenerator Design. 15-9. Regenerator Calculations.

16. The Gas-turbine Power Plant 456

16-1. Introduction. 16-2. Dimensionless Performance Parameters of the Stationary Plant. 16-3. Twin-shaft Plant. 16-4. Dimensionless Parameters of the Aircraft Plant. 16-5. Torque Characteristics of the Gas-turbine Plant. 16-6. Starting. 16-7. Performance of Gas-turbine Power Plants.

Appendix 473

Abridged Gas Tables
Abridged Steam Tables

Index 497

CHAPTER 1

STEAM-TURBINE TYPES

1-1. Introduction. The history of the steam turbine can be traced to ancient times when Hero of Alexandria described what might be regarded as a crude forerunner of the steam turbine. However, a practical form of the steam turbine did not appear until the end of the nineteenth century when De Laval designed a high-speed turbine as a prime mover for a cream separator, a function for which the steam engine was totally unsuited. This same era witnessed the introduction of turbine designs by Sir Charles A. Parsons and C. G. Curtis which laid the cornerstone for the development of the modern steam turbine.

Fig. 1-1. Hero's reaction turbine.

Following the turn of the century, the development and application of the steam turbine proceeded rapidly until today it is the most important of the large prime movers. In large capacities it has no peer. Only in the smaller sizes (100 to 5000 hp) does the steam turbine begin to find competition in the diesel engine and to some extent in the gas turbine. In the very smallest capacities both the steam engine and the diesel engine are competitors.

Modern steam turbines range in capacity from a few kilowatts to 200,000 kw and in speed from 1000 rpm to well over 15,000 rpm. Inlet steam pressures vary from atmospheric to 2400 psig with temperatures in excess of 1050 F and exhaust pressures as low as 1.5 in. Hg abs. The versatility of the steam turbine in meeting an extensive range of operation conditions is unparalleled by any other form of prime mover.

Among the advantages of the modern steam turbine are simplicity, reliability, and low maintenance costs. Space requirements for the steam turbine are much less than for the diesel or steam engine. The absence of reciprocating motion results in decreased vibration and permits lighter foundations. Lubrication in the steam turbine is simpler than in a reciprocating engine. Furthermore, the ability to deliver oil-free condensate or exhaust steam is a valuable consideration in the process industries. Because of this particular advantage, many manufacturing industries can generate their own electrical energy cheaply as a by-product to the production of process steam.

Steam turbines may be found as prime movers for large alternators in central stations or as reliable drives for fans, pumps, and other auxiliaries located in the power plant itself as well as in industry in general. The noncondensing steam turbine is well suited as a variable-speed drive as contrasted with large condensing units which in the production of electrical energy in central stations must operate at constant speed within close tolerances. This ability to drive variable-speed auxiliaries, coupled with the advantage of oil-free exhaust steam and condensate mentioned before, makes the steam turbine particularly suitable for marine requirements.

1-2. Nomenclature. Before undertaking a study of the steam turbine, it is essential to establish first a familiarity with at least some of the more common terms and their meanings. An understanding of the nomenclature will facilitate the description of the various types of turbines covered later in this chapter.

In general, it may be said that the steam turbine depends for its motive force almost entirely on the dynamic action of the steam. Some of the thermal energy of the steam is converted into kinetic energy through a drop in static pressure in a nozzle. The resulting high-velocity steam is directed by the nozzle into a passage which is integral with the moving part (rotor) of the turbine. In passing through the rotor flow passage, the direction of the steam is changed, causing a change of momentum, and as a result a dynamic force is translated into a turning force on the shaft and is therefore the motive force of the turbine.

If the static pressure drop occurs principally in a stationary nozzle with little or no static-pressure drop taking place in the rotor flow passage, the turbine may be broadly termed an impulse turbine. (A more complete definition of an impulse turbine will be given later in Sec. 8-7.) On the other hand if a substantial static-pressure drop occurs in the rotor flow passage, as well as in a preceding stationary nozzle, the turbine is generally called a reaction turbine. The static-pressure drop in the rotor flow passage causes a further conversion of thermal energy into kinetic energy. The resulting reactive force and the force associated with change of steam direction comprise the total dynamic force translated to the shaft as a turning force.

From the foregoing it may be concluded that the turbine has two important elements, a stationary nozzle and a rotor flow passage. The rotor flow passage, which consists of blades or buckets, and the stationary nozzle are described with reference to Fig. 1-2 for an impulse turbine as follows:

1. *Nozzles.* The stationary passage of an impulse turbine consists of

one or more stationary nozzles. The nozzle expands steam of comparatively low velocity and high static pressure to a lower static pressure with a considerable increase in velocity. The nozzle is so positioned as to direct the flow of steam into the rotor flow passages.

2. *Blades or buckets.* The blades or buckets form the rotor flow passage and serve to change the direction, and hence the momentum, of the steam received from the stationary nozzles.

With further reference to Fig. 1-2 the following components of the impulse steam turbine are described.

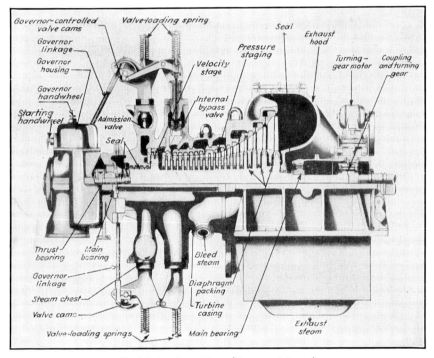

Fig. 1-2. Impulse turbine. (Courtesy of Power.)

3. *Guides or guide blades.* Often a turbine is arranged with a series of rotor flow passages. Intervening between the blade rows comprising the rotor passages are rows of stationary guides or guide blades. The purpose of the guides is to reverse the direction of the steam leaving the preceding moving blade row so that the general direction of the steam entering all the moving blade rows is similar. If guide blades were not provided, opposing forces would be exerted on the rotor which would largely negate each other. The use of guide blades will be discussed more fully in Sec. 1-3 in connection with the Curtis stage.

4. *Casing, shell, or cylinder.* The turbine enclosure is generally called

the casing although the other two names are in common use. The nozzles and guides are fixed to the casing, which in addition to confining the steam serves as a support for the bearings. Sometimes the term cylinder is restricted to the cylindrical form attached to the inside of the casing to which the guides are fixed.

5. *Shaft, rotor, spindle.* These terms are applied to the rotating assembly which carries the blades.

6. *Disc or wheel.* The moving blades are attached directly to the disc, which in turn is keyed to or shrunk on the shaft.

7. *Diaphragm.* The diaphragm, which is fixed to the cylinder or casing, contains the nozzles and serves to confine the steam flow to the nozzle passages.

8. *Packing.* Packing in the form of carbon rings or labyrinths minimizes the leakage in the annular space between the diaphragm and shaft or casing and shaft. More specific information on various types of packing will be given in Chap. 10.

9. *Thrust bearing.* A thrust bearing, usually a combination of the Kingsbury and the collar types, absorbs the axial forces (see Fig. 1-3).

10. *Exhaust hood.* The exhaust hood is that portion of the casing which collects and delivers the exhaust steam to the exhaust pipe or condenser.

11. *Steam chest.* The steam chest is the supply chamber from which steam is admitted to the nozzles.

12. *Governor.* The governing system may be designed to control steam flow so as to maintain constant speed with load fluctuations, to maintain constant pressure with variation of demand for process steam, or both. The operating principles and details will be covered in Chap. 11.

13. *Throttle or stop valve.* The throttle and stop valves are located in the steam supply line to the turbine. The stop valve is a hydraulically operated, quick opening and shutting valve designed to be either fully open or shut. On small turbines the stop valve may be manually operated but in any case is intended for emergency use or when fully shut down. The throttle valve is used in smaller turbines in addition to the stop valve as a means of regulating steam flow during the starting or stopping operation.

14. *Turning gear.* The term turning gear is applied to the mechanism which keeps the shaft rotating at about 1 to 20 rpm to avoid springing the shaft because of unequal expansions and contractions when warming or cooling the turbine. The turning gear consists of a gear integral with the turbine shaft which is driven by an electric motor through the necessary speed reduction equipment. The turning gear is used only with large turbines and therefore is not illustrated in Fig. 1-2.

15. *Main bearing.* The main bearings support the shaft and are

(a)

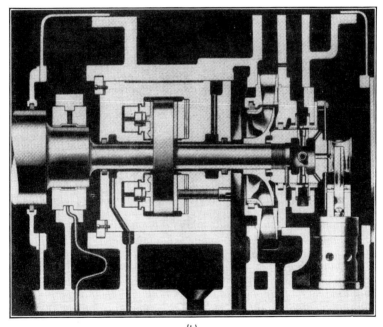

(b)

Fig. 1-3. (a) Thrust bearing, cage in place; (b) section of thrust bearing and housing. (*Courtesy of Westinghouse Electric Corporation.*)

usually of the journal type except in the case of small turbines, where ball bearings are sometimes used.

16. *Emergency trip mechanism.* An overspeed governor with a trip mechanism is usually provided to shut off the supply of steam. The trip mechanism may be also actuated by loss of lubricating oil pressure or condenser vacuum or in case of excessive axial thrust.

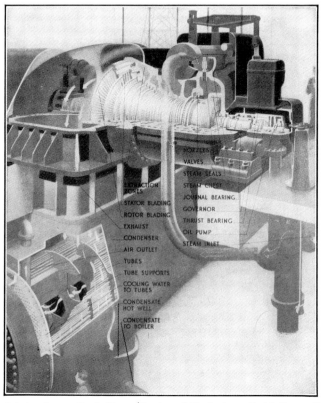

Fig. 1-4. Impulse-reaction turbine. (*Courtesy of Westinghouse Electric Corporation.*)

Figure 1-4 shows a reaction turbine which has many components in common with the impulse turbine. Items 4, 5, 8, 10, 11, 12, 13, 14, 15, and 16 are appropriate to either impulse or reaction turbines. The term nozzle is not widely used for the reaction turbine although in fact both the stationary and moving blades form expanding passages. The stationary blades of the reaction turbine are vaned partitions forming an annular ring of nozzle passages. Strictly speaking, the term bucket is not used either in reference to the stationary or moving reaction blades. Guides or guide blades are not used in reaction turbines since their function is taken over by the stationary blades. The moving blades of a reaction turbine are often fixed to a drum rather than to individual discs, as was shown in Fig. 1-2 for the impulse turbine. The term diaphragm is infrequently used in reaction turbines since the stationary blades always occupy the total annular area between the drum and casing. Although a thrust bearing is used, most of the thrust in reaction turbines is taken up in the balance or dummy position. A counterforce to the thrust is achieved by bringing extraction or condenser steam to bear against the face of the balance piston. A balance piston is shown at the high-pressure end of the turbine of Fig. 1-10.

The preceding list is not intended to be exhaustive as to detail or coverage of the many parts of the turbine. Other components and more detailed information concerning those components listed will be given at appropriate points in the text.

1-3. Classification of Turbines as to Flow Passages. As stated before, in the conversion of the thermal energy of the steam into work, two distinct functions are performed in the steam turbine.

1. The thermal or available energy of the steam is converted into kinetic energy.
2. The kinetic energy produces a turning force on the shaft.

These functions suggest a broad classification as to the manner in which they are carried out, namely, by impulse or reaction. The terms impulse and reaction were defined in general terms in the preceding section. Now some of the characteristics of the classical impulse and reaction turbines will be discussed.

Figure 1-5 shows a diagrammatic sketch of a simple impulse or De Laval stage. It will be noted that the steam in passing through the stationary nozzles experiences a static-pressure drop with an accompanying increase in velocity and an enthalpy drop. The specific volume of the steam increases along with dropping static pressure. In passing through the moving blades, the specific volume and enthalpy are constant and the absolute velocity decreases as work is done on the blading. If the steam must expand through a considerable static-pressure drop, it is clear that high velocities are likely to be generated in the stationary nozzles. The bucket velocity should be approximately one-half the jet velocity for good efficiency (as will be shown later), and therefore this type of turbine inherently has high rotational speeds.

In order to utilize efficiently the high-velocity jet with reasonable rotational speed, a Curtis or velocity-staged turbine may be used. Instead of absorbing all the kinetic energy in a single moving row of blades, it is divided among two or three moving rows with suitable guide blades placed between the rows. A diagrammatic sketch of the Curtis turbine is shown in Fig. 1-6. Again it will be observed that the entire pressure and enthalpy drop, with increasing velocity and specific volume, occur in the stationary nozzles. No change in pressure, enthalpy, or specific volume occurs in either the buckets or guide blades. The absolute velocity decreases in the moving blades but remains constant in the guide blades since no work is done. Actually a slight velocity drop is incurred in the guide blades owing to friction.

Another method for utilizing high-velocity steam at acceptable shaft speed is to employ Rateau or pressure staging. In this type of staging instead of taking the entire pressure drop in a single step it is taken in smaller increments, resulting in moderate steam velocities and consequently favorable rotational speeds. Pressure staging consists simply of

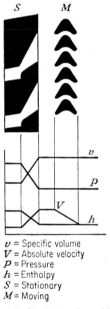

v = Specific volume
V = Absolute velocity
p = Pressure
h = Enthalpy
S = Stationary
M = Moving

Fig. 1-5. Simple impulse turbine.

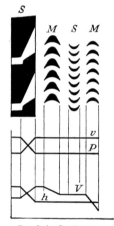

Fig. 1-6. Curtis stage.

a series of De Laval or simple impulse stages. The discharge from each moving row of blades is supplied to the stationary nozzles of the following stage. Figure 1-7 illustrates diagrammatically the flow characteristics through Rateau staging. Pressure and velocity staging may be accomplished with Curtis stages arranged in series.

The preceding turbines are all impulse turbines since the pressure and enthalpy drops occur chiefly in the stationary nozzles. Figure 1-8 shows the characteristics of a Parsons or reaction stage. It will be remembered that a pressure drop occurs in both the stationary and moving rows of blades with a corresponding enthalpy drop and specific volume increase. As indicated in the diagram, velocity increases in the stationary rows and decreases in the moving rows. The decrease in absolute velocity in the moving blades may appear to be inconsistent with a drop in pressure. However, it must be remembered that work is being done on the moving blades at the expense of the kinetic energy in the steam.

Although small turbines may exist in the forms outlined in the preceding paragraphs, medium and large turbines usually consist of a Curtis stage followed by reaction or Rateau staging. This arrangement permits better governing conditions and a reduction in turbine size. The theoretical and design aspects of staging will be covered in Chaps. 8 and 9.

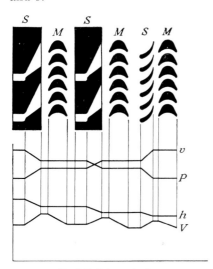

Fig. 1-7. Rateau staging.

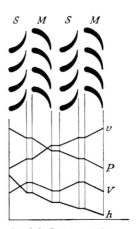

Fig. 1-8. Parsons staging.

1-4. Classification of Turbines as to Flow Arrangement. Various flow arrangements of steam turbines are illustrated in Fig. 1-9. In general, there are two principal reasons for the various arrangements. In the first place, for large flows of steam with high condenser vacuum, the volume of the steam becomes very large. This condition requires large annular flow areas and hence extremely long blades. Because of structural limitations it is not advisable to employ blades much longer than 25 in. in 3600-rpm turbines. By expanding the steam in a high-pressure turbine until the blade-height requirement begins to become a problem and then dividing the flow between two low-pressure turbines, reasonable blade heights may be maintained.

In the second place, compounding units permits the superposing of a high-pressure unit on an existing low-pressure plant or subposing a condensing turbine on an existing noncondensing plant. The vertical compound arrangement is used principally where an existing low-pressure plant is to be superposed and available floor space in the turbine room is restricted.   Some of the arrangements shown diagrammatically in Fig. 1-9 are illustrated in Figs. 1-10 to 1-16 inclusive.

1-5. Classification as to Use and Operating Conditions. Steam turbines may be also classified as condensing or noncondensing, and

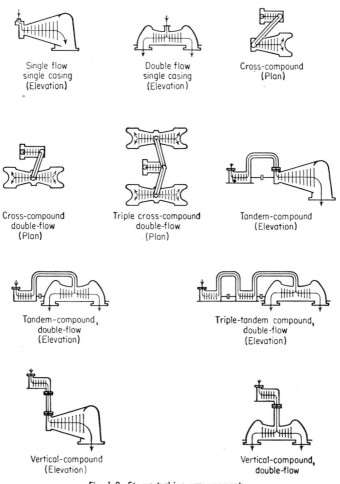

Fig. 1-9. Steam-turbine arrangements.

extraction* or nonextraction.   Figure 1-17 shows diagrammatically various types of condensing and noncondensing turbines.   Among the noncondensing types is the topping or superposed turbine which receives

* Strictly speaking an extraction turbine provides process steam at regulated pressures and quantities from various points along the turbine.   A bleeder turbine provides steam at pressures and quantities varying with load conditions.   When steam is taken from various points along the turbine solely for feedwater heating, it is good practice to refer to such a turbine as a regenerative turbine.

steam at very high pressure (900 to 2400 psig) and exhausts it at a pressure suitable for supplying an existing low-pressure plant operating at 200 to 600 psig. Another type of noncondensing turbine is the back-pressure turbine operating between 200 to 900 psig and 5 to 150 psig. When provided with an exhaust-pressure regulator, this turbine finds wide application where process steam at one pressure is desirable. If steam at pressures other than exhaust pressure is desired, back-pressure

Fig. 1-10. Single-flow single-casing condensing impulse-reaction turbine. (*Courtesy of Allis-Chalmers Manufacturing Company.*)

turbines arranged for extraction can be obtained. The back-pressure turbine may be used also as a house turbine in central stations where the exhaust steam and extraction steam, if any, may be used for feedwater heating and/or to supply steam for small turbines serving as auxiliary drives. The electrical output of the house turbine is used to meet the demands for electrical energy in the station itself. A third type of non-condensing turbine is the small auxiliary turbine operating at pressures of 200 to 600 psig and exhausting at pressures of 0 to 50 psig. These turbines are used as drives for fans, pumps, blowers, exciters, generator

sets, marine and power-plant auxiliaries, and stand-by emergency
drives.

Among the condensing types are the high-pressure (600 to 2400 psig)
regenerative turbines used in central stations and for marine propulsion.
These units exhaust at 2 to 1.5 in. Hg abs. The high-pressure (200 to
800 psig) turbine operating extracting or nonextracting may be used as a
generator drive, marine propulsion drive, or drive for large-capacity
blowers, compressors, or pumps in city waterworks. The reheat or
resuperheat turbine is one in which steam is withdrawn at some inter-

Fig. 1-11. Low-pressure spindle of tandem double-flow installation. (*Courtesy of Allis-Chalmers
Manufacturing Company.*)

mediate pressure, returned to the boiler or an auxiliary superheater, and
finally returned to the turbine at an elevated temperature for the balance
of the expansion. The reheat turbine has the dual advantage of improving the plant efficiency and avoiding excessively wet steam in the final
stages of the turbine. The mixed-pressure turbine expands high-pressure
steam (200 to 900 psig) to a suitable pressure where waste low-pressure
steam from processes, waste-heat boilers, or steam accumulators is
admitted to augment the flow. Normally the high-pressure steam is
regarded as supplementary and an attempt is made to utilize in so far as
possible all the low-pressure steam available.

The induction-extraction turbine is so arranged that it can admit steam
at a given pressure when available or provide extraction steam at the

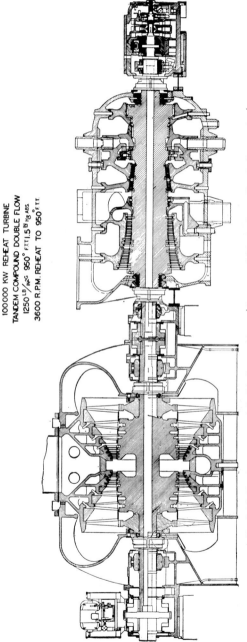

100,000 KW REHEAT TURBINE
TANDEM COMPOUND DOUBLE FLOW
1250 LB/IN² G 950° F. I.T. 1.5 IN. Hg ABS
3600 R.P.M. REHEAT TO 950° F. I.T.

Fig. 1-12. Tandem-compound double-flow turbine. (Courtesy of Westinghouse Electric Corporation.)

13

same pressure if required.   Occasionally a particular manufacturing process requires at times a large quantity of steam at a particular pressure
while at other times an abundance of waste steam is available at the same
pressure.   The induction-extraction turbine provides a convenient solution to this problem.

1-6. Other Classifications.   Turbines may be classified also as to
other distinguishing characteristics which are of less general significance.
One classification can be made with regard to the general direction of

Fig. 1-13. 80,000-kw tandem double-flow impulse-reaction turbine. *(Courtesy of Allis-Chalmers Manufacturing Company.)*

flow translation such as axial, radial, or tangential.   Nearly all turbines
used in the United States are axial flow with the exception of some very
small turbines which are of the tangential type.   In axial-flow turbines
the through-flow direction is substantially the same as that of the shaft.
In the tangential-flow turbine the steam flows in a direction which is
approximately tangential to the periphery of the rotor or wheel.   This is
accomplished by means of a reversing chamber equipped with stationary
blades which reverse the direction of the steam leaving the moving blades.
The process is continuous until the steam reaches the exhaust, consti-
tuting an ingenious method for accomplishing multivelocity staging in a

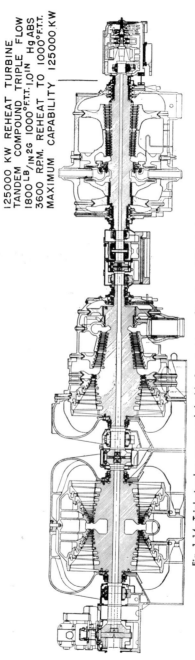

125000 KW REHEAT TURBINE
TANDEM COMPOUND TRIPLE FLOW
1800 LB/IN²G 1000°F.T.T. 1.0IN Hg ABS
3600 R.P.M. REHEAT TO 1000°F.T.T.
MAXIMUM CAPABILITY 125000 KW

Fig. 1-14. Triple-tandem-compound double-flow turbine. (Courtesy of Westinghouse Electric Corporation.)

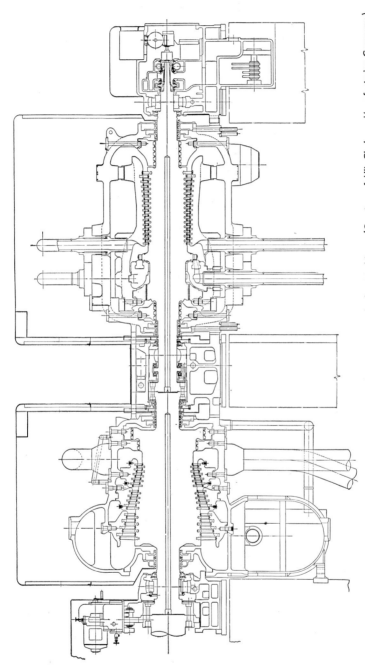

Fig. 1-15. Typical longitudinal cross section of HP and IP turbines of cross-compound reheat turbine. (Courtesy of Allis-Chalmers Manufacturing Company.)

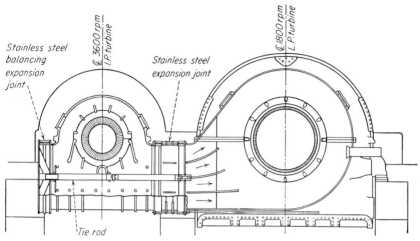

Fig. 1-16. Transverse section of crossover connection for close-coupled cross-compound reheat turbine (IP turbine and LP double-flow turbine). *(Courtesy of Allis-Chalmers Manufacturing Company.)*

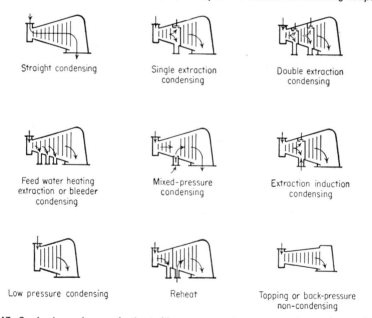

Fig. 1-17. Condensing and noncondensing turbine arrangements as to use and operating conditions.

single wheel. Figure 1-18 illustrates this type of turbine. It should be noted that although the steam flows in a corkscrew or approximately helical path the general direction of translation is tangential.

The radial-flow turbine is of no particular interest in the United States but has been put to use on a limited scale in Europe. In the radial-flow turbine, steam is introduced near the shaft and passes radially outward through successive moving blades arranged in concentric circles.   There are no fixed blades so that pressure drops are necessary in all blade passages.   Obviously the blades must rotate in opposite directions so that what are essentially two concentric shafts and two generators are required for each turbine.   The principal difficulties with this type of turbine lie in the elaborate packing, large size, and high first cost.

Turbines may be classified according to speed of rotation.   Since 60-cycle generators are in general use in the United States, turbines as

Fig. 1-18. Tangential-flow re-entry turbine.   (*Courtesy of Terry Steam Turbine Company.*)

prime movers are generally limited to 3600 rpm except in smaller units (up to 100 kw) where higher turbine speeds may be utilized with the incorporation of suitable reduction gears.   If 50-cycle generators are to be used, as is the general rule in Europe and to a limited extent in the United States, then the corresponding rotational speed is 3000 rpm.   A classification of turbines with respect to rotational speed loses much of its meaning when it is realized that even large turbines can be geared to meet a wide variety of speed requirements.   Ship-propulsion turbines which may rotate at a comparatively high speed and yet can be geared down to as little as 90 rpm for good propeller efficiency are an excellent example.

Still another classification can be made on the basis of whether the steam passes through the blades once or several times. The Terry tangential-flow turbine is a multipass or re-entry turbine in that a given mass of steam may be returned to the moving blades several times during its journey to the exhaust. Another type of re-entry turbine is shown in Fig. 1-21. All large turbines and most small turbines are single-pass.

1-7. Recapitulation of Classifications. The following outline of steam-turbine types according to classification is offered with a directory to the appropriate illustrative material.

I. With reference to flow passages
1. Impulse
   a. Simple impulse or De Laval (Fig. 1-5)
   b. Velocity-staged or Curtis (Fig. 1-6)
   c. Pressure-staged or Rateau (Fig. 1-7)
   d. Curtis followed by Rateau staging (Figs. 1-4 and 1-22)
2. Reaction
   a. Reaction-staged or Parsons (Fig. 1-8)
3. Impulse-reaction
   a. Curtis followed by reaction (Fig. 1-4)
   b. Rateau followed by reaction

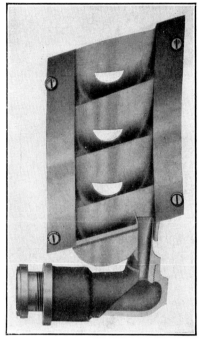

Fig. 1-19. Section of reversing chamber for turbine shown in Fig. 1-18. (*Courtesy of Terry Steam Turbine Company.*)

II. With reference to flow arrangement
1. Single-flow single-casing (Figs. 1-9 and 1-10)
2. Double-flow single-casing (Fig. 1-9)
3. Cross-compound (Fig. 1-9)
4. Cross-compound, double-flow (Fig. 1-9)
5. Triple-cross-compound, double-flow (Figs. 1-9, 1-15, and 1-16)
6. Tandem-compound (Fig. 1-9)
7. Tandem-compound, double-flow (Figs. 1-9, 1-12, and 1-13)
8. Triple-tandem-compound, double-flow (Figs. 1-9 and 1-14)
9. Vertical compound (Fig. 1-9)
III. With reference to operation and use
1. Noncondensing
   a. Topping (Fig. 1-17)

      b. Back pressure (Figs. 1-17, 1-22, 1-23, and 1-24)
      c. Atmospheric exhaust
   2. Condensing
      a. Straight condensing (Figs. 1-17 and 1-27)
      b. Single extraction (Figs. 1-17 and 1-25)

Fig. 1-20. General assembly of turbine shown in Fig. 1-18. (*Courtesy of Terry Steam Turbine Company.*)

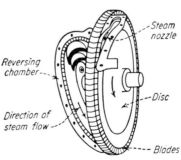

Fig. 1-21. Re-entry turbine.

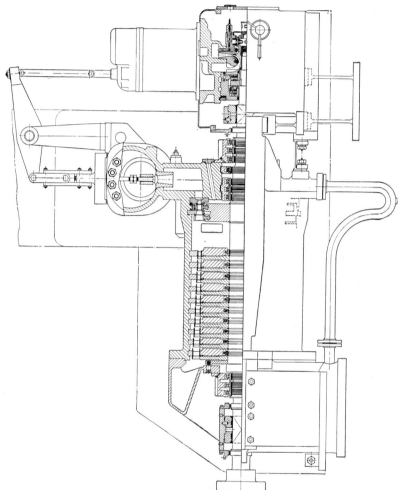

Fig. 1-22. Noncondensing impulse-reaction turbine. (Courtesy of Westinghouse Electric Corporation.)

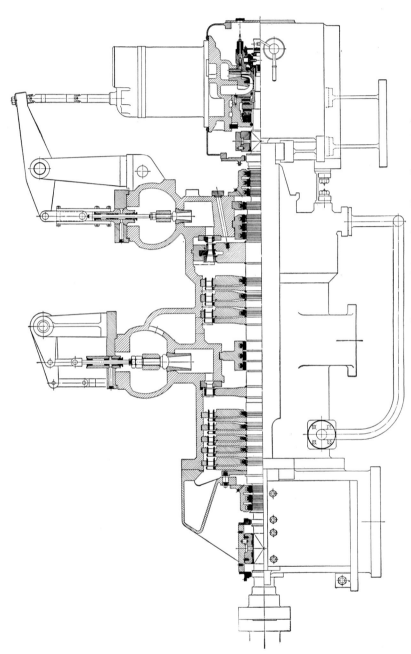

Fig. 1-23. Noncondensing single-extraction turbine. (Courtesy of Westinghouse Electric Corporation.)

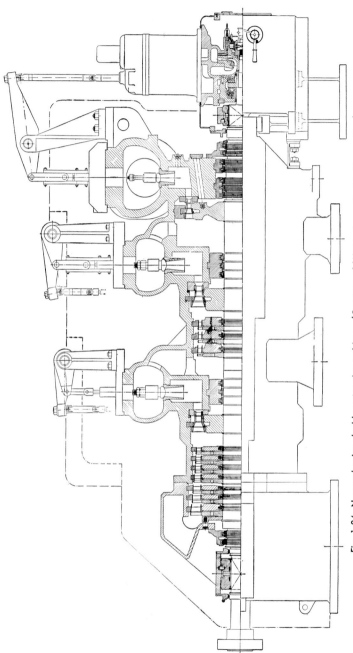

Fig. 1-24. Noncondensing double-extraction turbine. (Courtesy of Westinghouse Electric Corporation.)

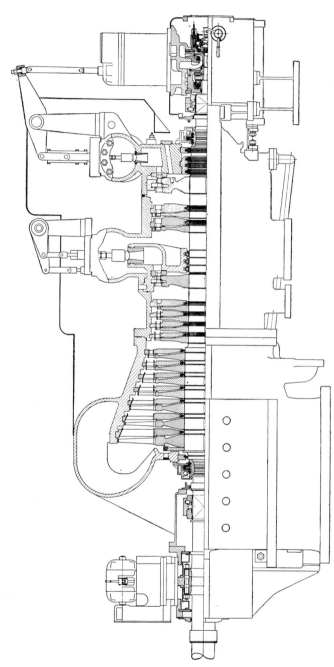

Fig. 1-25. Condensing single extraction or extraction-induction turbine. (Courtesy of Westinghouse Electric Corporation.)

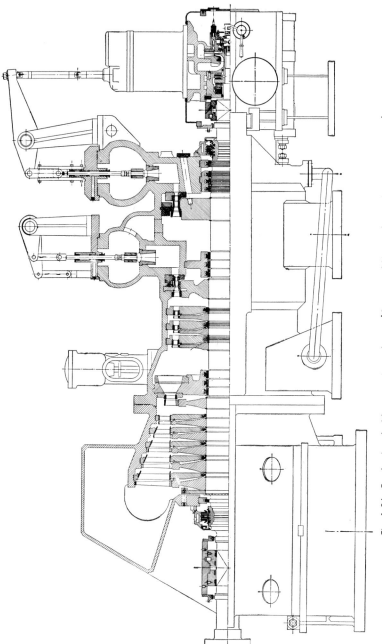

Fig. 1-26. Condensing double extraction turbine. (Courtesy of Westinghouse Electric Corporation.)

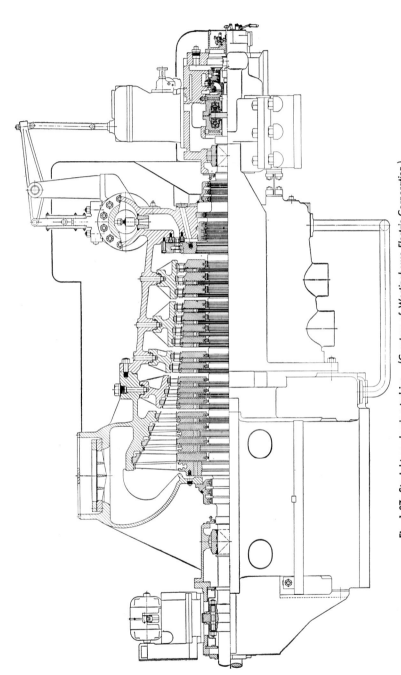

Fig. 1-27. Straight condensing turbine. (Courtesy of *Westinghouse Electric Corporation*.)

 c. Double extraction (Figs. 1-17 and 1-26)
 d. Regenerative (Fig. 1-17)
 e. Mixed pressure (Fig. 1-17)
 f. Extraction-induction (Figs. 1-17 and 1-25)
 g. Low pressure (Fig. 1-17)
 h. Reheat (Figs. 1-17, 1-12, 1-13, 1-14, 1-15 and 1-16)
IV. With reference to translational direction of flow in passages
 1. Axial-flow
 2. Tangential-flow (Figs. 1-18 to 1-20)
 3. Radial-flow (Fig. 1-28)

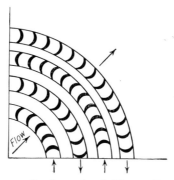

Fig. 1-28. Diagrammatic scheme of radial-flow or Ljungstrom turbine.

V. With reference to number of passes
 1. Single-pass
 2. Multipass (Figs. 1-18 to 1-21)

References

1. Church, E. F.: "Steam Turbines," McGraw-Hill Book Company, Inc., New York, 1950.
2. Economical Power, *Westinghouse Electric Corporation Bull.* B-3883, 1948.
3. "Stationary Steam Turbines," Socony Vacuum Company, 1948.
4. Steam Turbines, *Power*, December, 1948.
5. Turbine-generators, *General Electric Company Bull.* GEA-3277B, 1949.
6. Turbine-generators, *Worthington Corporation Bull.* 1960-A, 1947.
7. Wilson, C. D.: "Present-day Concepts in Steam Turbine Design," Pennsylvania Electric Association, 1952.

CHAPTER 2

GAS-TURBINE TYPES

2-1. Introduction. The gas turbine, as well as the steam turbine, can trace its ancestry back some 2000 years to the very same Hero of Alexandria. Hero's gas turbine, like his steam turbine, did not even remotely resemble the modern concepts of the gas turbine. In fact a gas turbine at

Fig. 2-1. Hero's gas turbine, 130 B.C. (*Courtesy of Allis-Chalmers Manufacturing Company.*)

all similar in principle to those currently in use did not appear until well into the nineteenth century.

Old literature is replete with references to machines of one type or another which could be classified as gas turbines. In the seventeenth century a gas turbine known as the "smokejack" was invented to operate a spit. The smokejack was placed in the chimney of an open fireplace and the passage of the hot flue gas exerted a force on a bladed wheel. The name of the inventor is lost in antiquity.

An important forerunner of the modern gas turbine was invented by

John Barber in England about 1791. Although crude as to form, Barber's gas turbine included a compressor, combustion chamber, impulse turbine, and even water injection to prevent exposing the turbine blades to excessive temperatures (see Fig. 2-2).

Another Englishman, John Dumbell, invented the first explosion type of gas turbine in 1808. Products of combustion from a coal fire passed through several rows of moving blades attached to a single rotor. It is significant that stationary guide blades were not utilized with the consequent forfeiture of the advantage of modern multistaging.

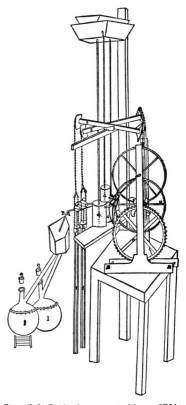

In 1872, F. Stolze, a German, invented a gas turbine very similar in concept to the modern plant (see Fig. 2-3). Atmospheric air was heated in an externally fired combustion chamber and finally expanded in a reaction turbine directly coupled to the compressor. The meager knowledge of aerodynamics which existed generally at that time did not permit design of efficient compressors, thereby dooming the whole project to failure. This limitation, of course, was felt in all gas-turbine development until modern times.

About 1884, Parsons attempted to utilize his reaction turbine in reverse as a compressor but the result was an inefficient machine. After considerable effort to improve the efficiency of his compressor Parsons finally abandoned the project on the appearance of the

Fig. 2-2. Barber's gas turbine, 1791. (Courtesy of Allis-Chalmers Manufacturing Company.)

more successful centrifugal compressor developed by Rateau in 1908.

The first successful attempt at a gas turbine was undertaken by two Frenchmen, Armengaud and Lemale, about 1905 (see Fig. 2-4). The unit consisted of a two-row impulse turbine driving a Rateau multistaged centrifugal compressor. Combustion took place in a combustion chamber by injecting and igniting a liquid fuel in the compressed-air stream on its journey from compressor to turbine. Turbine blades and discs were water-cooled to withstand the high gas temperatures. Thermal efficiencies slightly below 3 per cent were reported.

Fig. 2-3. The Stolze gas turbine, 1872.   (*Courtesy of Allis-Chalmers Manufacturing Company.*)

Fig. 2-4. The Armengaud and Lemale gas turbine, 1905.   (*Courtesy of Allis-Chalmers Manufacturing Company.*)

One other gas-turbine unit deserves mention. Hans Holzwarth, in 1908, began activity on what is known as an explosion or constant-volume gas turbine. This work is continued by his followers to this day. The explosion gas turbine as conceived by Holzwarth provides for intermittent combustion of a liquid fuel in a combustion chamber at constant volume and at elevated pressure. The hot products of combustion are expanded in a Curtis turbine. The high pressure in the combustion chamber is obtained by supplying combustion air under pressure. In one plant steam-turbine-driven centrifugal compressors are used to compress the combustion air, the steam being supplied by a waste-heat boiler located in the exhaust hood of the gas turbine.

Fig. 2-5. The Holzwarth gas turbine, 1910. (*Courtesy of Allis-Chalmers Manufacturing Company.*)

Although Holzwarth gas turbines have been built in Germany and Switzerland, they have not met with great favor because of their complicated design, intermittent combustion, bulkiness, and generally low efficiency. The highest thermal efficiency ever obtained with a Holzwarth unit is reportedly about 13 per cent. An earlier Holzwarth gas turbine is illustrated in Fig. 2-5.

The modern gas turbine may be regarded as successful although its full measure of success has not been reached by any means. The gas-turbine plant can be so simple as to include merely a compressor, combustor, and turbine. On the other hand, the plant may be so involved as to include large heat exchangers, two or more compressors with intercoolers, and two or more turbines with auxiliary combustors. Gas-turbine plants range in capacity from a few kilowatts to 27,000 kw, with even larger units in view.

Besides the familiar application of the gas turbine in jet aircraft it may be found in stationary power plants, industrial processes, locomotives, ships, and, on an experimental basis, in trucks. With the exception of aircraft and some industrial processes, the number of installations in the other fields mentioned is not great. It appears, however, that the installations in Europe are much more numerous, particularly in the field of stationary baseload power. It must be borne in mind that in any event the number of installations is no criterion of the eventual merit of the gas turbine. It has been only recently that really serious and concerted effort has been expended on the gas turbine, and although the development has proceeded at a remarkable pace, many years are needed before the full impact of this development will be felt in industrial applications.

2-2. Nomenclature. The nomenclature for the principal parts of the gas turbine proper closely parallels that of the steam turbine. Gas turbines operate on the impulse and reaction principles. However, where it is rare to find a steam turbine composed entirely of reaction blading it is not uncommon in the gas turbine. Another pronounced difference in gas-turbine blading stems from the intimacy of its development with aerodynamic principles. A type of blading in which the reaction principle is more pronounced, approaching the tip of the blade, is more generally employed than is the case with the steam turbine. This type of blading will be fully investigated in Chap. 9.

Other differences in turbine parts are directly a result of differences in the working medium and the high-temperature operating requirements.

2-3. Classifications. The gas-turbine power plant must be considered as a whole. In the case of the steam turbine, a treatment independent of the rest of the plant can be conceived. Such is not the case with the gas turbine, where interdependence of the compressor, burners, heat exchanger, and turbine is a fundamental consideration for an efficient and economical plant. Therefore, the gas turbine itself will be considered as a component or part of a greater heat engine, the gas-turbine power plant.

Gas-turbine power plants may be classified according to the following criteria:

I. Application
  1. Aircraft
      a. Jet propulsion
      b. Propjets
  2. Stationary
      a. Peak load
      b. Stand-by
      c. End-of-transmission line
      d. Base load
      e. Industrial

3. Locomotive
4. Marine
5. Transport
II. Cycle
  1. Open
  2. Closed
  3. Semiclosed
III. Arrangement
  1. Simple
  2. Single shaft
  3. Multishaft
  4. Intercooled
  5. Reheat
  6. Regenerative
  7. Combination
IV. Combustion
  1. Continuous
  2. Intermittent
V. Fuel
  1. Liquid
  2. Solid
  3. Gas

2-4. Classifications According to Application. In the jet-aircraft application of the gas-turbine power plant there are four essential components, namely, the diffuser, compressor, gas turbine, and exhaust cone.

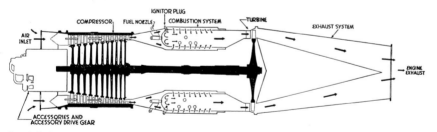

Fig. 2-6. Schematic flow diagram of General Electric TG-180 engine. (*Courtesy of General Electric Company.*)

The purpose of the diffuser is to convert the kinetic energy of the entering air into static pressure followed by a further static-pressure increase in the compressor. The compressed air leaving the compressor flows through the combustor where liquid fuel is ignited continuously, combustion being supported by the steady flow of air. The air plus the products of combustion leaving the combustor at high pressure and temperature are expanded sufficiently in the turbine to supply the work of compression.

Fig. 2-7. General Electric J-47 jet engine. *(Courtesy of General Electric Company.)*

Fig. 2-8. General Electric I-40 jet engine. Note centrifugal compressor. *(Courtesy of General Electric Company.)*

Finally, the exhaust gases from the turbine are expanded in the exhaust cone to a high velocity, the resulting reaction force propelling the aircraft. The turbine and compressor are mounted on a single shaft. Figures 2-6, 2-7, and 2-8 illustrate typical jet engines.

In the propjet, unlike the jet, the turbine utilizes nearly all the energy of the gas, the turbine output over and above that required to operate the

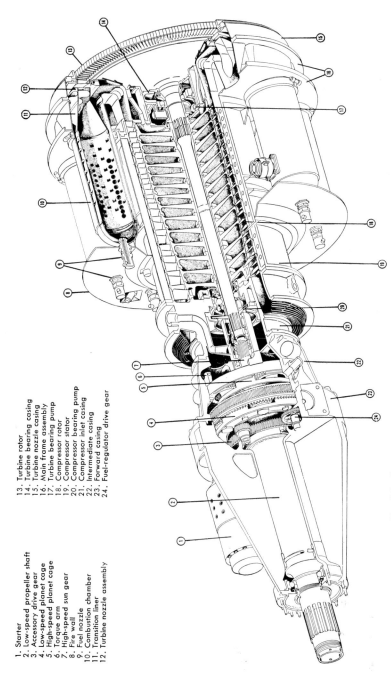

1. Starter
2. Low-speed propeller shaft
3. Accessory drive gear
4. Low-speed planet cage
5. High-speed planet cage
6. Torque arm
7. High-speed sun gear
8. Fire wall
9. Fuel nozzle
10. Combustion chamber
11. Transition liner
12. Turbine nozzle assembly

13. Turbine rotor
14. Turbine bearing casing
15. Turbine nozzle casing
16. Main frame assembly
17. Turbine bearing pump
18. Compressor rotor
19. Compressor stator
20. Compressor bearing pump
21. Compressor inlet casing
22. Intermediate casing
23. Forward casing
24. Fuel-regulator drive gear

Fig. 2-9. General Electric TG-100 propjet. (Courtesy of General Electric Company.)

35

compressor being used to drive a conventional propeller. The turbine exhaust gases are expanded in an exhaust cone, thereby assisting propulsion. The propjet offers many advantages which are of importance to commercial aircraft, such as more extensive range, shorter length of take-off required, large cargo capacity, and suitability to moderate speeds and altitudes. The jet-propelled aircraft is far superior for high-altitude and high-speed requirements and is, therefore, primarily of military interest although its commercial possibilities are bright. A propjet is shown in Fig. 2-9.

The stationary installations of the gas-turbine power plant, in point of number, are understandably far behind the aircraft installations. This

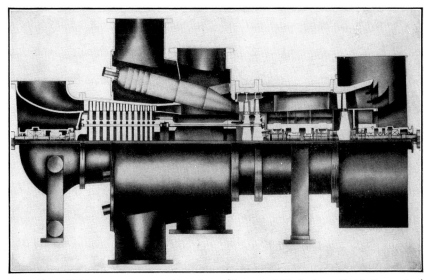

Fig. 2-10. A 5000-hp stationary gas-turbine plant. (*Courtesy of Westinghouse Electric Corporation.*)

is especially true of base-load power plants. However, the use of peak-load, stand-by, and end-of-transmission-line installations is increasing and will probably continue to increase as more operating experience is gained. The experience gained from these installations will undoubtedly be of great value in promoting the acceptance of the gas turbine for base loads. In fact some installations which were originally installed as peak-load or stand-by plants are now furnishing a substantial portion of the base load. Under some circumstances the gas turbine may be used in conjunction with a steam power plant, the turbine exhaust gases being used for feedwater heating. Two representative examples of this use of the gas turbine are Huey Station at Oklahoma City and Farmingdale Station at Farmingdale, Me. Figure 2-10 shows a cross-sectional view of a model of a 5000-hp stationary unit.

The industrial applications offer an opportunity to utilize the gas turbine in its simplest form, especially in oil refineries or chemical process industries in which the primary interest in the gas turbine is as an effective utilizer of abundant by-product hot compressed gases. For example, the Houdry cracking process requires large quantities of compressed air to intensify catalytic action. The waste gases from the process have enough energy to operate a gas turbine which in turn drives a compressor supplying compressed air for the process. Indeed the turbine develops sufficient excess power to drive a generator. A typical installation of this kind is at the Sun Oil Company refinery located at Marcus Hook,

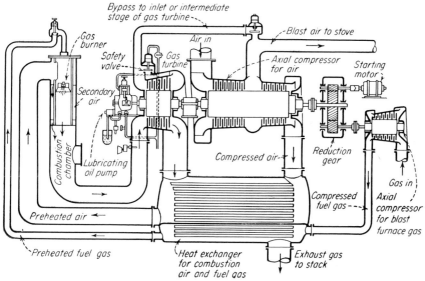

Fig. 2-11. Arrangement of gas-turbine-driven blast-furnace blower. (Courtesy of Brown Boveri Corporation.)

Pa. The turbine develops 5300 kw, of which 4400 kw are required for the compressor, leaving an excess of 900 kw for generating electrical energy. Other industrial applications include the steel industry where waste blast-furnace gases can be utilized as fuel (see Fig. 2-11). Compressed air in excess of that required for the turbine can be utilized with the exhaust from the turbine to supply the blast. The oil fields offer many important opportunities for the gas turbine when natural gas is available at low cost or even as waste. Other possibilities are suggested in the recovery of the heat from the turbine exhaust by means of a waste-heat boiler for the production of steam or hot water for process or building heating.

The locomotive application of the gas turbine bids fair to be the most promising of all. Here again light weight, compactness, and freedom from cooling water requirements make the simple gas turbine highly desirable. The gas turbine locomotive is much more efficient than the steam locomotive and although less efficient than the diesel it burns a cheaper fuel than the usual railroad diesel. The figures in Table 2-1

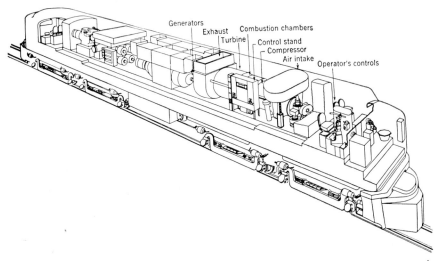

Fig. 2-12. A 4500-hp oil-burning gas-turbine locomotive. (*Courtesy of General Electric Company.*)

(published by J. I. Yellott of the Locomotive Development Committee) illustrate the comparison.

The Swiss Federal Railways have a 2200-hp unit burning the equivalent of No. 6 residual fuel oil, which has been in service since 1941. The long operating experience with the Swiss unit has been augmented by the recent experience in this country with a 4500-hp unit built by the General

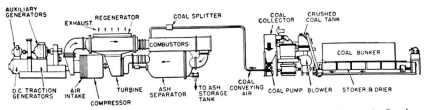

Fig. 2-13. Coal-burning gas-turbine locomotive. (*Courtesy of J. I. Yellott and the Locomotive Development Committee.*)

Electric Company for the Union Pacific Railroad. A coal-burning gas-turbine locomotive which has shown promising results on the test stand is ready for road trials. Figures 2-12 and 2-13 show schematic arrangements of the General Electric and coal-burning gas-turbine locomotives.

Marine applications of the gas turbine have received a great deal of

TABLE 2-1. COMPARATIVE EFFICIENCIES AND FUEL COSTS FOR LOCOMOTIVES

Type of locomotive	Thermal efficiency at rail, per cent	Fuel cost, cents per million Btu	Fuel cost, dollars per 1000 hp-hr
Modern steam locomotive......................	7	15	5.47
Diesel electric locomotive.....................	27	45	4.26
Gas-turbine locomotive, oil-burning (Bunker C) (for Eastern United States).................	21	30	3.64
Gas-turbine locomotive, oil-burning (Bunker C) (for Western United States).................	21	20	2.43
Gas-turbine locomotive, coal-burning..........	20	15	1.91

attention. Thus far several marine gas turbines have been constructed ranging from 1200 to 6000 hp. Three 3000-hp units have been built, two of which are installed in U.S. Navy ships and the third in a merchant

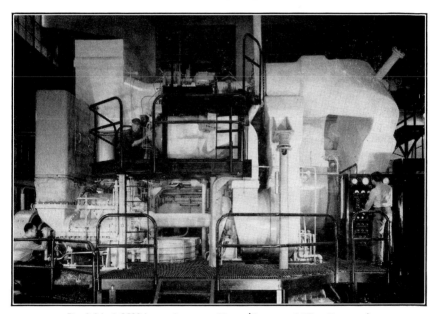

Fig. 2-14. A 2500-hp marine gas turbine. (*Courtesy of Elliott Company.*)

vessel. A 6000-hp unit has been installed in a British frigate. Figures 2-14 and 2-15 show a 2500-hp marine gas turbine equipped with a positive displacement Lysholm compressor. A phantom view of the Lysholm compressor is shown in Fig. 2-16. Figure 2-17 illustrates a 3500-hp experimental gas turbine built for the U.S. Navy. This unit is equipped with an axial-flow compressor.

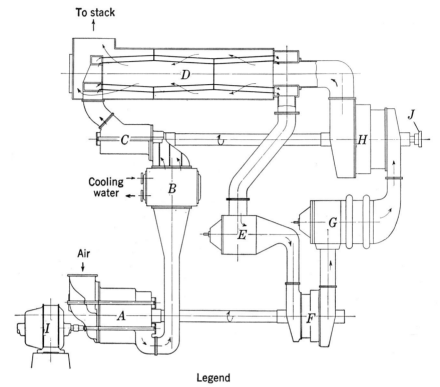

To stack

Cooling
water

Air

Legend
A Low-pressure compressor
B Intercooler
C High-pressure compressor
D Regenerator
E High-pressure combustion chamber
F High-pressure turbine
G Low-pressure combustion chamber
H Low-pressure turbine
I Starting motor
J Output shaft

Fig. 2-15. Schematic layout of marine gas turbine. (*Courtesy of Elliott Company.*)

The transport applications of the gas turbine which include automobiles, busses, trucks, launches, and streetcars are still in the experimental or development stage. Gas turbines have been installed in heavy trucks on a test basis, but it is too early to predict the extent of their general acceptance in this field of application.

2-5. Classification According to Cycle. The open-cycle gas-turbine plant is the most commonly used. The term open cycle means that air is being continuously drawn in from the atmosphere and the turbine exhaust gases are rejected whole to the atmosphere. After the unit is

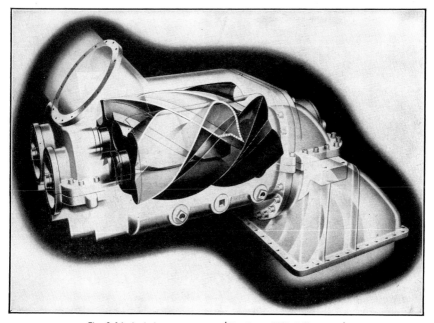

Fig. 2-16. Lysholm compressor. (*Courtesy of Elliott Company.*)

started by means of a starting motor or engine, atmospheric air is drawn into the compressor and raised to a static pressure several times that of the atmosphere. The high-pressure air flows to a combustor where fuel is injected, continuous combustion being maintained in the air stream. The products of combustion from the combustor still at high pressure (a very small static pressure drop occurring in the combustor) and at high temperature (1000 to 1800 F) expand in the turbine. The turbine exhaust gas, as stated before, is rejected to the atmosphere. The open cycle is in most general use since air is cheap and abundant and the resulting plant is considerably simpler than the closed-cycle plant.

The closed-cycle plant may use air or some other stable gas as a working medium. Instead of burning the fuel directly in the air stream, an

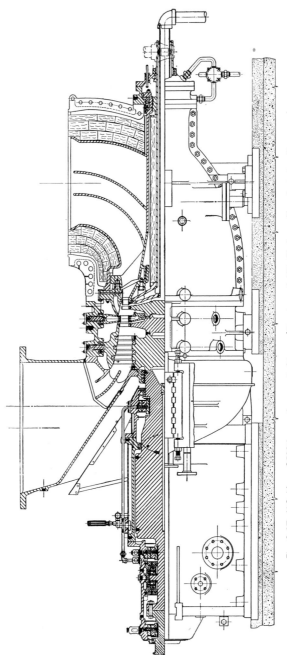

Fig. 2-17. U.S. Navy 3500-hp marine gas turbine. (Courtesy of Allis-Chalmers Manufacturing Company.)

externally fired combustion chamber is used and heat is transferred to the working medium through heat-transfer surfaces. Thus the working medium is uncontaminated by the products of combustion and is constantly recirculated. A cooler must be provided for the recirculated working medium before it enters the compressor in order to minimize compressor work and to make provision for the rejection of heat from the cycle. The thermodynamic principles involved in the incorporation of a cooler in the plant are discussed in the next chapter.

The closed-cycle plant has the advantages of flexibility as to type of fuel, uncontaminated working medium, and the possibility of using a gas exhibiting more desirable characteristics than air. Major disadvantages are size and complexity. Figures 2-18 and 2-19 show a 12,500-kw closed-cycle plant using a low-grade residual fuel oil.

A semiclosed-cycle plant is illustrated in Fig. 2-20. In this plant combustion takes place in the air stream just as in the open-cycle plant. The difference is that a major portion of the turbine exhaust gases is recirculated after passing through a cooler. The recirculated gases are augmented by air in order to maintain the oxygen content at a level which will effectively support combustion. This make-up air is compressed in an auxiliary compressor driven by a separate gas turbine. A serious disadvantage lies in the fact that the compressor performance, particularly with the axial-flow type, is adversely affected by deposits left in the compressor flow passages by the recirculated gases.

2-6. Classification According to Arrangement. Figure 2-21 illustrates schematically the various gas-turbine plant arrangements to be considered here.

The simple gas-turbine plant was described before. Figure 2-21a and b shows the simple plant with single-shaft and twin-shaft arrangements. The term "single-shaft" means that all compressors and turbines in the plant are coupled in a series arrangement. In the "multishaft" plant, two or more turbine-compressor combinations or turbines are carried on independent shafts. In each turbine-compressor combination the machines are, of course, coupled to each other in a series arrangement. Thus Fig. 2-21a, c, d, and e shows single-shaft arrangements. Figure 2-21b shows a twin-shaft arrangement in which two turbines operate independently of each other. Figure 2-21f illustrates a triple-shaft arrangement wherein two turbine-compressor combinations operate on independent shafts. A third shaft is provided for a low-pressure turbine. With the multishaft arrangement a compressor which operates more efficiently at a constant or high speed may be driven by a turbine on one shaft while another turbine operating on an independent shaft and at another speed may drive a slower or variable-speed machine. The multishaft plant is also advantageous when it is necessary to use a

1. LP compressor
2. MP compressor
3. Intercooler
4. HP compressor
5. Heat exchanger
6. Air heater, HP and LP heating surfaces combined
7. HP turbine

8. LP turbine
9. Generator
10. Starting motor
11. Circulating gas blower
12. Charging compressor
13. Exhaust turbine
14. Combustion air preheater

Fig. 2-18. Escher Wyss closed-cycle gas-turbine plant. Useful output 12,500 kw. (Arrangement for a more longitudinal surface.) (*Courtesy of Escher Wyss Company.*)

Fig. 2-19. Escher Wyss 12,500-kw closed-cycle gas-turbine plant. (*Courtesy of Escher Wyss Company.*)

reversing turbine as in marine applications or to suit a convenient layout when reheat and intercooling are utilized.

An intercooled plant arrangement is shown in Fig. 2-21c. In the intercooled plant, compression takes place in two or more steps, the air being cooled in the intercooler between these steps. Intercooling may be used in a single-shaft arrangement as shown in Fig. 2-21c or a multishaft arrangement as illustrated in Fig. 2-21f. The reasons for employing intercooling will be discussed in Sec. 5-9.

The reheat plant with a single-shaft arrangement is shown in Fig. 2-21d and with a multishaft arrangement in Fig. 2-21f. In the reheat plant, gas expansion takes place in two or more turbines with heat added

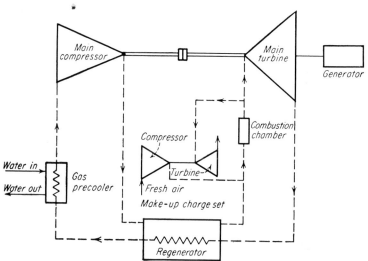

Fig. 2-20. Westinghouse semiclosed cycle.

to the gas between the turbines. The circumstances under which reheat is desirable are discussed in Sec. 5-11.

The regenerative plant (Fig. 2-21e) utilizes a heat exchanger to recover heat from the turbine exhaust gases. The heat exchanger or regenerator operates with exhaust gases on one side of the plates or tubes and air from the compressor on the other side. This operation decreases the heat required to be added in the combustor. Regeneration is discussed in more detail in Secs. 5-5 and 5-12.

The combination plant (Fig. 2-21f) utilizes reheat, intercooling, and regeneration. Due consideration is given to the relative importance of plant performance, simplicity, weight, bulkiness, and initial cost in determining which of the functions of reheat, intercooling, and regeneration are to be incorporated in the design. The relative merits of these functions in combined use are discussed further in Sec. 5-12.

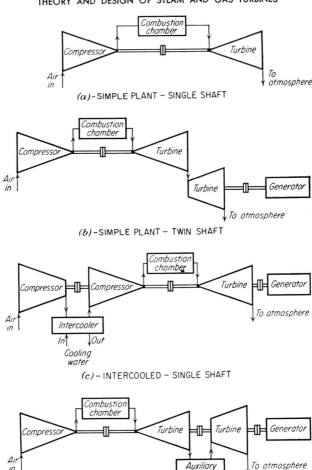

(a)-SIMPLE PLANT - SINGLE SHAFT

(b)-SIMPLE PLANT - TWIN SHAFT

(c)-INTERCOOLED - SINGLE SHAFT

(d)- REHEAT - SINGLE SHAFT

Fig. 2-21. Gas-turbine arrangements.

2-7. Classification According to Combustion. All the gas turbines described thus far operate with continuous combustion, *i.e.*, continuous ignition takes place in either an internally or externally fired combustion chamber as opposed to the intermittent combustion associated with the Otto or diesel engines.

The free-piston or power-gas plant is a type of gas-turbine plant operating with intermittent combustion. The free-piston unit takes the place of the combustor, heat exchanger, and air compressor. Figure 2-22 shows a diagrammatic arrangement of a free-piston plant similar to a 7000-hp unit constructed by Sulzer Brothers, Ltd. The free-piston unit operates

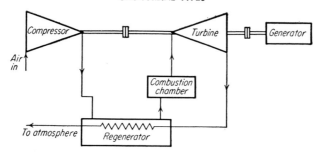

(e) – REGENERATION – SINGLE SHAFT

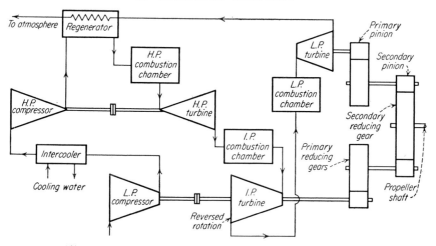

(f) – INTERCOOLING, REHEAT, REGENERATION, TRIPLE-SHAFT PLANT
FOR MARINE PROPULSION

Fig. 2-21. Gas-turbine arrangements (continued).

on a principle similar to that of the two-stroke (two-cycle) diesel engine. The charging compressor delivers air to the compressor cylinders where it is secondarily compressed by the outward movement of the pistons. The compressed air is then admitted to the firing chambers and fuel is injected. When the pistons come together, the charge of fuel and air is compressed and ignition takes place, driving the pistons outward. Upon reaching the extreme extended position, the pistons bounce back to compress the succeeding charge of air and fuel. In other words the outward movement of the pistons compresses the air in the air cylinders and the inward movement compresses the charge of fuel and air in the firing chamber. The motive force is obtained from the combustion of the fuel in the firing chamber.

2-8. Classification According to Fuel. Gas-turbine plants may be further classified according to fuel, such as oil, gaseous fuel (natural gas or waste combustible gas), or solid fuel in the form of coal or waste combustible solids.   Oil and gas are in most general use.   At this time the only coal-fired units used are in the coal-burning gas-turbine locomotive described previously.

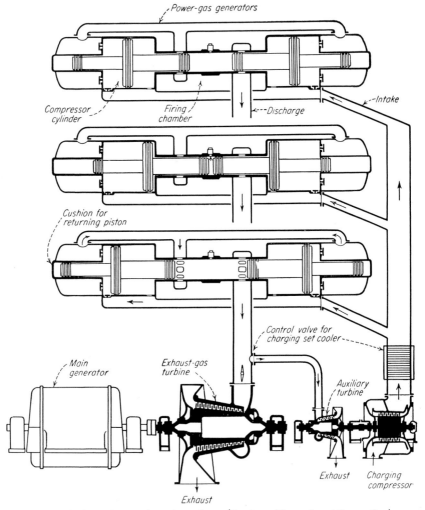

Fig. 2-22. Sulzer Brothers free-piston plant.   (Courtesy of Brown Boveri Corporation.)

2-9. Some Advantages of the Gas Turbine.   Some of the advantages of the gas turbine are apparent from the material previously covered. These advantages and some others will be reviewed here.   Further advantages and limitations will be discussed at appropriate points in the text after the necessary background material has been introduced.

Compared with reciprocating engines the gas turbine shares with the steam turbine the advantage of comparative freedom from vibration. This advantage is particularly desirable in marine and transport applications.

The size and weight of the gas-turbine plant compared with the steam power plant are low. However, the size of the gas-turbine plant may be appreciably greater than that of a high-speed diesel in the lower capacities. In the larger capacities, notably the stationary and marine types, the gas-turbine plant may have the advantage of lower size than a comparable diesel installation. Where size and weight are important considerations, as in aircraft, ships, and locomotives, the gas turbine would in general appear to occupy a favorable position. A further advantage is found in the generally cylindrical shape of the turbine and the compressor, making these units easier to install.

The gas-turbine power plant requires little or no water compared with the condensing steam power plant. This of course is a very decided advantage where an ample supply of water is not available. However, it must be remembered that the diesel engine requires very little water.

Lubrication for the gas-turbine power plant is required chiefly in the compressor and turbine main bearings and the bearings of auxiliary equipment. This is a decided advantage over the complicated lubrication system of the diesel with its expensive grades of lubricants.

Experience gained with the steam turbine and with existing gas-turbine installations indicates that maintenance costs should be lower than with the complicated diesel. However, this advantage is lessened when more complex forms of the gas-turbine plant are used. Considering the boiler and extensive auxiliary equipment required in the steam power plant, the comparative simplicity of the gas-turbine power plant is conducive to lower maintenance costs. A similar relationship exists between the initial costs of the gas-turbine plant and the steam power plant. In larger capacities the gas-turbine plant seems to have a slight advantage over the diesel engine as far as initial costs are concerned. The opposite appears to be true in the smaller capacities.

The gas-turbine plant can be started in about 6 to 15 min, which offers a decided advantage over the steam power plant for stand-by and peak-load service. Furthermore, no stand-by losses are involved such as are incurred in the steam power plant where the boiler must be kept in operation during periods when the turbine is off the line. The advantage of quick starting is not so great when the gas turbine is compared with the diesel engine.

The thermal efficiencies of gas turbines appear to be quite similar to those of steam power plants of comparable size. Much information is available in the literature as to the thermal efficiencies of gas-turbine plants but it is not always clear if the efficiencies claimed are based on computation, peak conditions, continuous operation, or on the higher or lower heating values of the fuel. In any case the thermal efficiencies of present installations of gas turbines appear to be considerably lower than those reported for stationary diesels. However, if the gas turbine operates on a No. 6 residual fuel oil the comparative cost with diesel fuel in some circumstances may make the gas turbine more attractive, its lower thermal efficiency notwithstanding.

References

1. Davy, N.: "The Gas Turbine," D. Van Nostrand Company, Inc., New York, 1914.
2. Fischer, F. K., and C. A. Meyer: The Gas Turbine-Harness for Hot Air, *Westinghouse Engineer*, May, 1944.
3. Gas Turbine Issue, *Powerfax*, Autumn, 1945.
4. Keller, C.: Some Technical Aspects and Applications of the Closed-cycle Gas Turbine System, *Paper* 2, Section *G*, Fourth World Power Conference, London, 1950.
5. Pfenninger, H.: Where Gas Turbines Will Fit in Future Power Fields, *Power*, November, 1946, and January, 1947.
6. Rettaliata, J. T.: The Combustion Gas Turbine, *Current Trends*, No. 4, 1939.
7. Rettaliata, J. T.: The Gas Turbine, *Current Trends*, No. 7, 1945.
8. Rowley, L. N., and B. G. A. Skrotzki: Gas Turbines, *Power*, October, 1946.
9. Smith, R. B., and C. R. Soderberg: The Gas Turbine as a Possible Marine Prime Mover, *Trans. Soc. Naval Architects and Marine Engrs.*, 1943.
10. Supplee, H. H.: "The Gas Turbine," J. B. Lippincott Company, Philadelphia, 1910.

CHAPTER 3

FUNDAMENTALS OF THERMODYNAMICS

3-1. Introduction. A knowledge of the principles of thermodynamics is a condition precedent to undertaking a study of steam and gas turbines. The science of thermodynamics finds its basis in two natural laws, namely, the first and second laws of thermodynamics. From these two laws are developed qualitative relationships among the observable dimensions or properties of matter without any thesis regarding the structure of matter. To determine the quantitative relationships among the properties of matter, one must resort to experiment. Classical thermodynamics predicts the qualitative relationships of matter predicated on the validity of the first and second laws, while engineering or applied thermodynamics incorporates the quantitative relationships observed through experimental and statistical methods.

The purpose of this chapter is to review some of the more important thermodynamic principles which are essential to a study of steam and gas turbines and their operating media. The reader who has recently completed a course in thermodynamics may omit this chapter if desired without any loss of continuity.

3-2. Thermodynamic Systems. A system is a region in space enclosing a definite quantity of matter. The boundary or surface enclosing the system may be real or imaginary and rigid or elastic. A real and rigid boundary may be a steel bomb enclosing a mass of gas. A real and elastic boundary may be a rubber balloon enclosing a mass of gas. An imaginary boundary may be either elastic or rigid and may be supposed to surround a given mass of fluid flowing in a passage, for example.

Systems are further defined as closed or open systems. An open system is one which experiences mass transfer. A closed system contains a constant mass with no mass transfer.

Any other system or systems of thermodynamic interest outside the system under consideration are termed the surroundings. Energy transfers in the form of heat and work may take place between a system and its surroundings. When no energy transfer takes place between system and surroundings, the system is known as an isolated system.

Systems may also be defined as being homogeneous or heterogeneous. A homogeneous system is one in which the matter exists in a single phase. A phase is a quantity of matter which is homogeneous in composition both chemically and physically but not necessarily in a molecular sense. For example, water may exist in the solid, liquid, or gaseous phase. A heterogeneous system is one in which the matter exists in two or more phases. For example, a heterogeneous system may contain a two-phase mixture such as wet steam.

Thermodynamics is concerned principally with systems which are in equilibrium. For example, an isolated system in which there are internal temperature variations will, if left to itself, attain a condition where the temperature is uniform throughout the system. This final state is said to be in thermodynamic equilibrium and one can speak of the temperature of the system. The same condition of equilibrium must apply to other properties such as pressure and density. Should the system be heterogeneous, as, for example, a system containing wet steam, an additional condition for equilibrium is constancy of the proportions of vapor and water, that is to say, the temperature and pressure must be each the same everywhere in the two-phase mixture. To be sure the density will not be the same in the two phases but within each phase, which is itself homogeneous, the density must be constant for equilibrium.

The state of a homogeneous system in equilibrium is completely specified in terms of pressure, temperature, and specific volume or density. A heterogeneous system in equilibrium requires in addition the concentration of the mixture. For example, in the case of wet steam the quality must be specified in addition to one of the properties of pressure, temperature, and density or specific volume. These dimensions which specify the state of a system are known as the properties, state variables, or thermodynamic coordinates.

3-3. Processes. When a system undergoes a change of state, that is, when the values of the properties are changed, the operation which brought about the change is known as a process. If the process is such that equilibrium is maintained at all times, that is to say, the properties are uniform at all times in each homogeneous phase, the process is said to be reversible. If uniformity of the properties is not maintained, the process is irreversible. The true significance of the concepts of reversibility and irreversibility is evident only in terms of the second law of thermodynamics, which will be discussed in a later section.

It should be emphasized here that the state of a system is defined in terms of the properties and is independent of the process which brought about the change. In other words, the state of a system is a point function of its properties.

3-4. Equations of State. The equation of state of a homogeneous substance is the mathematical relationship between the state variables of pressure, specific volume or density, and temperature.   The substance may be a solid, a liquid, or a gas.   Therefore

$$f(P,v,T) = 0$$

If the form of the function f is known and its value is calculated for a given substance, then any two of the properties P, v, and T will define the state.   However, the function f may be extremely complicated for a real substance.   Therefore it is usual to employ a simpler function which is more convenient to handle and a substance obeying such a simple equation of state is known as an ideal substance.

3-5. Equation of State of an Ideal Gas.   The equation of state of all gases near zero pressure has been found from extrapolated experimental data to be

$$Pv = RT \tag{3-1}$$

where P = pressure, psf

    v = specific volume, cu ft per lb

    R = gas constant = 1545/molecular weight

    T = absolute temperature, °R

An ideal gas is one which obeys this equation of state at all temperatures and pressures.   No real gas obeys exactly this equation at normal temperatures and pressures, but a very good approximation is obtainable for He, H_2, O_2, N_2, CO, and dry air.   At low pressures the equation of state of an ideal gas approximates the behavior of real gases.

It is clear from Eq. (3-1) that at constant pressure the specific volume of an ideal gas is a linear function of temperature and at constant volume the pressure is a linear function of temperature.   This approximation of the behavior of real gases at low pressures was observed by Charles and Gay-Lussac and led to what is known as the Charles or Gay-Lussac law.

It is also evident from Eq. (3-1) that if the temperature of an ideal gas is held constant, the product of P and v is constant.   This behavior is approximated for real gases at low pressures and is called Boyle's law after the discoverer.

3-6. Some Other Equations of State.   Many empirical equations of state for real gases have been proposed where the accuracy of the equation of state for an ideal gas is too crude an approximation.   The Beattie-Bridgeman equation of state correlates very closely with experimental data over a wide range of pressure, volume, and temperature and is given here.

$$Pv = \frac{RT}{v} (1 - \epsilon)(v + B) - \frac{A}{v} \tag{3-2}$$

where $A = A_0(1 - a/v)$

    $B = B_0(1 - b/c)$

    $\epsilon = c/vT^3$

Experimentally determined values for the constants in the Beattie-Bridgeman equation of state are given in Table 3-1.

TABLE 3-1. VALUES OF CONSTANTS IN BEATTIE-BRIDGEMAN EQUATION OF STATE

Gas	R, ft-lb/(lb)(°F)	A_o, ft⁴/lb	a, ft³/lb	B_o, ft³/lb	b, ft³/lb	c, (ft³)(°R³)/lb
Air	53.35	842	0.0107	0.0255	−0.00061	14×10^4
O_2	48.29	790	0.0128	0.0232	0.00211	14×10^4
CO_2	35.12	1,403	0.0260	0.0382	0.0263	14×10^5
H_2	766.6	26,400	−0.0402	0.167	−0.347	2.33×10^4
N_2	55.16	930	0.0149	0.0288	−0.00395	14×10^4
C_2H_4	55.13	4,240	0.0283	0.0693	0.0205	75.6×10^4

Equation (3-2) is in such form that it is not possible to solve for the specific volume v when the pressure and temperature are known. However, the equation may be expressed in the following form after a series transformation to permit solving for specific volume directly:

$$v = \frac{RT}{P} + \frac{\alpha}{RT} + \frac{\beta P}{R^2 T^2} + \frac{\gamma P^2}{R^3 T^3} \qquad (3\text{-}3)$$

where $\alpha = RTB_o - A_o - Rc/T^2$
$\beta = -RTB_o b + A_o a - RB_o c/T^2$
$\gamma = RB_o bc/T^2$

Another well-known equation of state is that of van der Waals and is usually given in the following form:

$$R'T = \left(P' + \frac{a}{v'^2}\right)(v' - b) \qquad (3\text{-}4)$$

where a and b = constants for a given gas
R' = gas constant = 0.729 atm ft³/(°R)(mole)
P' = pressure, atm
v' = specific volume, cu ft per mole
The values of a and b for a few gases are given in Table 3-2.

TABLE 3-2. VALUES OF THE CONSTANTS IN VAN DER WAALS' EQUATION OF STATE

Gas	a, atm-ft⁶/mole²	b, ft³/mole
Air	343.8	0.585
O_2	349.5	0.510
CO_2	924.2	0.685
H_2	63.02	0.427
N_2	346.0	0.618

A significant feature of van der Waals' equation of state is that at large specific volumes the term a/v'^2 becomes negligible, as does the term b giving the equivalent of the equation of state for an ideal gas. This fact is of course consistent with the applicability of Eq. (3-1) at large specific volumes or low pressures. It is clear that any equation of state must approach the equation of state of an ideal gas at large specific volumes.

Other equations of state which are in less general use are given below without discussion except to say that the constants given in the equations have values for each gas that are unique for the equation considered.

Dieterici:

$$P = \frac{RT^{-(a/RTv)}}{v - b^e}$$

Lees:

$$P = \frac{RT}{v - b} - \frac{aP^{1/3}}{Tv^{5/3}}$$

Clausius:

$$P = \frac{RT}{v - b} - \frac{c}{T(v + a)^2}$$

Callendar:

$$v = \frac{RT}{P} + b - \frac{c}{T^n} \quad \text{(for steam)}$$

3-7. Work. Work is defined as energy transfer between a system and its surroundings due to a force potential. For example, work is done when a boundary is displaced. If the force is exerted from the surroundings displacing the boundary inward on the system, the work expended is regarded as being negative. If the force acts from within the system displacing the boundary outward on the surroundings, the work done is considered to be positive.

Consider a system with an arbitrary boundary and containing a unit mass of a substance as shown in Fig. 3-1. The boundary is experiencing a change due to a force F. The work done on the system is $\int F \cos \theta \, ds$. Consider now a differential force dF exerted by the system due to an internal pressure P_i acting on a differential area dA. Then

$$dF = P_i \, dA$$

and if the element is displaced inward on the system a differential distance ds, the work done on the system against the internal pressure is

$$\dot{W} = dF \, ds = P_i \, dA \, ds$$

The total surface area is obtained by integrating over the boundary surface so that

$$\dot{W} = P_i A \, ds$$

Since $A \, ds$ represents the decrease in volume of the system, it may be expressed as dv and the work done on the system is expressed

$$\dot{W} = P_i \, dv \qquad (3\text{-}5)$$

If the process by which the displacement of the boundary takes place (or the system volume is changed) is a succession of equilibrium states, then at all times the system and surroundings will be in equilibrium and the internal pressure equals the external pressure. Therefore this equilibrium pressure P may be expressed in terms of v and T by means of the equation of state. The work may be then expressed

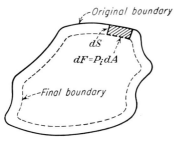

$$\dot{W} = P \, dv \qquad (3\text{-}6)$$

Now Eq. (3-6) is not a function of the state of the system before and after the work is done but is a function of the process or path by which the work is done.

Fig. 3-1. Displacement of boundary.

Therefore, $\dot{W}$ is an inexact differential (indicated by the dot over the differential sign) since it is not a function of the integration limits alone, but is dependent on the path. The real meaning of the differential $\dot{W}$ is a "small amount of work" and not a "small change in W."

If the path or process is defined, Eq. (3-6) may be integrated. For example, consider a reversible process represented by a line xy on a P-v plane as shown in Fig. 3-2. The work done by a small change dv is represented by the crosshatched area under the line representing the process. The total work done due to the increase of specific volume from x to y via the reversible path xy is

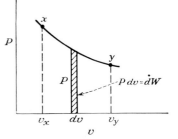

$$W = \int_{v_x}^{v_y} P \, dv \qquad (3\text{-}7)$$

Fig. 3-2. Reversible process on P-v diagram.

The work done is positive since the specific volume change is positive, indicating the work is done by the system. If the process is retraced from y to x, the work is negative and is done on the system.

Similarly $\int P \, dv$ may be evaluated for other processes as follows: In a constant-volume or isometric process, $\int P \, dv = 0$, since dv is constant. In a constant-pressure or isobaric process, the work done is

$$W = P \int_{v_x}^{v_y} dv = P(v_y - v_x) \qquad (3\text{-}8)$$

In a constant temperature or isothermal process and if the system is an ideal gas, from the equation of state, $P = RT/v$ and

$$W = \int_{v_x}^{v_y} \frac{RT}{v} \, dv = RT \ln \frac{v_y}{v_x} \tag{3-9}$$

Furthermore, since $P_x v_x = P_y v_y = RT = $ constant for an isothermal process, Eq. (3-9) may be put in the form

$$W = RT \ln \frac{P_x}{P_y} = P_x v_x \ln \frac{v_y}{v_x} = P_y v_y \ln \frac{v_y}{v_x} \tag{3-10}$$

Note that in Eqs. (3-8) to (3-10) the path is specified.

3-8. The First Law of Thermodynamics. The first law of thermodynamics is merely a restatement of the natural law of conservation of energy. Applied to a thermodynamic system, this law means that the energy change in a system is exactly equal to the resultant energy transfer across its boundary. By resultant energy transfer is meant the difference in energy transfer into and out of the system.

In the preceding section one form of energy transfer which can take place across the boundary of a system was discussed, namely, work. Another form of energy transfer may also take place across the boundary and it is known as heat. Heat may be defined as energy transfer across the boundary of a system resulting from a thermal potential and it is given the symbol Q to distinguish it from work. It will be noted that there is no implication of mass transfer across the boundary of the system in the definition of heat.

If at any and all times the energy stored within the system is assumed to be a function of the state of the system, then the change in stored energy may be expressed as an exact differential. The stored energy so defined is referred to as the internal energy of the system and given the symbol U. Then the first law of thermodynamics may be expressed

$$U_2 - U_1 = Q - W \tag{3-11}$$

where $U_1 = $ internal energy at start of process, Btu per lb
$U_2 = $ internal energy at end of process, Btu per lb
$Q = $ resultant heat transfer into system, Btu per lb
$W = $ resultant work done by system, Btu per lb

In the preceding section it was shown that dW is an inexact differential. The change in internal energy of a system is an exact differential and, therefore, does not depend on the process. Then, a priori, Q indeed depends on the process and is not a function of the state of the system. The differential of Q is inexact and is given as dQ. For an infinitesimal change of state, the first law may be expressed

$$dU = dQ - dW \qquad (3\text{-}12)$$

Equation (3-12) is known as the energy equation of a system.
Consider now a series of unspecified processes which change the state
of a system and eventually return it to its original condition. Such a
series of processes is known as a cycle. Since dU is an exact differential,
it is clear that for a cyclic change $dU = U_2 - U_1 = 0$. It follows that
for a cycle $dQ = dW$. This is a very important consequence of the first
law, for it says that the net heat transferred into a system must equal
exactly the resultant work done by the system. It is an obvious conclusion that no machine operating in complete cycles can do more work
than the equivalent energy absorbed by the machine in the form of heat.
A machine purported to violate this principle is said to be a perpetual-
motion machine of the first kind.

From the preceding discussion it is clear that the earlier assumption
that the internal energy of a system is a function of the state of the system must necessarily be true as a corollary of the first law.

3-9. Specific Heat. The equation of state of a homogeneous system
expresses a relationship between one dependent and two independent
variables so that any two of the state variables P, v, and T will define
the state of the system. The internal energy U is also a function of the
state of the system and, therefore, of the state variables P, v, and T.
Therefore, if T and P are considered to be the independent variables

$$U = f(T,P)$$

$$dU = \left(\frac{\partial U}{\partial T}\right)_P dT + \left(\frac{\partial U}{\partial P}\right)_T dP \qquad (3\text{-}13)$$

and, from the equation of state,

$$dv = \left(\frac{\partial v}{\partial T}\right)_P dT + \left(\frac{\partial v}{\partial P}\right)_T dP \qquad (3\text{-}14)$$

From Eqs. (3-6), (3-12), (3-13), and (3-14),

$$dQ = \left[\left(\frac{\partial U}{\partial T}\right)_P + P\left(\frac{\partial v}{\partial T}\right)_P\right] dT + \left[\left(\frac{\partial U}{\partial P}\right)_T + P\left(\frac{\partial v}{\partial P}\right)_T\right] dP \qquad (3\text{-}15)$$

This is the energy equation for the system in terms of the independent
variables T and P. The process by which the state variables change is
reversible by reason of using Eq. (3-6). However, the partial derivatives
do not have this restriction since they do not refer to any process at all.
Consider now a constant-pressure process; then $dP = 0$ and Eq. (3-15)

becomes

$$dQ = \left[\left(\frac{\partial U}{\partial T}\right)_P + P\left(\frac{\partial v}{\partial T}\right)_P\right] dT \tag{3-16}$$

The value of the bracketed expression in Eq. (3-16) may be obtained experimentally, and the heat transfer to a system may then be expressed in terms of this value and the temperature change of the system. The bracketed expression is identified by the symbol C_p and is known as the specific heat at constant pressure. In measuring the specific heat at constant pressure, the system may be kept at atmospheric pressure or any other convenient pressure. Quantities of heat may be then added to the system and the temperature changes observed. As a result Eq. (3-16) can be expressed

$$dQ = C_p\, dT_p \tag{3-17}$$

It is implied in Eq. (3-16) that the value of the specific heat depends on the process, in this case a constant-pressure process. It is also clear from the partial derivatives that the value of the specific heat also depends on the pressure and mean temperature at which the measurements are taken. Therefore, the value of the specific heat at constant pressure is a function of the mean temperature at which heat is added and the pressure of the system.

If T and v are taken as the independent variables, then

$$U = f(T,v)$$

or

$$dU = \left(\frac{\partial U}{\partial T}\right)_v dT + \left(\frac{\partial U}{\partial v}\right)_T dv \tag{3-18}$$

From Eqs. (3-6), (3-12), and (3-18),

$$dQ = \left(\frac{\partial U}{\partial T}\right)_v dT + \left[P + \left(\frac{\partial U}{\partial v}\right)_T\right] dv \tag{3-19}$$

If the volume is held constant, Eq. (3-19) becomes

$$dQ = \left(\frac{\partial U}{\partial T}\right)_v dT \tag{3-20}$$

and the partial derivative is called the specific heat at constant volume. The value of this specific heat is seen to depend on the mean temperature at which heat is transferred and the specific volume of the system. In other words, the value of the specific heat is not constant over a wide range of temperatures and pressures. Equation (3-20) may be expressed

$$dQ = C_v\, dT_v$$

where C_v is the specific heat at constant volume.

The value of C_v cannot be determined by direct experimental methods because of the practical difficulties of maintaining a constant-volume process. The principal difficulty exists in the impossibility of finding a rigid container which will not expand with increase of temperature. Usually the value of C_v is obtained in terms of the more easily measured C_p.

3-10. Joule's Law. Joule performed experiments in order to determine the change in internal energy of an expanding gas. The experimental technique consisted of permitting a gas to expand from one vessel into another vessel which had been evacuated. The apparatus is described diagrammatically in Fig. 3-3. As can be seen, the two vessels a and b are connected by means of a pipe and stopcock. The entire apparatus was immersed in a water bath and permitted to remain there until thermal equilibrium was reached between system and surroundings. No further heat transfer between system and surroundings could take place under these

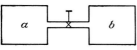

Fig. 3-3. Joule's apparatus.

conditions. The temperature of the gas was observed. Then the stopcock was opened and the gas expanded into the evacuated vessel. No work was done either by the system on the surroundings, or vice versa. After the system had reestablished thermal equilibrium, the final temperature of the gas was observed. No difference was observed between the final and initial temperatures of the gas. The temperature of the water bath also remained constant and, therefore, no heat transfer occurred. From these observations and from the first law of thermodynamics, Joule concluded that when a *gas expands without doing external work and without heat transfer, the temperature remains constant and the internal energy is constant.*

Now the pressure and the volume of the gas certainly changed so that it may be further concluded that the change in internal energy is a function of temperature only. Later it will be shown that Joule's law is valid only for ideal gases and that the change in internal energy of real gases is a function of P, v, and T.

3-11. Relationships between Specific Heats of Ideal Gases. For an ideal gas a relationship between C_p and C_v may be found as follows. If a system consisting of an ideal gas is heated at constant pressure through some temperature rise dT with a corresponding specific volume increase dv, the heat transferred to the system is

$$\dot{Q} = C_p \, dT \qquad \text{Btu} \qquad (3\text{-}21)$$

and the work done is

$$\dot{W} = P \, dv \qquad \text{ft-lb}$$

From the equation of state for an ideal gas and the condition that the pressure is constant

$$\frac{P \, dv}{J} = \frac{R}{J} \, dT \qquad \text{Btu}$$

and
$$dW = \frac{R}{J} \, dT \qquad \text{Btu} \qquad (3\text{-}22)$$

From Eq. (3-12) and Eqs. (3-21) and (3-22),

$$dU = C_p \, dT - \frac{R}{J} \, dT = \left(C_p - \frac{R}{J} \right) dT \qquad (3\text{-}23)$$

If the same ideal gas is now heated at constant volume between the same temperature limits

$$dQ = C_v \, dT \qquad \text{Btu} \qquad (3\text{-}24)$$

For a constant-volume process, $dW = P \, dv = 0$, and, from Eqs. (3-12) and (3-24),

$$dU = C_v \, dT \qquad \text{Btu} \qquad (3\text{-}25)$$

But since the temperature change for each process is the same, the change in internal energy must also be the same in accordance with Joule's law. Therefore, Eqs. (3-23) and (3-25) may be set equal to each other and

$$C_p - C_v = \frac{R}{J} \qquad (3\text{-}26)$$

or
$$\frac{C_p}{C_v} - 1 = \frac{R}{JC_v}$$

Denoting the ratio of the specific heats C_p/C_v by k,

$$k - 1 = \frac{R}{JC_v}$$

and hence
$$C_v = \frac{R}{J(k-1)} \qquad (3\text{-}27)$$

and
$$C_p = \frac{Rk}{J(k-1)} \qquad (3\text{-}28)$$

3-12. Adiabatic Processes. An adiabatic process is one in which the system is perfectly insulated thermally and $dQ = 0$. If, in addition to being adiabatic, the process is also reversible, the property entropy S is constant. Entropy will be discussed later as a consequence of the second law of thermodynamics.

Equation (3-19) may be expressed by substituting for $(\partial U/\partial T)_v$ the specific heat C_v and

$$dQ = C_v \, dT + \left[P + \left(\frac{\partial U}{\partial v} \right)_T \right] dv$$

Consider the process to be reversible and adiabatic; then

$$C_v \, dT = - \left[P + \left(\frac{\partial U}{\partial v} \right)_T \right] dv \tag{3-29}$$

If further an ideal gas is considered, the change in internal energy is a function of temperature only and $(\partial U/\partial v)_T = 0$ so that

$$C_v \, dT = -P \, dv = - \frac{RT}{v} \, dv \tag{3-30}$$

Integrating the preceding equation,

$$\frac{dT}{T} + \frac{R}{C_v} \frac{dv}{v} = 0$$

and

$$\ln T + \frac{R}{C_v} \ln v = \text{const}$$

$$Pv^{R/C_v} = \text{const}$$

Since the equation of state is a point function, $T = Pv/R$, and

$$Pv^{(R+C_v)/C_v} = \text{const}$$

Substituting from Eq. (3-26), keeping units consistent,

$$Pv^k = \text{const} \tag{3-31}$$

This is the equation of the path of a reversible adiabatic process on a P-v plane.

With the aid of Eq. (3-31) an expression can be developed for the work done in a reversible adiabatic process for an ideal gas

$$\dot{Q} = P \, dv$$

or

$$Q = \int_{v_1}^{v_2} P \, dv$$

and

$$Q = C \int_{v_1}^{v_2} v^{-k} \, dv$$

$$Q = \frac{1}{1-k} \left[C v^{1-k} \right]_{v_1}^{v_2}$$

or

$$Q = \frac{1}{1-k} (P_2 v_2 - P_1 v_1) \tag{3-32}$$

From the first law of thermodynamics for an adiabatic process

$$dU = -\dot{d}W$$

and for an ideal gas

$$W = U_1 - U_2 = C_v(T_1 - T_2) \tag{3-33}$$

3-13. Joule-Thomson Experiment. The Joule-Thomson apparatus is shown in Fig. 3-4. A constant flow of gas at a pressure P_1 and T_1 is pumped through a porous plug in a pipe and leaves at some lower P_2 and at a temperature T_2. The entire apparatus is insulated thermally. The apparatus is operated for a sufficient length of time until a steady state is reached, *i.e.*, there is no variation of pressure, specific volume, velocity, or temperature with time at any cross section of the apparatus. Therefore, heat flows from the gas to the walls of the apparatus are eliminated.

Consider an elementary mass of gas m entering the porous plug; then P_1A represents the force exerted on the upstream face where A is the cross-sectional area. Similarly, P_2A is the force exerted in the opposite direction on the downstream face. The length of the element of gas entering the plug is l_1 and leaving it is l_2. The length l_2 is greater than l_1

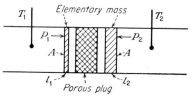

Fig. 3-4. Joule-Thomson apparatus.

because an expansion takes place with the decrease in pressure and the cross-sectional areas are constant. The net force is

$$F = P_2A - P_1A$$

and the work done by the gas is

$$W = P_2Al_1 - P_1Al_1$$

or

$$W = P_2v_2 - P_1v_1$$

Since the apparatus is insulated thermally, from the first law of thermodynamics and the preceding equation,

$$U_2 - U_1 = \frac{P_1v_1}{J} - \frac{P_2v_2}{J} \qquad (3\text{-}34)$$

The internal energy is not constant as was the case in the Joule experiment for an isolated system. If it is assumed that the gas is ideal and the specific heats are constant so that $C_p - C_v = R/J$,

$$C_p(T_1 - T_2) = \left(\frac{R}{J} + C_v\right)(T_1 - T_2)$$

or

$$C_p(T_1 - T_2) = \frac{RT_1}{J} - \frac{RT_2}{J} + C_v(T_1 - T_2) \qquad (3\text{-}35)$$

The change in internal energy of an ideal gas is a function of temperature change only. This is true regardless of the process since temperature is a function of the state of the gas. Then

$$U_2 - U_1 = f(T_2 - T_1)$$

If a constant-volume process is selected for convenience, the value of the function f may be readily determined for

$$\dot{Q} = C_v(T_2 - T_1) = U_2 - U_1$$

and $f = C_v$. Substituting for $C_v(T_1 - T_2)$ its equivalent $U_1 - U_2$ and for $(RT_1 - RT_2)/J$ its equivalent $(P_1v_1 - P_2v_2)/J$,

$$C_p(T_1 - T_2) = \frac{P_1v_1 - P_2v_2}{J} - (U_2 - U_1) \qquad (3\text{-}36)$$

But from Eq. (3-34), $(P_1v_1 - P_2v_2)/J = U_2 - U_1$, and Eq. (3-36) becomes

$$C_p(T_1 - T_2) = 0$$

Therefore, the temperature of an ideal gas does not change in the Joule-Thomson experiment.

Equation (3-34) may be rearranged as follows

$$U_1 + \frac{P_1v_1}{J} = U_2 + \frac{P_2v_2}{J} \qquad (3\text{-}37)$$

The expression $U + (PV/J)$ is composed of state functions and, therefore, the expression itself is a state function or property of the system.

3-14. Enthalpy. The expression $U + (PV/J)$ occurs in thermodynamic relationships whenever mass transfer into and out of a system is involved. It has been found convenient to give the expression a name and a symbol to identify it. The name is enthalpy and the symbol is h. The units are in Btu per pound. Since

$$h = U + \frac{PV}{J}$$

$$dh = dU + \frac{d(Pv)}{J} = dU + \frac{P\,dv + v\,dP}{J} \qquad (3\text{-}38)$$

But from the first law of thermodynamics

$$\dot{Q} = dU + \frac{P\,dv}{J}$$

Therefore

$$dh = dQ + \frac{v\,dP}{J} \qquad (3\text{-}39)$$

Consider a constant pressure process in which $dP = 0$ and $\dot{Q} = C_p\,dT$. Substituting in Eq. (3-39),

$$dh = C_p\,dT$$

or

$$\left(\frac{\partial h}{\partial T}\right)_p = C_p \qquad (3\text{-}40)$$

3-15. Steady-flow Energy Equation. Figure 3-5 represents an open system through which a constant mass rate of flow occurs. The flow is steady and the rates at which heat is transferred and work is done are uniform. The rates of mass flow entering and leaving the system are both constant and equal. The properties of the system at any point are invariable with time. In other words the system is incapable of storing

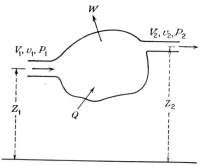

Fig. 3-5. Steady-flow open system.

mass or energy. The steady-flow energy equation for a unit mass flow per unit time is

$$\frac{Z_1}{J} + \frac{V_1^2}{2gJ} + U_1 + \frac{P_1 v_1}{J} + Q = \frac{Z_2}{J} + \frac{V_2^2}{2gJ} + U_2 + \frac{P_2 v_2}{J} + \frac{W}{J}$$

or

$$\frac{Z_1}{J} + \frac{V_1^2}{2gJ} + h_1 + Q = \frac{Z_2}{J} + \frac{V_2^2}{2gJ} + h_2 + \frac{W}{J} \tag{3-41}$$

where Z/J = the potential energy, Btu per lb

$V^2/2gJ$ = kinetic energy, Btu per lb

U = internal energy, Btu per lb

h = enthalpy, Btu per lb

Q = heat transfer, Btu per lb

W = work, ft-lb per lb

Not all the energy terms given in Eq. (3-41) need be used in some processes. For example, in an adiabatic process $Q = 0$. Another example is a nozzle where $Q \approx 0$, $W = 0$, and $\Delta Z \approx 0$. In the Joule-Thomson experiment $\Delta Z = 0$ and $Q = 0$ while $\Delta(v^2/2g)$ was negligible.

3-16. Second Law of Thermodynamics. It is significant to note that no direct reference has been made thus far to the second law of thermodynamics. To be sure, Joule's law could have been proved directly for an ideal gas by using the second law. Also, a more meaningful definition of heat, temperature, and entropy could have been made in consideration of the second law. Yet, without the truth of the second law, the science of thermodynamics would be without meaning.

The first law of thermodynamics states that the internal energy of an isolated system is constant regardless of what happens within the system. Yet to define the state or condition of the system it must be necessarily in equilibrium. What assurance is there that the system, if left alone, will reach equilibrium? Can the system get into a state of unequilibrium spontaneously? In which direction does the system attain equilibrium and can this direction be predicted? The answers to these and similar questions cannot be found in the first law. To find the answers, one must look to the second law of thermodynamics.

The second law of thermodynamics is stated in many ways. The most fundamental and general definition is given in terms of the property known as entropy. Since the internal energy of an isolated system is constant, this property can give no indication as to the direction in which a process proceeds. Clausius discovered in entropy a property of the system, that is, it is independent of the path and therefore is dependent only on the initial and final states of the system. Besides being a property, entropy has the unique characteristic of providing an arrow to predict in which direction a process must proceed.

The second law of thermodynamics is stated in terms of entropy as follows:

The entropy of an isolated system cannot decrease but must increase to a maximum in all real processes.

As a corollary of the second law it may be stated that when the entropy of an isolated system has reached a maximum no further change of entropy is possible and the system is in a state of equilibrium.

The entropy of a nonisolated system may decrease but then the entropy of the surroundings must increase. The boundary of the system may be extended to include those portions of the surroundings which react with the system, thus preserving the general nature of the statement of the second law.

3-17. The Reversible Cycle. A reversible cycle is a series of reversible processes through which a system undergoes a change of state. A classical reversible cycle is the one proposed by Carnot. The Carnot cycle consists of four reversible processes. The system takes in heat at constant temperature. That is, the temperatures of the system and the surroundings are each constant. Therefore the system is in equilibrium throughout the process and the process is reversible. This process requires that system and surroundings be infinite heat reservoirs so that the transfer of heat does not lower or increase the temperatures. The second process is a reversible adiabatic or isentropic expansion. Since this process is at constant entropy, it follows from the second law that the system is always in equilibrium and the process is reversible. The third process is isothermal and, therefore, reversible rejection of heat. The fourth process is an isentropic or reversible adiabatic compression.

The Carnot cycle is shown on T-S and P-v diagrams in Fig. 3-6. A type of Carnot heat engine utilizing a gas as a medium is shown in Fig. 3-7. The cylinder and piston are insulated thermally except for the cylinder head. First, the cylinder is placed in contact with a constant-temperature heat source and heat is added to the medium. This process is represented from (1) to (2) on the T-S and P-v planes. The system is assumed to be homogeneous and the process (1) to (2) proceeds with

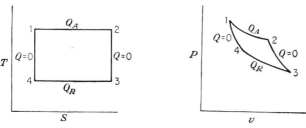

Fig. 3-6. Carnot cycle.

an increase in entropy and specific volume but a drop in pressure. The temperature of the system is constant. Next the cylinder is placed on a perfect insulator and a further increase in specific volume occurs with a drop in pressure and a drop in temperature to T_3. The entropy of the system is constant. This process is shown from (2) to (3). Now the cylinder is placed in contact with a constant-temperature heat sink and heat is rejected with the system at constant temperature $T_3 = T_4$. The

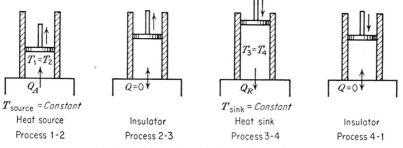

Fig. 3-7. An example of a Carnot heat engine.

process [illustrated from (3) to (4)] proceeds with a decrease in entropy, temperature, and specific volume but an increase in pressure. However, the entropy of the heat sink is increased. For the final process (4) to (1), the cylinder is again placed in contact with the insulator. Work is done on the system with an increase in pressure and temperature, a decrease in specific volume and at constant entropy.

Since this is a cyclic change of state, the internal energy is the same at the beginning and end of the cycle.   Therefore, from the first law,

$$Q - W = 0$$

But Q is the net heat added to the system or $Q_A - Q_R$ from which

$$W = Q_A - Q_R$$

Now the thermal efficiency of a heat engine is defined as the useful work output divided by the heat input, or

$$\eta_t = \frac{W}{Q_A} = \frac{Q_A - Q_R}{Q_A} \tag{3-42}$$

Concerning the isothermal addition and rejection of heat, the question arises as to the need to maintain equality of temperature between system and surroundings.   This would, of course, be a necessary requirement in order that equilibrium exist between system and surroundings.

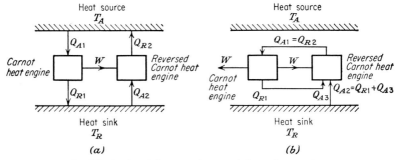

Fig. 3-8. Combined Carnot and reversed Carnot heat engines.

However, the concern here is for equilibrium within the system as a prerequisite for reversibility within the system.   It is a simple matter to arrange the boundary of the system so that any thermal unequilibrium which might exist between system and surroundings is placed outside the system.   In this way the irreversibility is in the surroundings and reversibility is maintained within the system.

3-18. Some Consequences of the Carnot Cycle.   The Carnot heat engine discussed in the preceding section utilized a gas as a working medium.   This restriction was made merely for convenience in representing the cycle on the P-v plane.   Actually, Carnot demonstrated that the efficiency of Carnot cycle is dependent only on the temperature at which heat is added to the system and the temperature at which heat is rejected. The demonstration consists of a Carnot heat engine receiving heat at T_A and rejecting heat at T_R and a reversed Carnot heat engine receiving heat at T_R and rejecting heat at T_A (see Fig. 3-8a).   The Carnot heat engine is arranged to drive the reversed Carnot engine. The net work output of this system is zero, since the work output of the Carnot heat engine is exactly equal to the work input of the reversed Carnot heat engine. Now suppose that some other medium is used which is assumed to be more efficient. This more efficient medium is used in the Carnot heat engine and the less efficient medium is retained in the reversed Carnot heat engine (see Fig. 3-8b). Under these conditions it might be expected that the Carnot heat engine will deliver more work than is needed to drive the reversed Carnot heat engine. A high-temperature source is not needed since the heat rejected by the reversed Carnot heat engine is equal exactly to the heat added to the Carnot heat engine. Consequently, the combined engine will produce work while receiving heat from a low-temperature source only. This conclusion is so utterly false in the light of man's observation of nature that the premise must be also false.

Therefore, the following conclusion must be true:

The thermal efficiency of a reversible heat engine depends entirely on the temperature at which heat is added to the system and the temperature at which heat is rejected.

Through the same process of reasoning it can be demonstrated that the following is true:

For given temperatures of source and sink no heat engine can be more efficient than a reversible heat engine and the thermal efficiencies of all reversible heat engines are the same. A system cannot transfer heat from a source of a given temperature to a sink of a higher temperature without receiving work.

Having established that the efficiency of a reversible cycle is dependent only on the temperature of source and sink, a thermodynamic scale of temperature can be developed:

$$\eta_t = f(T_A, T_R)$$

But

$$\eta_t = \frac{Q_A - Q_R}{Q_A} = 1 - \frac{Q_A}{Q_R}$$

and therefore

$$\frac{Q_R}{Q_A} = f'(T_A, T_R)$$

Lord Kelvin proposed that

$$\frac{Q_R}{Q_A} = \frac{T_R}{T_A} \qquad (3\text{-}43)$$

and the efficiency of the Carnot cycle would be, therefore,

$$\eta_t = 1 - \frac{T_R}{T_A} \qquad (3\text{-}44)$$

where T_A and T_R are the absolute thermodynamic temperatures. All existing scales such as the Fahrenheit and centigrade scales can be calibrated in terms of the absolute scale obtained from the preceding expression for the thermal efficiency of the Carnot cycle. To illustrate, the freezing point of water is taken as 32 F and the boiling point as 212 F. Suppose that a Carnot cycle operates between heat reservoirs at these temperatures. The heat added and the heat rejected are measured. Then, from Eq. (3-43),

$$\frac{x + 0}{x + 212} = \frac{Q_R}{Q_A}$$

where x is an additive correction factor to be applied to the Fahrenheit scale to obtain the absolute thermodynamic scale. Since Q_R and Q_A are known, x will be found to be very nearly 459.69. Therefore, the absolute thermodynamic scale in Rankine degrees is

$$°R = °F + 459.69 \tag{3-45}$$

It follows from such a definition of an absolute thermodynamic scale that a Rankine temperature of zero degrees or less is impossible. This fact may be shown as follows. From Eq. (3-43),

$$Q_R = Q_A \frac{T_R}{T_A}$$

But

$$W = Q_A - Q_R$$

and

$$W = Q_A - Q_A \frac{T_R}{T_A}$$

from which

$$T_R = T_A \left(1 - \frac{W}{Q_A} \right) \tag{3-46}$$

With fixed values for T_A and Q_A, the temperature T_R can be decreased only by increasing W. But, from the second law, $W < Q_A$, and therefore the lowest temperature which can be reached is above zero $°R$.

3-19. Entropy. The relationship of Eq. (3-43) for a Carnot cycle or any reversible cycle may be expressed

$$\frac{Q_A}{T_A} - \frac{Q_R}{T_R} = 0$$

Therefore, the change in Q/T is zero for a reversible cycle from which it may be concluded that Q/T is a property of any system employing a reversible cycle. For any reversible process, the change in Q/T can be computed:

$$\int_1^2 ds = \int_1^2 \frac{dQ}{T} \qquad \text{(reversible process)} \tag{3-47}$$

where S is called the entropy of a system. It will be noted that Eq. (3-47) permits calculation of changes of entropy only. However, in most practical problems the change in entropy is the significant consideration. Therefore, the entropy can be assumed to be zero at some arbitrary datum and relative values calculated from Eq. (3-47) for other states. Then the calculated entropy for any particular state is a function of the state of the system, and not the process, and may be expressed as a function of other state properties such as pressure and temperature.

The change in entropy is easily calculated for an isothermal reversible process by means of Eq. (3-47) since the temperature is constant. For reversible and nonisothermal processes, it is necessary to express $\dot{Q}$ and T in terms of each other or a single variable. Thus if the process is at constant pressure

$$\dot{Q} = C_p \, dT$$

and
$$\int_1^2 dS = \int_{T_1}^{T_2} C_p \frac{dT}{T}$$

For a constant-volume process,

$$\dot{Q} = C_v \, dT$$

and
$$\int_1^2 dS = \int_{T_1}^{T_2} C_v \frac{dT}{T}$$

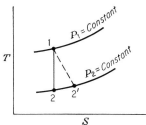

Fig. 3-9. Reversible and irreversible adiabatic compression process.

Suppose an irreversible process is considered. One might ask how the change in entropy can be calculated in view of the fact Eq. (3-47) is restricted to reversible processes. Since entropy is a property of the system and does not depend on the process, it is clear that an irreversible process may be replaced by a reversible process connecting the same two end states and the change in entropy of the system is identical.

Figure 3-9 shows reversible and irreversible adiabatic processes on a T-S diagram. A gas is expanded isentropically from (1) to (2) and from some pressure P_1 to a lower pressure P_2. An irreversible adiabatic expansion is indicated by the indeterminate line from (1) to (2′). For the isentropic or reversible adiabatic process,

$$dS = \int_1^2 \frac{\dot{Q}}{T} = 0$$

since $dS = 0$ and $\int_1^2 \dot{Q}/T = 0$ because $\dot{Q} = 0$. The internal energy of the system is reduced because the temperature is lowered from T_1 to T_2. Work is done by the system. Now if an irreversible and adiabatic expansion takes place between the same pressure limits as from (1) to (2′) less work is done by the system. Therefore, the internal energy of the system is higher at (2′) than at (2) as evidenced by $T_{2'} > T_2$ on the T-S diagram. An increase in entropy is also apparent from the T-S diagram. Therefore

$$\Delta S_{1\text{-}2'} > 0$$

and since the process is adiabatic

$$\int_1^{2'} \frac{dQ}{T} = 0 \quad \text{and} \quad \Delta S_{1\text{-}2'} > \int_1^{2'} \frac{dQ}{T}$$

If the process from (1) to (2′) is to be reversible, heat must be added to the system so that

$$\Delta S_{1\text{-}2'} = \int_1^2 \frac{dQ}{T} \quad \text{where } dQ = 0$$

Similar relationships may be established for other reversible and irreversible processes from which it may be concluded

$$dS = \int_1^2 \frac{dQ}{T} \quad \text{(reversible process)}$$

and $$dS > \int_1^2 \frac{dQ}{T} \quad \text{(irreversible process)} \tag{3-48}$$

Further reference to Fig. 3-9 will show that the work done by the system is greatest when an isentropic expansion occurs between the stated pressure limits. Since entropy is a property of the state of the system, it can be expressed in terms of the other properties, pressure and temperature. It is clear that a temperature lower than T_2 could be obtained only by a decrease in entropy which for an adiabatic process would be a violation of the second law. Then the energy at a temperature level lower than T_2 cannot be utilized to produce work and is termed the unavailable energy. The work done by the system as manifested by the temperature drop from T_1 to T_2 is a maximum within the limits of the second law and is equal to the "available energy." For the irreversible process from (1) to (2′), the entropy of the system must increase [Eq. (3-48)], and since $P_2 = P_2'$ and $S_2' > S_2$, it follows that $T_2' > T_2$. Therefore the unavailability of energy has been increased by the increase in entropy due to irreversibility. The available energy has been decreased. It will be noted that the total energy of system and surroundings has been conserved but entropy has been created. Two very important conclusions may be drawn from the preceding consideration.

Irreversibility with no heat transfer is accompanied by an increase in the unavailability of energy and a corresponding increase in entropy.

Although energy cannot be created or destroyed, entropy can be created, but once created cannot be destroyed.

3-20. Some Consequences of the First and Second Laws of Thermodynamics. The first law of thermodynamics is stated

$$dU = dQ - dW$$

The second law states

$$dQ = T \, dS$$

The first and second laws may then be stated

$$dU = T \, dS - dW \tag{3-49}$$

If $P \, dv$ work only is considered, Eq. (3-48) can be written

$$dU = T \, dS - P \, dv \tag{3-50}$$

Equation (3-50) contains no inexact differentials as is the case with the preceding equations, and therefore a great many thermodynamic relationships can be derived with comparative ease. Any of the four variables of Eq. (3-50) may be expressed as a function of any two variables, provided the system is homogeneous, consists of a single phase, and is in equilibrium.

Certain combinations of energy terms occur so frequently in thermodynamics that it is convenient to group them and give them a name. For example,

$$h = U + Pv = \text{enthalpy} \tag{3-51}$$
$$F = U - TS = \text{Helmholtz function} \tag{3-52}$$
$$G = U - TS + Pv = \text{Gibbs function} \tag{3-53}$$

The energy terms U, Pv, and TS have the units of energy to eliminate the need for the conversion factor. Equation (3-51) may be expressed in differential form

$$dh = d(U + Pv) = dU + P \, dv + v \, dP$$

and, from Eq. (3-50),

$$dh = T \, dS - P \, dv + P \, dv + v \, dP$$
or $$dh = T \, dS + v \, dP \tag{3-54}$$

Similarly, Eq. (3-52) may be expressed

$$dF = d(U - TS) = dU - S \, dT - T \, dS$$
or $$dF = T \, dS - P \, dv - T \, dS - S \, dT$$
and $$dF = -P \, dv - S \, dT \tag{3-55}$$

Equation (3-53) in differential form is

$$dG = d(U + Pv - TS) = dU + P \, dv + v \, dP - T \, dS - S \, dT$$
and $$dG = T \, dS - P \, dv + P \, dv + v \, dP - T \, dS - S \, dT$$
or $$dG = v \, dP - S \, dT \tag{3-56}$$

It will be noted the dU, dh, dF, and dG are all exact differentials. Then $U = f(S,v)$, from Eq. (3-50), or

$$dU = \left(\frac{\partial U}{\partial S}\right)_v dS + \left(\frac{\partial U}{\partial v}\right)_S dv$$

which, compared with Eq. (3-50), yields

$$\left(\frac{\partial U}{\partial S}\right)_v = T \quad \text{and} \quad \left(\frac{\partial U}{\partial v}\right)_P = -P \tag{3-57}$$

A similar treatment of Eqs. (3-54), (3-55), and (3-56) yields the following relationships:

$$\left(\frac{\partial h}{\partial S}\right)_P = T \quad \text{and} \quad \left(\frac{\partial h}{\partial P}\right)_S = v \tag{3-58}$$

$$\left(\frac{\partial F}{\partial v}\right)_T = -P \quad \text{and} \quad \left(\frac{\partial F}{\partial T}\right)_v = -S \tag{3-59}$$

$$\left(\frac{\partial G}{\partial T}\right)_P = -S \quad \text{and} \quad \left(\frac{\partial G}{\partial P}\right)_T = v \tag{3-60}$$

Now the second partial derivatives of U, h, F, and G, with respect to any two variables, are independent of the order of differentiation. Thus

$$\frac{\partial^2 U}{\partial S\, \partial v} = \frac{\partial^2 U}{\partial v\, \partial S}$$

or

$$\left(\frac{\partial T}{\partial v}\right)_S = -\left(\frac{\partial P}{\partial S}\right)_v \tag{3-61}$$

and similarly dh, dF, and dG in Eqs. (3-52), (3-59), and (3-60), respectively, yield

$$\left(\frac{\partial T}{\partial P}\right)_S = -\left(\frac{\partial v}{\partial S}\right)_P \tag{3-62}$$

$$\left(\frac{\partial S}{\partial v}\right)_T = \left(\frac{\partial P}{\partial T}\right)_v \tag{3-63}$$

$$\left(\frac{\partial S}{\partial P}\right)_T = -\left(\frac{\partial v}{\partial T}\right)_P \tag{3-64}$$

Equations (3-61) to (3-64) are known as the Maxwell equations. They relate the properties of P, T, v, and S for homogeneous systems. However, only $(\partial v/\partial T)_P$ can be directly measured.

The Maxwell equations provide a relationship which permits the direct measurement of specific heats of substances. Consider the specific heat at constant pressure which is defined

$$C_p = \frac{dQ}{T} \quad \text{at constant pressure}$$

It is not too difficult to measure the heat input to the system and at the same time measure the temperature rise; nor is it difficult to keep the system at constant pressure.

Now consider the specific heat at constant volume which is defined

$$C_v = \frac{dQ}{dT} \qquad \text{at constant volume}$$

The heat input and temperature can be measured simply, but it is practically impossible to find a vessel which can be maintained rigid because of the large stresses encountered when a solid is heated.

If the equation of state of a system can be expressed, $f(P,v,T) = 0$ and since S is a property of the system

$$S = f(v,T)$$

or

$$dS = \left(\frac{\partial S}{\partial T}\right)_v dT + \left(\frac{\partial S}{\partial v}\right)_T dv \qquad (3\text{-}65)$$

and

$$T\,dS = T\left(\frac{\partial S}{\partial T}\right)_v dT + T\left(\frac{\partial S}{\partial v}\right)_T dv$$

For a reversible process, $dQ = T\,dS$ and $C_v = T(\partial S/\partial T)_v$

Therefore

$$dQ = T\,dS = C_v\,dT + T\left(\frac{\partial S}{\partial v}\right)_T dv$$

But from the Maxwell equation, Eq. (3-63), and the preceding equation

$$dQ = T\,dS = C_v\,dT + T\left(\frac{\partial P}{\partial T}\right)_v dv \qquad (3\text{-}66)$$

Now S is also a function of P and T, or

$$T\,dS = T\left(\frac{\partial S}{\partial P}\right)_T dP + T\left(\frac{\partial S}{\partial T}\right)_P dT$$

and for a reversible process

$$dQ = T\,dS = C_p\,dT + T\left(\frac{\partial S}{\partial P}\right)_T dP$$

Substituting the Maxwell equation, Eq. (3-64),

$$dQ = T\,dS = C_p\,dT - T\left(\frac{\partial v}{\partial T}\right)_P dP \qquad (3\text{-}67)$$

From Eqs. (3-66) and (3-67),

$$C_p\,dT - T\left(\frac{\partial v}{\partial T}\right)_P dP = C_v\,dT + T\left(\frac{\partial P}{\partial T}\right)_v dv$$

Solving for dT,

$$dT = \frac{T(\partial v/\partial T)_p \, dP}{C_p - C_v} + \frac{T(\partial P/\partial T)_v \, dv}{C_p - C_v}$$

Since $T = f(P,v)$,

$$dT = \left(\frac{\partial T}{\partial P}\right)_v dP + \left(\frac{\partial T}{\partial v}\right)_P dv$$

Comparing the two preceding equations,

$$\left(\frac{\partial T}{\partial P}\right)_v dP = \frac{T(\partial v/\partial T)_P \, dP}{C_p - C_v} \tag{3-68}$$

from which

$$C_p - C_v = T\left(\frac{\partial v}{\partial T}\right)_P \left(\frac{\partial P}{\partial T}\right)_v \tag{3-69}$$

Similarly

$$\left(\frac{\partial T}{\partial v}\right)_P dv = \frac{T(\partial P/\partial T)_v \, dv}{C_P - C_v} \tag{3-70}$$

and

$$C_p - C_v = T\left(\frac{\partial v}{\partial T}\right)_P \left(\frac{\partial P}{\partial T}\right)_v \tag{3-69}$$

Now $P = f(v,T)$ or

$$dP = \left(\frac{\partial P}{\partial v}\right)_T dv + \left(\frac{\partial P}{\partial T}\right)_v dT$$

and

$$\frac{dP}{dv} = \left(\frac{\partial P}{\partial v}\right)_T + \left(\frac{\partial P}{\partial T}\right)_v \frac{dT}{dv}$$

and

$$\left(\frac{\partial P}{\partial v}\right)_T + \left(\frac{\partial P}{\partial T}\right)_v \left(\frac{\partial T}{\partial v}\right)_P = 0$$

Multiplying by $(\partial v/\partial P)_T$,

$$\left(\frac{\partial P}{\partial T}\right)_v \left(\frac{\partial T}{\partial v}\right)_P \left(\frac{\partial v}{\partial P}\right)_T = -1 \tag{3-71}$$

and

$$\left(\frac{\partial P}{\partial T}\right)_v = -\left(\frac{\partial v}{\partial T}\right)_P \left(\frac{\partial P}{\partial v}\right)_T$$

Substituting in Eq. (3-69),

$$C_p - C_v = -T\left(\frac{\partial v}{\partial T}\right)_P^2 \left(\frac{\partial P}{\partial v}\right)_T \tag{3-72}$$

The partial differentials in Eq. (3-72) are capable of direct measurement so that the difference between the specific heat at constant pressure and the specific heat at constant volume may be found. Since measurement of the specific heat at constant pressure offers no problem, the specific heat at constant volume may be found from Eq. (3-72) by subtraction.

3-21. Thermodynamic Properties of Gases. Many gases used in engineering practice, particularly air, satisfy the equation of state for an ideal gas within an acceptable tolerance. The thermodynamic properties which are of interest besides P, v, and T are U, S, and h. The relationships through which U, S, and h may be measured are derived as follows:

The internal energy U of a system is expressed by the first law

$$dU = T\,dS - P\,dv$$

But

$$S = f(T,v)$$

and

$$dS = \left(\frac{\partial S}{\partial T}\right)_v dT + \left(\frac{\partial S}{\partial v}\right)_T dv$$

or

$$T\,dS = T\left(\frac{\partial S}{\partial T}\right)_v dT + T\left(\frac{\partial S}{\partial v}\right)_T dv$$

Substituting in the first equation,

$$dU = T\left(\frac{\partial S}{\partial T}\right)_v dT + \left[T\left(\frac{\partial S}{\partial v}\right)_T - P\right] dv \qquad (3\text{-}73)$$

Now $T(\partial S/\partial T)_v = C_v$ from the Maxwell equation, Eq. (3-63),

$$\left(\frac{\partial S}{\partial v}\right)_T = \left(\frac{\partial P}{\partial T}\right)_v$$

and, from Eq. (3-68),

$$\left(\frac{\partial P}{\partial T}\right)_v = \frac{C_p - C_v}{T(\partial v/\partial T)_P}$$

which, substituted in Eq. (3-73), yields for a constant-temperature process

$$\left(\frac{\partial U}{\partial v}\right)_T = \frac{C_p - C_v}{(\partial v/\partial T)_P} - P \qquad (3\text{-}74)$$

All the terms on the right-hand side of Eq. (3-74) are measurable and hence $(\partial U/\partial v)_T$ can be obtained by measurement.

For a constant-volume process, Eq. (3-73) becomes

$$\left(\frac{\partial U}{\partial T}\right)_v = C_v \qquad (3\text{-}75)$$

If $S = f(T,P)$ is taken,

$$T\,dS = T\left(\frac{\partial S}{\partial T}\right)_P dT + T\left(\frac{\partial S}{\partial P}\right)_T dP$$

and

$$dU = T\left(\frac{\partial S}{\partial T}\right)_P dT + T\left(\frac{\partial S}{\partial P}\right)_T dP - P\,dv$$

But $T(\partial S/\partial T)_P = C_p$, and for a constant-pressure process

$$dU = C_p\,dT - P\,dv$$

from which

$$\left(\frac{\partial U}{\partial T}\right)_P = C_p - P\left(\frac{\partial v}{\partial T}\right)_P \qquad (3\text{-}76)$$

By similar means the following expressions may be derived:

$$\left(\frac{\partial U}{\partial P}\right)_T = \left(\frac{\partial P}{\partial v}\right)_T \left[P - \left(\frac{\partial T}{\partial v}\right)_P (C_p - C_v)\right] \tag{3-77}$$

$$\left(\frac{\partial U}{\partial P}\right)_v = C_v \left(\frac{\partial v}{\partial P}\right)_T \left(\frac{\partial T}{\partial v}\right)_P \tag{3-78}$$

$$\left(\frac{\partial U}{\partial v}\right)_P = \frac{C_p}{(\partial v / \partial T)_P} - P \tag{3-79}$$

For an ideal gas, the following relations result from a differentiation of the equation of state:

$$\left(\frac{\partial P}{\partial v}\right)_T = -\frac{P}{v} \tag{3-80}$$

$$\left(\frac{\partial v}{\partial T}\right)_P = \frac{R}{P} \tag{3-81}$$

If these relations are substituted in Eq. (3-72), a relationship between the specific heats for an ideal gas is obtained:

$$C_p - C_v = -T\left(\frac{R}{P}\right)^2 \left(-\frac{P}{v}\right) = \frac{R^2 T}{RT} = R \tag{3-82}$$

Substituting Eqs. (3-79) to (3-81) in Eqs. (3-74) to (3-79), respectively, yields the following relationships for an ideal gas:

$$\left(\frac{\partial U}{\partial v}\right)_T = R\frac{R}{P} - P = 0 \tag{3-83}$$

$$\left(\frac{\partial U}{\partial T}\right)_v = C_v \tag{3-84}$$

$$\left(\frac{\partial U}{\partial T}\right)_P = C_p - P\frac{R}{P} = C_v \tag{3-85}$$

$$\left(\frac{\partial U}{\partial P}\right)_T = -\frac{P}{v}\left(P - \frac{P}{R}R\right) = 0 \tag{3-86}$$

$$\left(\frac{\partial U}{\partial P}\right)_v = C_v\left(-\frac{v}{P}\right)\left(\frac{P}{R}\right) = -\frac{C_v v}{R} \tag{3-87}$$

$$\left(\frac{\partial U}{\partial v}\right)_P = P\frac{C_p}{R} - P = \frac{C_v P}{R} \tag{3-88}$$

It is clear from the above equations that the internal energy of an ideal gas is a function of temperature only. Therefore the subscript in Eq. (3-84) may be dropped and the equation written

$$dU = C_v\, dT \tag{3-89}$$

Entropy changes may be computed by means of measurable properties with considerable difficulty for a real gas but with comparative ease for an ideal gas. Three general expressions will be derived first for any substance and later modified for an ideal gas:

$$S = f(T,v)$$

and

$$T \, dS = T \left(\frac{\partial S}{\partial T} \right)_v dT + T \left(\frac{\partial S}{\partial v} \right)_T dv$$

Using the Maxwell equations,

$$T \, dS = C_v \, dT + T \left(\frac{\partial P}{\partial T} \right)_v dv$$

Substituting from Eq. (3-71),

$$dS = C_v \frac{dT}{T} + \frac{(\partial v/\partial T)_P}{(\partial v/\partial P)_T} \, dv \qquad (3\text{-}90)$$

Similarly

$$dS = C_p \frac{dT}{T} - \left(\frac{\partial v}{\partial T} \right)_P dP \qquad (3\text{-}91)$$

and

$$dS = \frac{C_p}{(\partial v/\partial T)_P} \frac{dv}{T} - \frac{C_v(\partial v/\partial P)_T}{(\partial v/\partial T)_P} \, dP \qquad (3\text{-}92)$$

Equations (3-90) to (3-92) can be integrated between equilibrium states, provided the coefficients of the integrals can be found in terms of their respective variables. This is normally an involved procedure making mandatory a graphical or machine integration. Occasionally it is possible to express the coefficients as an empirically determined power series.

The discussion here will be limited to an ideal gas and accordingly Eqs. (3-90) to (3-92) become

$$dS = C_v \frac{dT}{T} + R \frac{dv}{v}$$

$$dS = C_p \frac{dT}{T} - R \frac{dP}{P}$$

$$dS = C_p \frac{dv}{v} + C_v \frac{dP}{P}$$

Furthermore, if C_p and C_v can be regarded as being constant,

$$S_2 - S_1 = C_v \ln \frac{T_2}{T_1} + R \ln \frac{v_2}{v_1}$$

$$S_2 - S_1 = C_p \ln \frac{T_2}{T_1} - R \ln \frac{P_2}{P_1} \qquad (3\text{-}93)$$

$$S_2 - S_1 = C_p \ln \frac{v_2}{v_1} + C_v \ln \frac{P_2}{P_1}$$

It can be shown readily by means of the equation of state that the three preceding equations are equivalent.

One more property remains to be examined, namely, enthalpy. Equation (3-54) may be expressed as follows, if $h = f(T,P)$ is taken,

$$dh = T \left(\frac{\partial S}{\partial T} \right)_P dT + T \left(\frac{\partial S}{\partial P} \right)_T dP + v \, dP$$

or
$$dh = C_p \, dT - \left[T \left(\frac{\partial v}{\partial T} \right)_P - v \right] dP \qquad (3\text{-}94)$$

For a constant-enthalpy process such as the Joule-Thomson experiment, $dh = 0$ and the preceding equation may be expressed

$$\left(\frac{\partial T}{\partial P} \right)_h = \frac{1}{C_p} \left[T \left(\frac{\partial v}{\partial T} \right)_P - v \right] \qquad (3\text{-}95)$$

This is the equation for the slope of the Joule-Thomson inversion curve.

3-22. The Clausius-Clapeyron Equation. The equations discussed thus far apply to vapors or any substance (except rubber and like substances) with the exception of those equations restricted to ideal gases. Therefore, the Maxwell equation, Eq. (3-63),

$$\left(\frac{\partial P}{\partial T} \right)_v = \left(\frac{\partial S}{\partial v} \right)_T$$

can be applied to a vapor. However, if the vapor is wet (in other words a two-phase mixture in equilibrium), the pressure is a function of temperature only. Hence

$$\left(\frac{\partial S}{\partial v} \right)_T = \frac{S_g - S_f}{v_g - v_f} = \frac{S_{fg}}{v_{fg}}$$

and, from the previous equation,

$$\left(\frac{\partial P}{\partial T} \right)_v = \frac{S_{fg}}{v_{fg}} \qquad (3\text{-}96)$$

Now enthalpy may be expressed as a function of any other two properties such as S and P and

$$dh = \left(\frac{\partial h}{\partial S} \right)_P dS + \left(\frac{\partial h}{\partial P} \right)_S dP$$

But enthalpy is defined

$$dh = T \, ds + v \, dP$$

Comparing the two preceding equations,

$$T = \left(\frac{\partial h}{\partial S} \right)_P \quad \text{and} \quad v = \left(\frac{\partial h}{\partial P} \right)_S$$

Since pressure and temperature are interdependent,

$$T = \frac{h_{fg}}{S_{fg}} \tag{3-97}$$

Eliminating S_{fg} between Eqs. (3-96) and (3-97),

$$\frac{dP}{dT} = \frac{h_{fg}}{v_{fg}T} \tag{3-98}$$

This is the Clausius-Clapeyron equation for liquid-vapor equilibrium and is extremely useful in determining the properties of wet vapors.

References

1. Dodge, B. F.: "Chemical Engineering Thermodynamics," McGraw-Hill Book Company, Inc., New York, 1944.
2. Epstein, S.: "Thermodynamics," John Wiley & Sons, Inc., New York, 1937.
3. Fermi, E.: "Thermodynamics," Prentice-Hall, Inc., New York, 1937.
4. Keenan, J. H.: "Thermodynamics," John Wiley & Sons, Inc., New York, 1941.
5. Keifer, P. J., and M. C. Stuart: "Thermodynamics," John Wiley & Sons, Inc., New York, 1929.
6. Partington, J. R.: "Chemical Thermodynamics," Constable & Co., Ltd., London, 1924.
7. Roberts, J. K.: "Heat and Thermodynamics," Blackie & Son, Ltd., Glasgow, 1940.
8. Sears, F. W.: "Thermodynamics," Addison-Wesley Press, Inc., Cambridge, Mass., 1950.
9. Stodola, A., and L. C. Loewenstein: "Steam and Gas Turbines," McGraw-Hill Book Company, Inc., New York, 1927.
10. Zemansky, M. W.: "Heat and Thermodynamics," McGraw-Hill Book Company, Inc., New York, 1951.

Problems

3-1. Four pounds of air at a pressure of 165 psia occupy a volume of 6 cu ft. The air is expanded isentropically to 35 psia. Determine the work done, heat transfer, and the change in the following properties: P, v, T, U, and h.

3-2. One pound of a substance experiences a constant-pressure process in which the internal energy is increased by 160 Btu. The work done on the surroundings is 35,000 ft-lb. Determine the change in enthalpy.

3-3. A quantity of air undergoes a constant-pressure process, the initial pressure, temperature, and volume being 35 psia, 40 cu ft, and 110 F, respectively. The final temperature is 580 F. Determine the heat transfer, work done, and the change in the following properties: P, v, s, U, and h.

3-4. The Helmholtz free energy of a reactive mixture of gases before combustion is -135 energy units. After combustion the products are cooled to the original temperature and the Helmholtz free energy is -480 energy units. Determine the maximum work obtainable from the reaction, and show how the answer is obtained.

3-5. A cycle consists of the following processes which occur successively:

(a) Constant-pressure expansion
(b) Isentropic expansion

(c) Constant-pressure compression

(d) Constant-volume compression

The internal energy of the working fluid decreases 60 Btu per lb during the isentropic expansion. Determine the net work done after a complete cycle.

3-6. Another cycle consists of the following processes which occur successively:

(a) Constant-pressure expansion

(b) Isothermal expansion

(c) Constant-pressure compression

(d) Constant-volume compression

At the beginning of the isothermal expansion process the Gibbs function is -412 energy units above a datum at 32 F. At the end of this process the Gibbs function is -732 energy units. Determine the work done per pound of working fluid after a complete cycle.

3-7. Two identical fluids of equal mass m are mixed in an insulated system. Before mixing, Rankine temperatures are T_A and T_B. Prove that the entropy of the surroundings is increased by the amount

$$2m \ln \frac{(T_A + T_B)}{2 \sqrt{T_A T_B}}$$

3-8. An insulated box of 16 cu ft is partitioned into two chambers of equal volume. One chamber contains air at 600 psia and 400 F and the other is a perfect vacuum. Considering the air to be an ideal gas, determine if a change in entropy occurs when the partition is removed. Has the available energy of the system been changed?

3-9. An approximate check of Eq. (3-54) may be obtained by means of using data from the steam tables to compute ΔT and $T \Delta S + v \Delta P$ for small incremental changes of state. Make a comparison of the results obtained using any desired form of state change.

3-10. The specific volume, entropy, and enthalpy of superheated steam may be found from the steam tables as functions of temperature and pressure. Set up tables using pressure and temperature as arguments for each of the properties of specific volume, entropy, and enthalpy. A temperature range from 400 to 1600 F in increments of 200 F and a pressure range from 100 to 240 psia in increments of 20 psi may be selected.

(a) Compute the value of the following derivatives at 160 psia and 1000 F:

$$\left(\frac{\partial v}{\partial T}\right)_P; \left(\frac{\partial v}{\partial P}\right)_T; \left(\frac{\partial P}{\partial T}\right)_v$$
$$\left(\frac{\partial S}{\partial P}\right)_T; \left(\frac{\partial S}{\partial T}\right)_P; \left(\frac{\partial P}{\partial T}\right)_S$$

(b) Compute C_p and C_v. Compare the values of C_p obtained from Eqs. (3-40) and $C_p = T(\partial S/\partial T)_P$.

(c) Demonstrate the validity of the Maxwell relations.

(d) Compute $(\partial h/\partial P)_T$ at 160 psia and 1000 F from the tabulated data and compare with the value of $(\partial h/\partial P)_T$ obtained from Eq. (3-94).

3-11. The specific volume of compressed liquid water may be found from the steam tables as a function of temperature and pressure. Selecting values of the specific volume for a range of temperatures from 100 to 500 F in increments of 100 F and a range of pressures from 1000 to 3000 psia in increments of 500 psi, compute the difference between C_p and C_v at 2000 psia and 300 F.

CHAPTER 4

STEAM-TURBINE CYCLES

4-1. Introduction. A study of the steam turbine may be undertaken without specific reference to the cycle in which it is to operate. Clearly, a better understanding of design objectives can be obtained if the cycle, in which the steam turbine is the instrument for the expansion process, is given some consideration. Future improvements in the thermal efficiencies of steam power plants will be found by perfecting the components, of which the turbine is one, and by improvement of the cycle

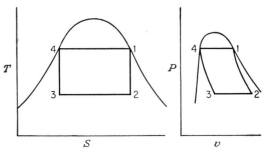

Fig. 4-1. Carnot cycle with steam as medium.

itself. Obviously, some modifications made in the cycle impose corresponding modifications in the turbine, as, for example, reheat and regenerative feedwater heating. Higher temperatures and pressures which are part and parcel of improving cycle efficiency also pose problems for the turbine designer.

4-2. Carnot Cycle. Since each of the processes of the Carnot cycle is completely reversible, it follows from the second law of thermodynamics that the optimum efficiency is to be obtained for stated temperatures of source and sink when operating on this cycle. Therefore it would appear that if at all possible the steam turbine should operate as part of the Carnot cycle or some cycle approximating it.

With reference to Fig. 4-1, which shows a T-S diagram for the Carnot cycle using steam as a medium, some generalizations may be made. First, since the heat added from (4) to (1) is latent heat of vaporization, the medium is at constant temperature and pressure. The isentropic expansion from (1) to (2) can be reasonably approached with a high efficiency turbine. Rejection of heat takes place from (2) to (3) at constant temperature and pressure as far as the medium is concerned since again this is latent heat. It will be noted that the condition of the fluid at (3) is a two-phase mixture or extremely wet steam. The two-phase mixture is compressed from (3) to (4) isentropically with a temperature rise corresponding to the work of compression. However, the work of compression would be great and the isentropic compression of a two-phase mixture well nigh impossible. If a large body of water such as the ocean is used, it reasonably could be assumed to be a constant-temperature sink. Similarly, the furnace could be taken as a reasonable, although fallible, approximation of a constant-temperature source with automatic combustion and temperature control. Counterflow heat transfer would complete the requirements for an approximation to isothermal addition and rejection of heat.

It would appear, therefore, that a steam power plant could be built to operate on a fair approximation of the Carnot cycle. However, one more fact must be considered and that is the work of compression. A little reflection will indicate that the work of compression would be of the same order of magnitude as the turbine work. This is so because it would be necessary to compress a two-phase mixture at turbine exhaust pressure to saturated liquid water at turbine inlet pressure. Actually if the compressor were very inefficient, as likely it would be, the net work from the cycle might be negative or at best a small amount of net work could be obtained. Greater net output could be obtained only by making the plant bigger until a plant of manifestly absurd proportions and excessive cost would be reached to produce an acceptable net output. Therefore an approach to the Carnot cycle as the ideal cycle would result in a plant completely unrealistic as to size and cost.

4-3. Rankine Cycle. The Rankine cycle shown on a T-S diagram in Fig. 4-2 provided the first workable cycle for a steam power plant. It will be observed that heat continues to be rejected in the condenser from (3') to (3) where saturated liquid water is obtained. A boiler feed pump is utilized to raise the static pressure of the condensate from condenser pressure (3) to boiler pressure (4). Since liquid water is substantially an incompressible fluid, the pump work is utilized solely for increasing the static pressure and the temperature rise is very small. Heat is supplied in a boiler to raise the temperature of the feedwater to the saturation temperature corresponding to boiler pressure, (4) to (5). The latent heat of vaporization is also supplied, (5) to (1), in the boiler. Obviously, the isothermal addition of heat is not maintained because of the extreme difficulty of maintaining a variable temperature source. Consequently, the cycle is irreversible and, according to the second law, its efficiency is inferior to the Carnot cycle operating between the same temperature limits.

However, the pump work is insignificant in comparison with the turbine work indicating a much smaller plant for a given net output as compared with the Carnot plant. Tolerable thermal efficiencies can be obtained with the Rankine cycle within attainable temperature and pressure limits. Straight condensing turbines, steam engines, and back-pressure turbines when the exhaust is used in the counterpart of a condenser (heating system or process with condensate recovery) operate on the Rankine cycle.

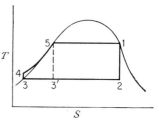

Fig. 4-2. Rankine cycle with steam as medium.

Usually it is not desirable to operate a turbine on the Rankine cycle as indicated in Fig. 4-2. It will be observed that the expansion process occurs entirely within the two-phase region and, if the moisture content becomes excessive (over 10 to 12 per cent), turbine efficiency will suffer along with erosion of the blades. To avoid this situation, the steam is superheated so that the expansion takes place without excessive moisture. The Rankine cycle with superheat is shown in Fig. 4-3. Superheating the steam also has the effect of raising the mean effective temperature* at which heat is added without increasing the pressure, resulting in an improvement of cycle efficiency. Also the turbine effi-

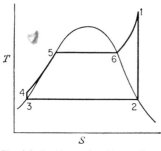

Fig. 4-3. Rankine cycle with superheat.

ciency is increased, since most of the expansion takes place in the superheat region with a reduction of the mechanical losses due to wet steam.

Inherently the Rankine cycle with superheat is less efficient than the straight Rankine cycle. Any increase in efficiency is attributable to the higher temperature at which heat is added and to the improvement of the turbine efficiency. The superheat is added from a constant-temperature source to a variable-temperature medium just as is the case in raising the boiler feedwater to saturated liquid temperature corresponding to boiler pressure. Superheating then serves to aggravate the degree of irreversibility in the heat addition process.

* The mean effective temperature is defined:

$$T_m = \frac{Q}{\Delta S}$$

4-4. Reheat Cycle. The reheat cycle is shown on a T-S diagram in Fig. 4-4. In the reheat cycle steam is withdrawn from the turbine after partial expansion, returned to a resuperheat section of the boiler or an auxiliary superheater, and then is readmitted to the turbine for expansion to final pressure. The reheat turbine may be in the form of a single spindle or two separate spindles, but in either case additional flow area must be provided after the reheated steam is admitted to accommodate the increased specific volume. Again, any increase in cycle efficiency over the Rankine cycle or Rankine cycle with superheat is due, primarily, to an increase in the mean effective temperature at which the heat is added. The reheat or resuperheat part of the cycle serves to increase the quantity of heat added at higher temperature, thereby increasing the

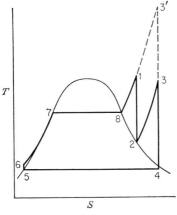

Fig. 4-4. Reheat cycle.

mean effective temperature at which the heat is added. Therefore, for optimum increase in thermal efficiency, the temperature at (2) should approach the temperature at (8) and conversely if the temperature at (2) approaches that at (4), the thermal efficiency may actually suffer.

Actually, reheating the steam results in a small increase in cycle efficiency to be balanced against increased first cost incurred by the additional piping, turbine modifications, and reheat section of the boiler. When fuel costs are high, as at present, the additional investment can be justified on the basis of fuel savings. A significant advantage of reheating, and in fact its only true justification, is the avoidance of the extremely high superheat temperatures required in high-pressure plants to keep the expansion substantially out of the wet region. An examination of Fig. 4-4 shows clearly that a considerably higher superheat temperature would be required with a straight superheat cycle in order to reach point (4).

4-5. Regenerative Cycle. The Rankine cycle may be modified as shown in Fig. 4-5 to incorporate regenerative feedwater heating. A portion of the steam is withdrawn at selected points along the turbine to heat the feedwater in a series of feedwater heaters. If it were feasible to employ an infinite number of feedwater heaters supplied with steam from a like number of extraction points, the Rankine cycle would become completely reversible and therefore would have the same thermal efficiency as the Carnot cycle for the same temperature limits. The turbine in effect would become a variable-temperature heat source corresponding to the variable temperature of the medium in this part of the heat addition process.

Since a finite number of heaters must be used, the effect of regenerative feedwater heating is to raise the temperature of the feedwater entering the boiler and therefore to increase the mean effective temperature at which heat is added. The result is an increase in thermal efficiency. As a matter of fact, despite the irreversibility of the regenerative cycle, its thermal efficiency may be higher than that of the reversible Rankine cycle. This apparent contradiction may be explained by noting that the mean effective temperature at which heat is added in the regenerative cycle is higher than in the reversible Rankine cycle even though the highest temperatures of heat addition may be the same. Pointedly, the mean effective temperature of heat addition and rejection are significant in defining the temperature limits.

In order to minimize the irreversibility of the regenerative cycle, the temperature rise should be equally divided among the heaters without regard to superheat. In practice, this condition may not always be met, since in large turbines the extraction points are established by the manufacturer and it may not be economical to use all of them.

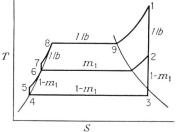

Fig. 4-5. Single extraction regenerative cycle.

In selecting the number of heaters to be used, the increase in thermal efficiency must justify the investment. The law of diminishing returns plays a large part here, since the incremental increase in thermal efficiency decreases with each heater added.

4-6. Effect of Temperature and Pressure on Cycle Efficiency. For the completely reversible cycle where all the heat is added at constant temperature and rejected at another and lower constant temperature, the thermal efficiency may be expressed in terms of the highest temperature at which the heat is added and the lowest temperature at which the heat is rejected. In other words, the highest and lowest temperatures of heat addition and rejection, respectively, define the temperature limits. The thermal efficiency may be expressed

$$\eta_t = \frac{T_A - T_R}{T_A}$$

It is clear that the thermal efficiency may be improved by raising T_A, lowering T_R, or doing both.

For an irreversible cycle with variable-temperature heat addition, such as the irreversible Rankine cycle, the above definition of the temperature limits is no longer applicable. This is so because all the heat is not added at the highest temperature. The mean effective temperature of heat addition and rejection may be used, and the thermal efficiency for such a cycle is

$$\eta_t = f\left(\frac{T_{mA} - T_{mR}}{T_{mA}}\right)$$

Once more the thermal efficiency of such a cycle may be increased by raising T_{mA}, lowering T_{mR}, or both.

Qualitatively, all other things being equal, the thermal efficiency of any cycle may be improved by raising and/or lowering the mean effective temperature of heat addition and rejection, respectively.

The mean effective temperature of heat addition may be increased by raising the highest temperature or adding a larger proportion of the heat at the higher temperatures. Therefore, examining the Rankine cycle with superheat, for example, it is observed that most of the heat added is latent heat at the saturation temperature, which greatly offsets the lower temperatures of heat addition in the liquid phase. The superheat is added at a still higher mean effective temperature, but its effect is not so pronounced because the quantity of heat added is small compared with the latent heat. Clearly, more effective increases in thermal efficiency are to be obtained with higher temperatures of latent heat addition, which for steam implies higher pressures. It is common practice among steam-power engineers to refer to "going to higher temperatures and pressures" to improve thermal efficiency. It must be remembered that it is the mean effective temperature of heat addition in which we are interested and the pressures are forced upon us by the properties of steam.

The thermal efficiency of the cycle may be also improved by lowering the mean effective temperature of heat rejection. Here again the saturation pressures corresponding to low steam temperatures (60 to 80 F) are correspondingly low (0.5 to 1.0 in. Hg abs approximately). It is convenient to state that the thermal efficiency is improved by increasing condenser vacuum, but the prime essential is to attain a low temperature of heat rejection. The fact that the lower temperatures for steam involve higher vacua is simply a disagreeable characteristic of steam. We should be better off if the saturation pressures corresponding to the attainable temperatures of heat rejection were above atmospheric pressure.

4-7. Thermal Efficiency. A few remarks regarding the meaning of thermal efficiency appear to be appropriate at this point. The thermal efficiency of a cycle or the cycle efficiency is defined as the net useful output divided by the heat added, all expressed in the same units, or

$$\eta_t = \frac{\text{net useful output}}{\text{heat added}} = \frac{W_{net}}{JQ_A} \tag{4-1}$$

As a corollary to the first law and from the definition of a cycle,

$$W_{net} = J(Q_A - Q_R) \tag{4-2}$$

where Q_R must include all losses from the cycle to the surroundings, and not merely the heat rejected in the condenser. In determining Q_R, the losses taken into account besides the heat rejected in the condenser are the losses in the boiler, turbine, piping, heaters, and other auxiliaries. The heat added Q_A is the heating value of the fuel fired in the boiler during the interval of time in which the net useful output is measured or Q_R occurs. In other words, a complete energy balance must be made for the cycle. For an ideal cycle which implies perfect components including the boiler and turbine, the thermal efficiency may be determined solely on the basis of energy changes in the medium.

Referring to the appropriate T-S diagrams, the ideal thermal efficiency may be written accordingly for the following cycles: Carnot (Fig. 4-1), Rankine (Fig. 4-2), and Rankine with superheat (Fig. 4-3).

$$\eta_t = \frac{(h_1 - h_2) - (h_4 - h_3)}{h_1 - h_4} \tag{4-3}$$

Reheat cycle (Fig. 4-4):

$$\eta_t = \frac{(h_1 - h_2) + (h_3 - h_4) - (h_6 - h_5)}{h_1 - h_6} \tag{4-4}$$

Single extraction regenerative cycle (Fig. 4-5):

$$\eta_t = \frac{(h_1 - h_2) + (1 - m_1)(h_2 - h_3) - (1 - m_1)(h_5 - h_4) - (h_7 - h_6)}{h_1 - h_7}$$

$$\tag{4-5}$$

The thermal efficiency of a steam turbine is quite another matter apart from the thermal efficiency of the cycle or plant. It would be obviously unfair to charge the turbine with all the losses occurring in the plant. Therefore, if thermal efficiency is to be an index of the turbine's ability to convert heat into work, clearly those losses which do not pertain to the turbine must be excluded. On the other hand, contributions made by the other components of the cycle must not be credited to the turbine. The thermal efficiency of the turbine may be then defined as the ratio of the turbine output to the heat chargeable or supplied in the cycle all expressed in similar units.

The turbine output may be taken on an ideal, internal, brake, or generator output basis. Quite obviously, if the value given for turbine thermal efficiency is to have any significance, the basis upon which the output was taken must be indicated. The ideal output is the available energy defined by the turbine operating conditions, and the internal output is the output of the spindle after deducting those losses which increase the entropy of the steam. The brake or shaft output may be measured by means of a dynamometer or calculated by deducting the internal and external losses, such as those which occur in the bearings, governor, etc., from the ideal output. Similarly, the generator output can be measured at the generator terminals or calculated by deducting all turbine and generator losses from the ideal output.

The heat chargeable or heat supplied may be defined as the actual enthalpy of the steam entering the turbine less the enthalpy of saturated liquid water at exhaust pressure. In effect, the turbine is charged with the heat actually delivered to the steam by the boiler plus the enthalpy rise due to pump work. This definition of heat chargeable is applicable to straight condensing and noncondensing turbines.

The basic definition for the heat chargeable must be modified for regenerative and reheat turbines. For the regenerative turbine, the heat transferred to the feedwater by the extraction steam, assuming perfect heaters, is credited to the turbine in determining the heat chargeable. For the reheat turbine, the heat delivered to the steam by the reheater is charged to the turbine. For more detailed definitions of heat chargeable for other than straight condensing and noncondensing turbines, the reader should consult "Steam Turbines: Power Test Codes," American Society of Mechanical Engineers, 1941.

4-8. Heat Rate and Steam Rate.

The heat rate is a modified reciprocal of the thermal efficiency and is in much wider use among steam-power and turbine engineers. The heat rate for a turbine is defined as the heat chargeable in Btu per kilowatt hour or horsepower-hour turbine output. Again the basis upon which the turbine output is taken should be specified. Turbine heat rate should not be confused with the heat rate of the steam-power plant known as the station heat rate. The station heat rate, like station thermal efficiency, takes into account all the losses from fuel to switchboard.

The heat rate for a straight condensing or noncondensing turbine is

$$\text{HR} = \frac{(h_1 - h_{f2})3413}{W} \qquad \text{Btu per kw-hr} \qquad (4\text{-}6)$$

or

$$\text{HR} = \frac{(h_1 - h_{f2})2545}{W} \qquad \text{Btu per hp-hr} \qquad (4\text{-}7)$$

where h_1 = enthalpy of throttle steam
$\quad h_{f2}$ = enthalpy of liquid water at exhaust pressure
$\quad W$ = output on any specified basis, Btu per lb of steam at throttle

Steam rate is defined as the mass rate of steam flow in pounds per hour divided by the power or rate of work development of the turbine in kilowatts or horsepower, giving pounds per kilowatthour or pounds per horsepower-hour. The steam rate, therefore, is the steam supplied per kilowatthour or horsepower-hour unit of output. The heat rate may be obtained by multiplying the steam rate by the heat chargeable.

4-9. Mechanical Efficiency. The mechanical efficiency of a turbine is the ratio of the brake output to the internal output. The mechanical efficiency is an index of the external losses.

4-10. Engine Efficiency. The engine efficiency is the ratio of the real output of the turbine to the ideal output. The engine efficiency is, primarily, of interest to the designer as a means of comparing the real turbine with the ideal. Just as in the case of thermal efficiencies, the output basis upon which the engine efficiency is determined must be designated.

References

1. Keller, A.: What Do You Mean by Thermal Efficiency? *Power Generation*, July, 1948.
2. Salisbury, J. K.: "Steam Turbines and Their Cycles," John Wiley & Sons, Inc., New York, 1950.
3. "Steam Turbines: Power Test Codes," American Society of Mechanical Engineers, 1941.

Problems

4-1. A steam turbogenerator has a steam rate of 11 lb per kwhr based on generator output. Steam is supplied at 390 psia and 750 F exhausting from the turbine at 1.5 in. Hg abs.

(a) Calculate the thermal efficiency of the turbine based on generator output.

(b) What is the quality of the exhaust steam if the generator efficiency is 0.96 and the mechanical efficiency of the turbine is 0.97?

4-2. Steam is delivered to a turbine at 300 psia and 650 F exhausting into a condenser in which the pressure is 1.5 in. Hg abs. The shaft output is 75 per cent of the available energy. The turbine is direct-connected to an alternator whose efficiency is 95 per cent. Determine (a) the steam rate based on generator output; (b) the heat rate and thermal efficiency based on generator output (Rankine cycle).

4-3. A steam turbogenerator delivers 15,000 kw at a steam rate of 10 lb per kwhr based on generator output. Steam is supplied to the turbine at 450 psia and 650 F exhausting at 28 in. Hg vacuum. The barometer reads 30 in. Hg. Determine the thermal efficiency, heat rate, and engine efficiency based on generator output.

4-4. A turbine is supplied with steam at 1250 psia and 800 F exhausting at 400 psia. Determine

(a) The available energy in Btu per pound

(b) The ideal thermal efficiency (Rankine cycle)

(c) The steam rate based on generator output if the brake engine efficiency of the turbine is 70 per cent and the generator efficiency is 95 per cent

(d) The condition of the exhaust steam if the internal engine efficiency is 80 per cent

4-5. The following data are assumed to have been obtained from a test of a steam turbine.

Pressure of steam supplied: 250 psia
Temperature of steam supplied: 600 F
Exhaust pressure: 20 psia
Mechanical efficiency: 0.95
Load: 500 kw
Steam flow: 10,000 lb per hr

Calculate:

(a) Internal output in kilowatts
(b) Work developed on an ideal, internal, and brake basis in Btu per pound
(c) Steam rate on ideal, internal, and brake basis in pounds per kilowatthour
(d) Heat rate on ideal, internal, and brake basis in Btu per kilowatthour
(e) Engine efficiency on an internal and brake basis
(f) The enthalpy, temperature, quality, and specific volume on an ideal and actual basis

4-6. The following information is assumed to be abstracted from test data on a steam turbogenerator.

Duration of test: 1 hr
Thermal efficiency based on generator output: 0.28
Pressure and temperature at turbine inlet: 250 psia and 600 F
Pressure and temperature at exhaust hood: 1 in. Hg abs and 79.03 F
Generator efficiency: 0.98
Bearing and radiation losses: 6 per cent of available energy
Steam flow: 5000 lb

Compute:

(a) The brake thermal efficiency
(b) The quality of the exhaust steam
(c) The internal thermal efficiency
(d) The brake engine efficiency
(e) The mechanical efficiency of the turbine

What other piece of test equipment might have been used, the information obtained therefrom greatly simplifying the above computations?   Hint: Pressure and quality fix the state of wet steam.

CHAPTER 5

GAS-TURBINE CYCLES

5-1. Introduction. Since the gas-turbine power plant is sensitive to the efficiency of its components, a fact which will be presently demonstrated, it follows that a thorough examination of not only the turbine but its interaction with other components is of the utmost importance. It is the purpose of this chapter to review the basic cycles with a view to their relative merits and to evaluate the behavior and characteristics of the

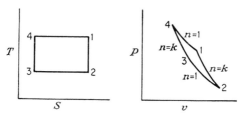

Fig. 5-1. Carnot cycle with gas as medium.

real cycles. Finally, the various component efficiencies will be weighed in the light of their effects on the over-all efficiency of the real cycle.

Other design and performance parameters, such as specific fuel consumption, air rate, fuel rate, cost, work ratio, weight, and size, are treated more appropriately in Chap. 16. It is felt that some of these parameters will be better understood after a study of the material in the succeeding chapters.

5-2. Carnot Cycle. The Carnot cycle utilizing a gas as a medium is shown on T-S and P-v diagrams in Fig. 5-1. It will be observed that the T-S diagram is unchanged by the medium (compare with Fig. 4-1). However, the P-v diagram is different from the one shown for steam in Fig. 4-1 in that heat addition and rejection are not at constant pressure. As a consequence, these processes almost of necessity would have to be nonflow, making the cycle totally unsuited for a gas-turbine power plant. Furthermore, slow speed of operation accompanies the slow rate of heat transfer through engine walls of severely limited surface area. Lubrication and metallurgical complications of great magnitude are involved because the engine surfaces need to be subjected continuously to temperatures greatly in excess of maximum cycle temperature to accomplish an acceptable heat-transfer rate.

Thus it must be concluded that the Carnot cycle can be useful only as a standard of comparison for the gas turbine.

5-3. Ideal Brayton or Joule Cycle.   Figure 5-2 illustrates the Brayton or Joule cycle.   An isentropic compression from (1) to (2) is followed by constant-pressure addition of heat from (2) to (3), an isentropic expansion from (3) to (4), and, finally, constant-pressure rejection of heat from (4) to (1).   The cycle has to be started by an auxiliary source of power after which atmospheric air is drawn in and compressed in a compressor, from (1) to (2); fuel is continuously injected and ignited in the air stream from (2) to (3); the products of combustion plus the heated air are expanded in

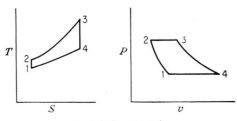

Fig. 5-2. Brayton cycle.

a turbine from (3) to (4); and the turbine exhaust gas with its heat is discarded to the atmosphere at atmospheric pressure from (4) to (1).

In analyzing the ideal cycle, the following assumptions are generally made, without serious error, in order to simplify the relationships:

1. Unchanged composition and mass rate of flow of the medium disregarding the comparatively small mass of fuel added in the combustion process.

2. Constant mean specific heat C_p throughout the cycle.

These assumptions will be applied to all open cycles covered in this chapter.

The ideal Brayton cycle may be considered reversible if it is assumed that variable-temperature heat source and sink are available (infinite number of heat reservoirs each at infinitesimally higher, or lower, temperature levels).   The thermal efficiency is expressed.

$$\eta_{tB} = \frac{Q_A - Q_R}{Q_A} = \frac{C_p(T_3 - T_2) - C_p(T_4 - T_1)}{C_p(T_3 - T_2)} \qquad (a)$$

$$\eta_{tB} = \frac{(T_3 - T_2) - (T_4 - T_1)}{T_3 - T_2} = 1 - \left(\frac{T_4 - T_1}{T_3 - T_2}\right) \qquad (b)$$

Since $P_2 = P_3$ and $P_1 = P_4$,

and
$$\frac{P_3}{P_4} = \frac{P_2}{P_1} \qquad \frac{T_3}{T_2} = \frac{T_4}{T_1}$$

then
$$\frac{T_3}{T_2} - 1 = \frac{T_4}{T_1} - 1 \qquad (c)$$

Substituting Eq. (c) in Eq. (b),

$$\eta_{tB} = 1 - \frac{T_1}{T_2} = \frac{T_2 - T_1}{T_2} \qquad (5\text{-}1)$$

or
$$\eta_{tB} = \frac{T_3 - T_4}{T_3} \qquad (5\text{-}2)$$

and also
$$\eta_{tB} = 1 - \left(\frac{P_1}{P_2}\right)^{(k-1)/k} = 1 - \frac{1}{(r_p)^{(k-1)/k}} \qquad (5\text{-}3)$$

designating $P_3/P_4 = P_2/P_1 = r_p$ as the pressure ratio.

A hasty glance at Eq. (5-1) would indicate that the thermal efficiency of the reversible Brayton cycle is equivalent to that of the Carnot. Closer scrutiny reveals, however, that T_2 is not the highest temperature of the Brayton cycle, and therefore Eq. (5-1) is not expressed in terms of the temperature limits as defined for the Carnot cycle. If Eq. (a) is expressed,

$$\eta_{tB} = \frac{Q_A - Q_R}{Q_A} = \frac{T_{mA}\,\Delta S_{3\text{-}2} - T_{mR}\,\Delta S_{4\text{-}1}}{T_{mA}\,\Delta S_{3\text{-}2}}$$

But from Fig. 5-2 it is clear that $\Delta S_{3\text{-}2} = \Delta S_{4\text{-}1}$ and therefore

$$\eta_{tB} = \frac{T_{mA} - T_{mR}}{T_{mA}}. \qquad (5\text{-}4)$$

Thus it is seen that the thermal efficiency of the Brayton cycle depends on the mean effective temperatures of heat addition and rejection.

Assuming the temperature of atmospheric air for a given cycle operation to be constant at T_1, it follows that T_2 will also be fixed for a given pressure ratio. Then the magnitude of the mean effective temperature of heat addition depends solely on the temperature rise due to heat addition. In other words, increasing the turbine inlet temperature T_3 will raise the mean effective temperature of heat addition. However, this will also raise the mean effective temperature of heat rejection since T_4 will be increased. The net result is an increase in thermal efficiency. It may, therefore, be concluded that the thermal efficiency is also a function of the highest temperature of heat addition. This conclusion is supported by Eq. (5-2).

If the pressure ratio is increased while keeping T_3 and T_1 constant, T_2 will be increased with the result that the mean effective temperature of heat addition also will be increased. The turbine exhaust temperature

T_4 will be decreased, causing a corresponding decrease in the mean effective temperature of heat rejection. The net effect again is an increase in thermal efficiency, a conclusion which is borne out by Eqs. (5-1) and (5-3). An expression for thermal efficiency similar to Eq. (5-3) may be derived by identical methods for the Carnot cycle. Such an expression might lead to the conclusion that the thermal efficiency of the Carnot cycle is independent of the temperature limits. Reflection, however, will establish the fact that with isothermal addition and rejection of heat in the Carnot cycle, the isentropic pressure ratio establishes the temperature limits. This is not the case with the Brayton cycle where the heat addition and rejection occur at varying temperatures. The following conclusions are then in order:

1. The thermal efficiencies of the reversible Brayton cycle and the Carnot cycle are the same if the isentropic pressure ratios are also the same and the media have identical specific heat ratios.

2. The thermal efficiency of either the Carnot or Brayton cycle in terms of pressure ratio is merely a derived expression, the fundamental basis for which rests in the defined temperature limits. For example, if Eq. (5-3) is applied to the Carnot cycle, as well it may be, it would appear that the thermal efficiency is dependent on the characteristics of the medium. For example, Argon with $k = 1.66$, compared with $k = 1.41$ for air, would seem to indicate a higher thermal efficiency for a cycle operating with Argon. That the Carnot cycle efficiency should depend on the characteristics of the medium is not supported by the previous examination of this efficiency. However, since $T_1 r_p^{(k-1)/k} = T_2$, it follows that T_2 will be increased for a fixed sink temperature. If the temperature limits are fixed, then T_2/T_1 is fixed, and the pressure ratio is decreased an amount corresponding to the increase in k so that $r_p^{(k-1)/k}$ is constant. The result is no change in the cycle efficiency. Therefore the increase in thermal efficiency, as evidenced by substituting a higher value of k in Eq. (5-3), is not due to an inherent characteristic of the medium, as one might be led to believe, but occurs simply because the temperature limits in the original relationship have been changed.

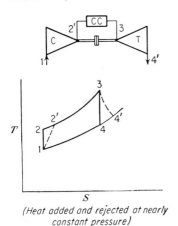

(Heat added and rejected at nearly constant pressure)

Fig. 5-3. Irreversible Brayton cycle.

5-4. Irreversible Brayton Cycle. The discussion of the Brayton cycle thus far has been based on the assumption of a completely reversible cycle. When the irreversibilities of the actual processes are taken into account, the picture changes completely. Figure 5-3 illustrates on the T-S and P-v diagrams the major irreversibilities of the Brayton cycle. The slight pressure drop in the combustion chamber is neglected. The thermal efficiency of the real cycle may be expressed

$$\eta_{tB} = \frac{W_{\text{net}}}{Q_A} = \frac{W_t - W_c}{Q_A} \qquad (a)$$

Expressing the turbine brake work in terms of the internal engine efficiency, the mechanical efficiency, and the isentropic enthalpy drop,

$$W_t = \eta_{mt}\eta_{et}(\Delta h_s)_{3\text{-}4} = (h_3 - h_{4'})\eta_{mt} \qquad (b)$$

Similarly, the compressor brake input may be expressed

$$W_c = \frac{(\Delta h_s)_{2\text{-}1}}{\eta_{mc}\eta_{ec}} = \frac{h_{2'} - h_1}{\eta_{mc}} \qquad (c)$$

The heat added in the form of fuel may be expressed in terms of the enthalpy rise in the combustion chamber and the combustion efficiency, or

$$Q_A = \frac{h_3 - h_{2'}}{\eta_b} \qquad (d)$$

Then the thermal efficiency is

$$\eta_{tB} = \frac{\eta_b[(h_3 - h_{4'})\eta_{mt} - (h_{2'} - h_1)/\eta_{mc}]}{h_3 - h_{2'}} \qquad (e)$$

or

$$\eta_{tB} = \frac{[(\Delta h_s)_{3\text{-}4}\eta_{et}\eta_{mt} - (\Delta h_s)_{2\text{-}1}/\eta_{ec}\eta_{mc}]\eta_b}{h_3 - h_{2'}} \qquad (f)$$

$$\eta_{ec} = \frac{h_2 - h_1}{h_{2'} - h_1} \qquad (g)$$

and since

$$\Delta h = C_p \, \Delta t$$

$$\eta_{ec} = \frac{T_2 - T_1}{T_{2'} - T_1} \qquad (h)$$

The isentropic temperature ratio, or pressure ratio, is defined by

$$\frac{T_2}{T_1} = \frac{T_3}{T_4} = \left(\frac{P_2}{P_1}\right)^{(k-1)/k} = r_p^{(k-1)/k} \qquad (i)$$

Solving Eq. (h) for $T_{2'}$ in terms of r_p,

$$T_{2'} = T_1\left(1 + \frac{r_p^{(k-1)/k} - 1}{\eta_{ec}}\right) \qquad (j)$$

Substituting in Eq. (f),

$$\eta_{tB} = \frac{\left[T_3\left(1 - \frac{T_4}{T_3}\right)\eta_{et}\eta_{mt} - \frac{T_1}{\eta_{ec}\eta_{mc}}\left(\frac{T_2}{T_1} - 1\right)\right]\eta_b}{T_3 - T_1\left(1 + \frac{r_p^{(k-1)/k} - 1}{\eta_{ec}}\right)} \qquad (k)$$

Substituting in Eq. (i),

$$\eta_{tB} = \frac{(r_p^{(k-1)/k} - 1)[(T_3\eta_{et}\eta_{mt}/r_p^{(k-1)/k}) - (T_1/\eta_{ec}\eta_{mc})]\eta_b}{T_3 - T_1\left(1 + \dfrac{r_p^{(k-1)/k} - 1}{\eta_{ec}}\right)} \tag{5-5}$$

Figure 5-4 was obtained by plotting thermal efficiency as obtained from Eq. (5-5) against pressure ratio. The component efficiencies were assumed to be as follows:

$$\eta_{et}\eta_{mt} = \eta_{ec}\eta_{mc} = 0.85$$
$$\eta_b = 1.00$$
$$\eta_{vc} = 0.87$$

The compressor inlet temperature was kept constant at 60 F. Figure 5-4 shows clearly that for a given pressure ratio, thermal efficiency improves

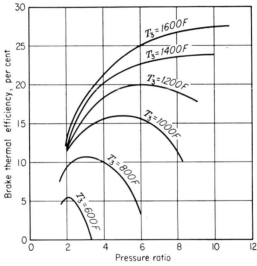

Fig. 5-4. Brake thermal efficiency as a function of pressure ratio and turbine inlet temperature, Brayton cycle.

considerably with higher turbine inlet temperature. Conversely, a drop in turbine inlet temperature at constant pressure ratio results in a serious drop in thermal efficiency. This fact is particularly significant since with constant-speed compressors the pressure ratio is substantially constant and output reduction is normally achieved by reducing turbine inlet temperature. Therefore poor part-load performance of the Brayton cycle can be expected. Another significant fact is the existence of a definite pressure ratio for maximum thermal efficiency. The optimum pressure ratio changes for various turbine inlet temperatures.

Figure 5-5 was obtained by holding the turbine inlet temperature constant at 1000 F while varying $\eta_{et}\eta_{mt} = \eta_{ec}\eta_{mc}$ for various pressure ratios. The combustion efficiency was assumed to be 100 per cent and $\eta_{mc} = 0.98$. Figure 5-5 reveals that the optimum pressure ratio is also a function of component efficiencies. Even more significant is the marked effect of component efficiencies on thermal efficiency. This very effect was the cause of much embarrassment to the early gas-turbine inventors.

The effect of another important parameter, compressor inlet temperature, is shown in Fig. 5-6. Since the compressor inlet temperature is the ambient temperature, the performance of the Brayton cycle can be expected to improve in winter or in colder climates. The curves of Fig.

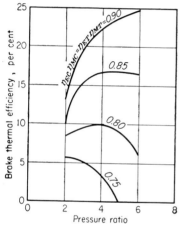

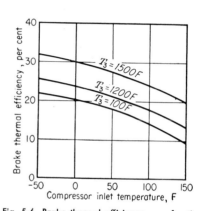

Fig. 5-5. Brake thermal efficiency as a function of pressure ratio and component efficiencies, Brayton cycle.

Fig. 5-6. Brake thermal efficiency as a function of compressor inlet temperature, Brayton cycle.

5-6 were obtained from Eq. (5-5) substituting the optimum pressure ratios from Fig. 5-4 for the temperatures indicated. Appropriate component efficiencies were selected and held constant for all the curves.

5-5. Ideal Brayton Cycle with Regeneration. The Brayton cycle with regeneration is shown on the T-S diagram of Fig. 5-7. The regenerative effect is indicated as heat transferred to the compressed air from (3) to (5) at the expense of the exhaust gases from (4) to (6). Heat is rejected from the cycle from (6) to (1), and heat is added in the combustion chamber from (5) to (3). Assuming perfect heat transfer, the temperature of the gas leaving the regenerator is equal to the temperature of the air leaving the compressor, or $T_6 = T_2$. Similarly, $T_5 = T_4$. The effect is to raise the mean effective temperature at which heat is added while lowering the mean effective temperature of heat rejection, thereby increasing the thermal efficiency of the cycle. Or looking at it another way, less heat is supplied from the heat source and less rejected to the heat sink. The thermal efficiency may be written

$$\eta_{tR} = \frac{(\Delta h_s)_{3\text{-}4} - (\Delta h_s)_{1\text{-}2}}{h_3 - h_5} = \frac{(h_3 - h_5) - (h_6 - h_1)}{h_3 - h_5} \tag{a}$$

$$\eta_{tR} = \frac{C_p(T_3 - T_5) - C_p(T_6 - T_1)}{C_p(T_3 - T_5)} \tag{b}$$

or $$\eta_{tR} = 1 - \frac{T_6 - T_1}{T_3 - T_5} \tag{c}$$

But $P_2 = P_5 = P_3$ and $P_1 = P_6 = P_4$ so that

$$\frac{T_6}{T_1} = \frac{T_2}{T_1} = \left(\frac{P_2}{P_1}\right)^{(k-1)/k} = \left(\frac{P_3}{P_4}\right)^{(k-1)/k} = \frac{T_3}{T_4} = \frac{T_3}{T_5}$$

or $$\frac{T_6}{T_1} - 1 = \frac{T_3}{T_5} - 1 \tag{d}$$

Substituting Eq. (d) in Eq. (c),

$$\eta_{tR} = 1 - \frac{T_1}{T_5} = \frac{T_5 - T_1}{T_5} \tag{5-6}$$

or $$\eta_{tR} = 1 - \frac{T_1}{T_3}\frac{T_3}{T_5} = 1 - \frac{T_1}{T_3}(r_p)^{(k-1)/k} \tag{5-7}$$

Equation (5-6) indicates that thermal efficiency is improved with higher values of T_5, which, for perfect regeneration assumed, is equivalent to

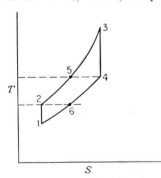

Fig. 5-7. Brayton cycle with regeneration (theoretical).

T_4. Obviously, the only way T_4 can be increased is by raising T_3, since T_4 is defined by the isentropic pressure ratio and T_3. This is substantiated by Eq. (5-7) if the pressure ratio is fixed. Equation (5-7) also suggests that thermal efficiency is increased with lower pressure ratio in contrast to the simple Brayton cycle. Lowering the pressure ratio reduces the isentropic temperature T_2 at the end of compression. For perfect regeneration, T_2 is equal to T_6, the temperature leaving the regenerator. Hence the mean effective temperature of the rejected heat is lowered. Theoretically, a pressure ratio of unity would raise the thermal efficiency to that of the Carnot cycle.

5-6. Irreversible Brayton Cycle with Regeneration. It is interesting to examine the effect of the principal irreversibilities on the thermal efficiency. The Brayton cycle with regeneration, taking into account the efficiency of the compressor, turbine, and heat exchanger, is shown in Fig. 5-8. The pressure drop in the burner and regenerator are neglected. The expressions for the turbine and compressor work are the same as before for the simple Brayton cycle. The regenerator is charged with the enthalpy difference $h_{4'} - h_{2'}$, the maximum quantity of heat

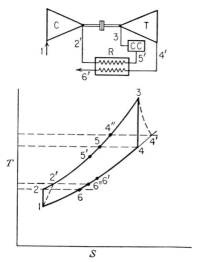

Fig. 5-8. Brayton cycle with regeneration (actual).

a perfect heat exchanger could transfer within the actual temperature limits. The efficiency of the regenerator may be expressed,

$$\eta_r = \frac{h_{5'} - h_{2'}}{h_{4'} - h_{6''}} = \frac{h_{5'} - h_{2'}}{h_{4'} - h_{2'}} \tag{a}$$

The heat added, solving Eq. (a) for $h_{5'}$ and expressing in terms of C_p and temperature, is

$$Q_A = \frac{C_p(T_3 - T_{5'})}{\eta_b} = \frac{C_p}{\eta_b}[T_3 - \eta_r(T_{4'} - T_{2'}) - T_{2'}] \tag{b}$$

Expressing $T_{2'}$ in terms of T_2, T_1, and η_{ec} and $h_{4'}$ in terms of T_3, T_4, and η_{et},

$$Q_A = \frac{C_p}{\eta_b}\left\{ T_3 - \eta_r T_3 \left[1 - \eta_{et}\left(1 - \frac{1}{r_p^{(k-1)/k}}\right)\right]\right.$$
$$\left. - T_1\left(\frac{r_p^{(k-1)/k} - 1}{\eta_{ec}} + 1\right)(1 - \eta_r)\right\} \tag{c}$$

The net work developed is given by the numerator of Eq. (5-5). The thermal efficiency may be then expressed:

$$\eta_{tR} = \frac{(r_p^{(k-1)/k} - 1)\left(\dfrac{T_3\eta_{et}\eta_{mt}}{r_p^{(k-1)/k}} - \dfrac{T_1}{\eta_{ec}\eta_{mc}}\right)\eta_b}{T_3 - \eta_r T_3\left[1 - \eta_{et}\left(1 - \dfrac{1}{r_p^{(k-1)/k}}\right)\right] + T_1\left(\dfrac{r_p^{(k-1)/k} - 1}{\eta_{ec}} + 1\right)(1 - \eta_r)}$$

$$(5\text{-}8)$$

For fixed values of T_1 and appropriate component efficiencies, the thermal efficiencies may be found from Eq. (5-8) in terms of pressure ratio for various turbine inlet temperatures. When the results are plotted, curves characteristically similar to those of Fig. 5-9 are obtained.

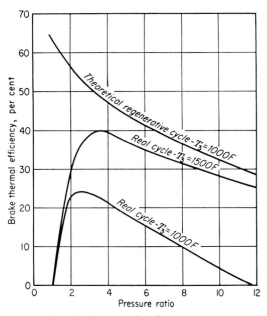

Fig. 5-9. Brayton cycle with regeneration.

The curves of Fig. 5-9 show clearly that the thermal efficiency of the real cycle is zero when the pressure ratio is unity. As pointed out previously, a pressure ratio of unity in the theoretical cycle would give the Carnot cycle efficiency. The curves also indicate that the efficiency of the real cycle improves with higher pressure ratio until the optimum pressure is reached. The curve for the theoretical cycle shows a steady decrease in thermal efficiency with increasing pressure ratio. As might be expected, a high turbine inlet temperature produces high thermal efficiency.

5-7. Stirling Cycle. The Stirling cycle is shown on the T-S diagrams of Fig. 5-10. Constant temperature expansion and addition of heat occurs from (3) to (4) followed by constant-volume rejection of heat from (4) to (1). Isothermal compression and rejection of heat take place from (1) to (2) followed by constant-volume addition of heat from (2) to (3). To approach the isothermal expansion and compression an

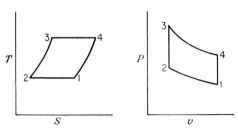

Fig. 5-10. The Stirling cycle.

infinite number of stages of reheat and intercooling, respectively, would be required. The thermal efficiency is

$$\eta_{ts} = \frac{Q_A - Q_R}{Q_A} = \frac{Q_{2\text{-}3} + Q_{3\text{-}4} - Q_{4\text{-}1} - Q_{1\text{-}2}}{Q_{2\text{-}3} + Q_{3\text{-}4}}$$

$$\eta_{ts} = \frac{C_v(T_2 - T_3) + T_3 \,\Delta S_{3\text{-}4} - C_v(T_4 - T_1) - T_1 \,\Delta S_{1\text{-}2}}{C_v(T_2 - T_3) + T_3 \,\Delta S_{3\text{-}4}}$$

but
$$\Delta S_{3\text{-}4} = \frac{R}{J} \ln \frac{P_3}{P_4}$$

and
$$P_3 v_3 = P_4 v_4 \qquad v_2 = v_3$$
$$P_1 v_1 = P_2 v_2 \qquad v_4 = v_1$$

Then
$$\frac{P_3}{P_4} = \frac{P_2}{P_1}$$

$$\Delta S_{3\text{-}4} = \frac{R}{J} \ln \frac{P_2}{P_1} = \Delta S_{1\text{-}2}$$

Therefore
$$\eta_{ts} = \frac{[(T_3 - T_2)/T_3](k - 1) \ln P_3/P_4}{[(T_3 - T_2)/T_3] - (k - 1) \ln P_3/P_4} \tag{5-9}$$

If the Stirling cycle is modified by the incorporation of a heat exchanger of infinite capacity, the heat rejected from (4) to (1) can be returned to the cycle from (2) to (3). The thermal-efficiency expression then appears

$$\eta_{tsR} = \frac{Q_{3\text{-}4} - Q_{4\text{-}1} - Q_{1\text{-}2}}{Q_{3\text{-}4}}$$

$$\eta_{tsR} = \frac{T_3 \,\Delta S_{3\text{-}4} - T_2 \,\Delta S_{1\text{-}2}}{T_2 \,\Delta S_{3\text{-}4}} = \frac{T_3 - T_2}{T_2} \tag{5-10}$$

Equation (5-10) indicates the Stirling cycle with regeneration has a thermal efficiency equivalent to that of the Carnot cycle when operating between the same temperatures of source and sink. Unfortunately, the Stirling cycle presents problems similar to those encountered with the Carnot cycle. Because of small volume changes in the Stirling cycle, low operating pressures are involved, resulting in a smaller and more compact plant than would be the case with the Carnot cycle. In view of this advantage, Stirling cycle reciprocating engines have been built in the past, but with very poor results from a thermal efficiency standpoint. The nonflow processes in the Stirling cycle make it totally unsuited for a gas-turbine plant.

5-8. Ideal Ericsson Cycle. The Ericsson cycle shown in Fig. 5-11 differs from the simple Brayton cycle in that isothermal compression and expansion are substituted for their isentropic counterparts in the Brayton cycle. Examining Fig. 5-11, it will be seen that isothermal compression occurs from (1) to (2), followed by constant-pressure heat addition from (2) to (3), isothermal expansion from (3) to (4), and constant-pressure

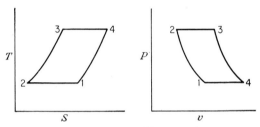

Fig. 5-11. Theoretical Ericsson cycle.

rejection of heat from (4) to (1). Heat is also added from (3) to (4) and rejected from (1) to (2) isothermally. The thermal efficiency is

$$\eta_{tE} = \frac{Q_{2\text{-}3} + Q_{3\text{-}4} - Q_{4\text{-}1} - Q_{1\text{-}2}}{Q_{2\text{-}3} + Q_{3\text{-}4}}$$

$$\eta_{tE} = \frac{C_p(T_3 - T_2) + T_3\,\Delta S_{3\text{-}4} - C_p(T_4 - T_1) - T_1\,\Delta S_{1\text{-}2}}{C_p(T_3 - T_2) + T_3\,\Delta S_{3\text{-}4}}$$

and by methods similar to those used in deriving the thermal efficiency of the Stirling cycle

$$\eta_{tE} = \frac{[(T_4 - T_1)/T_4][(k - 1)/k]\ln P_2/P_1}{[(T_4 - T_1)/T_4] + [(k - 1)/k]\ln P_2/P_1} \tag{5-11}$$

Equation (5-11) indicates clearly that the thermal efficiency of the Ericsson cycle depends on high turbine and low compressor inlet temperatures as well as high pressure ratio and high specific-heat ratio. It would appear from Eq. (5-11) that the thermal efficiency of the Ericsson cycle is somewhat worse than that of the simple Brayton cycle.

However, if a regenerator of infinite capacity or an infinite number of heat exchangers of finite capacity are used, the heat rejected from (4) to (1) may be recovered for readdition to the compressed air from (2) to (3). This would be theoretically possible because of the isothermal expansion and compression. The only external addition or rejection of heat would occur from (3) to (4) and from (1) to (2), respectively. The thermal efficiency may be written

$$\eta_{tER} = \frac{Q_{3\text{-}4} - Q_{1\text{-}2}}{Q_{3\text{-}4}}$$

$$\eta_{tER} = \frac{T_4\, \Delta S_{3\text{-}4} - T_1\, \Delta S_{1\text{-}2}}{T_4\, \Delta S_{3\text{-}4}} \qquad (5\text{-}12)$$

$$\eta_{tER} = \frac{T_4 - T_1}{T_4}$$

Therefore the thermal efficiency of the Ericsson cycle with regeneration is equivalent to that of the Carnot cycle within the same defined temperature limits.

It would appear that the Ericsson cycle with regeneration provides an excellent opportunity to improve the efficiency of a gas-turbine power plant. The isothermal compression could be approximated by inter-cooling between compressor stages and, similarly, the isothermal expansion by reheat between the turbine stages. The introduction of a counterflow regenerator of reasonable size would approximate the constant-pressure exchange of heat from the turbine exhaust gases to the compressed air leaving the compressor. In fact, it will be found that the improvement of gas-turbine efficiencies centers around the application of these modifications within the bounds of realizing a plant of reasonable first cost and size which is free from undue complexity.

Before undertaking an analysis of the effect of irreversibilities in the real plant on an over-all basis, it is well to consider each modification in detail, since a particular installation may not justify economically all of the modifications suggested by the theoretical Ericsson cycle with regeneration.

5-9. Theoretical Intercooling. The primary purpose of intercooling is to approach an isothermal compression, thereby decreasing the work of compression. Obviously, to approach a theoretical isothermal compression an infinite number of intercoolers is required with infinitesimal temperature difference. In the physical plant the isothermal compression is very crudely approximated by one or more stages of intercooling. There is rarely an economic justification for three stages of intercooling, and none whatsoever for any in excess of three.

Examining Fig. 5-12, which illustrates two stages of intercooling on the T-S and P-v diagram, the following is apparent:

a. Isentropic compression occurs from (1) to (2) to some intermediate pressure P_2.

b. Irreversible adiabatic compression occurs from (1) to (2′), indicating a higher specific volume and temperature increase than was the case under (*a*).

c. The first intercooler reduces the temperature (and specific volume) from (2′) to (3) at assumed constant pressure $T_3 = T_1$.

d. Compression continues in the second compressor from (3) to (4) isentropically, and from (3) to (4′) irreversibly and adiabatically to some pressure P_3.

e. The second intercooler lowers the temperature and specific volume from (4′) to (5), $T_5 = T_3 = T_1$.

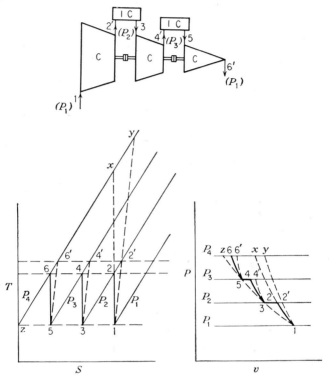

Fig. 5-12. Intercooled compression (two stages).

f. Final compression occurs isentropically from (5) to (6) and irreversibly and adiabatically from (5) to (6′) to the final pressure P_4. $T_{6'}$ is the temperature of the air after final compression since there is no advantage in cooling to the initial temperature T_1.

It is clear from the *P-v* diagram that the area under the intercooled compression curve (12′34′56′) is less than that under the isentropic curve 1-*x* or the irreversible adiabatic curve 1-*y*. Also, it is evident that with more stages of intercooling a better approach to the isothermal compression 1 *x*35*z* can be made.

An important consideration is the selection of the proper intermediate pressures. A closer approach to the isothermal compression is possible if the incremental temperature rise due to compression (or incremental temperature reduction in the intercooler) is constant. Then, necessarily, equal work of compression between intercoolers must be the case. If constant specific heat, specific-heat ratio, compression efficiency, and compression work between intercoolers, the intermediate pressure for a single stage of intercooling may be obtained as follows. Refer to Fig. 5-12 for compression from P_1 to P_3.

$$W_c = \frac{(h_2 - h_1) + (h_4 - h_3)}{\eta_{ec}\eta_{mc}} \tag{a}$$

or

$$W_c = \frac{C_p(T_2 - T_1) + C_p(T_4 - T_3)}{\eta_{ec}\eta_{mc}} \tag{b}$$

and

$$W_c = \frac{C_p T_1[(T_2/T_1) - 1] + C_p T_3[(T_4/T_3) - 1]}{\eta_{ec}\eta_{mc}} \tag{c}$$

But

$$\frac{T_2}{T_1} = \left(\frac{P_2}{P_1}\right)^{(k-1)/k} \quad \text{and} \quad \frac{T_4}{T_3} = \left(\frac{P_3}{P_2}\right)^{(k-1)/k}$$

and

$$T_1 = T_3$$

Therefore

$$W_c = \frac{C_p T_1}{\eta_{ec}\eta_{mc}} \left[\left(\frac{P_2}{P_1}\right)^{(k-1)/k} + \left(\frac{P_3}{P_2}\right)^{(k-1)/k} - 2 \right] \tag{d}$$

To find the optimum value of P_2,

$$\frac{dW_c}{dP_2} = \frac{d}{dP_2} \left\{ \frac{C_p T_1}{\eta_{ec}\eta_{mc}} \left[\left(\frac{P_2}{P_1}\right)^{(k-1)/k} + \left(\frac{P_3}{P_2}\right)^{(k-1)/k} - 2 \right] \right\} = 0 \tag{e}$$

so that

$$P_2 = \sqrt{(P_1 P_3)} \tag{5-13}$$

Similarly for two stages of intercooling,

$$P_2 = (P_1^2 P_4)^{1/3} \quad \text{and} \quad P_3 = (P_1 P_4^2)^{1/3} \tag{5-14}$$

5-10. Actual Intercooling. The intermediate optimum pressures derived in the previous section were derived on the assumption of no pressure drop in the intercooler. Although the pressure drop in the intercooler is small (about 1 per cent of the initial compressor inlet absolute pressure), some unbalancing of pressure ratios occurs with consequent unequal distribution of compression work. Equations (5-13) and (5-14) can be regarded only as a first approximation under the actual conditions of intercooling.

More often the intermediate pressures are selected on the basis of convenience in splitting the compression. Matching compressor characteristics may be a much more important determinant. Furthermore, Eqs. (5-13) and (5-14) are derived on the basis of obtaining the minimum work input, but optimum efficiency of compressor operation would occur at a pressure slightly higher than indicated by these equations.

Intercooling is effective only at high pressure ratios and when high turbine inlet temperatures are used. Even under the most favorable conditions there is very little gain in thermal efficiency when intercooling is used without the benefit of regeneration.

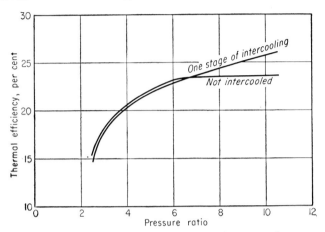

Fig. 5-13. Simple Brayton cycle with and without intercooling.

Figure 5-13 compares a simple Brayton cycle with one intercooler with another without intercooling. It can be seen that at lower pressure ratios the thermal efficiency actually suffers. This situation is brought about because the saving in compressor work is more than offset by the additional heat added to make up for the heat rejected to the intercooler.

Figure 5-14 shows that the decrease in work with one intercooler over nonintercooling is almost a straight-line function of pressure ratio. The curves of Figs. 5-13 and 5-14 take into account system pressure losses as well as component efficiencies.

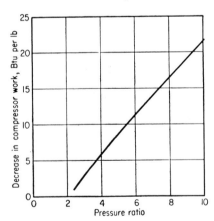

Fig. 5-14. Decrease in compressor work for single stage of intercooling compared with nonintercooling.

One important aspect of intercooling is the fact that the lower specific volumes obtained permit a smaller machine size. This factor, of course, is of greater significance when large quantities of air are to be handled.

Intercooling may be actually disadvantageous in some mobile applications where cooling water could be supplied only with great difficulty. It is possible to use atmospheric air as a coolant but only with design complications and additional bulk.

5-11. Reheat. Reheating the gas during turbine expansion is analogous to intercooling the air during compression. The purpose in reheating is to approach an isothermal expansion in order to increase the output of the turbine. The expansion process is broken up into two or more steps and heat is added to the gas by means of an auxiliary combustion chamber between the steps. Since the air-fuel ratio is so high in the main

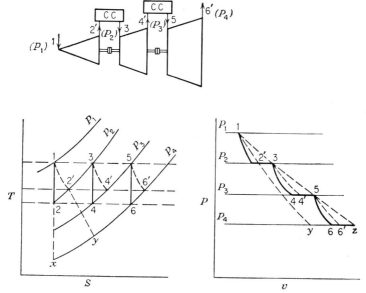

Fig. 5-15. Reheated expansion (two stages).

combustion chamber, there is more than ample oxygen in the gases to support combustion in the auxiliary combustion chambers.

Figure 5-15 illustrates a turbine expansion process with two reheaters. An isentropic expansion takes place from (1) to (2) and the irreversible adiabatic from (1) to (2′). Heat is added at constant pressure in the first auxiliary burner from (2′) to (3). The expansion in the second step takes place isentropically from (3) to (4) and irreversibly and adiabatically from (3) to (4′). Heat is added again at constant pressure in the second auxiliary burner from (4′) to (5). The final expansion takes place from (5) to (6) or (5) to (6′). The locus of points 1, 3, 5, and z establishes the isothermal expansion. The irreversible adiabatic expansion without reheat is indicated by the expansion line 1-y.

The optimum reheat pressures may be ascertained by methods similar to those used in determining the optimum intercooling pressure. For one reheater the reheat pressure is

$$P_2 = (P_1 P_3)^{1/2} \qquad (5\text{-}15)$$

and for two reheaters

$$P_2 = (P_1{}^2 P_4)^{1/3} \quad \text{and} \quad P_3 = (P_1 P_4{}^2)^{1/3} \qquad (5\text{-}16)$$

If the simple Brayton cycle is modified to incorporate reheat in the turbine expansion, the effect on thermal efficiency is about the same as when intercooling is used. At low pressure ratios the thermal efficiency will have a tendency to suffer but will be better at higher pressure ratios. This may be explained by the fact that at lower pressure ratios the increased turbine output is not enough to counterbalance the additional heat added and the higher temperature of heat rejection. At high pressure ratios the marginal increase in turbine output is more significant and the thermal efficiency of the cycle is improved.

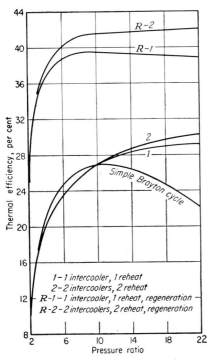

Fig. 5-16. Effect of intercooling and reheat on thermal efficiency.

The real value of reheat and intercooling is realized when regeneration is employed because the exhaust gases are nearer the highest temperature of the cycle and the air leaving the compressor is very nearly at the lowest temperature.

5-12. Combined Effects of Intercooling, Reheating, and Regeneration. The requirements and economics of a particular installation will dictate which modifications to the basic Brayton cycle are to be incorporated in the plant design. Additional complexities involve higher initial and maintenance costs which must be justified on the basis of fuel savings. Where space requirements are critical or weight is an important factor, some of the refinements must be omitted even though economically justified. It is significant then to examine the various combinations of intercooling, reheating, and regeneration in the light of their effects on thermal efficiency.

A comparison of a simple Brayton cycle (without regeneration) with the same cycle introducing reheat and intercooling is shown in Fig. 5-16.

These are characteristic curves, and the actual values would vary with turbine and compressor inlet temperatures and component efficiency. It may be seen from the curves that at low pressure ratios the thermal efficiency is worse than for a simple Brayton cycle but improves at higher pressure ratios. The true advantage of intercooling and reheat is more evident when used in conjunction with regeneration, as may be seen from the curves. Another fact is clear, and that is the slight improvement in thermal efficiency gained by using two stages of intercooling and reheat without regeneration. With regeneration, the additional stages of intercooling and reheat have a more pronounced effect in improving thermal efficiency.

Another characteristic of intercooling and reheat either with or without regeneration is the flatter efficiency curve, which is of importance at part load.

Figure 5-17 shows the comparative values of intercooling with varying regenerator efficiencies and regenerator pressure losses. Comparing curves (2) and (4) or (1) and (3) the effect of regenerator pressure losses is very apparent, as is the effect of regenerator efficiency in comparing curves (3), (4), (5), and (6).

5-13. Closed Cycles. The closed cycle gas turbine operates on a modification of the Ericsson cycle, *i.e.*, it may include intercooling, reheat, regeneration, or very probably all three. The closed and semiclosed cycles were described in Sec. 2-5.

Considering first the semiclosed plant, it is clear from the various equations derived that thermal efficiency does not depend on the magnitude of the pressures involved but on pressure ratio. However, if large flow quantities are involved, as in large plants, it is important that a high pressure level be maintained to decrease the specific volume of the gas, thereby reducing considerably the size of equipment required. To raise atmospheric air to such high pressure levels would require a prohibitive amount of energy for compression. Therefore it is essential that the pressure at compressor inlet be maintained at a high level, and to accomplish this a closed cycle must be employed. A semiclosed-cycle diagram is shown in Fig. 2-20. Heat is added by internal firing, as in the open cycle, followed by expansion in a turbine to some pressure above atmospheric. The turbine exhaust, still at a pressure above atmospheric, is sent through a regenerator and precooler before entering the compressor. An auxiliary turbocompressor supplies make-up air to sustain combustion. The make-up air is essential since the same gas is continuously recirculated and the oxygen would be eventually depleted. The precooler is required because it would be disadvantageous to compress a high-temperature gas; witness the effect of compressor inlet temperature on cycle thermal efficiency.

The externally fired closed cycle eliminates the auxiliary turbocompressor since make-up air is not required. Combustion takes place in an externally fired combustion chamber, and heat is transferred through tubes to the working medium, which is pure air. The combustion cham-

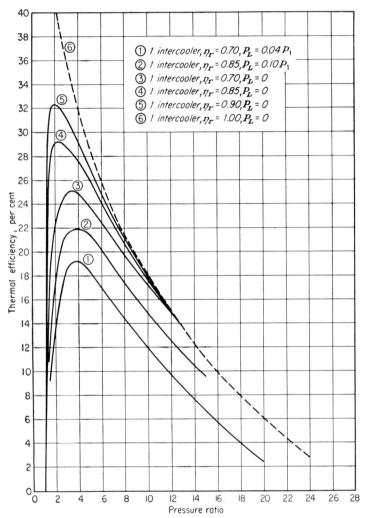

① *1 intercooler,* $\eta_r = 0.70, P_L = 0.04 P_1$
② *1 intercooler,* $\eta_r = 0.85, P_L = 0.10 P_1$
③ *1 intercooler,* $\eta_r = 0.70, P_L = 0$
④ *1 intercooler,* $\eta_r = 0.85, P_L = 0$
⑤ *1 intercooler,* $\eta_r = 0.90, P_L = 0$
⑥ *1 intercooler,* $\eta_r = 1.00, P_L = 0$

Fig. 5-17. Intercooling with regeneration (no reheat).

ber resembles a steam boiler and may use any form of fuel. The precooler and high compressor inlet pressures are retained as in the semiclosed cycle.

Besides the advantages mentioned for the semiclosed cycle, the closed cycle has the further advantages of a clean medium, use of cheaper fuels, and the possibility of utilizing a more suitable gas than air for the medium. Disadvantages of both types of closed cycles are the need for a precooler and design complications for certain components such as heat exchangers due to the high pressure level. A disadvantage of the externally fired closed cycle is the need for a combustion chamber comparable in size to a steam boiler with all the maintenance problems such an installation implies.

5-14. Operating Media Other than Air. The externally fired closed cycle permits the use of a gas other than air, and therefore it appears desirable to investigate the properties of some likely gases. The following characteristics are of interest in any proposed gas:

1. Stability
2. Cheapness and availability
3. Noninflammability
4. Nonexplosiveness
5. Nontoxicity
6. High specific heat, C_p
7. High specific heat ratio, k
8. High thermal conductivity, U
9. Noncorrosiveness
10. Gas constant, R

Gas	C_p	k	U at 32 F	R
Air..................	0.242	1.40	0.0140	53.34
Argon...............	0.124	1.66	0.00912	38.7
Helium..............	1.25	1.66	0.082	386.3
Hydrogen...........	3.42	1.41	0.099	766.8

For a given isentropic compression, the temperature at the end of compression is given by the expression

$$T_2 = T_1(r_p)^{(k-1)/k}$$

and the work done on the gas by

$$W_c = C_p(T_2 - T_1)$$

It is clear, therefore, that low values of k and C_p are conducive to lower compression work. On the other hand a high value of k and C_p are essential to high turbine output, assuming the same r_p. However, the net work out of the cycle, with high values of k and C_p, will always increase. This is because the increase in turbine output more than offsets the increased compressor work. It would seem, then, that the increased output per pound of media would permit a reduction in mass rate of flow.

It does not follow, however, that a reduction in mass rate of flow would permit the use of smaller machines. The specific volume of the gas must be considered, and therefore it is necessary to have, also, a low gas constant R.

An examination of the properties of some representative gases shown in the preceding table would indicate tnat when desirable values of C_p and k are available, they are accompanied by high values of R. Actually, no material change in turbine or compressor size would be indicated, since the net output per volume rate of flow is almost the same.

However, high values of thermal conductivity would result in appreciable savings in heat exchangers, *i.e.*, regenerators and intercoolers. The values given in the table for U are all based on 32 F for comparative purposes. Actually, these values would be considerably higher at the temperatures encountered in regenerators.

It must be concluded that any serious reduction in size of the gas-turbine plant by using a gas other than air would have to be realized in the heat exchangers. Of course a gas other than air could be used in an externally fired closed cycle. But it is there that a reduction in the size of heat exchanger is particularly important.

References

1. Rettaliata, J. T.: The Combustion Gas Turbine, *Current Trends*, No. 4, 1939.
2. Rettaliata, J. T.: The Gas Turbine, *Current Trends*, No. 7, 1941.
3. Rowley, L. N., and B. G. A. Skrotzki: Gas Turbines, *Power*, October, 1946.
4. Salisbury, J. K.: The Basic Gas Turbine Plant and Some of Its Variants, *Trans. ASME*, 1944.
5. Smith, R. B., and C. R. Soderberg: The Gas Turbine as a Possible Marine Prime Mover, *Trans. Soc. Naval Architects and Marine Engs.*, 1943.

Problems

5-1. The thermal efficiency of the ideal Brayton open cycle is given by Eq. (5-3). What would be the effect of irreversibilities in the compressor and turbine upon thermal efficiency, if

    (*a*) $100\% > \eta_c > \eta_t$

    (*b*) $100\% > \eta_t > \eta_c$

    (*c*) $\eta_c = \eta_t < 100\%$

Explain answers.

5-2. In an intercooled regenerative gas-turbine plant the temperatures of the air entering and leaving the low pressure compressor are 80 F and 210 F, respectively. The corresponding temperatures for the high-pressure compressor are 130 F and 270 F, respectively. Air leaves the regenerator at 650 F. The gas temperatures entering and leaving the turbine are 1600 F and 800 F, respectively. The atmospheric pressure of the air is 14.7 psia and the pressure ratio is 6. Cooling water enters the intercooler at 70 F and leaves at 85 F.

Compute:

(a) Net cycle output in Btu per lb of air

(b) The thermal efficiency of the cycle

(c) Cooling water required per pound of air

(d) Ratio of compressor input to turbine output

5-3. A simple Brayton cycle gas-turbine plant operates on a pressure ratio of 5. The temperature of the air entering the compressor is 70 F. Gas enters the turbine at 1300 F, expanding to atmospheric pressure at 14.7 psia. The compressor and turbine efficiencies are each 0.85, not including external losses. The mechanical efficiencies of compressor and turbine are each 0.96. The combustion efficiency is 0.98. The air flow is 85 lb per sec. Determine (a) the thermal efficiency of the cycle; (b) the output in kilowatts; (c) the thermal efficiency if a regenerator of 65 per cent efficiency is added.

5-4. If one stage of intercooling is introduced in the basic plant of Prob. 5-3, instead of regeneration, what will be the thermal efficiency of the cycle and the output? Intercooling is used at a point where the pressure is 33 psia and the air is cooled to 120 F. Find the thermal efficiency if intercooling and regeneration are used.

5-5. Suppose that reheating is introduced in the basic plant of Prob. 5-3 instead of regeneration and intercooling. Assuming that reheat takes place at a pressure of 33 psia and 1300 F, what will be the output and thermal efficiency of the plant? If the intercooling of Prob. 5-4 is added, what are the thermal efficiency and output of the plant? Suppose further that regeneration (in addition to intercooling) is added as in Prob. 5-3; what is the thermal efficiency of the plant?

5-6. Compute the thermal efficiency when reheating and regeneration, under the conditions previously specified, are added to the basic plant of Prob. 5-3. Compare the various thermal efficiencies obtained from Probs. 5-3 to 5-5 and the thermal efficiency obtained in this problem. In the light of this comparison discuss the relative merits of intercooling, reheat, and regeneration when used independently and in combination.

CHAPTER 6

ELEMENTARY GAS DYNAMICS

6-1. Introduction. Gas dynamics is concerned with the application of both the thermodynamic and the Newtonian laws to gases in motion. Since steam and gas turbines, compressors, combustors, and regenerators all utilize flowing gaseous fluids as working media, a basic understanding of elementary gas dynamics is essential.

The working medium may be assumed to obey the conditions of steady flow, *i.e.*, the mass rate of flow is constant at each and every cross section normal to the direction of flow. This condition of steady flow implies static pressure, specific volume, and velocity to be constant with respect to time at each and every cross section normal to the direction of flow.

In order for all the conditions of steady flow to be maintained, it is necessary for the discrete elements of fluid to flow in streamlines. Such streamline flow is often referred to as laminar or viscous flow. However, in most engineering applications the precise condition of steady flow of compressible fluids is seldom obtained, the usual condition being that of turbulence with microscopic variation in mass rate of flow. Nevertheless, if the variation of mass rate of flow is not great, the components of velocity tangent to the mean direction of flow may be considered as satisfactorily fulfilling the requirements for steady flow.

Flow may be considered as one-, two-, or three-dimensional under different circumstances. While most gas flows are in actuality three-dimensional, the flow may be approximated by one- or two-dimensional analyses as conditions dictate. Consider a particle of a gas moving in space as shown in Fig. 6-1. The direction of translation of the particle has three rectangular components in space. Consequently the resultant velocity of translation has three rectangular components. The flow of this particle is said to be three-dimensional.

Again referring to Fig. 6-1, if any one of the velocity components V_x, V_y, or V_z is zero, the flow is two-dimensional. For this condition it follows that the flow is identical in parallel planes. For example, if $V_z = 0$, then the flow in all planes parallel to the xy plane will be identical. Such flow is said to be two-dimensional and may be approximated if V_x, V_y, or V_z is small.

Similarly, if any two components are zero, then the flow is one-dimensional in the direction of the remaining component. This condition may also be approximated if the magnitudes of any two components are negligible.

In order to solve a problem in three-dimensional flow completely, it is necessary to find not only the three velocity components as illustrated but also the three components of density, static pressure, and temperature as functions of the space coordinates x, y, and z. For the solution, the laws of conservation of mass, conservation of energy, and the equations of state and conservation of momentum in the x, y, and z directions are available. Hence there are six equations upon which to support a solution.

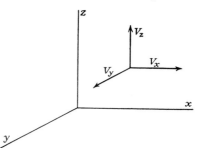

Fig. 6-1. Three-dimensional flow.

Although a rigorous treatment of the flow in turbine and compressor passages requires a consideration of three-dimensional effects, satisfactory results can be obtained by a one- or two-dimensional analysis with suitable modifications to predict reasonably close approximations to true conditions.

6-2. Continuity Equation. The continuity equation follows from the law of conservation of mass and the condition of steady flow. This equation may be expressed for three-dimensional flow (Fig. 6-1),

$$\frac{\partial}{\partial x}\left(\frac{V_x}{v}\right) + \frac{\partial}{\partial y}\left(\frac{V_v}{v}\right) + \frac{\partial}{\partial z}\left(\frac{V_z}{v}\right) = 0$$

For the one-dimensional case,

$$\frac{AV}{v} = G = \text{const} \tag{6-1}$$

where G = mass rate of flow, lb per sec
A = cross-sectional area normal to flow, sq ft
v = specific volume at section where area is noted, cu ft per lb
V = velocity at section where area is noted, fps

6-3. Isentropic Flow Relations. Consider the flow in a passage to be steady and one-dimensional as well as isentropic. For a particle of fluid, the net force in the direction of flow may be found from Newton's second law (conservation of momentum).

$$F = \frac{d(mv)}{dt}$$

Since the flow is steady and there is no change of m with time,

$$F = m \frac{dV}{dT}$$

From Fig. 6-2,

$$PA - (P + dP)(A + dA) + \left(P + \frac{dP}{2}\right) dA = \frac{A \; dl}{vg} \frac{dV}{dt} = F$$

Retaining only first-order differentials,

$$-A \; dP = \frac{A \; dl}{vg} \frac{dV}{dt}$$

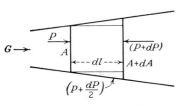

$G \longrightarrow$

Since $dl/dt = V$, the preceding equation reduces to

$$v \; dP + \frac{V \; dV}{g} = 0 \qquad (6\text{-}2)$$

Fig. 6-2. Forces exerted on an element of fluid flowing in a passage (frictionless).

Equation (6-2) may be recognized as the Bernoulli equation for isentropic steady flow.

Enthalpy is defined:

$$h = U + \frac{Pv}{J}$$

or

$$dh = dU + \frac{d(Pv)}{J}$$

But

$$dh = dU + \frac{P \; dv}{J} + \frac{v \; dP}{J} \qquad \text{and} \qquad dQ = dU + \frac{P \; dv}{J}$$

so that

$$dh = dQ + \frac{v \; dP}{J}$$

Since this is an isentropic flow process, $dQ = 0$,

and

$$dh = \frac{v \; dP}{J}$$

Therefore, substituting in Eq. (6-2),

$$J \; dh + \frac{V \; dV}{g} = 0 \qquad (6\text{-}3a)$$

or

$$(h_1 - h_2) + \frac{1}{2gJ} (V_2{}^2 - V_1{}^2) = \text{const} \qquad (6\text{-}3b)$$

Equation (6-3a) is the energy equation and is equivalent to Eq. (6-2) for isentropic flow.

Equations (6-2) and (6-3b) show that an increase in velocity is accompanied by a drop in static pressure and enthalpy. Conversely an increase in static pressure and enthalpy can be achieved only by a decrease in velocity. These equations are valid for isentropic steady flow in contact with solid boundaries. The fluid may be compressible or incompressible.

Referring to Eq. (6-2), if the pressure change is small, the change in specific volume may be disregarded. For this condition Eq. (6-2) can be integrated and

$$(P_2 - P_1) + \frac{1}{2gv}(V_2{}^2 - V_1{}^2) = \text{const} \qquad (6\text{-}4)$$

The first term is the static pressure and the second term the dynamic pressure each expressed in pounds per square feet. The sum of the static and dynamic pressures is the stagnation or total pressure. It may be noted that the stagnation pressure is constant.

Referring to Eq. (6-3b), the first term is the static enthalpy change which is a function of static temperature and static pressure changes. The second term is the dynamic enthalpy change and the sum of the first and second terms is the stagnation or total enthalpy change. The static and dynamic enthalpies each have units of Btu per pound. The stagnation enthalpy is a constant.

Further relations for stagnation enthalpy, pressures, and temperatures for compressible fluids are discussed in Sec. 6-10.

6-4. Sonic Velocity and Mach Number. The bulk modulus K by definition is the ratio of static-pressure change to the strain produced thereby per unit volume, or

$$K = -\frac{dP}{dv/v} = -v\frac{dP}{dv}$$

where K = bulk modulus, psf
dP = pressure change, psf
dv = volume change, cu ft
v = volume before change, cu ft

The negative sign indicates that an increase in pressure is accompanied by a decrease in volume.

The value of the bulk modulus depends on the process. For a polytropic process, the value of the bulk modulus may be found from the path equation, $Pv^n = $ constant.

Differentiating,

$$d(Pv^n) = 0$$

and
$$v^n\,dP + P\,dv^n = 0$$

or
$$v^n\,dP + nPv^{n-1}\,dv = 0$$

Dividing by Pv^n,

$$\frac{dP}{P} + n\frac{dv}{v} = 0$$

or
$$-\frac{dP}{dv/v} = nP = K_n$$

where K_n = polytropic bulk modulus, psf
$\quad\quad n$ = polytropic exponent
$\quad\quad P$ = pressure, psf
For an isothermal process, $n = 1$ and the bulk modulus is $K = P$. For an isentropic process, $n = k$ and therefore

$$K_s = kP$$

where K_s = isentropic bulk modulus, psf
$\quad\quad k$ = ratio of specific heats, C_p/C_v
From Eq. (6-2),

$$dV = -\frac{vg\,dP}{V}$$

The continuity equation, Eq. (6-1), may be expressed for constant A as follows

$$\frac{G}{A} = \frac{V}{v} = \text{const}$$

or in differential form

$$d\left(\frac{G}{A}\right) = d\left(\frac{V}{v}\right) = 0$$

whence
$$v\,dV + V\,dv = 0$$

or
$$dV = -\frac{V\,dv}{v}$$

Then
$$dV = \frac{vg\,dP}{V} = V\frac{dv}{v}$$

and
$$V = \sqrt{gv\frac{dP}{dv/v}}$$

or
$$V = \sqrt{gvK_n}$$

If the isentropic bulk modulus is used, then

$$a = V = \sqrt{gkPv} = \sqrt{gkRT} \tag{6-5}$$

The velocity obtained from this equation is the velocity of sound in a gas (also known as the sonic or acoustic velocity). This is the velocity at which a disturbance such as a pressure change propagates itself in a gas.

The Mach number is a dimensionless number expressing the ratio of the local velocity of a gas to the velocity of sound in the same gas. The velocity of sound is calculated from Eq. (6-5) for the conditions existing at the point where the local velocity is observed:

$$M = \frac{V}{a} = \frac{V}{\sqrt{gkRT}} \tag{6-6}$$

where M = Mach number

V = local velocity of fluid, psf

a = velocity of sound in fluid, psf

The Mach number is an important flow parameter and much use will be made of it in the succeeding sections.

6-5. Mach Waves. High-speed flows (sonic or supersonic) are often encountered in connection with steam and gas turbines, compressors, jet aircraft, rockets, and projectiles. The compressibility effects of disturbances in a gas decelerating from a supersonic to a subsonic velocity are

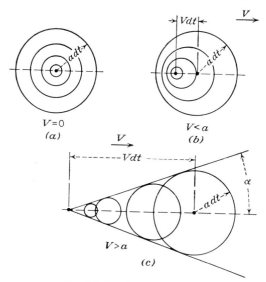

Fig. 6-3. Sound waves in a gas.

important considerations for the designer of any of the previously mentioned devices.

Consider a spherical disturbance such as an intermittent electric spark or pressure change in a quiescent gas. The resulting phenomenon is illustrated by Fig. 6-3a. The wave front caused by the disturbances propagates itself in all directions at the velocity of sound in the gas. Suppose the gas is in motion with a velocity of flow less than that of sound in the gas. Figure 6-3b represents this case. The net velocity of propagation of the wave front upstream is $a - V$ and downstream $a + V$. Since $a > V$, the wave front moves upstream as well as downstream. Another situation where the velocity of flow is supersonic is shown in Fig. 6-3c. Since $V > a$, the net velocity of wave propagation upstream is negative and thus the wave front does not move upstream at all.   It is clear from Fig. 6-3a and b that the wave front can move to infinity.   However, Fig. 6-3c shows that all spherical wave fronts lie within the envelope of a cone whose apex is the original location of the disturbance.   This is a consequence of the negative net velocity of wave propagation upstream.   It should be noted that the velocity of propagation normal to the sides of the cone is always sonic.

Considering Fig. 6-3c, the half angle α of the cone may be expressed

$$\alpha = \arcsin \frac{a}{V}\frac{dt}{dt} = \arcsin \frac{a}{V} = \arcsin \frac{1}{M} \tag{6-7}$$

Angle α is called the Mach angle because of the relation shown in the previous equation.   The waves are known as Mach waves and the sides of the cone as Mach lines.   These waves are very weak and the energy transitions across their boundaries take place isentropically.   Therefore, the use of the isentropic bulk modulus in Eq. (6-5) is justified.

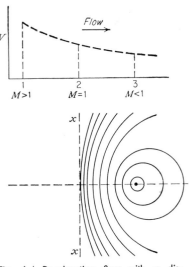

6-6. Plane Normal Shock Waves. Consider the case of a decelerating flow from supersonic to subsonic velocity as represented in Fig. 6-4. A disturbance occurs in the subsonic region, and the wave front moves upstream at a velocity $a - V$ until point 2 is reached where $V = a$, $V - a = 0$, and $M = 1$. It is evident that the wave front cannot pass the sonic barrier. The wave fronts accumulate as they approach xx as a limit creating a large disturbance which results in a discontinuity with

Fig. 6-4. Decelerating flow with a disturbance in subsonic region (plane normal shock).

attendant shock.   The xx line is the Mach line and the Mach angle is 90° consistent with a Mach number equal to unity.   Since there is no change in direction of flow, the shock wave appears as a standing wave in a plane normal to the direction of flow as shown in Fig. 6-4.   Hence this type of shock wave is referred to as a plane normal shock wave.

If an accelerating flow is considered where the fluid velocity accelerates from subsonic to supersonic, normal shock will not occur.   The wave front moves downstream at a velocity $a + V$ and therefore is never zero. Upstream movement of the wave front emanating from a disturbance in the subsonic region is at a net velocity $a - V$ and since $a > V$ this sum never can be equal to zero and no shock occurs.   Disturbances occurring in the supersonic region are propagated upstream at velocity $a - V$, where $V > a$, and therefore never reach the sonic threshold.

Shock is an event which occurs so rapidly that it may be regarded as an essentially adiabatic process. Since no work is done, it follows from the first law that the total energy of the system must be constant. However, there is an increase of entropy with a consequent decrease in the availability of energy. The decrease in availability is, of course, a source of loss. This phenomenon is therefore of great interest to the compressor and turbine designer. It would appear that shock compression is a condition to be avoided, although currently much attention is being directed to the possible use of this phenomenon to achieve compression in air compressors.

Nothing in the foregoing material shows that a rarefaction shock is not possible. A rarefaction shock is the opposite of compression shock as previously described. If rarefaction shock were possible instead of a static-pressure rise through shock, the flow would be accelerated from subsonic to supersonic velocity. Although the impossibility of a rarefaction can be demonstrated by rigorous analysis, a qualitative analysis is satisfactory for the purposes of this chapter. Since compression shock is accompanied by an increase in entropy, rarefaction would have to occur with a decrease in entropy. A decrease in entropy with constant total energy through shock would be a clear violation of the second law of thermodynamics. Therefore, only a compression shock is possible.

6-7. Relationship of State Properties through Plane Normal Shock. The plane in which normal shock occurs may be regarded as infinitesimally thin so that the action can be assumed to occur between parallel streamlines. If the conditions before shock are represented by the subscript 1 and after shock by subscript 2, then from Eq. (6-1) for continuity, assuming constant area control surface and an ideal gas,

$$\frac{G}{A} = \frac{V_1}{v_1} = \frac{V_2}{v_2}$$

From conservation of momentum

$$F = \frac{G}{g} dV = P_2 A - P_1 A = \frac{G}{g} (V_1 - V_2)$$

$$P_2 - P_1 = \frac{G}{Ag} (V_1 - V_2)$$

$$P_2 - P_1 = \frac{V_1^2}{v_1 g} - \frac{V_2^2}{v_2 g}$$

Substituting for v its equivalent RT/P from the equation of state,

$$P_2 - P_1 = \frac{P_1 V_1^2}{gRT_1} - \frac{P_2 V_2^2}{gRT_2}$$

But $\dfrac{V_1{}^2}{gkRT_1} = M^2$ and $P_2 - P_1 = k(P_1 M_1{}^2 - P_2 M_2{}^2)$

$$\frac{P_2}{P_1} = \frac{kM_1{}^2 + 1}{kM_2{}^2 + 1} \tag{6-8}$$

This is one form of the Rayleigh equation for plane normal shock for an ideal gas in isentropic flow.

The energy equation [Eq. (6-2)] for an ideal gas may be expressed as follows:

$$\frac{V_2{}^2 - V_1{}^2}{2gJ} = C_v(T_1 - T_2) + \frac{P_1 v_1 - P_2 v_2}{J}$$

and since $C_v = \dfrac{R}{J(k-1)}$,

$$\frac{V_2{}^2 - V_1{}^2}{2g} = \frac{k}{k-1}(P_1 v_1 - P_2 v_2)$$

or $\quad \dfrac{V_1{}^2}{2g}\dfrac{(k-1)}{k} + P_1 v_1 = \dfrac{V_2{}^2}{2g}\dfrac{(k-1)}{k} + P_2 v_2$

and $\quad P_1 v_1 \left[1 + \dfrac{V_1{}^2(k-1)}{2gkP_1 v_1} \right] = P_2 v_2 \left[1 + \dfrac{V_2{}^2(k-1)}{2gkP_2 v_2} \right] \tag{6-9}$

From the equation of state, $Pv = RT$, and $M = V/\sqrt{gkPv}$,

$$T_1 \left[\frac{2 + (k-1)M_1{}^2}{2} \right] = T_2 \left[\frac{2 + (k-1)M_2{}^2}{2} \right]$$

or $\quad \dfrac{T_2}{T_1} = \dfrac{2 + (k-1)M_1{}^2}{2 + (k-1)M_2{}^2} \tag{6-10}$

Equation (6-10) gives the ratio of absolute temperatures before and after shock for an ideal gas.

In Eq. (6-9), noting that V/v is constant and that $V = M\sqrt{gkRT}$,

$$P_1 M_1 \sqrt{gkRT_1} \left[\frac{2 + (k-1)M_1{}^2}{2} \right] = P_2 M_2 \sqrt{gkRT_2} \left[\frac{2 + (k-1)M_2{}^2}{2} \right]$$

Substituting Eq. (6-10),

$$P_1 M_1 \left[\frac{2 + (k-1)M_1{}^2}{2} \right]^{1/2} = P_2 M_2 \left[\frac{2 + (k-1)M_2{}^2}{2} \right]^{1/2} \tag{6-11}$$

Equation (6-11) is a form of the Fanno equation for an ideal gas.

From Eqs. (6-8) and (6-11),

$$\frac{M_2 \left[\dfrac{2 + (k-1)M_2{}^2}{2} \right]^{1/2}}{1 + kM_2{}^2} = \frac{M_1 \left[\dfrac{2 + (k-1)M_1{}^2}{2} \right]^{1/2}}{1 + kM_1{}^2} \tag{6-12}$$

Equation (6-12) gives the relationship between the Mach numbers before and after shock in terms of the specific heat ratio. It is clear that one solution of Eq. (6-12) is $M_1 = M_2$ for undisturbed flow without discontinuity. Therefore, $M_1 - M_2$ is one factor. Squaring Eq. (6-12), cross multiplying, and dividing through by $(M_1 - M_2)$, the result is

$$M_2{}^2 = \frac{2 + (k - 1)M_1{}^2}{2kM_1{}^2 - (k - 1)} \tag{6-13}$$

Equations (6-8) and (6-10) may now be solved in terms of the Mach number before shock, so that

$$\frac{P_2}{P_1} = \frac{2kM_1{}^2 - (k - 1)}{k + 1} \tag{6-14}$$

$$\frac{T_2}{T_1} = \frac{[2kM_1{}^2 - (k - 1)][2 + (k - 1)M_1{}^2]}{(k + 1)^2 M_1{}^2} \tag{6-15}$$

Since $Pv = RT$, from Eq. (6-15),

$$\frac{P_2 v_2}{P_1 v_1} = \frac{T_2}{T_1} = \frac{[2kM_1{}^2 - (k - 1)][2 + (k - 1)M_1{}^2]}{(k + 1)^2 M_1{}^2}$$

Substituting for P_2/P_1, its equivalent, from Eq. (6-14),

$$\frac{v_2}{v_1} = \frac{2 + (k - 1)M_1{}^2}{(k + 1)M_1{}^2} \tag{6-16}$$

Since

$$\frac{V_1}{v_1} = \frac{V_2}{v_2},$$

$$\frac{V_2}{V_1} = \frac{2 + (k - 1)M_1{}^2}{(k + 1)M_1{}^2} \tag{6-17}$$

Thus the ratio of state properties through one-dimensional plane normal shock in an ideal gas in isentropic flow may be expressed in terms of the Mach number before shock and the ratio of the specific heats. At very high values of M_1, a large change of temperature is evident through shock necessitating an allowance for varying specific heats.

6-8. Inclined or Oblique Waves. Section 6-5 included a discussion of the formation of inclined Mach lines in a supersonic gas stream caused by a disturbance producing spherical waves which propagate at the velocity of sound in the gas. If a thin symmetrical wedge (θ very small) is submerged in the gas so that the bisector of θ is parallel to the direction of the approach velocity, two-dimensional waves similar to Mach lines are produced. Like the Mach lines described in Sec. 6-5, these two-dimensional waves are weak oblique shock waves. The changes in state properties of the gas through weak shock are very small, and the process may be regarded as essentially isentropic. The angle of inclination of a weak oblique shock wave referred to the direction of approach velocity is equivalent to the Mach angle α (see Fig. 6-5).

Consider supersonic flow of a gas along the wall of a diverging passage where a slight change of direction $d\theta$ occurs as shown in Fig. 6-6. This is analogous to the flow past the lower surface of the thin wedge of Fig. 6-5. Assuming uniform velocity distribution in the approaching stream of gas, then V_1 represents the approach velocity and a_1 its component normal to

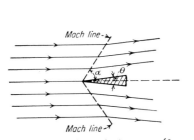

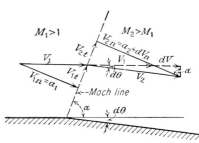

Fig. 6-5. Weak oblique shock waves (θ very small).

Fig. 6-6. Weak oblique shock wave in a diverging passage ($d\theta$ very small).

the Mach line. The normal component a_1 is equal to the velocity of sound, as it was in Fig. 6-3c. Because there is no static-pressure change along the Mach line, there is no change in the velocity components of V_1 and V_2 parallel to the Mach line. Then it is clear that since V_2 is parallel to the new direction of the passage wall the normal component of V_2 must increase an amount ΔV over a_1. Consequently, V_2 must be greater than

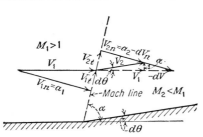

Fig. 6-7. Weak oblique shock wave in a converging passage (θ very small).

V_1 in magnitude. It follows that a drop in static pressure occurs, accompanied by an increase in Mach number and specific volume. It may be inferred from Fig. 6-6 that the magnitude of these changes is a function of the magnitude of $d\theta$. Thus for vanishingly small values of $d\theta$ ($2°$ or less), whereby $M_1 \approx M_2$, the angle of the Mach line is very nearly given by $\alpha = \arcsin (1/M)$.

A similar analysis may be extended to a converging passage as illustrated in Fig. 6-7 with its attendant compression.

Referring to Fig. 6-6 and taking the same assumptions that were pertinent in deriving the relationships through plane normal shock to be appropriate for the components normal to an oblique wave, then

$$\frac{G}{A} = \frac{V_{1n}}{v_1} = \frac{V_{2n}}{v_2} = \text{const}$$

or in differential form,

$$v \, dV_n + V_n \, dv = 0$$

or

$$dV_n = -V_n \frac{dv}{v}$$

From Eq. (6-2),

$$dV_n = \frac{vg \, dP}{V_n}$$

From the two preceding equations,

$$V_n = \sqrt{gv \frac{dP}{dv/v}}$$

Since the process is assumed to be isentropic ($d\theta$ very small),

$$K_S = kP = \frac{dP}{dv/v}$$

so that $a = V_n = \sqrt{gkPv}$.

Therefore, the components of the stream velocity normal to the Mach line are equal to the velocity of sound in the gas as previously stated.

The Mach angle $\alpha = \arcsin (V_n/V) = \arcsin (1/M)$. Now the components of V_1 and V_2 parallel to the Mach line are equal and the increase in magnitude of V_1 after the Mach line is

$$dV = dV_n \sin \alpha$$

The change in direction of V_1

$$d\theta = \frac{dV_n \cos \alpha}{V_1}$$

From the two preceding equations,

$$\frac{dV}{V_1} = \tan \alpha \, d\theta$$

and

$$\frac{dV}{V_1} = \frac{d\theta}{\sqrt{M^2 - 1}} \tag{6-18}$$

Thus the flow field consists of two zones separated by the Mach line at angle α. The velocity in each of these zones is constant, but the velocity change which occurs between the two zones is a function of $d\theta$, as shown by Eq. (6-18). The change in velocity magnitude is naturally accompanied by a change in the Mach number. It is desirable, therefore, to establish a relationship between the Mach number and velocity to take into account the variation of sonic velocity and gas velocity. To establish this relationship, it is convenient to write an energy equation for the section in the passage where the gas velocity is V_1 and some other section where the gas velocity is exactly equal to the sonic velocity. This value of the sonic velocity is known as the critical sonic velocity and is designated as a^*. The critical sonic velocity is then a characteristic constant for the flow

$$\frac{V_1^2}{2g}\left(\frac{k}{k-1}\right) + P_1v_1 = \frac{a^{*2}}{2g}\left(\frac{k}{k-1}\right) + P^*v^*$$

and

$$\frac{V_1^2}{a^{*2}} = \frac{(k+1)M_1^2}{M_1^2(k-1)+2} \qquad (6\text{-}19)$$

For convenience V_1^2/a^{*2} may be represented by $\bar{V}^2$, solving Eq. (6-19) for M_1^2 in terms of $\bar{V}^2$ and substituting in Eq. (6-18),

$$d\theta = \frac{d\bar{V}}{\bar{V}}\sqrt{\frac{\bar{V}^2 - 1}{1 - [(k-1)/(k+1)]\bar{V}^2}} \qquad (6\text{-}20)$$

Suppose that in the zone following this Mach line another change in direction of flow occurs through a second Mach line with Eq. (6-20) applicable again. For infinitesimal values of $d\theta$, an exact solution may be found for the total of the two zones. By extension an exact solution may be found for an infinite number of successive infinitesimal values of $d\theta$, and a reasonably good solution for very small values of $d\theta$. If $\theta_1 = 0$ at

$$M = 1 = \bar{V}$$

is substituted as a limit, Eq. (6-20) may be integrated, using Eq. (6-19), to give

$$\theta = \sqrt{\frac{k+1}{k-1}}\arctan\sqrt{\frac{k-1}{k+1}}\sqrt{M^2-1} - \arctan\sqrt{M^2-1} \qquad (6\text{-}21)$$

It should be noted that θ is the angle through which the flow would turn if M_1 were equal to unity at the corner in which the passage wall changes direction and if the final static pressure around this corner permitted full expansion to M_2. Suppose the flow before the corner is supersonic and therefore $M_1 > 1$, then it follows that some expansion must take place before the corner to satisfy the requirement that $M = 1$ at the corner. If θ_1 is the angle related to M_1, the ability of the flow to expand through θ_1 is depleted. Therefore the true angle of turning of the flow is given as $\beta = \theta_1 - \theta_2$, where θ_2 is the angle related to M_2. Values of θ corresponding to various Mach numbers are given in Fig. 6-8.

As an example of the use of Eq. (6-21) or Fig. 6-8, suppose that the flow of a gas along a wall is at $M = 3$ and the wall turns through an angle of $12°$ as shown in Fig. 6-9. Find M_2. From Fig. 6-8 or Eq. (6-21) for $M_1 = 3$, $\theta_1 = 49.76°$. $\beta = 12°$, so that $\theta_2 = 61.76°$. Solving Eq. (6-21) for M_2 or from Fig. 6-8, $M_2 = 3.7013$.

Equation (6-21) is a form of the Prandtl-Meyer equation. The method of approach to the problem is known as the "method of characteristics." Figure 6-9 shows that the limiting turning angle β which can be maintained occurs when the limiting value of $\theta_1 = 0$ at $M_1 = 1$,

$$P_1/P_0 = 0.5283$$

and $\theta_2 = 130.5°$ at $M_2 = 3.615$, $P_2/P_0 = 0$. Clearly P_2 would have to equal zero or a perfect vacuum would have to exist after turning the corner. Therefore the maximum turning angle that can be maintained with expansion to a perfect vacuum is $\beta = \theta_1 - 130.5°$. If the static pressure beyond the corner is such as to require a lower value for β than the physical corner provides, the flow will separate from the surface expanding to the actual static pressure P_2. If the physical value of β would require θ_2 to be greater than 130.5°, the flow will not turn through the physical angle but through a smaller angle again with flow separation.

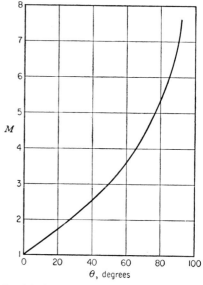

Fig. 6-8. Mach number vs. θ, as obtained from Eq. (6-21).

Figure 6-10 illustrates the condition which exists when a supersonic stream of gas is turned around smooth outside and inside corners. The latter case represents diffusion or compression. In Fig. 6-10a it may be noticed that the Mach lines do not intersect. However, if the angle of turning is great enough for an inside corner, as shown in Fig. 6-10b, the Mach lines are likely to intersect. Two Mach lines intersecting in this way merge into a single wave whose strength is the sum of the individual Mach lines. The resulting single wave will intersect with another Mach line to form an even stronger wave, and so on. Suppose the number of Mach lines to be infinite. Then an oblique shock wave would be formed whose strength would increase with its length. In an actual case, should the intensity of shock become great, the "method of characteristics" would not apply, since the approximation of isentropic conditions would not hold. Other methods are available for handling such a situation.

From the foregoing remarks it may be concluded that diffusion processes require great care in the design of the flow passages to avoid compression shock with consequent loss. It also follows that the flow pas-

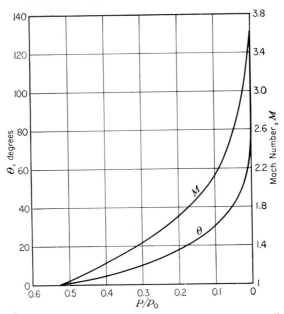

Fig. 6-9. M and θ as functions of the ratio of local static pressure to stagnation pressure.

sages for expansion processes may be designed with comparative freedom from the possibility of strong shock.

6-9. Strong Oblique Shock Waves. Strong oblique shock waves differ from weak oblique shock waves in intensity. For the weak oblique

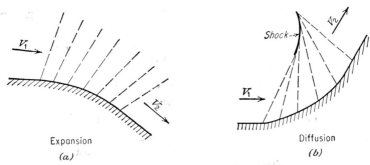

Fig. 6-10. Supersonic flow around outside and inside corners.

shock wave, the disturbance is infinitesimally small and the process is essentially isentropic. With strong oblique shock, the disturbance is so intense that the process can be no longer regarded as isentropic. There is an irreversible and adiabatic decrease in stagnation pressure. Strong oblique shock can occur only in diffusion or compression with a larger value of wall deflection angle δ.

Consider Fig. 6-11 which illustrates supersonic flow past a wall in which the deflection angle δ is large enough to induce an intense or strong shock. The components of velocity parallel to the shock are equal, but the normal components decrease through shock with a corresponding decrease in Mach number and increase in static pressure. The angle θ_w, called the wave angle, is no longer equal to the Mach angle.

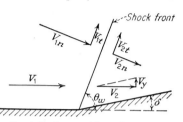

Fig. 6-11. Strong oblique shock wave.

The momentum, continuity, and energy equations may be set up for oblique shock, utilizing the components of velocity normal and parallel to the shock wave. The wave and deflection angles may be expressed in terms of V_1, V_2, and V_y. Finally, if the dimensionless ratios

$$\frac{V_1}{a^*} = \bar{V}_1 \qquad \frac{V_2}{a^*} = \bar{V}_2 \qquad \text{and} \qquad \frac{V_y}{a^*} = \bar{V}_y$$

are utilized, the following equation may be derived:

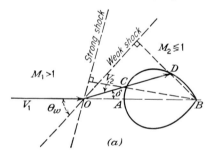

(a)

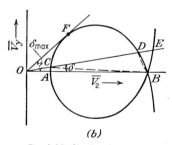

(b)

Fig. 6-12. Shock polar.

$$\bar{V}_y{}^2 = (\bar{V}_1 - \bar{V}_2) \cdot \left[\frac{\bar{V}_1 \bar{V}_2 - 1}{1 + \left(\frac{2}{k+1}\right)\bar{V}_1{}^2 - \bar{V}_1 \bar{V}_2} \right] \quad (6\text{-}22)$$

For stated values of $\bar{V}_1$, Eq. (6-22) becomes cubic in $\bar{V}_2$. Then plotting $\bar{V}_y$ vs. $\bar{V}_2$ for a fixed $\bar{V}_1$, a curve similar to that of Fig. 6-12 is obtained. This curve is known as a hodograph, since its coordinates represent the horizontal and vertical components of V_2. This particular hodograph may be referred to as a shock polar since it relates the velocities after shock. A family of curves may be obtained by taking different values for $\bar{V}_1$.

Some features of oblique shock waves now may be presented conveniently in terms of Eq. (6-22) and the shock polar. Equation (6-22) shows that when $\bar{V}_1 = \bar{V}_2$, V_y must be equal to zero, and therefore the wave is a weak or Mach wave. Point B in Fig. 6-12a represents this situation where $\bar{V}_2 = OB = \bar{V}_1$. $\bar{V}_y = 0$ when $\bar{V}_1\bar{V}_2 = 1$ or $V_1V_2 = a^2$, a condition of normal shock shown as point A in Fig. 6-12a. Between the Mach wave of point B and the normal shock wave of point A there is an infinite number of shock waves accompanied by flow deflection. For example, the ray OE with flow deflection angle δ cuts the curve at C, D, and E. This is true since Eq. (6-22) is cubic in $\bar{V}_2$. A line drawn normal to the curve segment BD cuts the abscissa or $\bar{V}_2$ coordinate at an angle θ_w, the wave angle. Similarly the wave angle for the curve segment BC may be obtained. As D approaches B, the chord BD approaches as a limit the tangent at B. The normal to the tangent at B cuts the $\bar{V}_2$ coordinate at the Mach angle α. Therefore, as D approaches B, the shock becomes very weak. On the other hand, as C approaches A, the chord BC approaches the chord AB and the wave angle formed by the normal to AB is 90°. This corresponds to a normal shock wave. It may be concluded that the two conditions C and D represent two solutions—the one at C for a strong shock and at D for weak shock. The third solution indicated at E imposes an increase in velocity or a rarefaction which is physically impossible.

It is clear that there exists no unique solution for a given value of $\bar{V}_1$ and θ. Two solutions are physically possible, one with weak shock accompanied by a small decrease in velocity and a small pressure rise. The flow may remain supersonic through weak shock. The other solution is strong shock with a large velocity decrease and a large pressure rise. The flow becomes subsonic through strong shock.

It may be observed from Fig. 6-12 that as the deflection angle δ increases, the intensity of the weak shock increases. But for smaller values of δ, the intensity of strong shock decreases and as δ approaches zero the wave approaches a Mach wave. The deflection angle δ may increase to a maximum so that a ray originating at O would be tangent to the curve at one point such as F. Now OF is not equal to $\bar{V}_2 = 1$ and point F does not signify the subdivision between supersonic and subsonic velocities. What happens through shock for maximum deflection actually depends on the particular family of curves. One family may result in supersonic flow through shock while another family may result in a reduction to subsonic velocity.

Suppose that the deflection angle of a wedge placed in a flow stream at a certain value of $\bar{V}_1$ is greater than the maximum deflection angle as indicated by the shock polar. In such an instance it is clear that no solution exists for which the shock wave is attached to the leading edge of the wedge. Instead a detached standing shock wave normal to the approaching flow direction will form just ahead of the wedge. The detached shock wave becomes more oblique on both sides of the wedge center line, as shown in Fig. 6-13. The region between the detached shock and the leading edge of the wedge and extending out some distance on both sides of the wedge center line is subsonic. At the very tip of the wedge leading edge a near stagnation condition exists. It is statistically improbable that the intensity of shock would increase along the shock wave pro-

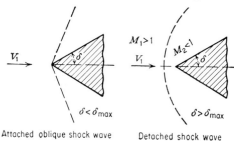

Attached oblique shock wave   Detached shock wave

Fig. 6-13. Attached and detached shock waves.

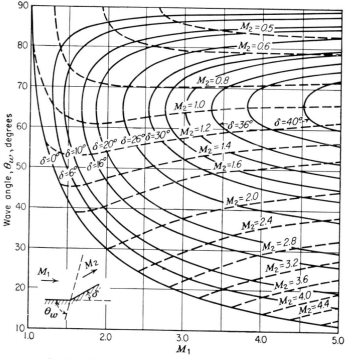

Fig. 6-14. Transformed shock polar for oblique shock waves.

ceeding out from the wedge center line. This is true since the entropy increase across shock would have to become infinite for increasing intensity. Actually the strength of shock decreases until at infinity the wave becomes a Mach wave.

Figure 6-14 represents a transformed shock polar which provides a convenient means for solving for properties of a gas through oblique shock. A detached shock wave may be solved by supposing the wave to be composed of many small segments corresponding to a portion of an oblique shock wave. These segments may be approximated by a straight line. The flow properties may then be computed from the shock equations for each point.

6-10. Stagnation Temperature, Enthalpy, and Pressure. Brief reference to stagnation enthalpy and pressure was made in Sec. 6-3 for a substantially uncompressed gas. A stagnation state exists when a high-velocity gas is brought completely to rest isentropically. If this definition of a stagnation state and Eqs. (6-2) and (6-3) are applied to an isentropic flow process, it is clear that the stagnation enthalpy is greater than the static enthalpy by the Btu equivalent of the kinetic energy. Similarly the stagnation pressure exceeds the static pressure by the pressure equivalent of the velocity. It will be demonstrated presently that the stagnation enthalpy is a function of stagnation temperature and stagnation pressure. Therefore the stagnation temperature exceeds the static temperature by the temperature equivalent of the velocity. When velocity effects are negligible, it follows that the static enthalpy, pressure, and temperature do not differ appreciably from their stagnation counterparts. The stagnation relationships are developed as follows for an ideal gas in isentropic flow.

The momentum equation is given by Eq. (6-2):

$$v\,dP + \frac{V\,dV}{g} = 0 \qquad (6-2)$$

But
$$Pv^k = \text{const}$$

which permits Eq. (6-2) to be integrated so that

$$\frac{k}{k-1}Pv + \frac{V^2}{2g} = \text{const}$$

Designating stagnation conditions by the superscript °

$$\frac{k}{k-1}P^\circ v^\circ = \frac{k}{k-1}Pv + \frac{V^2}{2g} = \text{const}$$

Since
$$C_p = \frac{Rk}{J(k-1)}$$

$$P^\circ v^\circ = R\left(T + \frac{V^2}{2gJC_p}\right)$$

But the term $V^2/2gJC_p$ is the temperature equivalent of the velocity, or the dynamic temperature, and

$$P^\circ v^\circ = RT^\circ \qquad (6-23)$$

Denoting conditions at two different sections of a flow passage by the subscripts 1 and 2, it follows, from Eq. (6-23) and the ideal gas relations for isentropic flow,

$$\frac{P_1}{P_1^\circ} = \left(\frac{T_1}{T_1^\circ}\right)^{k/(k-1)} \quad \text{and} \quad \frac{P_2}{P_2^\circ} = \left(\frac{T_2}{T_2^\circ}\right)^{k/(k-1)}$$

from which

$$\frac{P_1}{P_2^\circ} = \left(\frac{T_1}{T_2^\circ}\right)^{k/(k-1)} \tag{6-24}$$

and similarly

$$\frac{P_1^\circ}{P_2^\circ} = \left(\frac{T_1^\circ}{T_2^\circ}\right)^{k/(k-1)} \tag{6-25}$$

The preceding expressions show clearly that the ideal gas relations and the equation of state may be extended to the stagnation state properties.

The introduction of the Mach number to the stagnation temperature relationships provides a welcome convenience in calculations:

$$T^\circ = T + \frac{V^2}{2gJC_p} = T\left(1 + \frac{V^2}{2gJC_pT}\right)$$

Substituting Eq. (6-5), $a = \sqrt{gkRT}$, and $C_p = Rk/[J(k-1)]$

$$T^\circ = T\left[1 + \left(\frac{k-1}{2}\right)M^2\right] \tag{6-26}$$

Substituting Eq. (6-26) in Eq. (6-24),

$$P^\circ = P\left[1 + \left(\frac{k-1}{2}\right)M^2\right]^{k/(k-1)} \tag{6-27}$$

The energy equation [Eq. (6-3)] gives the relationship between static and stagnation enthalpies so that

$$h^\circ = h + \frac{V^2}{2gJ} = \text{const} \tag{6-28}$$

For adiabatic flow in which no work is done, even in the presence of friction, the stagnation enthalpy and temperature are constant at all sections of the flow passage so that

$$h_1^\circ = h_2^\circ = \text{const} \tag{6-29a}$$
$$T_1^\circ = T_2^\circ = \text{const} \tag{6-29b}$$

If the flow is isentropic with no work done, the stagnation pressures are equal at all sections and

$$P_1^\circ = P_2^\circ = \text{const} \tag{6-29c}$$

6-11. Isentropic Flow in a Passage of Varying Cross-sectional Area.

Equation (6-1) may be expressed

$$dG = d\left(\frac{AV}{v}\right) = 0$$

or

$$\frac{dA}{A} + \frac{dV}{V} - \frac{dv}{v} = 0$$

From the isentropic bulk modulus,

$$K_S = kP = -\frac{dP}{dv/v} \tag{6-30}$$

$$-\frac{dv}{v} = \frac{1}{k}\frac{dP}{P} \tag{6-31}$$

From Eq. (6-2), dividing through by V^2,

$$\frac{dV}{V} = -\frac{gv\,dP}{V^2} \tag{6-32}$$

Substituting Eqs. (6-31) and (6-32) in Eq. (6-30),

$$\frac{dA}{A} - \frac{gv\,dP}{V^2} + \frac{1}{k}\frac{dP}{P} = 0$$

or

$$\frac{dA}{A} = \frac{1}{k}\left(\frac{gkPv}{V^2} - 1\right)\frac{dP}{P}$$

The expression $gkPv/V^2$, it may be noted, is the square of the reciprocal of the Mach number, and

$$\frac{dA}{A} = \frac{1}{k}\left(\frac{1}{M^2} - 1\right)\frac{dP}{P} \tag{6-33}$$

From Eq. (6-31),

$$-v\,dP = kP\,dv$$

which, substituted in Eq. (6-2), yields

$$kP\,dv = \frac{V\,dV}{g}$$

or

$$\frac{dv}{v} = \frac{V\,dV}{gkPv}$$

Since

$$a = \sqrt{gkPv}$$

$$\frac{dv}{v} = \frac{V\,dV}{a^2}$$

which, substituted in Eq. (6-30), gives

$$\frac{dA}{A} + \frac{dV}{V} - \frac{V\,dV}{a^2} = 0$$

or

$$\frac{dA}{A} = \frac{V\,dV}{a^2} - \frac{dV}{V} = (M^2 - 1)\frac{dV}{V} \tag{6-34}$$

From Eq. (6-31),

$$-dP = kP \frac{dv}{v}$$

Substituting in Eq. (6-32),

$$\frac{dV}{V} = \frac{gkPv}{V^2} \frac{dv}{v}$$

or

$$\frac{dV}{V} = \frac{1}{M^2} \frac{dv}{v} \qquad (6\text{-}34)$$

Substituting the preceding expression in Eq. (6-30),

$$\frac{dA}{A} = \left(1 - \frac{1}{M^2}\right) \frac{dv}{v} \qquad (6\text{-}35)$$

Equations (6-2), (6-33), (6-34), and (6-35) are of such fundamental significance in studying isentropic flow that they are repeated here for convenience:

$$v\, dP + \frac{V\, dV}{g} = 0 \qquad (6\text{-}2)$$

$$\frac{dA}{A} = \frac{1}{k}\left(\frac{1}{M^2} - 1\right) \frac{dP}{P} \qquad (6\text{-}33)$$

$$\frac{dA}{A} = (M^2 - 1)\frac{dV}{V} \qquad (6\text{-}34)$$

$$\frac{dA}{A} = \left(1 - \frac{1}{M^2}\right)\frac{dv}{v} \qquad (6\text{-}35)$$

Several flow conditions will be examined in connection with the preceding equations.

Case I. M < 1 and Pressure Dropping. From Eq. (6-2) if dP is negative, then dV must be positive. With $M < 1$, the expression in parentheses of Eq. (6-33) is positive, and since dP is negative, dA must also be negative. The same result is obtained from Eq. (6-34) since the expression in parentheses is negative, dV is positive and dA has to be negative. The change in specific volume with cross-sectional area may be obtained from Eq. (6-35), which shows it to be increasing. To summarize, if the velocity entering a passage is subsonic and the static pressure in the passage is dropping, then the passage must be converging with increasing specific volume and velocity.

Case II. M > 1 and Pressure Dropping. Again from Eq. (6-2) if dP is negative, dV is positive. The expression in parentheses of Eq. (6-33) is negative, and since dP is also negative, dA must be positive. Similarly, Eq. (6-34) substantiates that dA is positive. Equation (6-35) establishes that the specific volume is increasing. To summarize, if the velocity entering a passage is supersonic and the static pressure in the passage is dropping, then the passage must diverge with increasing specific volume and velocity.

Case III. $M < 1$ *and Pressure Increasing.* Equation (6-2) shows dV to be negative when dP is positive. The expression in parentheses of Eq. (6-33) is positive and dA is positive. This condition is satisfied also by Eq. (6-34). Equation (6-35) shows that the specific volume decreases. To summarize, if the velocity entering a passage is subsonic and the static

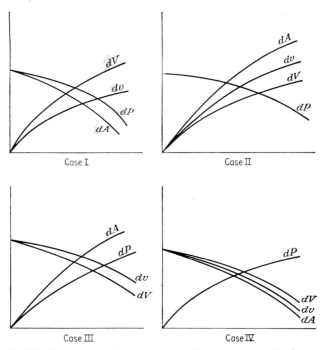

Fig. 6-15. Flow characteristics in a passage of varying cross-sectional area.

pressure in the passage is increasing, then the passage must diverge with decreasing velocity and specific volume.

Case IV. $M > 1$ *and Pressure Increasing.* Equation (6-2) shows dV is negative. Equation (6-33) indicates that dA is negative, a condition which is satisfied also by Eq. (6-34). Equation (6-35) shows increasing specific volume. To summarize, if the velocity entering a passage is supersonic and the static pressure in the passage is increasing, then the passage must converge with decreasing velocity and specific volume.

Case V. $M = 1$ *and Pressure Increasing or Decreasing.* If the Mach number is unity at a section in a passage, from Eqs. (6-33) to (6-35), dA is equal to zero. Therefore the slope of the curve of area vs. Mach number is zero when $M = 1$, a point of inflection is reached, and cross-sectional area is a minimum. For this condition, Eq. (6-30) reduces to

$$\frac{dV}{V} - \frac{dv}{v} = 0$$

or

$$d\left(\frac{V}{v}\right) = 0 \tag{6-36}$$

and

$$\frac{G}{A} = \frac{V}{v} = \text{maximum} \tag{6-37}$$

A point of deflection is reached on the curve of V/v vs. Mach number when $M = 1$ and the ratio V/v is a maximum. Therefore, when $M < 1$, the velocity increases much more rapidly than the specific volume until $M = 1$ is reached, after which ($M > 1$) the specific volume increases more rapidly than the velocity.

For a given minimum cross-sectional area ($dA = 0$ at $M = 1$), it follows from the continuity equation and Eq. (6-36), as expressed in Eq. (6-37), that the maximum mass rate of flow occurs at $M = 1$. Therefore the mass rate of flow in a passage is controlled by the conditions at $M = 1$, unless of course $M = 1$ is not reached, whereupon the passage exit conditions control the flow. These conclusions are consistent with the fact that disturbances such as pressure changes cannot move upstream after $M = 1$ is reached and therefore are unable to affect the flow.

The flow characteristics analyzed in the previous five cases apply to nozzles, venturi tubes, and diffusers. A transonic or converging-diverging nozzle exhibits the characteristics of Cases I, V, and II in that order. A venturi tube has the characteristics of Cases I, V, and III consecutively. The diffuser of a ram jet or supersonic jet aircraft shows the characteristics of Case IV while the jet itself is characterized by Case I.

6-12. Reynolds Number. Like the Mach number, the Reynolds number is another important flow parameter. The Reynolds number is defined as the ratio of the inertia forces to the viscous forces acting on a fluid in flow. The Reynolds number is dimensionless if consistent units are employed.

The inertia force can be represented as the product of mass and acceleration. The viscous force is the product of surface area of a particle of the fluid, velocity change, and coefficient of viscosity. If a characteristic dimension, such as passage diameter, is denoted by l, the inertia force may be expressed

$$\text{Inertia forces} = ma = f\left[(l^3\rho)\left(\frac{l}{t^2}\right)\right] = f(\rho, l^2, V^2)$$

where t = time, sec
ρ = density, slugs per cu ft

Similarly,

$$\text{Viscous forces} = f\left[(l^2)\left(\frac{V}{l}\right)(\mu) \right] = f(\mu,l,V)$$

where μ = absolute viscosity in slugs per second-foot.   The constant of proportionality is the Reynolds number

$$\text{Re} = \frac{\rho l^2 V^2}{\mu l V} = \rho\frac{Vl}{\mu} \tag{6-38}$$

Since $u = \rho\nu$,

$$\text{Re} = \frac{Vl}{\nu} \tag{6-39}$$

where ν = kinematic viscosity in square feet per second.

For gas flows, the principal forces are the inertia and viscous forces. It can be predicted by dimensional analysis and demonstrated by experiment that dynamically similar gas flows through geometrically similar passages or around geometrically similar objects are characterized by constancy of the Reynolds number.   Conversely, dynamic and geometric similarity may be maintained by adjustment of V, l, μ, or ρ so that the Reynolds number is constant.

6-13. Adiabatic Flow with Friction in a Passage of Constant Cross-sectional Area.   The energy equation for adiabatic flow gives no implicit

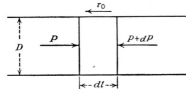

clue as to the effect of boundary friction loss.   The total energy of the gas remains the same, the friction loss manifesting itself by an increase in entropy.   There are two methods of accounting for frictional loss.   One method is to calculate the entropy increase and the other to utilize the

Fig. 6-16. Forces acting on an element of gas in a constant cross-sectional area passage.

momentum relationship, treating friction as a resisting force to flow. The latter method is in more general use and will be investigated first.

Figure 6-16 shows a section of straight pipe in which a high-velocity gas is flowing.   The pipe is insulated so that the flow process may be assumed to be adiabatic.   The friction force is indicated by τ_0.   The forces acting on an element of gas in the differential length of pipe dl are

$$F = \frac{\pi D^2}{4}\Big[P - (P + dP)\Big] - \tau_0\pi D\, dl$$

But $\tau_0 = f(V^2/2gv)$ in pounds, where f is the Fanning friction factor. Then

$$F = -dP\frac{\pi D^2}{4} - f\frac{V^2}{2gv}\pi D\, dl$$

The force F exerted on the element of gas is equal to the product of its mass and acceleration. The mass of the elements in slugs is

$$m = \frac{\pi D^2 \, dl}{4gv}$$

and the acceleration may be expressed

$$\frac{dV}{dt} = \frac{dV}{dl}\frac{dl}{dt} = V\frac{dV}{dl}$$

Then
$$-dP\,\frac{\pi D^2}{4} - f\frac{V^2}{2gv}\pi D \, dl = \frac{\pi D^2}{4g}\frac{dl}{v}\frac{V\,dV}{dl}$$

or
$$v\,dP + \frac{V\,dV}{g} + 2f\frac{V^2}{g}\frac{dl}{D} = 0 \qquad (6\text{-}40)$$

This is the momentum equation for adiabatic flow with friction. Equation (6-40) cannot be integrated easily in its present form and is of little practical use. However, when Eq. (6-40) is expressed in terms of Mach number, the integration may be carried out with much less difficulty.

It was stated in Sec. (6-10) that the stagnation temperature is constant at all sections of a passage if the flow is adiabatic. Substituting for the static temperature in Eq. (6-26) its equivalent from the equation of state, it follows that

$$Pv\left[1 + \left(\frac{k-1}{2}\right)M^2\right] = \text{const} \qquad (6\text{-}41)$$

Substituting Eq. (6-6) in Eq. (6-41),

$$Pv + \left(\frac{k-1}{k}\right)\frac{V^2}{2g} = \text{const} \qquad (6\text{-}42)$$

Equations (6-41) and (6-43) are the equations of state for the adiabatic flow of an ideal gas with friction.

Differentiating Eq. (6-6),

$$\frac{dT}{T} = 2\frac{dV}{V} - 2\frac{dM}{M}$$

Differentiating Eq. (6-1) and substituting for v its equivalent RT/P $(G/A = \text{constant since } A = \text{constant})$,

$$\frac{dP}{P} = \frac{dT}{T} - \frac{dV}{V}$$

From the two preceding equations

$$\frac{dP}{P} = \frac{dV}{V} - 2\frac{dM}{M}$$

From Equations (6-6) and (6-40) and $Pv = RT$,

$$\frac{dP}{P} = -kM^2 \frac{dV}{V} - 2kfM^2 \frac{dl}{D}$$

Eliminating dP/P between the two preceding equations,

$$2\frac{dM}{M} = \frac{dV}{V}(kM^2 - 1) + 2kfM^2 \frac{dl}{D} \tag{6-43}$$

From Equations (6-6) and (6-26),

$$V = M\sqrt{\frac{gkRT^\circ}{1 + [(k-1)/2]M^2}}$$

Differentiating the preceding equation, noting that T° is constant for adiabatic flow,

$$\frac{dV}{V} = \frac{dM}{\left[1 + \left(\dfrac{k-1}{2}\right)M^2\right]M} \tag{6-44}$$

Substituting Eq. (6-44) in Eq. (6-43),

$$4f\frac{dl}{D} = \frac{2(1 - M^2)\,dM}{kM\left[1 + \left(\dfrac{k-1}{2}\right)M^2\right]} \tag{6-45}$$

Equation (6-45) may be integrated for the conditions at inlet and outlet of passage. The Fanning friction factor may be assumed to be an average value. For the Reynolds numbers usually obtained in high-speed compressible fluid flow (250,000 to 600,000) the value of the Fanning friction factor has been found experimentally to be fairly constant at 0.005 (NACA TM 844). Then

$$\int_0^l 4f\frac{dl}{D} = \int_{M_1}^{M_2} \frac{2(1 - M^2)\,dM}{kM\left[1 + \left(\dfrac{k-1}{2}\right)M^2\right]}$$

or

$$4f\frac{l}{D} = \frac{k+1}{2k}\ln\frac{M_1^2\left[1 + \left(\dfrac{k-1}{2}\right)M_2^2\right]}{M_2^2\left[1 + \left(\dfrac{k-1}{2}\right)M_1^2\right]} + \frac{M_2^2 - M_1^2}{kM_1^2 M_2^2} \tag{6-46}$$

With the use of Eqs. (6-41), (6-42), and (6-6), Eq. (6-46) may be transformed to

$$4f\frac{l}{D} = \frac{k+1}{2k}\ln\left(\frac{V_1}{V_2}\right)^2 + \frac{1}{k}\left[1 - \left(\frac{V_1}{V_2}\right)^2\right]\left[\frac{1}{M_1^2} + \frac{k-1}{2}\right] \tag{6-47}$$

Equation (6-47) is a functional expression for the velocity change in an insulated pipe in terms of the friction parameter, $4f(l/D)$ and entering Mach number.

Equations (6-46) and (6-47) do not indicate implicitly the maximum value of the flow parameter. It will be shown presently that this maximum value is reached when the final Mach number is unity or when the velocity reaches the local velocity of sound. To find an expression for the

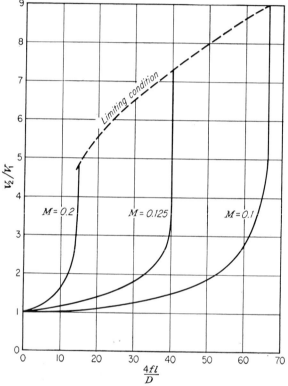

Fig. 6-17. Friction parameter for compressible flow of a gas in a constant-diameter insulated pipe ($k = 1.4$).

maximum value of the flow parameter, it is only necessary to set $M_2 = 1$ in Eq. (6-46).

$$\left(4f\,\frac{l}{D}\right)_{\text{max}} = \frac{k+1}{2k}\,\ln\frac{(k+1)M_1{}^2}{2+(k-1)M_1{}^2} + \frac{1-M_1{}^2}{kM_1{}^2} \tag{6-48}$$

Figure 6-17 shows a plot of V_2/V_1 vs. the friction parameter for several entering Mach numbers. These curves are obtained from Eq. (6-47). The dotted curves represent the limiting values of the friction parameter and the corresponding velocity ratios V_2/V_1. The curves of Fig. 6-18 are obtained by plotting the friction parameter as a function of entering Mach number using Eq. (6-48). It is significant that the friction parameter is a minimum when the entering Mach number is unity. For subsonic entering velocities, the effect of friction is to accelerate the flow until a maximum velocity equal to the velocity of sound is reached at $M = 1$. For supersonic entering velocities, the opposite effect is true with friction decelerating the flow to the velocity of sound at $M = 1$.

The limiting velocity and its related friction parameter are most readily found in terms of the Fanno line. Equation (6-11) is one form of the

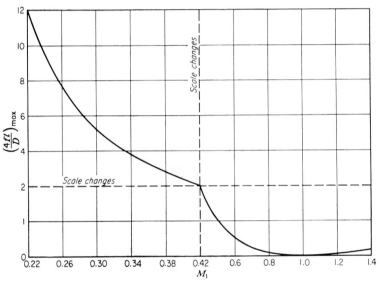

Fig. 6-18. Limiting friction parameter for compressible flow of a gas in a constant-diameter insulated pipe ($k = 1.4$).

Fanno equation in terms of static pressures for a perfect gas through normal shock. Another form of the Fanno equation now will be derived which is useful in determining the losses due to friction. If Eq. (6-28) for stagnation enthalpy is applied,

$$h° = h_1 + \frac{V_1{}^2}{2gJ} = h_2 + \frac{V_2{}^2}{2gJ} \tag{6-49}$$

This equation holds for any adiabatic flow process regardless of losses, provided no work is done. Substituting for velocity in the above equation its equivalent from the equation of state and noting that a constant cross-sectional-area passage is under consideration,

$$h° = h_1 + \frac{G^2v_1{}^2}{A^2 2gJ} = h_2 + \frac{G^2v_2{}^2}{A^2 2gJ} \tag{6-50}$$

Now the specific volume is a function of entropy and enthalpy and Eq. (6-50) may be represented on an h-S diagram. This equation is another form of the Fanno equation and its representation on an h-S diagram is a form of the Fanno line. Figure 6-19 shows such a Fanno line.

Figure 6-19 illustrates very clearly some important characteristics of adiabatic flow with friction. The stagnation enthalpy is constant and for subsonic flow a drop in static enthalpy occurs with an increase in velocity and entropy. The velocity and entropy reach a maximum at sonic velocity. Beyond this point any further increase in velocity would be accompanied by a decrease in entropy, which is inconsistent with the second law of thermodynamics.

The stagnation-enthalpy equation may be expressed in differential form

$$dh + \frac{V\,dV}{gJ} = 0$$

which is also the energy equation for adiabatic flow with no external work done. Since $T\,dS = dQ$, $dQ = 0$ and $T\,dS = 0$ for adiabatic and nonisentropic flow. Entropy may be defined

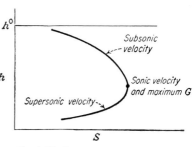

Fig. 6-19. Fanno line on h-S diagram.

$$dh = T\,dS + \frac{v\,dP}{J}$$

which, substituted in the energy equation, yields

$$\frac{v\,dP}{J} + \frac{V\,dV}{gJ} + T\,dS = 0 \tag{6-51}$$

Comparing Eq. (6-51) with Eq. (6-40),

$$T\,dS = 2f\,\frac{V^2}{g}\frac{dl}{D}$$

and

$$dS = 2f\,\frac{V^2}{gJT}\frac{dl}{D} \tag{6-52}$$

Equation (6-52) shows a very definite relationship between frictional loss and increase in entropy. Suppose the maximum increase in entropy has occurred for given initial conditions. If more frictional length is added to the pipe beyond the maximum length satisfying maximum dS in Eq. (6-52), the velocity must decrease. A consequence of reducing the velocity is a reduction in mass rate of flow, a condition known as choking or flow constriction. The entropy increase is fixed between two points on the Fanno line. For the inlet and discharge pressures defined by these two points on the Fanno line, the addition of more frictional length of pipe can only result in decrease of velocity and choking the flow.

Also, it is clear that if the limiting condition of sonic velocity is reached in a pipe, any further decrease in pressure brought about by a device such as a suction pump cannot increase the flow since the pressure impulses cannot move upstream. However, if the inlet pressure is increased, it is tantamount to moving the initial point on the Fanno line back with an increase in dS. This latter case suggests a means for relieving the condition of choking flow when the limiting condition of sonic velocity is not reached.

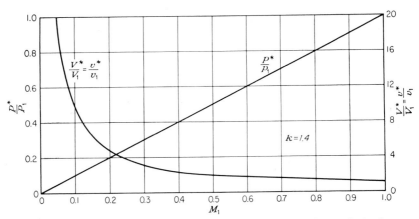

Fig. 6-20. Limiting values of static pressure, velocity, and specific volume of a gas flowing in a constant diameter.

The limiting velocities and static pressures may be obtained from Eq. (6-41) and the continuity equation, if written for conditions entering the passage and leaving at $M = 1$.

$$P_1 v_1 \left[1 + \left(\frac{k-1}{2} \right) M_1^2 \right] = P^* v^* \left[1 + \left(\frac{k-1}{2} \right) \right] \qquad (6\text{-}53)$$

Since $\dfrac{G}{A} = \dfrac{V_1}{v_1} = \dfrac{V^*}{v^*}$ and $a = \sqrt{gkPv}$, from Eq. (6-53),

$$\frac{P^* v^*}{P_1 v_1} = \frac{a^*}{a_1} = \left(\frac{k-1}{k+1} \right) \left(\frac{2}{k-1} + M_1^2 \right)$$

and

$$\frac{a^*}{V_1} = \left[\left(\frac{k-1}{k+1} \right) \left(1 + \frac{2}{M_1^2(k-1)} \right) \right]^{\frac{1}{2}}$$

and

$$\frac{v^*}{v_1} = \frac{V^*}{V_1} = \left[\left(\frac{k-1}{k+1} \right) \left(1 + \frac{2}{(k-1)M_1^2} \right) \right]^{\frac{1}{2}} \qquad (6\text{-}54)$$

Equation (6-54), substituted in Eq. (6-53), yields

$$\frac{P^*}{P_1} = M_1{}^2 \left[\left(\frac{k-1}{k+1} \right) \left(1 + \frac{2}{(k-1)M_1{}^2} \right) \right]^{1/2} \tag{6-55}$$

Figure 6-20 shows the results of plotting Eqs. (6-54) and (6-55) for various values of M_1 and $k = 1.4$.

6-14. Compressible Frictionless Flow with Heat Transfer in a Passage of Uniform Section. The flow in compressors, steam and gas turbines, and ducts under normal conditions may be assumed to be adiabatic with negligible error. In the case of combustors, regenerators, and intercoolers such an assumption is not at all valid. The term heat transfer refers to heating or cooling of the flow medium by an external system. The addition of heat may be accomplished by the injection and ignition of fuel in the gas stream. The mass transfer of fuel will be regarded, for the purposes of this section, to be so small in comparison to that of the stream as to be negligible.

In studying the effect of heat transfer between gas flow and its surroundings, some assumptions are made in order to simplify the relationships. These assumptions are:

1. No external work is done by the gas. This is normally the case in all practical applications of concern in this text.

2. The flow is frictionless. This assumption greatly simplifies the relationships. Actually, heat transfer is always accompanied by frictional loss in the flow process. However, the frictional effects can be accounted for separately.

3. The gas is ideal. This assumption is adequate for some gases but the conclusions can be extended qualitatively to all real gases and vapors.

4. The flow passage is of uniform cross section. This is a much more severe restriction, but again the conclusions can be extended to varying section passages.

5. The gas has no free surface, and therefore gravity forces are not present. This condition is normally true of all gas flows.

The momentum equation, Eq. (6-2), may be expressed

$$\frac{V}{v} \frac{dV}{g} = -dP$$

For a passage of uniform section, $\dfrac{G}{A} = \dfrac{V}{v} = $ constant, and

$$\frac{V}{gv} \int_1^2 dV = - \int_1^2 dP$$

or

$$\frac{V_2{}^2}{gv_2} - \frac{V_1{}^2}{gv_1} = P_1 - P_2$$

But
$$\frac{V^2}{gkPv} = M^2 \quad \text{or} \quad \frac{V^2}{v} = gkPM^2$$

Substituting the latter expression in the preceding equation,

$$kP_2M_2^2 - kP_1M_1^2 = P_1 - P_2$$

or
$$P_2(kM_2^2 + 1) = P_1(kM_1^2 + 1)$$

and
$$\frac{P_2}{P_1} = \frac{1 + kM_1^2}{1 + kM_2^2} \tag{6-56}$$

Since $\dfrac{G}{A} = \dfrac{V}{v}$, $M = \dfrac{V}{\sqrt{gkRT}}$, and $v = \dfrac{RT}{P}$, then

$$\frac{G}{A} = \frac{V}{v} = \frac{M\sqrt{gkRT}}{v} = \frac{PM\sqrt{gkRT}}{RT} = PM\sqrt{\frac{gk}{RT}} = \text{const} \tag{6-57}$$

Substituting Eq. (6-26) in Eq. (6-57),

$$\frac{G}{A} = PM\sqrt{\frac{gk}{RT^\circ}}\sqrt{1 + \frac{k-1}{2}M^2} = \text{const}$$

or $\dfrac{G}{A}\sqrt{\dfrac{R}{gk}} = \dfrac{P_1M_1}{\sqrt{T^\circ}}\sqrt{1 + \dfrac{k-1}{2}M_1^2} = \dfrac{P_2M_2}{\sqrt{T^\circ}}\sqrt{1 + \dfrac{k-1}{2}M_2^2} = \text{const}$

from which

$$\frac{T_2^\circ}{T_1^\circ} = \frac{P_2^2M_2^2}{P_1^2M_1^2}\left[\frac{2 + (k-1)M_2^2}{2 + (k-1)M_1^2}\right] \tag{6-58}$$

Substituting from Eq. (6-56) in Eq. (6-58),

$$\frac{T_2^\circ}{T_1^\circ} = \left[\frac{2 + (k-1)M_2^2}{2 + (k-1)M_1^2}\right]\left[\frac{(1 + kM_1^2)M_2}{(1 + kM_2^2)M_1}\right]^2 \tag{6-59}$$

Substituting Eq. (6-26) in Eq. (6-59),

$$\frac{T_2}{T_1} = \left[\frac{(1 + kM_2^2)M_2}{(1 + kM_1^2)M_1}\right]^2 \tag{6-60}$$

From the equation of state, $\dfrac{v_2}{v_1} = \dfrac{T_2P_1}{T_1P_2}$, and from Eq. (6-56) and Eq. (6-60),

$$\frac{v_2}{v_1} = \frac{T_2P_1}{T_1P_2} = \frac{(1 + kM_1^2)M_2^2}{(1 + kM_2^2)M_1^2} \tag{6-61}$$

and
$$\frac{V_2}{V_1} = \frac{v_2}{v_1} = \frac{(1 + kM_1^2)M_2^2}{(1 + kM_2^2)M_1^2} \tag{6-62}$$

Substituting Eq. (6-27) in Eq. (6-57),

$$\frac{P_2^\circ}{P_1^\circ} = \left[\frac{1 + kM_1^2}{1 + kM_2^2}\right]\left[\frac{2 + (k-1)M_2^2}{2 + (k-1)M_1^2}\right]^{k/(k-1)} \tag{6-63}$$

One more relationship remains to be found, namely, the entropy change. From the first and second laws of thermodynamics,

$$dQ = T \, dS = dh - \frac{v \, dP}{J} \tag{6-64}$$

or

$$dS = C_p \frac{dT}{T} - \frac{R}{J} \frac{dP}{P} \tag{6-65}$$

Since $v = RT/P$ and $C_p = Rk/[J(k-1)]$,

$$dS = \frac{R}{J} \frac{k}{(k-1)} \frac{dT}{T} - \frac{R}{J} \frac{dP}{P}$$

and

$$\frac{dS}{R/J} = \frac{k}{k-1} \int_1^2 \frac{dT}{T} - \int_1^2 \frac{dP}{P} \tag{6-66}$$

or

$$\frac{\Delta S}{R/J} = \frac{k}{k-1} \ln \frac{T_2}{T_1} + \ln \frac{P_1}{P_2}$$

and

$$\Delta S = C_p \ln \left[\frac{T_1}{T_2} \left(\frac{P_1}{P_2} \right)^{(k-1)/k} \right] \tag{6-67}$$

Substituting Eq. (6-56) and Eq. (6-60) in Eq. (6-67),

$$\Delta S = C_p \ln \left[\left(\frac{M_2}{M_1} \right)^2 \left(\frac{1 + kM_1^2}{1 + kM_2^2} \right)^{(k+1)/k} \right] \tag{6-68}$$

Equations (6-56), (6-59), (6-60), (6-62), and (6-63) give the state variables for ideal gases when heat transfer takes place and the passage is of uniform section. However, no limitation on the possible amount of heat transfer is given explicitly. To find these limitations, one must examine Eq. (6-68). This equation indicates that entropy increases until a maximum is reached when $M_2 = 1$. Further addition of heat or a further increase in M_2 results in a decrease in entropy, a condition which is physically impossible in view of the second law of thermodynamics. Four possibilities are suggested:

1. No further heat addition is possible after $M_2 = 1$ is reached, if $M_1 < 1$.

2. If $M_1 > 1$, cooling must take place until $M_2 = 1$ is reached, after which no further cooling can take place.

3. M_2 can exceed unity in the case of $M_1 < 1$ if heat is added until $M = 1$ followed by cooling for $M_2 > 1$.

4. When $M_2 = 1$ is reached, choking of flow will occur, and if $M_1 < 1$ the flow will adjust itself until the final increment of heat addition takes place at $M_2 = 1$. In effect, M_1 is lowered. This condition is known as thermal choking and is analogous to friction choking described in Sec. 6-13.

A clear picture of the foregoing possibilities may be obtained from an examination of the Rayleigh line. The Rayleigh line is defined as the locus of states for a process. The state properties can be found from the relations of Eqs. (6-56), (6-59), (6-60), (6-62), (6-63), and (6-68). Plotted on a T-S plane the Rayleigh line has the form of the curve shown in Fig. 6-21. The Rayleigh line indicates that heating a gas in subsonic flow results in an acceleration until maximum entropy is reached at $M = 1$. Further acceleration has to be accomplished by cooling. It will be noted that maximum static temperature is reached before maximum entropy. This condition is due to the fact that the heat addition exactly equals the rate of velocity increase at the maximum static temperature point. Beyond this point the rate of velocity increase is so great that not only all the heat addition but also some of the internal energy is required. As a consequence the static temperature drops.

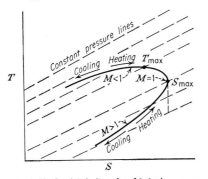

Fig. 6-21. Rayleigh line for frictionless compressible flow in a uniform section passage with heat transfer.

Also clear is the fact that the acceleration of velocity occurs with a drop in static pressure. Furthermore, the stagnation temperature increases since the entropy increase is a function of heat addition only in the absence of friction. The static enthalpy increases with static temperature until a point is reached corresponding to the maximum static temperature. Beyond this point the enthalpy drops with dropping static temperature until maximum entropy is reached.

The condition of thermal choking can be illustrated by means of the Rayleigh line. When M_1 is decreased, it is evident that the change in entropy is increased and therefore the quantity of heat added. Thermal choking, in effect, moves M_1 back on the Rayleigh line. *to another Rayleigh line*

The pressure loss due to heat addition may be expressed:

$$\frac{P_1 - P_2}{P_1} = 1 - \frac{P_2}{P_1}$$

Substituting Eq. (6-56),

$$\frac{P_1 - P_2}{P_1} = 1 - \frac{1 + kM_1^2}{1 + kM_2^2} \tag{6-69}$$

and in terms of stagnation pressures, using Eq. (6-63),

$$\frac{P_1^\circ - P_2^\circ}{P_1^\circ} = 1 - \left[\frac{1 + kM_1^2}{1 + kM_2^2}\right]\left[\frac{2 + (k - 1)M_2^2}{2 + (k - 1)M_1^2}\right]^{k/(k-1)} \tag{6-70}$$

If friction is also present, the combined pressure loss is the sum of the pressure losses due to friction and heat addition.

6-15. Isentropic Flow in Nozzles. The energy equation for isentropic flow in a nozzle may be written

$$\frac{V \, dV}{gJ} = -dU - \frac{d(Pv)}{J} \tag{6-71}$$

Integrating and neglecting the entering velocity as being negligible,

$$\frac{V_1^2}{2gJ} = U_2 - U_1 + \frac{P_2 v_2}{J} - \frac{P_1 v_1}{J} \tag{6-72}$$

If the gas is ideal, the internal energy is a function of temperature only, or

$$U_2 - U_1 = C_v(T_2 - T_1)$$

Substituting $C_v = R/[J(k-1)]$ and $Pv = RT$,

$$U_2 - U_1 = \frac{RT_2 - RT_1}{J(k-1)} = \frac{P_2 v_2 - P_1 v_1}{J(k-1)} \tag{6-73}$$

Substituting Eq. (6-73) in Eq. (6-72),

$$\frac{V_2^2}{2g} = \frac{k}{k-1}(P_2 v_2 - P_1 v_1)$$

From the path equation for the isentropic expansion of an ideal gas, $Pv^k = \text{constant}$, it follows that

$$P_1 v_1 = P_2 v_2 \left(\frac{P_1}{P_2}\right)^{(k-1)/k}$$

which, substituted in the preceding equation, yields

$$\frac{V_2^2}{2g} = \frac{k}{k-1}\left[P_1 v_1 - P_1 v_1 \left(\frac{P_2}{P_1}\right)^{(k-1)/k}\right]$$

Designating the ratio of the exit pressure to entrance pressure by r, the preceding equation may be expressed

$$V_2 = \sqrt{2g \frac{k}{k-1} P_1 v_1 (1 - r^{(k-1)/k})} \qquad \text{fps} \tag{6-74}$$

It should be carefully noted that this is the expression for the exit velocity, provided the entering velocity is negligible, the expansion is isentropic, and the fluid is an ideal gas.

If Eq. (6-74) is substituted in the continuity equation,

$$G = \frac{A_2}{v_2} \sqrt{2g \frac{k}{k-1} P_1 v_1 (1 - r^{(k-1)/k})} \tag{6-75}$$

Again, from the path equation for the isentropic expansion of an ideal gas, $v_2 = v_1 r^{-1/k}$ which, substituted in Eq. (6-75), yields

$$G = A_2 \sqrt{2g \frac{k}{k-1} \frac{P_1}{v_1} \left(r^{2/k} - r^{(k+1)/k} \right)} \tag{6-76}$$

For a given set of conditions it follows that the mass rate of flow given by Eq. (6-76) is a maximum when the expression $r^{2/k} - r^{(k+1)/k}$ is a maximum. The value of r for which this expression is a maximum may be found when

$$\frac{d}{dr} \left(r^{2/k} - r^{(k+1)/k} \right) = 0$$

or

$$\frac{2}{k} r^{(2-k)/k} + \frac{k+1}{k} r^{1/k} = 0$$

Solving for r,

$$r^* = r = \left(\frac{2}{k+1} \right)^{k/(k-1)} \tag{6-77}$$

This value is known as the critical-pressure ratio and is designated as r^*.

It will be shown presently that the critical pressure and sonic velocity are reached simultaneously. The ratio of this critical pressure to the entering pressure is the critical-pressure ratio. Values of r^* may be obtained from Eq. (6-77) if the value of k is known for the gas under consideration. Average values of r^* for some gases and vapors encountered in turbine practice are as follows:

Gas or Vapor	r^*
Air (cold)	0.527
Gas-turbine gases	0.525
Dry saturated or wet steam	0.577
Superheated steam	0.546

The relation of the critical pressure to sonic velocity can be found if the value of r^* obtained from Eq. (6-77) is substituted in Eq. (6-74):

$$V_2 = \sqrt{2g \frac{k}{k+1} P_1 v_1} \tag{6-78}$$

From the path equation, $P_1 v_1 = P^* v^* (r^*)^{(1-k)/k}$ and

$$P_1 v_1 = P^* v^* \frac{k+1}{2}$$

Substituting the preceding equation in Eq. (6-78),

$$V^* = a = \sqrt{gk P^* v^*}$$

Therefore the velocity of the gas is sonic when the critical pressure is reached. The maximum mass rate of flow now may be calculated

$$G_{max} = \frac{A^*}{v^*} \sqrt{gkP^*v^*} \tag{6-79}$$

An alternate expression for the maximum mass rate of flow may be obtained by substituting r^* from Eq. (6-77)

$$G_{max} = A^* \sqrt{2g \frac{k}{k-1} \frac{P_1}{v_1} \left[\left(\frac{2}{k+1} \right)^{2/(k-1)} - \left(\frac{2}{k+1} \right)^{(k+1)/(k-1)} \right]} \tag{6-80}$$

Although the relations derived in this section are useful in examining the flow pattern in nozzles, the turbine designer takes advantage of simpler relations in terms of the properties of the gas or vapor obtained from appropriate tables of thermodynamic properties. The design relations will be covered in the next chapter.

6-16. Two-dimensional Concentric Circulatory Flow. Consider steady two-dimensional and isentropic concentric flow as illustrated in Fig. 6-23. The flow in planes parallel to that of the page is assumed to be identical.

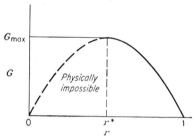

Fig. 6-22. Mass rate of flow as a function of pressure ratio.

The radii of the concentric streamlines are designated as r and the velocity component tangent to the streamlines as V_w. An infinitesimal element of gas at distance r has a height of dr and an area of A along the curved surface at r. The area along the curved surface at $r + dr$ is $A + dA$. The static pressure at r is P and at $r + dr$ it is $P + dP$. Then the resultant force toward the center of curvature is

$$(P + dP)(A + dA) - PA - \left(P + \frac{dP}{2} \right) dA = A\, dP$$

The centrifugal force is $\rho A\, dr(V_w^2/r)$ which equated to the previous equation yields

$$\frac{dP}{dr} = \rho \frac{V_w^2}{r}$$

From Eq. (6-2),

$$dP = -\rho V\, dV$$

Therefore

$$-\rho \frac{V_w\, dV_w}{dr} = \rho \frac{V_w^2}{r}$$

or

$$\int_1^2 \frac{dV_w}{V_w} = -\int_1^2 \frac{dr}{r}$$

and

$$rV_w = \text{const} = \Omega = \text{vorticity} \tag{6-81}$$

Therefore, the tangential velocity V_w varies inversely as the radial distance r. If Eq. (6-81) is solved for V_w, it is clear that when r approaches zero as a limit, V_w will approach infinity. Now such a condition is obviously a physical impossibility. One of two possibilities must exist. Either the flow takes place in a region surrounding the outer periphery of a cylinder so that $r = 0$ is a fictitious point or Eq. (6-81) does not reflect a true relationship as $r \to 0$. Actually, the viscous effects which were not considered in the derivation of Eq. (6-81) are so pronounced as $r \to 0$ that the gas behaves like a rotating solid body with the result:

$$V_w = \omega r$$

The physical condition then when $r = 0$ exists in the flow field is a central core rotating like a solid body outside of which is a transition region and outside the transition region is still another region where the viscous effects are negligible and Eq. (6-81) applies. The flow in this last region is known as free-vortex flow while that in the central core is referred to as forced-vortex flow.

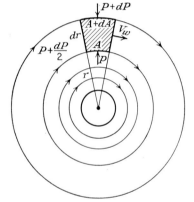

Fig. 6-23. Streamlines and volume element for concentric circulatory flow.

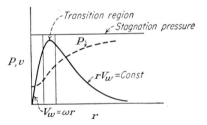

Fig. 6-24. Concentric circulatory flow.

From the initial assumption of isentropic flow it follows that the stagnation pressure is constant everywhere in the free-vortex region and from Eq. (6-81) the static pressure varies directly as radial distance. Static-pressure and velocity variations radially are shown in Fig. 6-24.

6-17. Elementary Airfoil Theory. An airfoil may be defined as a streamlined form bounded principally by two flattened curves and whose length and width are very large in comparison with thickness. Some airfoils are shown in Fig. 6-25. Figure 6-25a shows a symmetrical airfoil placed in a stream of gas so that the axis of symmetry of the airfoil lies in the same direction as the undisturbed velocity of approach. It will be noted that a local disturbance is created in the gas stream but no permanent deflection of the main stream is imposed. The flow merely divides around the airfoil at the leading edge and rejoins at the trailing edge. The only significant forces exerted on the airfoil are due to friction and the local disturbance.

Figure 6-25b shows a nonsymmetrical airfoil inclined with the direction of the undisturbed approaching flow at an angle α_0, known as the angle of attack. Now a more pronounced disturbance is created and a correspondingly greater local deflection of the flow. The flow far in advance or far behind the airfoil is, nevertheless, uniform with parallel streamlines. It is clear that the airfoil must exert a force on the gas stream in order to cause its deflection and an equal and opposite reaction is exerted by the gas stream on the airfoil. These forces may be expressed in terms of force

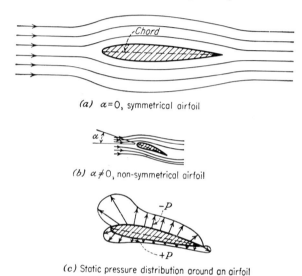

(a) $\alpha = 0$, symmetrical airfoil

(b) $\alpha \neq 0$, non-symmetrical airfoil

(c) Static pressure distribution around an airfoil

Fig. 6-25. Gas flow around airfoils. (a) $\alpha = 0$, symmetrical airfoil; (b) $\alpha \neq 0$, nonsymmetrical airfoil; (c) static pressure distribution around an airfoil.

per unit of projected area or static pressure. For constant stagnation pressure everywhere in the flow field, it follows that the local changes in static pressure are accompanied by corresponding inverse changes in velocity. An examination of the airfoil of Fig. 6-25b shows that a gas particle following a streamline above the airfoil must travel at a higher velocity to meet beyond the trailing edge a similar particle which has traveled along a streamline under the airfoil. This condition is represented by more closely spaced streamlines above the airfoil as compared with those underneath. It may be concluded from the condition of constant stagnation pressure that the static pressure under the airfoil is greater than that above it and therefore a net upward force or lift is experienced by the airfoil. Figure 6-25c shows the static pressure distribution about an airfoil.

For a more meaningful explanation of the lift phenomenon, it is mandatory that two-dimensional considerations be introduced. Actually, the flow around an airfoil is both rectilinear and circulatory. The velocity deflections imposed on the flow by the airfoil manifest themselves as a circulatory velocity imposed on the rectilinear velocity.

The circulatory flow may be generalized in terms of the concept of circulation which has a very precise mathematical meaning but may be defined physically as the speed of rotation of the gas as a solid body. Mathematically

$$\Gamma = \oint V \cos\theta \, dl \tag{6-82}$$

or, circulation is equal to the line integral of $V \cos\theta \, dl$ around a simple (without loops) closed path. Figure 6-26 illustrates such a path.

Now instead of an airfoil, a cylinder which has rectilinear velocity in a stationary gas is considered (see Fig. 6-27). Assume the cylinder has also

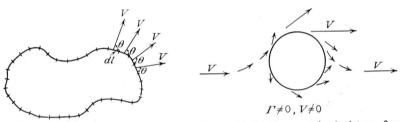

Fig. 6-26. Simple and closed path.   Fig. 6-27. Rectilinear and circulatory flow around a cylinder.

a clockwise circulation. Then above the cylinder the rectilinear and circulation velocities are in the same direction and therefore are additive. Under the cylinder, rectilinear and circulation velocities are in opposite directions, and thus the circulation velocity is subtracted from the rectilinear velocity. Therefore a static pressure differential exists between the upper and lower surfaces of the cylinder and a lift is exerted. If the flow of gas is steady, two-dimensional, frictionless, and without velocity discontinuities, the lift on an infinitely long cylinder may be related to the circulation by the Kutta-Joukowsky equation which follows:

$$L' = \rho V_\infty \Gamma \tag{6-83}$$

where L' = lift per unit length of cylinder and perpendicular to the direction of approach velocity

ρ = density of gas, slugs per cu ft

V_∞ = undisturbed velocity of approach, fps

$\Gamma = \oint V \cos\theta \, dl$ = circulation, sq ft per sec

Equation (6-83) may be proved rigorously, but such a proof is beyond the scope of this text.

It is clear from Eq. (6-83) that if $\Gamma = 0$ there is no lift. Consider the symmetrical airfoil of Fig. 6-25a which has an angle of attack equal to zero. Clearly the circulation also must be equal to zero since the product of $V \cos \theta$ and each element of upper surface dl is exactly equal and opposite in direction to the corresponding product of $V \cos \theta$ and dl of the lower surface. Consequently, $\Gamma = \oint V \cos \theta \, dl = 0$ and no lift is exerted. When an angle of attack α_0 is introduced, the flow is no longer symmetrical about the airfoil. If in addition the airfoil itself is nonsymmetrical, the nonsymmetry of the flow is accentuated. Now circulation exists and a lift is exerted on the airfoil. It may be inferred from this that circulation about an airfoil is a function of the airfoil curvature and magnitude

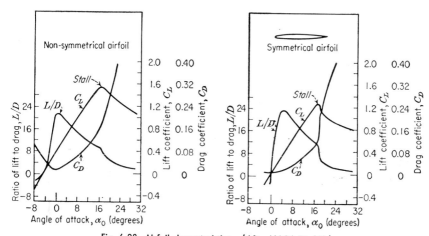

Fig. 6-28. Airfoil characteristics. (After NACA TR 460.)

of the angle of attack. Actually, there is a limit to the extent the curvature of the airfoil and angle of attack may be increased before flow separation is introduced at the leading edge with a sharp drop in lift (see Fig. 6-28).

It is observed that the units of Γ are square feet per second which may be expressed $V \times$ length. If c, the chord, is selected as a characteristic dimension of the airfoil, then the total lift exerted on the airfoil in a direction normal to the approach velocity can be expressed in the form

$$L = f(\rho, V_\infty^2, c)$$

If further r represents the finite length of the airfoil and the velocity is expressed in terms of dynamic pressure,

$$\frac{dL}{dr} = f\left(\rho, \frac{V_\infty}{2}, c\right)$$

The function f, known as the coefficient of lift, is identified by the symbol C_L

$$dL = C_{L}\rho \frac{V_\infty^2}{2} c \, dr \qquad (6\text{-}84)$$

Similarly the drag force may be expressed

$$dD = C_{D}\rho \frac{V_\infty^2}{2} c \, dr \qquad (6\text{-}85)$$

The total or resultant force exerted normal to the airfoil consists of two

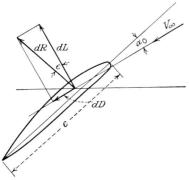

components, one of which is the lift and is normal to the direction of the approach velocity. The other component is the drag, which is parallel to the direction of the approach velocity. The ratio of drag to lift from Eqs. (6-84) and (6-85) is

$$\frac{dD}{dL} = \frac{C_D}{C_L}$$

Figure 6-29 illustrates the forces acting on an airfoil. Since the ratio of drag to lift is very small (0.02 to

Fig. 6-29. Forces acting on an airfoil.

0.06) and consequently ϵ is correspondingly small, then

$$\tan \epsilon \approx \epsilon = \frac{C_D}{C_L} \qquad (6\text{-}86)$$

6-18. Induced Drag, Shock, and Compressibility Burble. In addition to profile drag an airfoil of finite length experiences what is termed induced drag. In an airfoil of finite length, the higher static pressure under the airfoil influences the flow direction toward the ends. Thus when the flow from above the airfoil meets the flow from underneath, which is now in a different direction, a sheet of small trailing vortices is developed. Furthermore, at the very ends of the airfoil the flow moves outward and upward toward the region of lower static pressure above the airfoil. This condition results in a much larger trailing vortex turning inward above the airfoil. Since these trailing vortices do not contribute to exerting a lift on the airfoil, they represent a loss of energy. This loss is called the induced drag. The conditions contributing to induced drag are illustrated in Fig. 6-30.

Another source of loss is the occurrence of shock waves in the flow over an airfoil. Even when the velocity of the gas approaching an airfoil is subsonic, the local velocity above the airfoil may be accelerated until it is

supersonic. It is entirely possible that the local velocity above the airfoil may reach a maximum value which is 50 per cent higher than that of
the approach velocity. The extent to which the local velocity is accel-

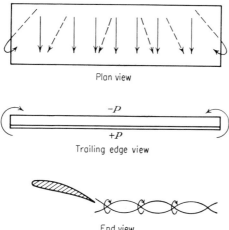

Plan view

Trailing edge view

End view
Fig. 6-30. Secondary flows produced by an airfoil of finite length.

erated is, of course, a function of the magnitude of the angle of attack and
the curvature of the airfoil. Now it was learned earlier that when supersonic flow is decelerated a shock wave will be formed. Therefore when

the supersonic flow above the airfoil
is decelerated to match at the trailing edge the lower velocity flow
from underneath the airfoil, shock
is introduced.

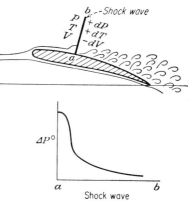

Fig. 6-31. Shock wave with boundary layer
separation in flow over an airfoil.

In addition to the loss attendant
to shock itself, other losses are introduced as a consequence of shock.
These latter losses require an examination of the boundary layer for
explanation. The thin layer of gas
in immediate contact with the upper
boundary of the airfoil has a sharp
velocity gradient dropping to zero at
the boundary surface itself owing to
friction. The static pressure across the shock wave increases with an
accompanied decrease in velocity so that the flow in general is retarded.
In the boundary layer where the velocity is already small, the effect of
shock is to stop all motion completely. This causes the boundary layer
to thicken just before shock and may even cause the boundary layer after

shock to separate from the boundary surface with the formation of a vortex trail. This latter condition is called compressibility burble and is a source of more severe loss than shock itself.

If the stagnation pressure is found by traverse in advance and to the rear of an airfoil when compressibility burble occurs, the loss of stagnation pressure will be found to vary somewhat as shown in Fig. 6-31.

References

1. Ackeret, J.: "Handbuch der Experimental Physik," Springer-Verlag, Berlin, 1927.
2. Bailey, N. P.: The Thermodynamics of Air at High Velocities, *J. Aeronaut. Sci.*, July, 1944.
3. Busemann, A.: "Handbuch der Physik," Akademische Verlagsgesellschaft, H. Leipzig, 1931.
4. "Handbook of Supersonic Aerodynamics," *Navord Rept.* 1488, Vol. I, U.S. Navy, 1950.
5. Keenan, J. H., and J. Kaye: "Gas Tables," John Wiley & Sons, Inc., New York, 1948.
6. Liepmann, H. W., and A. E. Puckett: "Aerodynamics of a Compressible Fluid," John Wiley & Sons, Inc., New York, 1947.
7. Sauer, R.: "Theoretical Gas Dynamics," Edwards Bros., Inc., Ann Arbor, Mich., 1947.
8. Shapiro, A. H., and W. R. Hawthorne: The Mechanics and Thermodynamics of Steady, One-dimensional Gas Flow, *Trans. ASME*, 1947.
9. Sibert, H. W.: "High-speed Aerodynamics," Prentice-Hall, Inc., New York, 1948.

Problems

6-1. Air at 12 psia and 0 F approaches a diffuser at a velocity of 2000 fps. If plane normal shock occurs at the entrance to the diffuser, find the following for the state behind shock:

(a) Mach number
(b) Static temperature of air
(c) Sonic velocity
(d) Velocity of air
(e) Static pressure
(f) Specific volume or density

If isentropic subsonic diffusion continues behind shock to a final velocity of 500 fps, find the above data for the final state.

6-2. Compare the static temperature rise through the normal shock of Prob. 6-1 with the static temperature rise for isentropic compression between the same pressure limits. Compute the increase in entropy through shock.

6-3. Air flows in a straight passage of constant cross-sectional area with an inlet Mach number of 0.4 and an exit Mach number of 0.7. Calculate the value of $4fl/D$. What is the maximum value of $4fl/D$ that can be attained?

6-4. Discuss the conditions under which shock can occur in a nozzle. If plane normal shock occurs in a nozzle and the Mach number before shock is 1.8, find the Mach number behind shock and the static-pressure ratio. Assume an ideal gas with $k = 1.35$.

6-5. Assuming that the velocity distribution in a cyclone is closely approximated by the conditions for free-vortex flow, determine the static-pressure distribution from the storm center out.

CHAPTER 7

DESIGN OF NOZZLES

7-1. Introduction. The flow passages of any turbine are formed by nozzles and blades. The stationary passages of impulse turbines and both the stationary and moving passages of reaction turbines are composed of nozzles. The function of the nozzle is to convert some of the thermal energy of the gas or steam into kinetic energy, an important intermediate step in converting heat to work. It is essential, therefore, that the nozzles perform their function efficiently. The preceding chapter reviewed some elementary concepts based on perfect gas relations and idealized flow. While these concepts are valuable in fostering an understanding of flow phenomena on a broad scale, in general they are not in sufficiently convenient or usable forms to support design computations. The purpose of this chapter is to present the factors which govern the nozzle design procedure generally in use. Some of these factors are based on experimental results and a few are empirical in nature, but all of them have been widely accepted as giving results reasonably close to actual conditions.

Steam-nozzle design poses some difficulties not encountered in gas-nozzle design because steam is a vapor and in some instances may be a two-phase mixture. Special attention will be given to the problems which are peculiar to the steam nozzle in addition to those factors common to the design of all nozzles regardless of flow medium.

7-2. Nozzle Construction. Probably the most common physical conception of the nozzle is the converging-diverging, transonic, or De Laval type, although its application in turbine design is somewhat limited. More generally in use is the converging or subsonic nozzle. The types of nozzle construction common in turbine practice are reamed, or round, and foil nozzles.

Examples of the reamed or round nozzle are shown in Figs. 7-1 and 7-2. The principal advantages of the reamed nozzle are low cost, ease of manufacture, and adaptability to standardization. The principal disadvantages are lower efficiency, somewhat greater length, and an inability to utilize effectively for flow purposes the area of a given flow annulus.

Fig. 7-1. Reamed nozzles in process of being reamed in block.   (*Courtesy of De Laval Steam Turbine Company.*)

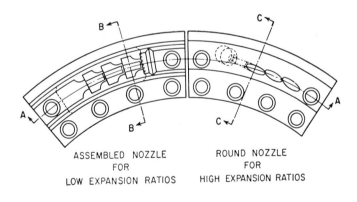

ASSEMBLED NOZZLE
FOR
LOW EXPANSION RATIOS

ROUND NOZZLE
FOR
HIGH EXPANSION RATIOS

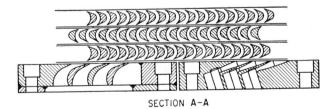

SECTION A-A

Fig. 7-2. Foil and reamed nozzles.   (*Courtesy of Westinghouse Electric Corporation.*)

The reamed nozzle is used primarily in the high-pressure impulse stages of steam turbines.

Figure 7-3 shows the characteristics of an ideal nozzle designed for uniform pressure drop which is principally characterized by a flaring bell-shaped profile. Such a shape results in a costly nozzle which is difficult

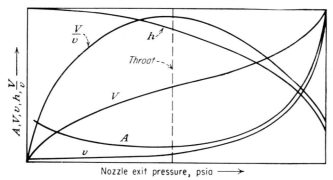

Fig. 7-3. Characteristics of flow through an ideal nozzle with uniform pressure drop.

to manufacture and fails to give a well-directed concentrated jet. The reamed straight conical nozzle eliminates these objections with only a slight decrease in efficiency. Figure 7-4 shows the flow characteristics of a reamed nozzle and it will be noticed that none of the functions has a uniform rate of change along the nozzle axis except for area.

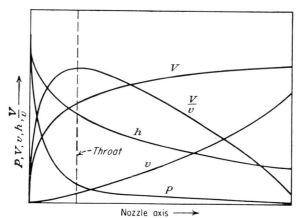

Fig. 7-4. Characteristics of flow through a reamed nozzle.

The angle of divergence in reamed nozzles is usually about 12° and rarely over 15°, in order to avoid flow separation with its attendant loss. The converging part of the nozzle is not critical as far as shape is concerned and a good fillet or rounded entrance is usually all that is required.

The transonic nozzle which is usually of the reamed type finds its application in small simple impulse steam turbines or velocity compounded stages where large enthalpy drops are required. Occasionally a small turbine may operate condensing and at other times noncondensing. For this condition of service, two sets of reamed nozzles may be employed with the inappropriate set shut off or cut out by means of needle valves furnished with each nozzle and operated either manually or by governor action. The needle valve offers an opportunity to cut out individual nozzles to vary the flow area within close limits during part-load operation.

The foil nozzle is formed by curved airfoil sections or facsimiles of airfoils. This type of nozzle is characterized by its high efficiency. The nozzle is short with well-rounded entrance edges and sharp exit edges affording clear definition to the issuing jet. Figures 7-2 and 7-5 show foil nozzle blocks. The block is made by welding the individual foils between sections of concentric rings. The block is then welded in place between the outer and inner shrouds. Typical foil partitions are shown in Fig. 7-6.

The foil nozzle finds wide application especially in Rateau stages of large steam turbines and is used universally in gas turbines where turbine efficiency is of extreme importance to cycle performance.

7-3. Critical-pressure Ratios. The critical-pressure ratio is a significant function in nozzle design. It is important to have correct values of the critical-pressure ratios over the range of temperatures and pressures encountered in practice. The values of the critical-pressure ratios given in the foregoing chapter were based on the average ratio of specific heats.

Figure 7-7 shows values of the critical-pressure ratio for superheated and wet steam taking into consideration the variation of specific heats with temperature and pressure. The procedure in using Fig. 7-7 for steam initially superheated is to determine the critical-pressure ratio from curve a for superheated steam, noting from the Mollier diagram if the critical pressure occurs in the superheat region. If it does, then the critical-pressure ratio selected from curve a is the correct one. If the critical pressure had occurred in the wet region, then the correct critical-pressure ratio should be selected from curve b for saturated and wet steam. An ambiguous situation might occur when the critical-pressure ratio selected from curve a puts the critical pressure in the wet region, indicating that curve b should be used. Now the higher critical-pressure ratio from curve b may put the critical pressure back in the superheat region. When this situation arises, curve a should be used until values obtained from curve b actually fall in the wet region. This latter procedure results in overrunning the saturation curve approximately 5 Btu, which is excusable in view of the phenomenon of super-saturation to be explained in a later section.

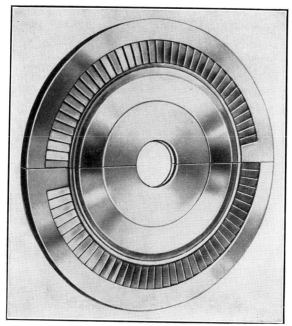

Fig. 7-5. Foil nozzle block. (Courtesy of Worthington Corporation.)

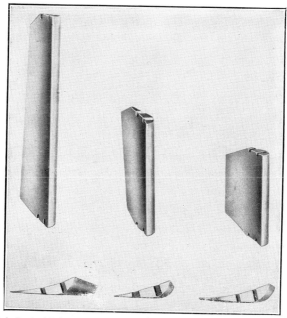

Fig. 7-6. Typical foil nozzle partitions. (Courtesy of Worthington Corporation.)

Figure 7-8 shows values of the critical-pressure ratio for air which are generally satisfactory for the gases normally used in gas turbines. The critical-pressure ratio is given in terms of the temperature entering the

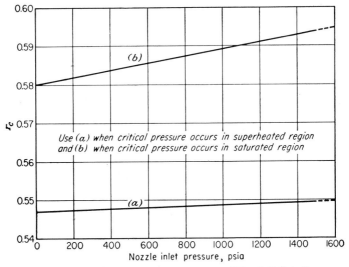

Fig. 7-7. Critical-pressure ratios for steam.   (After Rettaliata.[8])

nozzle, taking into account the variation in specific heats over a wide range of temperatures and for the pressures used in gas-turbine practice.

7-4. Nozzle Losses.   Nozzle losses are taken into account by means of a velocity coefficient defined as the ratio of the actual velocity to the

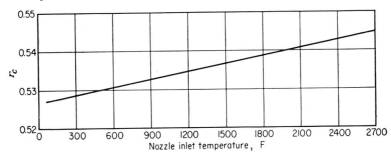

Fig. 7-8. Critical-pressure ratios for air.

theoretical or ideal velocity. The theoretical velocity is derived from the general energy equation as follows:

$$h_0 + \frac{V_0{}^2}{2gJ} = h_1 + \frac{V_1{}^2}{2gJ}$$

and

$$_tV_1 = 223.7 \sqrt{(h_0 - h_1)_s + \frac{V_0{}^2}{2gJ}} \qquad (7\text{-}1)$$

or, if the velocity of approach is negligible,

$$_tV_1 = 223.7 \sqrt{h_0 - h_1)_s} \tag{7-2}$$

Then the velocity coefficient

$$k_n = \frac{\text{actual velocity}}{\text{theoretical velocity}} = \frac{_aV_1}{_tV_1} \tag{7-3}$$

The velocity coefficient depends on many factors and its value is determined experimentally. While it is not true that a given set of velocity coefficients will apply precisely to all nozzles, even of the same type, nevertheless reasonable agreement may be expected. In general, the velocity coefficient depends on:

1. *Size of nozzle.* Large nozzles are more efficient with a sharp drop in k_n for very small nozzles.

2. *Surface roughness.* Surfaces should be very smooth for high values of k_n.

3. *Nozzle length.* Long nozzles are accompanied by increased friction losses.

4. *Roundness of entrance.* Entrance edges should be well rounded so as not to create disturbances which increase losses.

5. *Sharp curvature of short radius.* Sharp curvature increases friction losses or may cause flow separation with attendant loss.

6. *Divergence angle.* Too great a divergence angle causes flow separation with increased losses.

7. *Space between nozzles.* The wide spaces between reamed nozzles and the thickness of entrance edge of foil nozzles introduce disturbances at entrance which are carried into the nozzle passage and are a source of loss.

8. *Moisture.* Wet steam causes considerable loss, as will be explained in a later section.

9. *Trailing edge.* The thickness of nozzle edges or partitions at exit should be small to avoid losses due to trailing vortices.

Figure 7-9 gives average values of k_{ng} for reamed or foil nozzles in terms of theoretical velocity. It will be noticed that k_{ng} varies little in the subsonic range, but when the sonic velocity is exceeded by very much, k_{ng} drops off rather sharply. This is explained in terms of the Reynolds number. Boundary layer effects are important with Reynolds numbers less than 100,000, showing a marked decrease in efficiency with lower Reynolds numbers. With Reynolds numbers exceeding 100,000 and subsonic velocity there is very little variation of k_{ng} with velocity. Inasmuch as turbines are generally designed with Reynolds numbers above 200,000, the velocity effects on k_{ng} are nearly constant until velocities exceeding Mach 1.2 to 1.3 are encountered.

Figure 7-9 may be used for nozzles operating with gas or superheated steam. A preferable method for determining losses in foil nozzles will be discussed under blading design in Chap. 9.

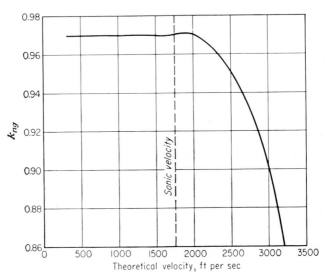

Fig. 7-9. Typical values of velocity coefficient for superheated steam or gas. (*After Keenan*[4] *and Kraft.*[5])

The nozzle efficiency is defined as the fraction of available energy which is converted into velocity or kinetic energy. There is a very definite relationship between nozzle efficiency and velocity coefficient:

$$\eta_n = \frac{\Delta h_{\text{actual}}}{\Delta h_s}$$

and, from Eqs. (7-2) and (7-3),

$$_aV_1 = 223.7 k_n \sqrt{\Delta h_s} = 223.7 \sqrt{\Delta h_s \, k_n^2}$$

Obviously $\Delta h_S \, k_n^2 = \Delta h_{\text{actual}}$ so that

$$k_n^2 = \eta_n \qquad (7\text{-}4)$$

7-5. Divergence and Position Angles. The angle of divergence in a reamed nozzle is defined as the total angle included by the sides. It can be readily seen from the geometry of the reamed nozzle that the angle of divergence and required areas control the nozzle length. Too wide an angle of divergence results in a widely dispersed jet lacking unified direction and concentration. On the other hand, if the angle of divergence is too small, the nozzle will be extremely long, thus increasing the friction losses. While it is possible to achieve reasonable results in some cases with an angle as high as 20°, the most effective angle lies somewhere between 12° and 15°.

The position angle, usually referred to as the nozzle angle, is the angle made by the nozzle axis with the path of rotation of the blades. It will be shown in Chap. 8 that the kinetic energy of the medium leaving a nozzle is most efficiently utilized when the nozzle angle is zero degrees. Practical considerations rule out such a possibility; therefore a compromise angle must be selected which is reasonably small consistent with the requirements of a short nozzle to reduce friction losses. The practical value of the nozzle angle for best results is close to 15° although angles ranging from 12° to 20° are not uncommon.

7-6. Wet Steam. The flow of wet steam in nozzles introduces a source of loss not reflected in the velocity coefficients obtained from Fig. 7-9, which are for superheated steam. Although most turbines operate with steam initially superheated, the steam in the last stages may be wet. During initial condensation, droplets of moisture appear to have the same velocity as the steam, but with falling pressure their velocity lags behind that of the steam. The presence of the moisture droplets slows down the velocity of the steam, since the droplets are accelerated at the expense of the steam velocity. This interference in addition to viscous effects tends to decrease the velocity of the two-phase mixture. Goodenough gives the following expression for modifying the velocity coefficient obtained from Fig. 7-9 for the effect of moisture in the steam:

$$k_{nw} = k_{ng} \sqrt{q + f(1 - q)} \qquad (7\text{-}5)$$

where k_{nw} = velocity coefficient for wet steam

k_{ng} = velocity coefficient for superheated steam obtained from Fig. 7-9

q = quality of steam entering the nozzle expressed as a decimal

f = the square root of the ratio of enthalpy drop of saturated liquid to enthalpy drop of saturated steam, or

$$f = \sqrt{\frac{h_{f0} - h_{f1}}{h_{g0} - h_{g1}}}$$

The question arises as to how to handle an expansion which begins in the superheated region and proceeds into the wet region. This situation poses a different problem which is discussed in the following section.

7-7. Supersaturated Steam. When steam passing through a nozzle crosses the saturation line into the two-phase region, condensation would be normally expected to begin the instant the saturation line is crossed. Because the transition is so rapid in a nozzle (about 0.00002 sec) condensation does not actually take place until a lower temperature and pressure are reached. Condensation may then take place suddenly with the formation of multitudinous minute droplets. From the time the steam crosses the saturation line until condensation actually begins to appear, it is in a state of supersaturation. Steam in this metastable condition is at a lower temperature than would be indicated for equilibrium conditions and therefore is said to be subcooled.

During more leisurely expansion, when condensation begins, the molecules have insufficient kinetic energy to resist intermolecular attraction and they group together attracting other molecules until droplets of moisture are formed. However, in a nozzle where expansion is extremely

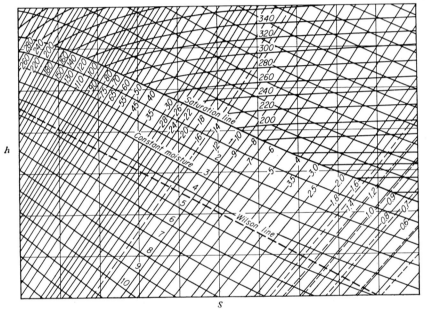

Fig. 7-10. Supersaturation limit.

rapid the temperature of the steam is dropping much more rapidly than the speed at which the molecular groups are formed. Hence when the temperature becomes considerably lower than that indicated for equilibrium, condensation suddenly appears.

Figure 7-10 shows a portion of a Mollier diagram showing the locus of points where condensation ultimately occurs. This locus is known as the Wilson* line, and condensation begins when this line is reached regardless of initial temperature and pressure of the steam. It will be noticed that the Wilson line is in the neighborhood of the 4 to 5 per cent

* There is considerable disagreement among investigators as to the actual location of the Wilson line. However, no serious error is introduced in assuming its location to be in the vicinity of the 4 per cent moisture line. This location appears to be a rather fair compromise.

moisture line. For the nozzles encountered in steam-turbine practice, condensation may be assumed to begin at the 4 per cent moisture line. Since convergent nozzles are usually short, if supersaturation occurs, there is little likelihood of recovery within the nozzle because of the short time available for equilibrium to be established. In convergent-divergent nozzles there is a possibility that equilibrium might be reached before the steam passes out of the nozzle providing supersaturation begins near the throat.

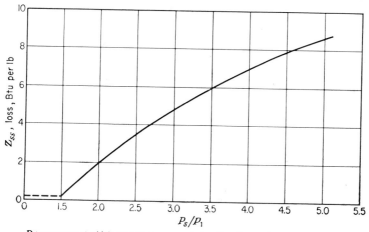

P_s = pressure at which expansion crosses saturation line, psia
P_1 = pressure at which condensation begins or exit pressure if recovery does not take place, psia

Fig. 7-11. Losses due to supersaturation.

The losses due to supersaturation may be found from Fig. 7-11, which shows the loss in Btu per pound plotted against the ratio of the absolute pressure at which supersaturation begins to the absolute pressure at which condensation actually begins (or nozzle exit pressure if recovery does not take place within the nozzle). The value of the velocity coefficient for a nozzle in which supersaturation occurs may be found as follows:

$$k_{ns} = k_{ng} \sqrt{\frac{(h_0 - h_1)_s - Z_s}{(h_0 - h_1)_s}} \qquad (7\text{-}6)$$

where k_{ns} = velocity coefficient for nozzle in which supersaturation occurs

k_{ng} = velocity coefficient for superheated steam obtained from Fig. 7-9

$(h_0 - h_1)_s$ = isentropic enthalpy drop in entire nozzle, Btu per lb

Z_s = losses due to supersaturation, Btu per lb, obtained from Fig. 7-11

7-8. Shock Waves in Nozzles. An examination of Eq. (6-76) reveals that for a given set of initial conditions and constant mass rate of flow there is a definite nozzle cross-sectional area associated with a particular pressure ratio. Figure 7-12 shows the result of plotting pressure ratio against area ratio for a converging-diverging nozzle whose cross-sectional area characteristics are similar to those of the nozzle shown in Fig. 7-3. From Fig. 7-12 it can be seen that for an area ratio less than unity there are two pressure ratios which satisfy Eq. (6-76). One pressure ratio is related to an expansion (converging nozzle) and the other ratio to a compression (diffuser). In a converging-diverging passage, expansion continues to the throat, after which further expansion or recompression may

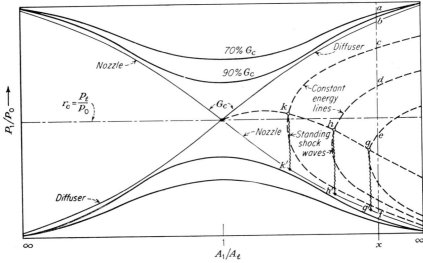

Fig. 7-12. Pressure variations in converging-diverging nozzle.

take place depending on the exit pressure. Since nozzles are under consideration here, recompression is to be avoided as undesirable.

Assume that a converging-diverging nozzle is designed for a given set of entrance and exit pressures, the pressure ratio is designated by f and the correct ratio of exit area to throat area by x in Fig. 7-12. When the true pressure ratio deviates from the design pressure ratio corresponding to the area ratio, certain phenomena are apparent. Suppose that the pressure ratio is increased to some point a, by increasing the back pressure, by decreasing the entrance pressure, or by a combination of each, then the flow is shockless, the only effect being a decrease in the mass rate of flow. It is evident that the nozzle would be operating with shockless recompression. The increase in pressure ratio is compensated by an adjustment in flow. This possible because the flow is subsonic and hence affected by the back pressure. Suppose the pressure ratio had been increased to some point between b and f such as point c, d, or e. Taking c as the new pressure ratio, it will be observed that expansion continues beyond the throat to some point k' where an abrupt increase in pressure takes place with compression shock up to k. From k' to c normal recompression takes place. A similar situation occurs at any pressure ratio between b and f. The abrupt increase in pressure with compression shock is an irreversible adiabatic transformation and, therefore, is a source of loss. A nozzle which operates under these conditions is said to be overexpanding.

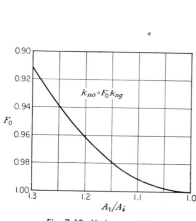

Fig. 7-13. Underexpansion.

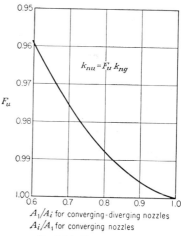

Fig. 7-14. Overexpansion.

If the pressure ratio is decreased below point (f), the design pressure ratio, the mass rate of flow is unaffected, since this is a region of super-sonic velocity. Hence the flow is expanded in the nozzle down to the design back pressure, further expansion taking place explosively beyond the nozzle exit. When this situation occurs, the nozzle is said to be underexpanding.

While overexpansion and underexpansion are both sources of loss, overexpansion is more serious, since the compression shock takes place within the nozzle itself. It should be clear that overexpansion can never occur in a simple converging nozzle generating subsonic velocities because an increase in back pressure under conditions of subsonic flow would merely lead to an adjustment in the mass rate of flow. Therefore, another reason is apparent for confining nozzles to the converging type wherever possible in turbine design, since the more serious source of loss, overexpansion, is completely avoided. If converging-diverging nozzles are used, the areas should be so proportioned that underexpansion rather than overexpansion takes place under all load conditions and expansion ratios encountered in service.

Figures 7-13 and 7-14 show approximately the losses experienced from underexpansion and overexpansion. The losses indicated are not conclusive but are sufficiently close to the average of test results to be satisfactory for preliminary design. The loss factors in both figures are plotted against the ratio of the actual exit area of the nozzle to the theoretically correct exit area. The theoretical exit area may be obtained from the equation of continuity assuming an isentropic expansion.

7-9. Nozzle Discharge Coefficients. The nozzle discharge coefficient is defined as the ratio of the actual discharge from a nozzle to the theoretical discharge. The actual discharge is obtained by test, and the theoretical discharge is computed from the continuity relationships assuming an isentropic expansion. For gases the discharge coefficient is always less than unity, but for steam it may be under certain circumstances even greater than unity. An accurate determination of the discharge coefficient in turbine design is not as critical as is the case with velocity coefficients, since turbine performance is not sensitive to slight variation in nozzle discharge.

Among the factors affecting the discharge coefficient the following are apparent:

1. Deviation of actual expansion from the isentropic
2. Accuracy of computation of theoretical discharge
3. Accuracy of test equipment and observation of test data
4. Accuracy of compressibility factors
5. For condensable vapors such as steam, the presence of condensate and supersaturation

The discharge coefficient for nozzles expanding gases varies from 0.98 to 0.99, the higher value being applicable to larger nozzles. The same values apply to superheated steam.

The discharge coefficient for wet steam may be greater than unity. The reason for this occurrence lies in the fact that the theoretical discharge is computed on the assumption that wet steam is a homogeneous mixture of dry steam and moisture in which the droplets of moisture are accelerated at the same velocity as the dry steam. Comparing the weight of moisture to the weight of the entire mixture, the ratio may be appreciable, whereas a similar volume ratio may be inconsequential, because of the negligible specific volume of the moisture. Then, of course, the velocity of the steam is considerably greater than the velocity of the mixture, resulting in a higher discharge than indicated by the theoretical value calculated by the conventional methods. The coefficient of discharge for wet steam may be obtained from Goodenough's formula

$$C_{dw} = \frac{C_d}{\sqrt{q + f(1 - q)}} \tag{7-7}$$

where C_d = coefficient of discharge normally applied to a nozzle when expanding superheated steam

C_{dw} = coefficient of discharge for wet steam

All other symbols have the same meaning as in Eq. (7-5).

When supersaturation occurs, the discharge coefficient again may be greater than unity. This is explained by the fact that supersaturated steam behaves as though it were superheated and the expansion exponent is essentially the same. This expansion exponent is greater than the exponent for saturated steam. The higher value of the discharge coefficient indicates that the specific volume and velocity of supersaturated steam are lower than for saturated steam. Now the decreased specific volume of supersaturated steam more than compensates for the decreased velocity, and consequently the discharge is greater than is indicated by calculation for wet steam.

Comparing the actual discharge with the theoretical discharge which does not consider the phenomenon of supersaturation, the result is obviously a discharge coefficient greater than unity. The effect of supersaturation is to increase the coefficient of discharge normally used for superheated steam from 2.4 to a maximum of 3 per cent for each per cent of moisture at the nozzle throat. The discharge correction factor to be applied to the normal discharge coefficient to allow for supersaturation may be found from Fig. 7-15.

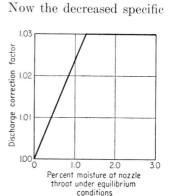

Fig. 7-15. Discharge correction factor for supersaturated steam.

7-10. Nozzle Calculations

Example 1. Design a nozzle to expand 6.5 lb per sec of steam from 300 psia and 560 F to 100 psia. Velocity of approach is negligible.

From Figure 7-7, using curve a,

$$r_c = 0.5475 \qquad P_c = 0.5475P_0 \qquad P_c = 0.5475 \times 300 = 164.3 \text{ psia}$$

Since the back pressure P_1 is lower than the critical pressure P_c, the nozzle will be obviously converging-diverging.

	Entering	Throat	Exit
P	300 psia	164.3 psia	100 psia
T	560 F		
h	1293	1233 (isentropic)	1190 (isentropic)
Δh_S	. . . .	60	103

The theoretical exit velocity is

$$_tV_1 = 223.7 \sqrt{(h_0 - h_1)_s}$$
$$_tV_1 = 223.7 \sqrt{1293 - 1190}$$
$$_tV_1 = 2270 \text{ fps}$$

From the Mollier diagram it can be seen that the entire expansion takes place in the superheat region, and therefore the velocity coefficient for superheated steam is appropriate. From Fig. 7-9 $k_{ng} = 0.963$ so that the actual velocity leaving the nozzle is

$$_aV_1 = k_{ng} \, _tV_1 = 0.963 \times 2270 = 2180 \text{ fps}$$

The theoretical throat velocity is

$$_tV_c = 223.7 \sqrt{(h_0 - h_c)_s}$$
$$_tV_c = 223.7 \sqrt{1293 - 1233} = 1732 \text{ fps}$$

From Figure 7-9, $k_{ng} = 0.97$

$$_aV_c = k_{ng} \, _tV_c = 0.97 \times 1732 = 1680 \text{ fps}$$

The actual enthalpy drop to the throat is

$$(h_0 - h_c)_s \, k_{ng}^2 = 60 \times (0.97)^2 = 56.5 \text{ Btu per lb}$$

from which the actual enthalpy at the throat including reheat is

$$h_c' = h_0 - 56.5 = 1293 - 56.5 = 1236.5 \text{ Btu per lb}$$
$$V_c' = 3.09 \text{ cu ft per lb}$$
$$(h_0 - h_1)k_{ng}^2 = 103(0.963)^2 = 95 \text{ Btu per lb}$$
$$h_1' = h_0 - 95 = 1293 - 95 = 1198 \text{ Btu per lb}$$
$$v_1' = 4.57 \text{ cu ft per lb}$$

A coefficient of discharge $C_d = 0.98$ might be expected:

$$A_c = \frac{GV_c}{C_d \, _aV_c} = \frac{6.5 \times 3.09}{0.98 \times 1680} \times 144 = 1.76 \text{ sq in.}$$
$$A_1 = \frac{Gv_{1'}}{C_d \, _aV_1} = \frac{6.5 \times 4.57}{0.98 \times 2180} \times 144 = 2 \text{ sq in.}$$

Example 2. The steam leaving the nozzle of Example 1 is expanded further to 30 psia in another nozzle arranged in series. Calculate the exit velocity assuming that only 20 per cent of the velocity in the steam leaving the first nozzle is available as approach velocity, the balance having been converted into work by intervening turbine blades.

From Fig. 7-7, using curve b, $r_c = 0.581$

$$P_c = 0.581 P_1 = 58.1 \text{ psia}$$

The nozzle is converging-diverging.

	Entering	Exit
P	100 psia	30 psia
h	1198	1130
Δh_S	. . . .	68

Taking into account the approach velocity, the theoretical exit velocity is

$$_tV_1 = 223.7 \sqrt{68 + \frac{(2180 \times 0.20)^2}{2gJ}}$$

$$_tV_1 = 1896 \text{ fps}$$

To find the actual exit velocity, supersaturation must be taken into account. From Fig. 7-9, $k_{ng} = 0.97$. It can be observed from the Mollier diagram that the steam crosses the saturation line at 85 psia and recovery from supersaturation occurs at the 4 per cent moisture line with a pressure of 45 psia. The loss due to supersaturation may be found from Fig. 7-11, noting that the supersaturation pressure ratio is

$$85 \div 45 = 1.89$$

yielding $Z_s = 1.8$ Btu per lb. Then, from Eq. (7-6),

$$k_{ns} = 0.97 \sqrt{\frac{68 - 1.8}{68}}$$

$$k_{ns} = 0.955$$

$$_aV_1 = k_{ns} \, _tV_1 = 0.955 \times 1896 = 1830 \text{ fps}$$

If the normal discharge coefficient when passing superheated steam is assumed to be 0.98, then the discharge coefficient for supersaturated steam is

$$C_d = 0.98 \times 1.03 = 1.01$$

The discharge correction factor is obtained from Fig. 7-15 after noting that the per cent of moisture at $P_c = 58.1$ psia is over 2 per cent.

Example 3. If wet steam at 50 psia and 5 per cent moisture is expanded to 30 psia, calculate the actual exit velocity. From Fig. 7-7, $r_c = 0.5805$

$$P_c = 0.5805 \times 50 = 29.03 \text{ psia}$$

The nozzle is converging and the exit pressure controls the discharge rate.

	Entering	Exit
P	50 psia	30 psia
$(1 - q)$	5	7.5
h	1128	1091 (isentropic)
Δh_S	. . . .	37
h_f	250.1	218.8
Δh_f	. . . .	31.3

From Fig. 7-9, $k_{ng} = 0.97$ and, from Eq. (7-5),

$$k_{nw} = 0.97 \sqrt{0.95 + 0.92(1 - 0.95)}$$
$$k_{nw} = 0.966$$

The factor f in the above equation was obtained as follows:

$$f = \sqrt{\frac{31.3}{37}} = 0.92$$

The actual exit velocity is

$$_aV_1 = k_{nw} \, _aV_t = 0.966 \times 1361 = 1320 \text{ fps}$$

The procedure for gas nozzles is identical to that for steam except that enthalpies from the air tables are used and the effects of moisture and supersaturation are not present.

Example 4. A gas-turbine nozzle has been designed to expand 3 lb per sec of gas from 80 psia and 1200 F to 60 psia. Calculate the exit velocity if the nozzle is used with an exit pressure of 50 psia.

From Fig. 7-8, $\quad\quad r_c = 0.535$
$$P_c = 80 \times 0.535 = 42.8 \text{ psia}$$

The nozzle is converging and the back pressure controls the flow.

	Entering	Design exit	Operating exit
P	80 psia	60 psia	50 psia
T	1200 F	1081.6 F	1010.7
P_r	82.83	62.12	51.78
h	411.82	380.5	361.44
Δh_s	. . . .	31.3	50.4

Design exit velocity:

$$_tV_1 = 223.7 \sqrt{31.3} = 1252 \text{ fps}$$

From Fig. 7-9, $k_{ng} = 0.97$

$$_aV_1 = 0.97 \times 1252 = 1212 \text{ fps}$$

Operating exit velocity:

$$_tV_1 = 223.7 \sqrt{50.4} = 1588 \text{ fps}$$

Design exit enthalpy, temperature, and specific volume:

$$h_{1'} = h_0 - 31.3(0.97)^2 = 411.82 - 29.4 = 382.4 \text{ Btu per lb}$$
$$T_{1'} = 1090 \text{ F}$$
$$v_{1'} = \frac{RT}{P} = \frac{53.34(1090 + 460)}{60 \times 144} = 9.55 \text{ cu ft per lb}$$

Operating exit specific volume:

$$v_1 = \frac{RT}{P} = \frac{53.34(1010.7 + 460)}{50 \times 144} = 10.9 \text{ cu ft per lb}$$

Design exit area:

$$A_1 = \frac{Gv_{1'}}{C_d \, _aV_1} = \frac{3 \times 9.55}{0.98 \times 1212} \times 144 = 3.48 \text{ sq in.}$$

Theoretical operating exit area:

$$A_t = \frac{Gv_1}{v_1} = \frac{3 \times 10.9 \times 144}{1588} = 2.97 \text{ sq in.}$$

Then

$$\frac{A_t}{A_1} = \frac{2.97}{3.48} = 0.854$$

and from Fig. 7-13, $F_U = 0.993$.   From Fig. 7-9, $k_{ng} = 0.97$.

$$k_{nw} = 0.993 \times 0.97 = 0.964$$
$$_aV_1 = 0.964 \times 1588 = 1530 \text{ fps}$$

References

1. Binnie, A. M., and M. W. Woods: Pressure Distribution in Convergent-divergent Steam Nozzles, *Proc. IME*, 1938.
2. Dollin, F.: Investigation of Steam Turbine Nozzle and Blading Efficiency, *Proc. IME*, 1941.
3. Goodenough, G. A.: Supersaturation and Flow of Wet Steam, *Power*, 1927.
4. Keenan, J. H.: Reaction Tests of Turbine Nozzles for Supersonic Velocities, *Trans. ASME*, 1949.
5. Kraft, H.: Reaction Tests of Turbine Nozzles for Subsonic Velocities, *Trans. ASME*, 1949.
6. Martin, H. M.: A New Theory of the Steam Turbine, *Engineering*, 1918.
7. Rettaliata, J. T.: Undercooling in Steam Nozzles, *Trans. ASME*, 1937.
8. Rettaliata, J. T.: *Current Trends*, No. 2, 1939.
9. Shapiro, A. H.: Nozzles for Supersonic Flow without Shock Fronts, *Trans. ASME*, 1944.

10. Stodola, A., and L. C. Loewenstein: "Steam and Gas Turbines" McGraw-Hill Book Company, Inc., New York, 1927.
11. Warren, G. B., and J. H. Keenan: An Experimental Investigation of Nozzle Efficiency, *Trans. ASME*, 1926.
12. Yellott, J. I., and C. K. Holland: The Condensation of Flowing Steam, *Trans. ASME*, 1937 and 1938.

Problems

7-1. Gas-turbine gases enter a nozzle at 60 psia and 1400 F and expand to 40 psia. Find (*a*) if nozzle is converging-diverging or converging; (*b*) exit velocity; (*c*) exit area; (*d*) temperature and pressure ratio.
Assume gas to have the properties of air.

7-2. A nozzle expands 2 lb per sec of steam from 200 psia and 580 F to 80 psia. Calculate the required cross-sectional area at the throat. What is the velocity coefficient and the nozzle efficiency if the actual discharge velocity is 1950 fps?

7-3. A nozzle expands 1 lb per sec of steam from 150 psia and 2 per cent moisture to 15 psia. It is required to plot certain flow variables and nozzle characteristics against static pressure for incremental pressure drops of 15 psi. To do this, first construct a table with the following column headings, filling in the data for each static pressure station along the nozzle.

1. P_x, static pressure at each station, psia
2. h_x, enthalpy after isentropic expansion from initial conditions to pressure at station under consideration
3. $h_1 - h_x$, available energy, Btu per pound, where h_1 = enthalpy of steam entering nozzle
4. V_x, ideal velocity at pressure station under consideration
5. v_x, specific volume of steam at pressure station under consideration
6. V_x/v_x
7. A_x, cross-sectional area in square inches, at pressure station under consideration
8. D_x, diameter of nozzle, in inches, at pressure station under consideration

(*a*) Taking data from the table just constructed, plot A_x, D_x, v_x, and V_x against P_x on a single sheet of graph paper.

(*b*) Select the critical pressure from the curve and calculate the critical-pressure ratio.

(*c*) What significant relationship exists between V_x, v_x, and V_x/v_x?

(*d*) Compare the V_x and v_x curves before and after the critical pressure. Discuss.

(*e*) Discuss the merits and disadvantages of the nozzle profile.

(*f*) How do the conclusions reached from an examination of the curves compare with the material of Sec. 6-11?

7-4. Determine the mass rate of flow in pounds per second in a nozzle expanding steam from 300 psia and 600 F to 150 psia if the minimum cross-sectional area is 0.75 sq in.

7-5. A nozzle expands 4000 lb per hr of air from 80 psia and 1500 F to 60 psia. The initial velocity is 600 fps. Find the exit velocity and exit area. What is the nozzle efficiency?

CHAPTER 8

ENERGY INTERCHANGES IN FLUID MACHINERY

8-1. Introduction. The purpose of this chapter is to examine the theoretical interchanges of energy between a fluid and the rotor of fluid machinery. Some general relationships are developed which are applicable to all fluid machinery and for any fluid regardless of compressibility. After the general treatment, attention is directed to the energy interchanges between a compressible fluid and the rotor of axial-flow turbines and axial-flow compressors.

In the general treatment, expressions are developed for the energy received or delivered by the rotor and for the energy changes in the fluid resulting therefrom. The energy received or delivered by the rotor may be examined kinematically by what is known as streamline theory, by the theory of gas dynamics, or by a combination of the two theories. The fundamental kinematic relationships hold for any fluid machine, the introduction of gas dynamic theory being a refinement. Each of these theories and their applications are discussed.

THE GENERAL THEORY

8-2 Momentum Principles. The momentum principles are statements of Newton's laws of motion and form the basis upon which the kinematic analysis of fluid machinery is established. The most fundamental of these laws is that the time rate of change of momentum is equal to the sum of the external forces acting on a body. Momentum is defined as the product of the mass of a body and its velocity, the momentum having the same direction as the velocity, or

$$(MM) = mV = \frac{w}{g} V$$

where (MM) = momentum
m = mass, slugs
V = velocity
w = mass, lb

From Newton's law,

$$\sum F = \frac{d}{dt}\left(\frac{w}{g} V\right) \tag{8-1}$$

If Eq. (8-1) is applied to a continuum of particles in steady flow,

$$w = \int dw$$

and

$$\sum F = \frac{d}{dt} \int V \frac{dw}{g}$$

or

$$\sum F = \frac{d(MM)}{dt} \tag{8-2}$$

Another important postulate is the law of conservation of momentum. This law is simply a specific statement of the law of conservation of energy since momentum is a form of energy. Thus, for example, where momentum interchanges occur between two bodies, the total momentum is conserved and the momentum given up by one body exactly equals the momentum received by the second body.

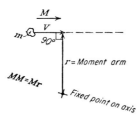

Fig. 8-1. Moment of momentum of a particle.

The angular momentum or the moment of momentum of a particle of mass about a stationary axis is defined as the product of the momentum of the particle and the moment arm drawn perpendicular to the velocity direction from a fixed point on the axis. The elements of this definition are illustrated in Fig. 8-1.

Angular momentum is a vector quantity inasmuch as the momentum itself is a vector quantity. Let

r_x = moment arm of momentum vector
r_y = moment arm of force vector

Then for a given mass consisting of a number of particles, the following expression may be written:

$$Fr_y = \frac{d}{dt} \sum \left(\frac{W}{g} V \right) r_x \tag{8-3}$$

This equation is simply another way of stating that the time rate of change of the angular momentum of a body about a fixed axis is equal to the resultant moment of the applied forces.

8-3. Streamline Theory. To simplify the analysis of the energy interchanges between fluid and rotor in accordance with streamline theory, some assumptions are necessary. It follows then that the results obtained from such an analysis are theoretical or ideal. This limitation offers no serious handicap since the ideal relationships can be modified later by suitable design coefficients to yield practical results. The assumptions made are given as follows.

1. The flow through the passages is steady and uniform at entrance and exit cross sections. This assumption implies that pressure and velocity disturbances caused by the passage partitions themselves are negligible or at least do not affect the uniformity of entrance and exit velocities.

2. The flow is laminar or occurs in streamlines. Therefore the passages are completely filled by the fluid and no friction is encountered.

3. The rotor turns at a constant angular velocity.

4. None of the fluid by-passes the passages, i.e., no leakage occurs.

5. No heat transfer takes place between the fluid and its surroundings.

Figure 8-2 shows an arbitrary rotor turning at a constant angular velocity about an axis xx. All the foregoing assumptions are considered to be applicable. The fluid may be compressible or incompressible and may

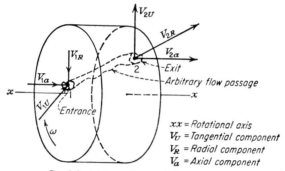

Fig. 8-2. Arbitrary flow path through a rotor.

enter the passages at any point and leave at any other point on the radius. In other words the fluid is general and the path it traces through the rotor is also general. The pressure of the fluid and cross-sectional areas of the passages may change or remain constant. V_1 represents the absolute uniform velocity of the fluid entering the rotor passage and V_2 the absolute uniform velocity leaving the rotor passage. V_{1U} and V_{2U} represent the entering and leaving tangential components, respectively. The tangential component is the component of velocity tangent to the path of angular rotation of the rotor. V_{1a} and V_{2a} represent, respectively, the axial components of the entering and leaving velocities. The axial component is the component parallel to the axis of rotation of the rotor. V_{1R} and V_{2R} represent the radial components of the entering and leaving velocities, respectively. The radial component lies in a plane normal to the axis of rotation.

Figure 8-3 shows side and front elevations of the rotor of Fig. 8-2 together with the plane projections of the entering and leaving velocities and their components. It is clear from this figure that the only component of significance in studying the rotational force effects on rotor or fluid are the tangential components.   The axial components merely exert a thrust on the entire rotor assembly.   The radial components, of course, result in a force normal to the axis of rotation.   Furthermore, the angular momentum must be expressed in terms of the tangential velocity.   From

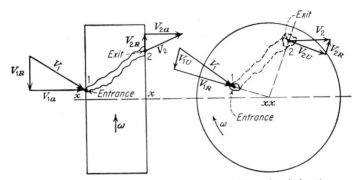

Fig. 8-3. Arbitrary flow passage through a rotor, side and end elevations.

Eq. (8-3) the angular momentum of the entering fluid is for the condition of steady flow,

$$\text{Angular momentum} = Fr_1 = \frac{dw}{g\,dt}(V_{1U})r_1$$

where r_1 = the radial distance from rotational axis to V_{1U}

w = mass, lb

Similarly for the fluid leaving the rotor,

$$\text{Angular momentum} = Fr_1 = \frac{dw}{g\,dt}(V_{2U})r_2$$

Designating $dw/dt = G$ and noting that dw/dt is the mass of fluid flowing per unit time in pounds, then

$$T = (MM)_1 - (MM)_2 = \frac{G}{g}(r_1 V_{1U} - r_2 V_{2U}) \qquad (8\text{-}4)$$

where T = torque exerted by rotor on fluid, or vice versa, ft-lb

MM = angular momentum

The power is given by the product of torque and angular velocity and, from Eq. (8-4),

$$P = T\omega = \omega \frac{G}{g}(r_1 V_{1U} - r_2 V_{2U}) \qquad (8\text{-}5)$$

The energy transfer for 1 lb per sec of flow is

$$E = \frac{\omega}{g}(r_1 V_{1U} - r_2 V_{2U}) \qquad \text{ft-lb} \qquad (8\text{-}6)$$

The expression rV_U is the whirl or vorticity of the fluid (see Eq. 6-81). If the vector difference of r_1V_{1U} and r_2V_{2U} is positive, the rotor is a turbine, and if the vector difference is negative, the rotor is a compressor.

Equation (8-6) indicates clearly that the energy transfer is dependent wholly on the resultant value of r_1V_{1U} and r_2V_{2U} and therefore is independent of the type of flow passage. The shape of the flow passage, of course, influences the value of the change of whirl. But any number of different flow passages could possibly give the same change of whirl. Therefore it is the change of whirl that is significant and not the actual shape of the passage.

Noting that the linear velocity of a point on the rotor is given by ωr and designating the linear velocity of such a point by the symbol U, from Eq. (8-6),

$$E = \frac{1}{g}(U_1V_{1U} - U_2V_{2U}) \qquad \text{ft-lb} \qquad (8-7)$$

This equation is sometimes called the Euler equation for energy transfer between a fluid and a rotor after Leonhard Euler who in the eighteenth century first recognized this relationship.

8-4. Momentum and Circulation. Consider a rotor consisting of n vanes or passage partitions. Figure 8-4 shows a conical section YZ through the rotor. If the circulation around each passage partition in section YZ is given by Γ_b, it can be shown that the total circulation of the section is

$$\Gamma = n\Gamma_b \qquad (8-8)$$

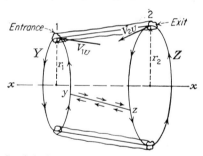

The total circulation is measured around the two circles Y and Z which have a common axis. These two circles Y and Z are in planes before and after the system. They are located sufficiently far apart so that local velocity disturbances do not cause

Fig. 8-4. Conical section through rotor showing closed contours for total circulation of section.

fluid velocity variations about the circles. Consider the two contours formed by circles Y and Z to be joined by two lines yz and zy which are opposite in direction but coincident. Thus the two circles are joined in a single closed contour. A physical picture of this is obtained by cutting a section of paper tubing along the side. The perimeter of the resulting shape is a closed contour. Applying Eq. (6-82),

$$\Gamma = 2\pi rV_{1U} + \int_x^y V \cos \theta \, dl - 2\pi rV_{2U} + \int_y^x V \cos \theta \, dl \qquad (8-9)$$

But
$$\int_x^y V \cos \theta \, dl = -\int_y^x V \cos \theta \, dl$$

since the integrations apply to the same line but proceed in opposite directions. Therefore Eq. (8-9) becomes

$$\Gamma = 2\pi(r_1V_{1U} - r_2V_{2U}) \qquad (8\text{-}10)$$

A comparison of Eqs. (8-6) and (8-10) reveals that the energy transfer to or from the rotor and circulation each depend on the change of whirl. In fact the Kutta-Joukowski equation [Eq. (6-83)] relates the lift to circulation. It is clear then that a relationship must exist between circulation and the energy transfer between a fluid and a rotor.

From Eq. (8-8) and Eq. (8-10) it follows that

$$\frac{\Gamma}{2\pi} = \frac{n\Gamma_b}{2\pi} = r_1V_{1U} - r_2V_{2U} \qquad (8\text{-}11)$$

From Eqs. (8-6) and (8-11) the following relationship is obtained for the energy exchange between a fluid and a rotor in terms of circulation:

$$E = \frac{\omega\Gamma}{g2\pi} = \frac{\omega n\Gamma_b}{g2\pi} \qquad (8\text{-}12)$$

Equation (8-12) is a very useful expression, particularly in the design of axial-flow compressors. Further discussion will not be given here inasmuch as the generality of the expression would necessarily be destroyed. Γ_b depends on coefficients which require a consideration of the passage form.

8-5. Energy Changes in the Fluid. The equations developed thus far give the energy transferred to the rotor or from the rotor to the fluid. If no losses are encountered, the energy transferred to the rotor from the fluid exactly equals the difference between the energy of the fluid entering and leaving the rotor. Similarly, the energy increase of the fluid passing through the rotor exactly equals the energy transferred to the fluid by the rotor. For such an ideal case the energy transfer can be expressed

$$E = \frac{\omega}{Jg}(r_1V_{1U} - r_2V_{2U}) = -\left[(h_1 - h_2) + \left(\frac{V_1{}^2 - V_2{}^2}{2gJ}\right)\right] \qquad (8\text{-}13)$$

Expressions for energy changes in the fluid when losses are involved will not be equal to the energy change in the rotor but will differ by the magnitude of the losses. Relationships for the energy changes in the fluid when losses are incurred are best developed separately for compressors and turbines and therefore are discussed in Chaps. 9, 12, and 13.

THE IMPULSE TURBINE

8-6. Introduction. As stated previously, the function of turbine blading is to convert the energy of the fluid flowing in the blade passages into useful work. The purpose of this division is to analyze the action of steam or gas on the blading of impulse turbines. Turbines may be broadly classified as impulse or reaction in accordance with whether the dynamic force of impulse or reaction predominates. It is essential, therefore, to understand clearly at the outset the exact meaning of impulse and reaction force.

8-7. Impulse and Reaction Forces. Newton's second law may be expressed

$$F_U = ma = \frac{w \, dV_U}{g \, dt}$$

For conditions of steady flow, $m/dt = G = $ constant and

$$F_U = \frac{G}{g} \, dV_U \tag{8-14}$$

where F_U = tangential force, lb
  G = mass rate of flow, lb per sec
  V_U = tangential component of fluid velocity V, fps
  g = acceleration of gravity, ft per sec^2

With Eq. (8-14) as a basis, an impulse force is defined as the force resulting from a decrease in magnitude or a change in direction of the

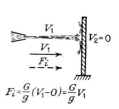

Fig. 8-5. Impulse force due to velocity decrease.

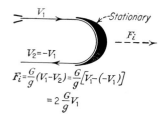

Fig. 8-6. Impulse force due to change of direction of velocity.

tangential velocity of the fluid. A reaction force takes place when the tangential velocity of the fluid is increased and is opposite in sense to the direction of the velocity. Figure 8-5 illustrates an impulse force due to a decrease in the velocity of the fluid. Here the velocity V_1 is effectively reduced to zero upon impact with the wall, resulting in an impulse force in the direction of the fluid jet. In Fig. 8-6, an impulse force is exerted on a cylindrical blade owing to a change in direction of velocity. Since the blade is stationary and frictionless, there is no decrease in magnitude of the velocity. It is interesting to note in this particular case that the total force exerted on the blade is actually partly impulse and partly reaction. The impulse force is exerted on the entrance half of the blade where the jet impinges, exerting a force to the right. In the exit half the leaving jet exerts a reactive force on the blade which is also to the right. This latter force is called the reactive force to distinguish it from the reaction force, as defined earlier. The combined effort of the two forces on an impulse blade is arbitrarily referred to as an impulse force.

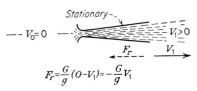

$$F_r = \frac{G}{g}(0 - V_1) = -\frac{G}{g}V_1$$

Fig. 8-7. Reaction force due to acceleration of velocity.

Figure 8-7 illustrates a reaction force exerted on a nozzle by reason of acceleration of the fluid.

8-8. Relative Velocity. Absolute velocity is defined as the velocity of an object relative to the earth. Relative velocity is the absolute velocity of one moving object compared with the absolute velocity of another object. If the absolute velocity of a jet is denoted as V, then its velocity relative to a moving blade whose absolute velocity is U is equal vectorially to $V - U = W$, where W represents the relative velocity. In Fig. 8-8, V_1 is the absolute velocity of the fluid leaving the nozzle and entering the blade. Since the blade has an absolute velocity U, the relative velocity of the jet is $V_1 - U = W_1$. Assuming frictionless contact between the jet and blade, the relative velocity leaving the blade W_2 is equal in magnitude to the entering relative velocity or $W_1 = -W_2 = -(V_1 - U)$. The absolute velocity V_2 leaving the blade equals $(V_1 - U) - U$ or $V_1 - 2U$, and since the direction is opposite to V_1, it becomes $-(V_1 - 2U) = 2U - V_1$. Applying Eq. (8-14),

Fig. 8-8. Relative velocities.

$$F_U = \frac{G}{g}(W_1 - W_2)$$
$$= \frac{G}{g}[(V_1 - U) - (-V_1 - U)]$$
$$= 2\frac{G}{g}(V_1 - U) \qquad (8-15)$$

A similar result can be obtained by substituting the absolute velocities in Eq. (8-14).

$$F_U = \frac{G}{g}(V_1 - V_2)$$
$$= \frac{G}{g}[V_1 - (2U - V_1)]$$
$$= 2\frac{G}{g}(V_1 - U) \qquad (8-15a)$$

8-9. Blade Velocity. Nearly all steam and gas turbines are of the axial-flow type and therefore the radial-flow type will not be considered here. Generally speaking in axial-flow fluid machinery r_1 and r_2 of Eqs.

(8-4) to (8-6) may be assumed equal. However, it is clear that there can be considerable variation of the value of r from root to tip of a blade. This fact raises a question as to what is meant by the linear velocity of a blade since $U = \omega r$. Consider Fig. 8-9 which shows a portion of a turbine rotor with a single blade attached. The radii to the blade root and tip are designated r_r and r_t, respectively. These radii describe two concentric circles which form the flow annulus. An element of area of the blade of radial depth dr is defined by circular arcs of radii r_x and r_y. This element of area can be considered to have substantially a constant linear velocity over its radial depth equivalent to the linear velocity at the mean radius r_m given by the following expression:

$$r_m = \sqrt{\frac{r_x{}^2 - r_y{}^2}{2}}$$

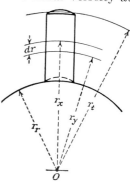

The radius r_m is then the root mean square of the radii and divides the annulus between r_x and r_y into two annuli of equal area and therefore of equal mass rates of flow. The linear velocity of this element of blade is then $U = \omega r_m$. It is clear that if the blade is comparatively short then the mean linear velocity of the blade is fairly representative. However, when the blade is

Fig. 8-9. Turbine blade radii.

long, the deviation at root and tip from the mean linear velocity is rather marked. For the present it will be assumed that short blades are under consideration or U is the mean blade linear velocity and representative of the entire blade.

In accordance with the foregoing remarks, Eq. (8-7) may be reduced to

$$E = \frac{U}{g}(V_{1U} - V_{2U}) \tag{8-16}$$

8-10. Blade Work and Efficiency—Ideal Impulse Blades. An examination of Eq. (8-16) reveals that no work is done when $U = 0$ or when $V_{1U} = U$. For a blade of the form similar to the one shown in Fig. 8-8, $V_{1U} = V_1$. For such an ideal blade, the condition for maximum work or energy transfer to the rotor must lie between the conditions of $U = 0$ and $V_1 = U$. To find this condition, Eq. (8-16) is first modified as follows:

$$E = 2\frac{UV_1}{g}\left(1 - \frac{U}{V_1}\right)$$

and denoting U/V_1 by ν, the symbol for the velocity ratio,

$$E = 2\frac{UV_1}{g}(1 - \nu)$$

$$\nu = \frac{U}{V_1}$$

Then multiplying and dividing by U/V_1,

$$E = 2 \frac{V_1^2}{g} \nu(1 - \nu) \qquad (8\text{-}17)$$

and finally differentiating with respect to ν in order to find the optimum value of ν,

$$2 \frac{V_1^2}{g} - 4 \frac{V_1^2}{g} = 0$$

and
$$\nu = \tfrac{1}{2} \qquad (8\text{-}18)$$

Therefore the maximum energy is delivered to a frictionless blade whose form permits parallel entering and exit fluid velocities when the absolute velocity of the entering fluid is twice the blade linear velocity. Substituting $\nu = \tfrac{1}{2}$ in Eq. (8-17),

$$E_{\max} = 2 \frac{V_1^2}{g} \frac{1}{2} \left(1 - \frac{1}{2}\right) = \frac{V_1^2}{2g}$$

which is equal to the kinetic energy of the entering fluid. It is evident that in order for this condition to be satisfied the blade must be 100 per cent efficient and the velocity of the fluid leaving the blades is zero. A leaving velocity of zero requires an infinite area at the exit of the blade passages. Furthermore, it is impossible to use a cylindrical blade form, since it would necessitate placing the nozzles which produce the jet directly in the path of blade rotation. Similarly, the flow leaving the blades would strike the backs of the following blades, causing a retarding force. Because of these physical limitations the flow must enter and leave the blades at some angle greater than zero degrees so that only the tangential components of the entering and exit velocities can contribute to the impulse force.

From the preceding considerations it is clear that a blade of 100 per cent efficiency must of necessity be hypothetical and that any real blade will have at best a somewhat lower efficiency even if frictionless.

8-11. Velocity Diagrams. Figure 8-10 shows extended velocity diagrams for a simple impulse turbine. The velocity vector V_1 represents the magnitude of the speed and direction of the flow leaving the nozzle and entering the blade. The direction is given by the nozzle angle α. The velocity vector U represents the blade velocity and $V_1 - U$ vectorially gives the entering relative velocity vector W_1. The triangle formed by velocity vectors V_1, W_1, and U is known as the entrance velocity triangle. The fluid entrance angle is indicated by β. The velocity vector V_{1u} is the tangential component of the absolute entering velocity V_1 and is sometimes called the entering absolute velocity of whirl.   This whirl velocity is often designated by the more descriptive term "rotative component" of entering absolute velocity.

Similarly W_{1U} is the tangential component of the entering relative velocity W_1, or entering relative whirl velocity.   The exit relative velocity is indicated by the vector W_2 and γ is the flow exit angle.   Adding W_2 and U vectorially gives V_2, the absolute exit velocity.   The vector V_{2U} is the exit absolute whirl velocity.   The absolute exit angle of the fluid is δ.   The triangle formed by vectors V_2, W_2, and U is known as the exit velocity triangle.

It is clear from the velocity diagrams that the forces exerted on the blades are due to changes in the whirl velocity and are somewhat less than in the hypothetical case of zero entrance and exit angles.

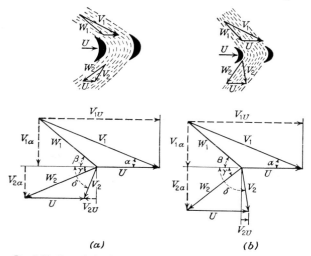

Fig. 8-10. Extended velocity diagrams for a simple impulse turbine.

It should be emphasized that the velocity directions given in the velocity diagrams represent the directions of the uniform velocities of the fluid and not the angles established by the blades.

From the velocity diagram and Eq. (8-16) the following expression may be written for the energy transferred to the blades:

$$E = \frac{U}{g} (V_1 \cos \alpha - V_2 \cos \delta) \dagger \qquad (8\text{-}19)$$

If the relative whirl velocities are substituted in Eq. (8-16), the result is equivalent to Eq. (8-19).   Usually it is more convenient to express the

† Care must be taken with Eq. (8-19) that the proper direction is accorded to V_2 cos δ.   While α is measured from U, the angle δ is not, in keeping with customary notation.   If a sign is used for δ, it must be the sign appropriate to the complementary angle.

energy transferred to the rotor in terms of the absolute whirl velocities. Therefore in the future only the absolute whirl velocities will be used and they will be referred to simply as the whirl velocities.

The axial components of the entering and exit absolute velocities are indicated on the velocity diagrams as V_{1a} and V_{2a}, respectively. The change in axial components obviously exerts no motive force on the blades but transmits a thrust in the direction of the turbine shaft. However, the thrust due to the exit axial velocity is opposite in direction to that of the entrance axial velocity and the net thrust is small in an impulse turbine. This small net thrust can be handled easily by means of a thrust bearing.

Other types of velocity diagrams are used for impulse turbines besides the extended diagram, usually to emphasize some feature or to condense the diagram. Figure 8-11 shows a velocity diagram which differs from the extended diagram of Fig. 8-10 in that the exit velocity triangle is

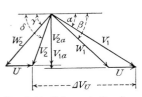

Fig. 8-11. Polar velocity diagram.

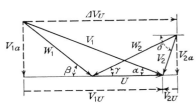

Fig. 8-12. Condensed velocity diagram for a simple impulse turbine.

placed beside the entrance velocity triangle with a common origin for all the velocity vectors except, of course, the blade velocity vector.

Another type of velocity diagram frequently used is shown in Fig. 8-12. Here the entrance velocity triangle keeps the same position as in the extended diagram of Fig. 8-10. The exit velocity triangle is folded upon vector U as a bending axis.

The effect of friction may be shown in the velocity diagram by decreasing the magnitude of W_2 by the velocity lost due to friction in the blade passage. Friction is accounted for by the blade friction factor

$$k_b = W_2/W_1$$

The velocity diagram is an extremely important device for analyzing the flow through turbine passages. The effect of blade velocity, flow entrance and exit angles, and friction can be shown graphically by means of a suitable velocity diagram. If the velocity diagram is drawn with care and to a sufficiently large scale, it can be used to provide a graphical solution for many of the values required for design purposes.

8-12. Theoretical Work and Efficiency of the Simple Impulse Stage.

The energy transferred to the rotor of an impulse turbine can be expressed by the general expression of Eq. (8-16) which is applicable to any axial-flow fluid machine. However, it is desirable to express the energy delivered to the blading in several ways in order to study the effects produced by varying certain conditions. Some of these expressions are developed in this section and the effects evaluated.

A fundamental expression for the energy transferred to impulse blading where the only loss considered is that due to friction is given by the change in kinetic energy of the fluid in flowing through the blade passages. Thus

$$E = \frac{1}{2g}(V_1{}^2 - V_2{}^2) - \frac{W_1{}^2}{2g}(1 - k_b) \tag{8-20}$$

where $W_2 = k_b W_1$. The term $W_1{}^2(1 - k_b)/2g$ represents the kinetic energy lost due to friction.

The energy transferred to the blading may also be computed from Eq. (8-19) and with the aid of a velocity diagram such as shown in Fig. 8-10,

$$E = \frac{U}{g}(V_1 \cos \alpha - U + W_2 \cos \gamma)$$

Substituting $W_2 = k_b W_1$,

$$E = \frac{U}{g}(V_1 \cos \alpha + k_b w_1 \cos \gamma - U)$$

Substituting $W_1 \cos \beta = V_1 \cos \alpha - U$

$$E = \frac{U}{g}\left[V_1 \cos \alpha - U + k_b(V_1 \cos \alpha - U)\frac{\cos \gamma}{\cos \beta}\right]$$

or

$$E = \frac{U}{g}(V_1 \cos \alpha - U)\left(1 + k_b\frac{\cos \gamma}{\cos \beta}\right) \tag{8-21}$$

and substituting $\nu = U/V_1$,

$$E = \frac{U^2}{g}\left(\frac{\cos \alpha}{\nu} - 1\right)\left(1 + k_b\frac{\cos \gamma}{\cos \beta}\right)$$

The efficiency of the blading may be obtained by dividing Eqs. (8-16), (8-19), (8-20), or (8-21) by the kinetic energy of the fluid entering the blade passages. Thus from Eq. (8-16), substituting $\nu = U/V_1$,

$$\eta_b = \frac{2\nu^2(V_{1U} - V_{2U})}{U} \tag{8-22}$$

Similarly Eq. (8-19) yields

$$\eta_b = \frac{2\nu^2(V_1 \cos \alpha + V_2 \cos \delta)}{U} \tag{8-23}$$

and, from Eq. (8-20),

$$\eta_b = \frac{V_1^2 - V_2^2 - W_1^2(1 - k_b^2)}{V_1^2} \tag{8-24}$$

From Eq. (8-21),

$$\eta_b = 2\nu \left(1 + k_b \frac{\cos \gamma}{\cos \beta}\right)(\cos \alpha - \nu) \tag{8-25}$$

Assuming α, k_b, and $\cos \alpha / \cos \beta$ are constant in Eq. (8-25), which is the equation of a parabola, differentiating with respect to ν and equating to zero,

$$\frac{d\eta_b}{d\nu} = \frac{d}{d\nu}\left[2\nu(1 + k_b)\frac{\cos \gamma}{\cos \beta}\right](\cos \alpha - \nu) = 0$$

and

$$2\left(1 - k_b \frac{\cos \gamma}{\cos \beta}\right)(\cos \alpha - 2\nu) = 0$$

from which

$$\nu = \frac{\cos \alpha}{2} \tag{8-26}$$

for maximum blade efficiency.

Substituting $\nu = \cos \alpha/2$ in Eq. (8-25),

$$\eta_{b\,max} = \left(1 + k_b \frac{\cos \gamma}{\cos \beta}\right)\frac{\cos^2 \alpha}{2} \tag{8-27}$$

In the case where $\gamma = \beta$, or very nearly so, Eq. (8-27) becomes

$$\eta_b = (1 + k_b)\frac{\cos^2 \alpha}{2} \tag{8-28}$$

If the blade is frictionless,

$$\eta_b = \cos^2 \alpha \tag{8-29}$$

It is apparent from Eqs. (8-23), (8-25), and (8-27) that small values of α and γ are essential for high blade efficiency. However, care must be taken not to make α too small in order to avoid long nozzles which are accompanied by higher friction losses. In practice a nozzle angle α equal to about 15° results in reasonably short nozzles without undue increase in friction loss.

The blade exit angle γ cannot be made too small either for another reason. Since there is supposedly no pressure drop across impulse blading, the cross-sectional area of the flow passages must not be decreased. But decreasing γ decreases the width of the flow passage at exit, and to maintain a given cross-sectional area at exit, the exit height of the blades can be increased within reasonable limits. Generally satisfactory results are obtained with γ equal to about 20° to 21°. Actually it is customary, as a compromise, to decrease the flow passage exit area slightly, permitting a reaction of 5 to 10 per cent.

Many of the efficiency equations involve the velocity ratio ν. It is significant to note that the efficiency depends on ν or the ratio of U to V_1 and not on the individual value of U or V_1.

It is interesting to compare the optimum values of ν for the hypothetical impulse blade given by Eq. (8-18) ($\nu = 0.5$) with that of ν for a simple impulse blade from Eq. (8-26) ($\nu = \cos \alpha/2$). For the usual range of values of α, Eq. (8-26) yields a value for $\nu = 0.48$.

Also instructive is a comparison of the maximum efficiency of the hypothetical blade with that of the simple impulse blade without friction as given by Eq. (8-29). For the usual range of values of α, Eq. (8-29) indicates $\eta_{b\,\mathrm{max}}$ equal to about 91 per cent. This shows that the impulse-blade deflection angles can never yield an efficiency of 100 per cent even if frictionless.

8-13. Combined Nozzle and Blade Efficiency—Simple Impulse Stage.

The combined nozzle and blade efficiency may be obtained by multiplying any of the previous equations for blade efficiency by the nozzle efficiency η_n. The combined nozzle and blade efficiency is given the symbol η_{nb} and for the case of maximum blade efficiency, as given by Eq. (8-27),

$$\eta_{nb} = \eta_n \left(1 + k_b \frac{\cos \gamma}{\cos \beta} \right) \frac{\cos^2 \alpha}{2} \tag{8-30}$$

or

$$\eta_{nb} = k_n{}^2 \left(1 + k_b \frac{\cos \gamma}{\cos \beta} \right) \frac{\cos^2 \alpha}{2} \tag{8-31}$$

Of course the proper velocity coefficient must be used, taking into account moisture, supersaturation, and overexpansion and underexpansion if appropriate.

8-14. Impulse Turbine Staging.

The simple impulse turbine is severely limited in its applications when a large pressure drop is necessary. In the simple impulse turbine the total pressure drop is necessarily taken in one row of stationary nozzles, and if the pressure drop is large, high nozzle velocities will result. This implies high blade speed with attendant blade and disc stress problems and high rotational speed. Because of stress considerations, the blade speed may not exceed 1400 ft per sec as a practical maximum so that large leaving losses are inevitable when a large pressure drop is attempted in a simple impulse turbine.

The simple impulse turbine is used where a small compact turbine operating at high speed is desirable or where only a small pressure drop is available. Sometimes gears are used if slower rotational speed is necessary.

For applications requiring the conversion of large amounts of thermal energy into work, such as in the prime mover for a large generator, the simple impulse turbine is out of the question. In this case a turbine capable of operating at 1800 or 3600 rpm and of converting large quantities of thermal energy into work is essential.

Two schemes are available to avoid the difficulties inherent in the simple impulse turbine. One method is to employ what is known as velocity

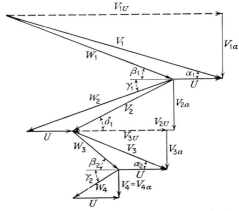

Fig. 8-13. Extended velocity diagram for a two-row Curtis turbine.

or Curtis staging. In this type of staging the entire pressure drop occurs in a single row of stationary nozzles but no attempt is made to absorb all the energy of the fluid in a single row of moving blades. Instead, a portion of the kinetic energy of the fluid is absorbed in the first row of moving blades, the fluid leaving the blades at a high velocity. A row of fixed blades turns the flow around so as to direct it against another row of moving blades which absorb more of the kinetic energy of the fluid. The flow may pass through more rows of fixed and moving blades if desired. Because of the high friction loss the efficiency of this arrangement is usually low but the turbine operates at a reasonable speed.

The other method is pressure or Rateau staging which really consists of simple impulse turbines in series on a single shaft and within a common casing. The total pressure drop is taken in increments in the successive stages so that the resulting kinetic energy of the fluid leaving any stationary row of nozzles can be absorbed in the following row of moving blades with reasonable blade speed. The frictional loss in pressure staging is considerably less than that in a comparable velocity stage but the arrangement results in a more costly turbine.

8-15. Curtis Staging. It is interesting to examine both an extended velocity diagram (Fig. 8-13) and a condensed velocity diagram (Fig. 8-14) for Curtis stages consisting of two and three rows of moving blades. These velocity diagrams show that the flow entrance and exit angles increase, resulting in flatter blades from row to row. As a consequence the whirl velocities decrease from row to row also. It is obvious that the total energy delivered to the rotor is equal to the sum of the energies delivered to each moving row. It is also clear that since the whirl velocities decrease from row to row the energy delivered to the moving rows decreases in the same order.

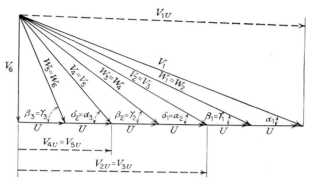

Fig. 8-14. Polar velocity diagram for a three-row Curtis turbine with symmetrical blade and no blade friction.

Some conception of the relative magnitude of the energy delivered to each row may be obtained from examining Fig. 8-14 and writing Eq. (8-16).

$$E = \frac{U}{g} \left[(V_{1U} - V_{2U}) + (V_{3U} - V_{4U}) + (V_{5U} + V_{6U}) \right] = \frac{U}{g} \sum \Delta V_U$$

(8-32)

Substituting from Fig. 8-14,

$$E = \frac{U}{g} \left[(6U + 4U) + (4U + 2U) + (2U + 0) \right]$$

(8-33)

or

$$E = 18 \frac{U^2}{g}$$

since $V_{1u} = 6U$, $V_{2u} = 4U$, etc.

From the above equations it can be readily established that the energy delivered to each row of moving blades is in the proportion 5:3:1. Since the total energy delivered to the rotor is 18 units, the first row absorbs $^{10}/_{18}$ or $^{5}/_{9}$ of the total energy, the second row $^{6}/_{18}$ or $^{3}/_{9}$, and the third row $^{2}/_{18}$ or $^{1}/_{9}$. In a four-row Curtis stage the proportions are 7:5:3:1 and in a five-row stage, 9:7:5:3:1. It is obvious that the proportion of the total energy absorbed in any row beyond the second row is negligible. Therefore there is little point in building Curtis stages consisting of more than two moving rows.

8-16. Velocity Ratio for Optimum Efficiency—Curtis Staging. Just as there is a specific value of ν for maximum blading efficiency for the simple impulse turbine so also there is a definite value of ν for maximum blading efficiency for the Curtis stage. Assuming frictionless and symmetrical blading for a Curtis stage consisting of two rows of moving blades, the sum of the whirl velocities is (Fig. 8-13),

$$\Sigma \, \Delta V_U = \Delta_1 V_U + \Delta_2 V_U$$

and
$$V_{1U} = W_1 \cos \beta_1 + W_2 \cos \gamma_1$$

but since $W_1 = W_2$ and $\beta_1 = \gamma_1$, .

$$\Delta_1 V_U = 2W_1 \cos \beta_1$$

or
$$\Delta_1 V_U = 2(V_1 \cos \alpha_2 - U)$$

Similarly
$$\Delta_2 V_U = 2(V_3 \cos \alpha_2 - U)$$

or
$$\Delta_2 V_U = 2(V_1 \cos \alpha_1 - 3U)$$

Then
$$\Sigma \, \Delta V_U = 4(V_1 \cos \alpha_1 - 2U)$$

and
$$\eta_b = \frac{8U}{V_1{}^2} (V_1 \cos \alpha_1 - 2U) \tag{8-34}$$

Substituting $\nu = U/V_1$,

$$\eta_b = 8(\nu \cos \alpha_1 - 2\nu^2)$$

Differentiating and equating to zero,

$$\frac{d\eta_b}{d\nu} = 8 \frac{d}{d\nu} (\nu \cos \alpha_1 - 2\nu^2)$$

and
$$8 \cos \alpha_1 - 32\nu = 0$$

from which
$$\nu = \frac{\cos \alpha_1}{4} \tag{8-35}$$

This is exactly one-half the value of ν for the simple impulse turbine given in Eq. (8-26). Substituting this value of ν in Eq. (8-34), the maximum blade efficiency is

$$\eta_{b\,max} = \cos^2 \alpha \tag{8-36}$$

which is the same value obtained in Eq. (8-29) for symmetrical and frictionless simple impulse blading. However, if friction had been taken into account the blading efficiency of the Curtis stage would be considerably lower than the efficiency of the simple impulse blading.

It should be stressed that the values of ν obtained thus far have been based on ideal and theoretical considerations. In real turbines some sacrifice of efficiency must be made in the interests of enonomy of manufacture and the production of a machine of reasonable weight and size. Therefore in practice it is found that for a two-row Curtis stage design values of ν range from 0.20 to 0.22.

8-17. Mixed Staging. Often it is not possible to absorb all the available energy in one Curtis stage and still maintain the desired blade speed with a practical number of moving rows. In such a situation a possible solution is to utilize two or more Curtis stages in series on a single shaft and within a common casing.

Another possible arrangement is to provide one or more Curtis stages followed by Rateau or reaction staging. The Curtis stages reduce the pressure of the fluid to a moderate level with a high proportion of work per stage and then the more efficient Rateau or reaction stages absorb the balance of the energy available. This arrangement makes it possible to reduce the over-all length of the turbine and consequently represents a saving in initial cost which more than offsets the lower efficiency.

THE REACTION TURBINE

8-18. Introduction. The principal distinguishing characteristic of the reaction turbine as compared with the impulse turbine is the fact that a pressure drop occurs in both stationary and moving rows, while in the impulse turbine, theoretically at least, the total pressure drop occurs in the stationary nozzles. The stationary blade passage in the reaction turbine serves to increase the velocity of the fluid and direct it at the moving blades. Hence the function of the stationary blades in the reaction and impulse turbine is identical. In fact, the passages formed by the stationary blades in a reaction turbine are nozzles though never conical in cross section.

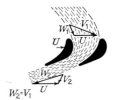

Fig. 8-15. Reaction blading.

For a clearer understanding of what takes place in the moving blades, Fig. 8-15 shows that the fluid leaving the stationary blading impinges on the moving blades, exerting a force to the right. The direction of the fluid is changed and its velocity increased, resulting in a reaction force also to the right. It is obvious then that the force exerted on the moving blades is not purely reaction but a combination of impulse and reaction forces, the magnitude of the impulse force being a function of the pressure drop in the stationary blading. If a reaction stage is defined as one row of stationary blading and one row of moving blades and if the enthalpy drop is equally distributed between the moving and stationary rows, then it may be said that the stage is a 50 per cent reaction stage. Other ratios of enthalpy drop may be used. Consideration will be given here only to the 50 per cent reaction stage.

8-19. Velocity Diagrams. The velocity diagram of the reaction turbine is similar in principle to that of the impulse turbine. Figure 8-16 shows one noticeable difference in that the relative velocity leaving the blade passage is considerably greater than the entering relative velocity. This is due to the fact that the moving blade passages are in effect nozzles. It will be noted also that $W_1 = V_2$, $W_2 = V_1$, $\alpha = \gamma$, and

$\beta = \delta$. Hence the entrance and exit velocity diagrams are congruent. This is so because the blading is "symmetrical," *i.e.*, the stationary and moving blades are identical in cross section providing a welcome opportunity for economy in the manufacture of short blades.

Care must be taken to distinguish between the term "symmetrical" as applied to reaction blading in contrast to impulse blading. Symmetrical blading in a reaction turbine results in a 50 per cent reaction stage.

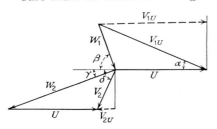

Condensed velocity diagrams may be drawn for reaction stages similar in principle to those drawn for impulse stages.

Fig. 8-16. Extended velocity diagram—Reaction stage.

8-20. Theoretical Work and Efficiency—Symmetrical Reaction Stage. The energy transferred to a rotor whether the blading is reaction or impulse is given by the general expression of Eq. (8-16):

$$E = \frac{U}{g}\,(V_{1U} - V_{2U})$$

or

$$E = \frac{U}{g}\,(V_1 \cos \alpha - V_2 \cos \delta) \tag{8-37}$$

From Fig. 8-16 it can be readily seen that $V_2 \cos \delta = W_2 \cos \gamma - U$ and $W_2 \cos \gamma = V_1 \cos \alpha$. Therefore $V_2 \cos \delta = V_1 \cos \alpha - U$. Substituting in Eq. (8-37),

$$E = \frac{U}{g}\,(V_1 \cos \alpha + V_1 \cos \alpha - U)$$

or

$$E = \frac{U}{g}\,(2V_1 \cos \alpha - U) \tag{8-38}$$

and substituting $\nu = U/V_1$,

$$E = \frac{V_1{}^2}{g}\,(2\nu \cos \alpha - \nu^2) \tag{8-39}$$

Before deriving an expression for the blading efficiency, it is first necessary to determine the energy available for delivery to the blading in each moving row. For symmetrical staging, the isentropic enthalpy drop across the stage is evenly divided between the stationary and moving rows so that

$$(\Delta h_S)_{\text{row}} = \frac{(\Delta h_S)_{\text{stage}}}{2}$$

Assuming the same nozzle efficiency for both stationary and moving rows, the thermal energy converted to kinetic energy per row is $\eta_n(\Delta h_S)_{stage}/2$. Now the kinetic energy associated with the leaving velocity of the preceding stage is available to do work just as the kinetic energy of the fluid leaving the stage under consideration is available to the following stage. Of course some loss is involved in the journey from one stage to the next and is taken into consideration by what is known as the efficiency of carry-over. Hence the kinetic energy leaving one stage and available to the next is given by $\eta_{co}V_2^2/2g$, where η_{co} is the efficiency of carry-over. Therefore the energy available for transfer to the blading is

$$\frac{V_1^2}{2g} - \eta_{co}\frac{V_2^2}{2g} = J\eta_n\frac{(\Delta h_S)_{stage}}{2}$$

which is for one row and for a flow of 1 lb per sec. For a stage consisting of two rows, the energy available is

$$J(\Delta h_S)_{stage} = \frac{2}{\eta_n}\left(\frac{V_1^2 - \eta_{co}V_2^2}{2g}\right) \tag{8-40}$$

The combined nozzle and blade efficiency is obtained by dividing Eq. (8-39) by Eq. (8-40) as follows:

$$\eta_{nb} = \frac{V_1^2/g(2\nu\cos\alpha - \nu^2)}{2/\eta_n[(V_1^2 - \eta_{co}V_2^2)/2g]}$$

or

$$\eta_{nb} = \eta_n\frac{2\nu\cos - \nu^2}{1 - \eta_{co}(V_2^2/V_1^2)} \tag{8-41}$$

From Fig. 8-16, $V_2^2 = W_2^2 + U^2 - 2UW_2\cos\alpha$ and $W_2 = V_1$ for symmetrical staging so that $V_2 = V_1^2 + U^2 - 2UV_1\cos\alpha$. Hence

$$\frac{V_2^2}{V_1^2} = 1 + \nu^2 - 2\nu\cos\alpha$$

Substituting in Eq. (8-41),

$$\eta_{nb} = \eta_n\frac{2\nu\cos - \nu^2}{1 - \eta_{co}(1 + \nu^2 - 2\nu\cos\alpha)} \tag{8-42}$$

From Eq. (8-42) it can be seen that for $\eta_{co} = 1$, the combined nozzle and blade efficiency is equivalent to the nozzle efficiency alone so that any losses which occur are due to the nozzle action. Also it will be noted that the combined nozzle and blade efficiency is independent of ν and α if $\eta_{co} = 1$.

For the condition of zero carry-over velocity, Eq. (8-42) becomes

$$\eta_{nb} = \eta_n(2\nu\cos\alpha - \nu^2)$$

which is the efficiency of a single row. Assuming zero carry-over velocity and $\eta_n = 1$,

$$\eta_b = \nu(2 \cos \alpha - \nu) \tag{8-43}$$

To find the value of ν for maximum efficiency, differentiate Eq. (8-43) with respect to ν and equate to zero, or

$$\frac{d\eta_b}{d\nu} = \frac{d}{d\nu} [\nu(2 \cos \alpha - \nu)] = 0$$

and

$$2 \cos \alpha - 2\nu = 0$$

from which

$$\nu = \cos \alpha \tag{8-44}$$

Substituting this value of ν in Eq. (8-43) the result is

$$\eta_{b \ max} = \cos^2 \alpha \tag{8-45}$$

Comparing Eq. (8-45) with Eqs. (8-26) and (8-35), the optimum value of ν for reaction blading is twice that of simple impulse blading and four times that of Curtis blading. A comparison of Eqs. (8-29), (8-36), and (8-45) reveals that the optimum efficiencies for simple impulse, Curtis, and reaction blading are all equal. However, when friction is taken into account, the reaction stage is usually found to be the most efficient, followed by Rateau and Curtis staging in that order. The reason the friction losses are less significant in the reaction stage lies in the fact that the flow velocities are lower.

8-21. Comparison of Energy-absorbing Abilities of Various Stages. Some concept of the relative abilities of the various types of stages to absorb energy may be obtained as follows. From Eqs. (8-29), (8-36), and (8-45),

Simple impulse:

$$\nu^2 = \frac{\cos^2 \alpha}{4} = \frac{U^2}{V_1^2}$$

$$V_1^2 = \frac{4U^2}{\cos^2 \alpha}$$

Curtis:

$$\nu^2 = \frac{\cos^2 \alpha}{16} = \frac{U^2}{V_1^2}$$

$$V_1^2 = \frac{16U^2}{\cos^2 \alpha}$$

Reaction:

$$\nu^2 = \cos^2 \alpha = \frac{U^2}{V_1^2}$$

$$V_1^2 = \frac{U^2}{\cos^2 \alpha}$$

Assuming that the kinetic energy entering the impulse blades is available for absorbtion by the blades and that twice this amount is available to the reaction stage (50 per cent reaction with equal velocities generated in stationary and moving rows),

Simple impulse:

$$E = \frac{V_1^2}{2g} = \frac{4U^2}{\cos^2 \alpha} \frac{1}{2g} = \frac{2U^2}{g \cos^2 \alpha}$$

Curtis:

$$E = \frac{V_1^2}{2g} = \frac{16U^2}{\cos^2 \alpha} \frac{1}{2g} = \frac{8U^2}{g \cos^2 \alpha}$$

Reaction:

$$E = \frac{2V_1^2}{2g} = \frac{2U^2}{\cos^2 \alpha} \frac{1}{2g} = \frac{U^2}{g \cos^2 \alpha}$$

If further U and α are kept constant for purposes of comparison, the following approximate conclusions may be drawn. The energy absorbing ability of the Curtis stage is four times that of the simple impulse and eight times that of the reaction stage while the energy-absorbing ability of the simple impulse stage is twice that of the reaction stage.

It must be stressed that actual conditions will change the above ratios materially and the ratios derived are merely to convey some concept of the order of magnitude.

THE AXIAL-FLOW COMPRESSOR

8-22. Introduction. As far as the concept of energy transfer between fluid and rotor is concerned the axial-flow compressor may be viewed as a reversed turbine. However, the turbine represents an expansion process and therefore the passage shapes are less critical than for a diffusing process such as is experienced in the axial-flow compressor. It will be recalled from Sec. 6-9 that change of flow direction must be carefully considered in a diffusing process. Hence the passage of axial-flow air compressors must be designed in accordance with the principles of gas dynamic theory. The result is a machine which is very different in appearance and design approach from the turbine.

Chapter 13 is devoted to a development of a design theory and procedure for the axial-flow compressor. Discussion in the present section is limited to some fundamental relationships which are independent of the particular design theory followed.

8-23. Velocity Diagrams. The velocity diagrams for the axial-flow compressor are constructed according to the same principles as for the turbine. However, some differences are apparent. Referring to Fig. 8-17, it is observed that the direction of the absolute velocity V_0

approaching the stationary blades is given by an angle α_0 measured from the axis of rotation of the compressor. This is simply a convention peculiar to air-compressor design practice. It will be remembered that the velocity vectors in the turbine velocity diagram were oriented with the plane of blade rotation. The stator or stationary blades may merely deflect the direction of flow or they may act as diffusers effecting a static-pressure rise with an accompanied velocity drop. The direction of the absolute velocity V_1 leaving the stator is given by the angle α_1. V_1 is also the direction and magnitude of the absolute velocity entering the rotor.

The rotor transfers energy to the fluid increasing the magnitude of the absolute velocity from V_1 to V_2 and changing the direction of flow so that the absolute velocity V_2 leaving the rotor is in the direction δ_1. The blade passages of the rotor are diffusers and a static-pressure rise occurs with a decrease in the magni-

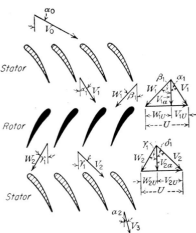

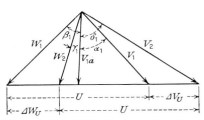

Fig. 8-17. Axial-flow compressor velocity triangles.

Fig. 8-18. Axial-flow compressor velocity diagram.

tude of the relative velocity from W_1 to W_2. The directions of the entering and exit velocities are given by the angles β_1 and γ_1, respectively.

The second stator shown in the figure accomplishes the same purpose as the first stator. The absolute velocity leaving the second stator is V_3 at angle α_3. In general, the absolute velocity entering the second stator, V_2 at angle δ_1, is equal to the absolute velocity entering the first stator, V_0 at angle α_0, in both magnitude and direction.

The two velocity triangles shown in Fig. 8-17 may be combined in a single velocity diagram as indicated in Fig. 8-18.

8-24. Energy Transfer from Rotor to Fluid. Equation (8-7) is applicable to compressors and turbines. Since axial-flow compressors are under consideration, Eq. (8-7) may be expressed

$$E = \frac{U}{g}(V_{2U} - V_{1U}) = \frac{U}{g}\Delta V_U \qquad (8\text{-}46)$$

It is evident that the energy transfer is also given by

$$E = \frac{U}{g} \Delta W_U \qquad (8\text{-}47)$$

From Fig. 8-18, $\Delta V_U = V_{2U} - V_{1U}$, $\Delta V_U = V_{1a}(\tan \delta_1 - \tan \alpha_1)$, and $\Delta W_U = W_{1U} - W_{2U} = V_{1a}(\tan \beta_1 - \tan \gamma_1)$. Substituting in Eqs. (8-46) and (8-47),

$$E = \frac{UV_{1a}}{g}(\tan \delta_1 - \tan \alpha_1) \qquad (8\text{-}48)$$

or

$$E = \frac{UV_{1a}}{g}(\tan \beta_1 - \tan \gamma_1) \qquad (8\text{-}49)$$

A relationship between U and V_{1a} may be established as follows:

$$U = V_{1U} + W_{1U} = V_{1a}(\tan \alpha_1 + \tan \beta_1)$$

or

$$\frac{1}{\phi} = \frac{U}{V_{1a}} = \tan \alpha_1 + \tan \beta_1$$

where ϕ is termed the flow coefficient, and

$$U = V_{2U} + W_{2U} = V_{1a}(\tan \delta_1 + \tan \gamma_1)$$
$$\frac{1}{\phi} = \frac{U}{V_{1a}} = \tan \delta_1 + \tan \gamma_1$$

Substituting in Eqs. (8-48) and (8-49),

$$E = \frac{U}{g}[U - V_{1a}(\tan \alpha_1 + \tan \gamma_1)] \qquad (8\text{-}50)$$

Equation (8-50) represents the energy delivered by the rotor to the air, but of course some of it is not effective in increasing the total pressure but instead is dissipated as friction. However, it can be seen that an increase in axial velocity or in the angles α_1 and γ_1 must necessarily result in a decrease in energy transfer to the fluid. For high energy input then the blade speed must be high while the axial velocity and blade angles corresponding to α_1 and γ_1 should be low.

The stagnation-temperature rise of the fluid in the compressor stage may be found from Eq. (8-48) or (8-49) regardless of the efficiency of compression. Thus, from Eq. (8-48),

$$\Delta T^\circ = \frac{UV_{1a}}{gJC_p}(\tan \delta_1 - \tan \alpha_1) \qquad (8\text{-}51)$$

If the velocities entering and leaving the stage are equal, the dynamic temperatures will also be equal and therefore for this condition Eq. (8-51) is valid for the static-temperature rise.

The ideal pressure rise can be computed on the basis of an isentropic compression so that the work of compression is given by

$$
\begin{aligned}
E = (h_2 - h_1)_S &= U_2 - U_1 + P_2 v_2 + P_1 v_1 \\
&= J C_v (T_2 - T_1) + P_2 v_2 - P_1 v_1 \\
&= \frac{R}{k-1}(T_2 - T_1) + P_2 v_2 - P_1 v_1 \\
&= \frac{k}{k-1}(P_2 v_2 - P_1 v_1)
\end{aligned}
$$

and
$$
E = \frac{k}{k-1} P_1 v_1' \left[\left(\frac{P_2}{P_1} \right)^{(k-1)/k} - 1 \right] \tag{8-52}
$$

Equations (8-48) and (8-52) are equal so that

$$
\frac{k}{k-1} P_1 v_1 \left[\left(\frac{P_2}{P_1} \right)^{(k-1)/k} - 1 \right] = \frac{U V_{1a}}{g}(\tan \delta_1 - \tan \alpha_1)
$$

and
$$
\frac{P_2}{P_1} = \left[\frac{(k-1) U V_{1a}(\tan \delta_1 - \tan \alpha_1)}{g k P_1 v_1} + 1 \right]^{k/(k-1)}
$$

Substituting $\phi = V_{1a}/U$,

$$
\frac{P_2}{P_1} = \left[\frac{U^2 \phi (k-1) \left(1 - \dfrac{\tan \alpha_1}{\tan \delta_1} \right)}{g k P_1 v_1} + 1 \right]^{k/(k-1)}
$$

Several conclusions may be drawn from Eq. (8-53). It is evident that all other things being constant the pressure rise is a function of the square of the blade speed. Low values of α_1 and high values of δ_1 are conducive to high pressure rise. Since $Pv = RT$, it is also clear that low temperature or low specific volume for a given compressor inlet temperature makes possible a higher pressure rise.

References

1. Church, E. F.: "Steam Turbines," McGraw-Hill Book Company, Inc., New York, 1950.
2. Heinze, F. J.: Thermodynamics and Turbine Design, Westinghouse Lectures, 1948.
3. Moss, S. A., C. W. Smith, and W. R. Foote: Energy Transfer between a Fluid and a Rotor, *Trans. ASME*, 1942.
4. Stodola, A., and L. C. Lowenstein: "Steam and Gas Turbines," McGraw-Hill Book Company, Inc., New York, 1927.
5. Wislicenus, G. F.: "Fluid Mechanics of Turbo-machinery," McGraw-Hill Book Company, Inc., New York, 1947.

Problems

8-1. Make the necessary calculations and draw an extended velocity diagram to scale for a simple impulse turbine; determine the energy transferred to the rotor per pound per second flow of steam, the blade efficiency, and the combined nozzle and blade efficiency, the following data being given:

$$P_1 = 150 \text{ psia} \qquad T_1 = 400 \text{ F} \qquad P_2 = 2 \text{ in. Hg abs}$$
$$k_n = 0.90 \qquad \alpha = 20° \qquad k_b = 0.85 \qquad U = 1250 \text{ fps}$$

Solve the problem for symmetrical and nonsymmetrical impulse blades. For the nonsymmetrical blades, take $\gamma = (\alpha + \beta)/2$.

8-2. Draw to scale the velocity diagram for a Curtis stage consisting of two moving rows. The blades are not symmetrical, $\alpha_1 = 15°$, and the absolute velocity entering the first row is 2600 fps. Select a suitable value of ν, and assume k_b for the first two rows of blades is 0.87 and for the last row $k_b = 0.94$. Calculate the blading efficiency and the energy transferred to the blades per pound per second of fluid flow.

8-3. Solve Prob. 8-2 trigonometrically.

8-4. The following data are applicable to a simple impulse turbine.

$$P_1 = 200 \text{ psia}, \ T_1 = 500 \text{ F}$$
$$P_2 = 4 \text{ in. Hg abs}$$
$$\alpha = 15$$
$$k_b = 0.80$$
$$U = 1000 \text{ fps}$$

Power developed by blades = 500 kw
Blading: symmetrical

Including nozzle losses, determine:

(a) Velocity diagram
(b) Steam flow in pounds per hour (blade output basis)
(c) Nozzle area at exit (assume 12 nozzles)
(d) Blade efficiency
(e) Combined blade and nozzle efficiency
(f) Steam rate (blade output basis)
(g) Heat rate (blade output basis)
(h) Engine efficiency (blade output basis)
(i) Thermal efficiency (blade output basis)

8-5. The following information applies to fluid machinery consisting of turbines and compressors using air as a working medium. The entrance conditions are indicated by the subscript 1 while the exit conditions are represented by the subscript 2. The direction of rotation of all the rotors is clockwise.

Machine	Magnitude and direction of tangential components of absolute fluid velocities	Radii
A	$+V_{1U}; \ -V_{2U} = -3V_{1U}$	$r_1; \ r_2 = 3r_1$
B	$-V_{1U}; \ +V_{2U}; \ |V_{1U}| = |V_{2U}|$	$r_1 = 3r_2; \ r_2$
C	$+V_{1U}; \ -V_{2U}; \ |V_{1U}| = |V_{2U}|$	$r_1 = r_2$
D	$V_{1U} = 0; \ +V_{2U}$	$r_1; \ r_2 = 3r_1$

(a) Determine which machines are turbines and which are compressors.
(b) If the magnitude of V_{1U} for machines A, B, and C and the magnitude of V_{2U} in machine D is 500 fps, the value of r_1 in all machines is 0.75 ft, the rotational speed of all machines is 6000 rpm, the mass rate of flow in all machines is 200 lb per sec, determine the pressure ratio and horsepower of each machine, neglecting all losses.

CHAPTER 9

DESIGN OF TURBINE FLOW PASSAGES

9-1. Introduction. The designer of turbine flow passages is primarily concerned with the shape and arrangement of nozzles (stationary blades) and moving blades. The blading is by far the most important element in any turbine design. It is the shape of the blades which determines the form of the flow passages and the energy transferred from the fluid to the rotor is dependent chiefly on the nature of the flow through these passages. Then clearly it is important that careful attention be given to developing the correct blade shape. Any deviation from the correct blade shape is accompanied by loss of efficiency.

The flow passages must also provide sufficient annular area to accommodate the entire flow of fluid. An adequate number of blades must be provided to ensure well-defined flow passages. Yet the use of too many blades may increase unduly the resistance to flow. Special consideration must be given to the stresses imposed on turbine blades by the pressures, temperatures, dynamic forces, and rotational speeds encountered under all conditions of operation.

The arrangement of the flow passages in stages has a marked effect not only on the efficiency of the turbine but on manufacturing costs as well. The best design is a harmonious compromise between operating efficiency, size of unit, and cost. Although there is no infallible rule to be followed in making such a compromise, a great deal can be learned from existing designs to assist in future decisions.

9-2. Isentropic Velocity Ratio. In developing design relationships, it is convenient to use the isentropic velocity ratio instead of the actual velocity ratio as previously defined. This is particularly true in dealing with blading other than impulse, since no assumptions need be made about the efficiency of the stationary passages. The isentropic velocity ratio for an impulse stage is defined as the ratio of the blade velocity to the velocity equivalent of the stage isentropic enthalpy drop, or

$$\nu'_i = \frac{U}{223.7 \sqrt{(\Delta h_S)_{\text{stage}}}} \tag{9-1}$$

For a reaction stage, the isentropic velocity ratio is defined as the ratio of the blade velocity to the velocity equivalent of one-half of the stage isentropic enthalpy drop. A reaction stage is considered to consist of a stationary and a moving row of nozzles. Thus

$$\nu'_r = \frac{U}{223.7 \sqrt{\dfrac{(\Delta h_S)_{\text{stage}}}{2}}} \qquad (9\text{-}2)$$

9-3. Energy Distribution in Turbines. Before attempting an analysis of the energy distribution in a turbine, some assumption must be made about the stage efficiency and the number of stages to be employed. Although the stage efficiency may be calculated with reasonable accuracy after the energy distribution has been established, some prediction of its magnitude must be made in the preliminary phase of design. The stage efficiency is defined

$$\eta_s = \frac{\text{output of stage, Btu per lb}}{(\Delta h_S)_{\text{stage}}} \qquad (9\text{-}3)$$

The combined nozzle and blade efficiency has been derived as a function of actual velocity ratio in the preceding chapter. The stage efficiency is somewhat less than the combined nozzle and blade efficiency because it takes into account other losses which may occur in the stage such as disc friction, windage losses, leakage, etc. These additional losses, referred to as stage parasitic losses, will be discussed in the next chapter. Suffice it to say here that the parasitic losses may be expressed as a percentage of the available energy in the stage. The stage efficiency may then be expressed

$$\eta_s = \eta_{nb} \left(1 - \frac{\text{parasitic losses, \%}}{100} \right) \qquad (9\text{-}4)$$

If reaction turbines are under consideration, it is more convenient to regard each row as a stage which requires the blade efficiency for the row to be substituted for η_{nb} in Eq. (9-4). In the discussion of energy distribution in reaction turbines it will be the practice in this text to treat each row as a separate expansion.

Figures 9-1 and 9-2 show what can be expected in the way of stage efficiency for various arrangements of flow passages as a function of actual or isentropic velocity ratio. These curves apply equally well to steam- and gas-turbine stages.

The assumption is made that the portion of available energy not converted into work in the stage remains in the fluid or is returned to the fluid at constant pressure. Hence the actual enthalpy of the fluid leaving the stage is somewhat higher than is indicated for an isentropic expansion.

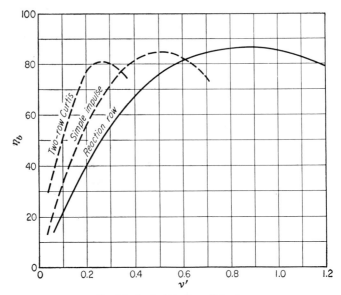

Fig. 9-1. Typical blading efficiencies.

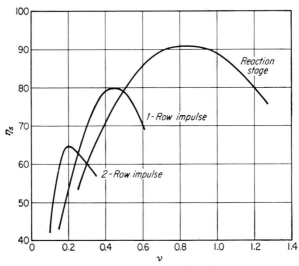

Fig. 9-2. Typical stage efficiencies.

The portion of the available energy remaining in the fluid is termed the reheat. Although the assumption that reheat takes place at constant pressure is open to serious question, the results obtained from such an assumption appear to be quite in keeping with actual conditions. A single-stage expansion with reheat is shown in Fig. 9-3.

Figure 9-4 shows the expansion in a four-stage turbine, taking into account the effects of reheat. Examining Fig. 9-4, the following characteristics of the expansion are apparent:

1. Reheat takes place with an increase in entropy.

2. The reheat in a given stage is available to do work in the succeeding stage with the exception of the last stage where the reheat is a total loss.

3. The constant-pressure lines diverge with increasing entropy, thereby increasing the enthalpy drop for the same pressure drop.

4. Because of (2) and (3) the sum of the available energies for each stage is greater than the available energy for the entire turbine.

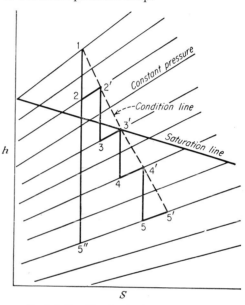

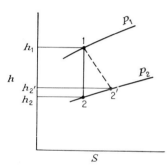

$$\Delta h_S = h_1 - h_2$$
$$\Delta h_{actual} = h_1 - h_2' = \eta_s (h_1 - h_2)$$
$$Reheat = h_2' - h_2 = (1 - \eta_s)(h_1 - h_2)$$

Fig. 9-3. Expansion in single stage with reheat.

Fig. 9-4. Condition line for four-stage turbine.

5. The condition line representing the actual expansion in the turbine is approximately the locus of points indicating the actual conditions at the exit of each stage.

The effect of item (4) may be expressed, assuming equal available energy per stage, by a term called the reheat factor

$$RF_N = \frac{N(\Delta h_S)_{stage}}{(\Delta h_S)_{turbine}} = \frac{\Sigma(\Delta h_S)_{stage}}{(\Delta h_S)_{turbine}} \tag{9-5}$$

where RF_N = reheat factor for N stages

N = number of stages or expansions

It follows then that if the reheat factor is known in advance, the available energy per stage for equal energy distribution may be obtained as follows:

$$(\Delta h_S)_{stage} = \frac{RF_N(\Delta h_S)_{turbine}}{N} \tag{9-6}$$

A relationship for the reheat factor assuming an infinite number of stages or expansions at constant stage efficiency may be derived as follows.* Referring to Fig. 9-5, it will be observed that the isentropic expansion for the turbine is designated by the curve ab, whereas the expansion representing the sum of the individual stage expansions is designated by the curve ab'. Since the latter expansion is assumed to take place in an infinite number of steps, it can be fairly represented by a smooth curve. Two additional assumptions are made, namely, that the isentropic expansion for the turbine and the stage isentropic expansions

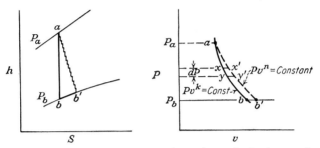

Fig. 9-5. Turbine isentropic expansion and sum of stage isentropic expansion.

are satisfied by the equations $Pv^n = \text{constant} = C$ and $Pv^k = \text{constant}$, respectively.

For an isentropic expansion in a single stage (a differential expansion),

$$dU = -P\,dv$$

Substituting from $Pv^k = C$,

$$dU = -C\frac{dv}{v^k}$$

Integrating,

$$U = -C\frac{v^{1-k}}{1-k} + C_1$$

or

$$U = -\frac{Pv}{1-k} + C_1$$

and

$$dU = d\left(\frac{Pv}{1-k} + C_1\right) = \frac{P\,dv + v\,dP}{1-k} \tag{9-7}$$

From the general energy equation for an isentropic expansion, assuming no appreciable change in kinetic energy entering or leaving the differential stage or expansion,

$$dh_S = -v\,dP \tag{9-8}$$

the negative sign is used since dP is negative. Now the reheat is given as

$$\text{Reheat} = (1 - \eta_s)\,dh_S \tag{9-9}$$

* This derivation was first conceived by Goudie.[5]

For a differential expansion, the area under the curves for the isentropic expansion for the turbine and the sum of the stage isentropic expansions may be considered to be very nearly equal, and from Eqs. (9-7) and (9-8),

$$\text{Reheat} = -(1 - \eta_s)v \, dP \tag{9-10}$$

Applying the first law of thermodynamics to the expansion consisting of the sum of the stage isentropic expansions,

$$\dot{Q} = dU + dW \tag{9-11}$$

where the only heat transfer occurs internally due to the reheat. Substituting from Eqs. (9-7) and (9-10) in Eq. (9-11),

$$-(1 - \eta_s)v \, dP = \frac{P \, dv + v \, dP}{k - 1} + P \, dv$$

or

$$[k - \eta_s(k - 1)]\frac{dP}{P} + k\frac{dv}{v} = 0$$

Integrating,

$$[k - \eta_s(k - 1)] \ln P + k \ln v = 0$$

and

$$Pv^{k/[k-\eta_s(k-1)]} = \text{const} \tag{9-12}$$

Therefore the exponent for the expansions represented by the sum of the stage isentropic expansions is

$$n = \frac{k}{k - \eta_s(k - 1)}$$

Now the sum of the stage isentropic enthalpy drops may be obtained by taking n as the expansion exponent. The enthalpy drop for a process following $Pv^n = C$ may be expressed

$$\Delta h = \left(U_1 + \frac{P_1 v_1}{J}\right) - \left(U_2 + \frac{P_2 v_2}{J}\right)$$

or

$$\Delta h = U_1 - U_2 + \frac{P_1 v_1 - P_2 v_2}{J}$$

Substituting from Eq. (6-73),

$$\Delta h = \frac{P_1 v_1 - P_2 v_2}{J(n - 1)} + \frac{P_1 v_1 - P_2 v_2}{J}$$

$$= \frac{n}{n - 1}(P_1 v_1 - P_2 v_2)$$

Multiplying and dividing by $P_1 v_1$ and substituting $Pv^n = C$,

$$\Delta h = \frac{nP_1 v_1}{n - 1}\left[1 - \left(\frac{1}{r}\right)^{(n-1)/n}\right] \tag{9-13}$$

where r = the expansion ratio or P_2/P_1.

Similarly for the turbine isentropic drop,

$$\Delta h_S = \frac{kP_1v_1}{k-1}\left[1 - \left(\frac{1}{r}\right)^{(k-1)/k}\right] \tag{9-14}$$

Applying Eqs. (9-13) and (9-14) to the sum of the stage isentropic enthalpy drops and the turbine enthalpy drop, respectively, and substituting in Eq. (9-5),

$$RF_\infty = \frac{n(k-1)[1 - (1/r)^{(n-1)/n}]}{k(n-1)[1 - (1/r)^{(k-1)/k}]}$$

Substituting from $n = k/[k - \eta_s(k - 1)]$,

$$RF_\infty = \frac{1}{\eta_s}\frac{1 - (1/r)^{\eta_s(k-1)/k}}{1 - (1/r)^{(k-1)/k}} \tag{9-15}$$

Equation (9-15) may be used for steam as well as gas. However, the equation is limited in that the simplifying assumption of an ideal gas is

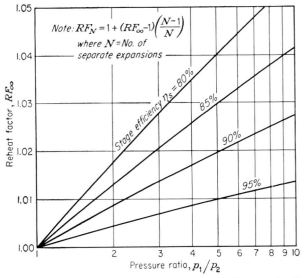

Fig. 9-6. Reheat factors for gas. (Courtesy of Allis-Chalmers Manufacturing Company.)

implied in its derivation. Furthermore, Eq. (9-15) is rather awkward to handle, but RF_∞ may be obtained conveniently from Fig. 9-6 for gas and Fig. 9-7 for steam.

The reheat factor for an infinite number of stages must be corrected for a finite number of stages, the only possible exception being when a great many stages are employed. The value of RF_∞ obtained from Fig. 9-6 may be corrected to yield the reheat factor for the number of stages involved, by the expression

$$\mathrm{RF}_N = 1 + (\mathrm{RF}_\infty - 1)\left(\frac{N-1}{N}\right) \qquad \text{gas} \qquad (9\text{-}16)$$

where N = number of stages (rows for reaction turbines). The value of RF_N for steam may be obtained by utilizing RF_∞ obtained from Fig. 9-7.

$$\mathrm{RF}_N = (\mathrm{RF}_\infty - 1)\left(1 - \frac{1}{N}\right)\left(\frac{1 - \eta_s}{0.2}\right) + 1 \qquad \text{steam} \qquad (9\text{-}17)$$

The number of stages used in a given turbine must always be a compromise between cost and efficiency. The optimum number of stages

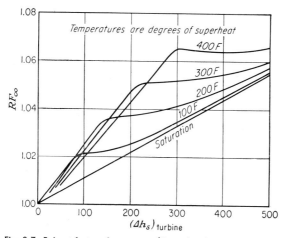

Fig. 9-7. Reheat factors for steam. (*Reproduced from Robinson.*[10])

from the standpoint of efficiency may be determined from the relations already derived. Solving Eq. (9-5) for the number of stages,

$$N = \frac{\mathrm{RF}_N(\Delta h_S)_{\text{turbine}}}{(\Delta h_S)_{\text{stage}}} \qquad (9\text{-}18)$$

Now, from the definition of the isentropic velocity ratio for an impulse stage,

$$2gJ(\Delta h_S)_{\text{stage}} = V_1{}^2 = (\nu_i')^2 U^2$$

or

$$(\Delta h_S)_{\text{stage}} = (\nu_i')^2 \frac{U^2}{2gJ} \qquad (9\text{-}19)$$

which substituted in Eq. (9-5) yields

$$N = \mathrm{RF}_N \frac{2gJ(\Delta h_S)_{\text{turbine}}}{U^2}(\nu_i')^2 \qquad (9\text{-}20)$$

Similarly for a reaction stage,

$$N = \mathrm{RF}_N \frac{2gJ(\Delta h_S)_{\text{turbine}}}{U^2} (\nu_r')^2 \qquad (9\text{-}21)$$

where U = mean blade velocity.

An examination of Figs. 9-1 and 9-2 shows that optimum stage efficiencies are expected with relatively high velocity ratios. However, Eqs. (9-20) and (9-21) indicate that the number of expansions increases with higher velocity ratios. Therefore if a given blade speed is to be maintained, a balance must be struck between a costly machine with many stages and a machine of fewer stages and lower efficiency.

One more relation remains to be developed in connection with reheat factor and stage efficiency. The internal engine efficiency, more commonly called simply the internal efficiency, is defined as the sum of the actual outputs of the stages divided by the turbine available energy. From Figure 9-4,

$$\eta_i = \frac{h_1 - h_{5'}}{h_1 - h_{5''}}$$

or

$$\eta_i = \frac{N\eta_s(\Delta h_S)_{\text{stage}}}{(\Delta h_S)_{\text{turbine}}}$$

and

$$\eta_i = \eta_s \, \mathrm{RF}_N \qquad (9\text{-}22)$$

Thus it is clear that the internal efficiency of a turbine consisting of more than one stage is always greater than the stage efficiency since the reheat factor is greater than unity.

9-4. Effect of Carry-over Velocity on Energy Distribution. In the preceding section no account was taken of the availability of the kinetic energy leaving a particular stage to do work in the succeeding stage. Although this omission of carry-over velocity from the treatment does not affect the validity of the conclusions reached, the carry-over would have a marked effect in decreasing the static enthalpy drop required in the succeeding stage for a given output.

In taking the carry-over velocity into account, it is important to consider its magnitude relative to the passage in which it is to be utilized. For example, if the carry-over to a moving row of blades is considered, it is the relative approach velocity which is considered. This has been done all along. However, if the approach velocity to a stationary row of blades is under consideration, then the absolute velocity leaving the preceding row of moving blades is appropriate.

Figure 9-8 illustrates carry-over velocity for a two-row stage. The stage illustrated happens to be a reaction stage, but a similar analysis is possible for impulse stages. The static enthalpy drops are shown as taking place between the appropriate static pressures yielding a typical condition curve (dashed line). The static pressure entering the first stationary row is given as P_0. The dynamic enthalpy equivalent of the kinetic energy entering the stationary row is Δh_{da0} and the stagnation pressure is P_0^0. The isentropic static enthalpy drop in the stationary row is shown as $(\Delta h_s)_{row}$, while the actual static enthalpy drop is indicated

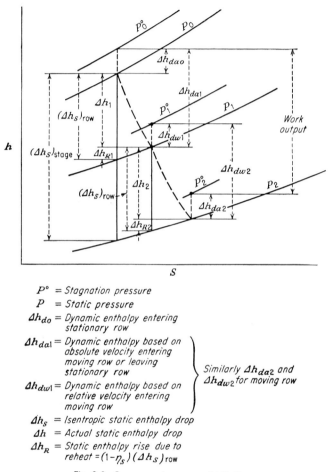

P^0 = Stagnation pressure

P = Static pressure

Δh_{do} = Dynamic enthalpy entering stationary row

Δh_{da1} = Dynamic enthalpy based on absolute velocity entering moving row or leaving stationary row

Δh_{dw1} = Dynamic enthalpy based on relative velocity entering moving row

Δh_s = Isentropic static enthalpy drop

Δh = Actual static enthalpy drop

Δh_R = Static enthalpy rise due to reheat = $(1-\eta_s)(\Delta h_s)_{row}$

Similarly Δh_{da2} and Δh_{dw2} for moving row

Fig. 9-8. Carry-over in energy distribution.

as (Δh_1). The static enthalpy rise due to reheat in the stationary row is shown as Δh_{R1}. Now the actual static enthalpy drop in the stationary row is converted into kinetic energy which in addition to the kinetic energy entering the stationary row gives the total magnitude of the kinetic energy leaving the stationary row. The sum of these two kinetic energies expressed in Btu is the dynamic enthalpy of the fluid leaving the stationary row, or

$$\frac{V_0^2}{2gJ} + \Delta h_1 = \Delta h_{da0} + h_1 = \Delta h_{da1}$$

Now if the velocity of the fluid leaving the stationary row is looked at from a vantage point on the moving blades, it appears as a relative velocity. In other words the approach velocity or carry-over velocity to the moving blades is the relative velocity and not the absolute velocity. This has been taken into account heretofore, perhaps unnoticed, by means of drawing the entrance velocity diagram. The Btu equivalent of this relative kinetic energy is indicated as Δh_{dw1} on the diagram.

Since this is a reaction stage, a static enthalpy drop occurs in the moving blades with an increase in the relative velocity. The total magnitude of the relative kinetic energy leaving the moving row is

$$\Delta h_2 + \Delta h_{dw1} = \Delta h_{dw2}$$

However, when the exit velocity triangle is drawn, it is found that the absolute velocity is considerably lower in magnitude than the relative velocity leaving the moving row. The Btu equivalent of the absolute kinetic energy leaving is shown as Δh_{da2}. If additional stages had been illustrated, the next row would be stationary and Δh_{da2} would be the Btu equivalent of the carry-over kinetic energy. Then it would be handled in the same way as Δh_{da0}.

If the dynamic pressure increase corresponding to Δh_{da2} is added to the static pressure P_2, the result is the stagnation pressure P_2° leaving the stage.

It is clear that if another stage is to follow the one illustrated Δh_{da2} does not represent a loss as far as the turbine is concerned since it is available to do work in the next stage. However, if the stage illustrated represents the very last stage, then Δh_{da2} must be regarded as a complete loss. The kinetic energy in the fluid leaving the last stage as manifested by the absolute velocity is termed the "leaving loss." The ratio of this loss to the turbine isentropic enthalpy drop is called the "per cent leaving loss," or

$$\% \text{ leaving loss} = 100 \cdot \frac{\Delta h_{da2}}{(\Delta h_S)_{\text{turbine}}}$$

Every attempt is made to reduce the leaving loss by means of increasing the annular area available for flow in the last stage and decreasing the exit angle γ. It would appear that the use of diffusion after the last stage could provide a means of recovering some of the leaving loss in the form of a vacuum or increased vacuum. This would increase the turbine output considerably in view of the increased expansion ratio. Although this method would be beneficial from an efficiency standpoint, the greater length, weight, bulk, and initial cost make it impractical for most applications.

IMPULSE TURBINE FLOW PASSAGES

9-5. Impulse Blade Profiles. Since no pressure drop occurs in impulse blade passages the purpose of the blades is to give the flow the maximum deflection consistent with high efficiency. Losses due to friction, turbulence, and shock must be kept to a minimum. The impulse blade profiles considered in this section are regarded as being constant along the entire length of blade. Therefore the velocity diagram for the mean blade height is assumed to be appropriate in determining the blade angles at all sections along the blade. However, it must be remembered that the velocity diagrams establish the fluid angles and not the geometric angles of the blades. The relationship between fluid angles obtained from the velocity diagrams to the geometric angles of the blades will be discussed in a later section. Figure 9-9b shows a type of impulse blade profile known as the plate blade which is rarely used at present. It is observed that the fluid streamlines are unable to follow the convex surface of the blade, resulting in flow separation with its attendant

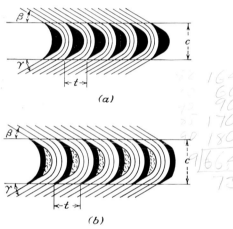

Fig. 9-9. Impulse blade profiles.

loss. To avoid such severe local deflections of the fluid, it is customary to fill out the blade profile as shown in Fig. 9-9a. The increased efficiency of the blading is usually sufficient to make such a change profitable.

Figure 9-10 illustrates typical parallel section impulse blades preceded by a row of foil nozzles.

9-6. Blade Pitch and Width. Two factors must be considered in determining the number of impulse blades which can be placed on a given disc. It is obvious that an excessive number of blades is bound to increase the loss due to friction. Yet if the blades are too few, they will fail to give clear definition to the flow, permitting the fluid to pass through without full deflection. Again the efficiency is decreased since the energy transfer to the rotor is dependent on the magnitude of the fluid deflection.

An examination of Fig. 9-9a shows clearly that in determining the number of blades which can be accommodated on a given disc consideration must be given to the thickness and width of the blade profile. It is difficult to establish a rational relationship among all these factors so that the optimum number of blades or pitch is a matter of empirical determination. Experience indicates that the optimum blade pitch is obtained when the ratio of blade pitch to width, t/c, is kept between 0.5 and 0.6.

Blade width c is determined largely on the basis of stress considerations, although wider blades are in some measure more efficient than narrow ones. However, it is desirable to keep the blade as narrow as possible in order to reduce the over-all length of the rotor.

Fig. 9-10. Typical impulse blades preceded by foil nozzles. (*Courtesy of General Electric Company.*)

The relationship between blade width and stress is discussed in Chap. 10. In general, it may be stated that the blade width is some function of blade height and the magnitude of the fluid velocity entering the blade passage. Therefore in pressure-staged turbines the blade width increases toward the low-pressure end with increasing blade height. However, in a Curtis stage the blade width decreases because of the decrease in fluid velocity. In a large pressure-staged impulse turbine the blade widths range from $\frac{3}{4}$ to 2 in. at the high-pressure end up to about 6 in. at the lower-pressure end. Small and intermediate turbines consisting of two-row Curtis stages may have blading of constant width ranging from $\frac{5}{8}$ to 1 in. Larger turbines composed of two-row Curtis stages may have blade widths ranging from $1\frac{1}{2}$ to 3 in. for the first moving row, $1\frac{1}{4}$ to $2\frac{1}{2}$ in. for the fixed blades, and $1\frac{1}{2}$ to $2\frac{1}{2}$ in. for the second moving row.

9-7. Blade Height. Blade height is a function of the total annular area required to pass the flow of fluid without a pressure drop. The annular area is in turn a function of mass rate of flow, specific volume, and velocity ratio. In computing the net annular area available for flow, account must be taken of the edge thickness of the blades and the blade angles. From Fig. 9-11 it can be seen readily that the area available for flow at exit of one nozzle passage is approximately

$$A = oh_n \qquad (9\text{-}23)$$

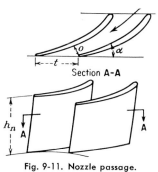

Section A-A

where A = area available for flow at exit of nozzle, sq in.

o = width of flow passage at exit at mean nozzle height, in.

h_n = nozzle height, in.

Then $\qquad A = (t \sin \alpha - m)h_n$

Fig. 9-11. Nozzle passage.

where t = nozzle pitch at mean nozzle height, in.

m = edge thickness of nozzle, in.

α = nozzle angle, degrees

Denoting an edge thickness factor for the nozzle as

$$k_{tn} = \frac{t \sin \alpha - m}{t \sin \alpha}$$

where k_{tn} = edge thickness factor for nozzle. Then

$$A = k_{tn}h_n t \sin \alpha$$

Assuming full peripheral admission, i.e., the nozzle diaphragm is completely occupied by nozzles, the number of nozzles is

$$z = \frac{\pi d_m}{t}$$

where z = number of nozzles

d_m = diameter of the mean nozzle ring, in.

Then the total nozzle area is

$$A_n = \pi d_m h_n k_{tn} \sin \alpha$$

Similarly it can be shown that the area available for flow at the entrance to the blades is

$$A_b = \pi d_m h_b k_{tb} \sin \beta$$

From the continuity equation it follows that

$$Gv = AV = V_1 \pi d_m h_n k_{tn} \sin \alpha = W_1 \pi d_m h_t k_{tb} \sin \beta$$

For all practical purposes it can be assumed that $k_{tn} = k_{tb}$ so that

$$\frac{h_b}{h_n} = \frac{V_1 \sin \alpha}{W_1 \sin \beta} = \frac{V_{1a}}{W_{1a}} = 1 \qquad (9\text{-}24)$$

since $V_{1a} = W_{1a}$ always.

By similar reasoning it can be shown that for a two-row Curtis stage as illustrated in Fig. 9-12,

$$h_{b2} = h_n \frac{V_{1a}}{V_{2a}} \qquad (9\text{-}25)$$

$$h_{b4} = h_n \frac{V_{1a}}{V_{3a}} \qquad (9\text{-}26)$$

$$h_{b6} = h_n \frac{V_{1a}}{V_{4a}} \qquad (9\text{-}27)$$

Although Eq. (9-24) indicates that the blade height at entrance is equal to the nozzle height at exit, it is customary to increase the blade entrance height slightly. This is done in order to avoid spilling the fluid issuing

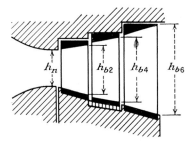

Fig. 9-12. Two-row Curtis stage.

from the nozzle passages. This increase in the blade entrance height is called the step-up or overlap and is apportioned equally at root and tip of the blade. The amount of step-up taken is purely arbitrary and varies from $\frac{1}{16}$ in. in high-pressure stages to $\frac{3}{4}$ in. in the low-pressure stages of large turbines. A step-up is applied to the entrance height of all fixed and moving blades in Curtis stages.

Equations (9-25) to (9-27) do not take into consideration the increase in specific volume of the fluid in the blade passages due to reheat. However, there is serious doubt that the reheat influences the specific volume of the fluid while the fluid is still in the blade passages. Therefore it is usual to neglect any slight increase in specific volume which might occur.

If round or conical nozzles are used, the entrance height of the following row of moving blades is equal to the nozzle exit diameter plus the overlap. It is evident that the area available for flow in a bladed annulus is greater than if the same annulus were occupied by round or conical nozzles. Compare the nozzle blocks shown in Fig. 9-13. Now the blade exit height cannot be determined from Eqs. (9-25) to (9-27) since this would result in increasing the exit height considerably more than is needed. Therefore a straight-tipped blade is used with entrance and exit heights equal. The flow area of the blades at exit can be brought more nearly in line with the nozzle exit area by depressing the blade exit angle. This procedure is of course at the same time beneficial in increasing the exit whirl with a consequent improvement in efficiency.

When full peripheral admission is maintained in high-pressure turbines, since the specific volume is extremely small in the high-pressure end, the diameter of each nozzle will be of necessity very small. Experience and experiment have shown that small-diameter nozzles are much less efficient than those of larger diameter. Furthermore, the blades following the nozzles are very short with the result that the root and tip profile disfigurations become too significant in their effect on the flow in the blade passages. As a consequence marked turbulence ensues with a decrease in

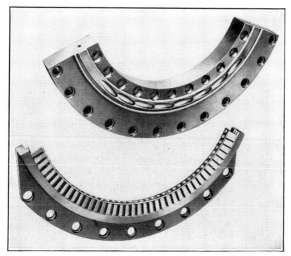

Fig. 9-13. Conical and foil nozzle blocks.

blade efficiency. Although blades as short as $\frac{3}{8}$ in. are used, it is advisable to establish a minimum height of $\frac{3}{4}$ in. in view of the foregoing considerations.

If a minimum height of $\frac{3}{4}$ in. is established for the blades, then the nozzle height at exit cannot be much less than $\frac{3}{4}$ in. Consequently partial admission must be adopted. That is, the annulus defined by the nozzle exit height is not completely occupied by nozzles. With partial admission, the discharge from a single nozzle flows through an arc on the blading annulus equal to the nozzle pitch.

It is clear that with partial admission a given blade passage will not receive flow from the nozzles at all times. The alternating exposure to high velocity flow subjects the blade to vibrations which may become destructive in long blades. This condition of course imposes a limit to the height of the blades.

The maximum blade height is fixed also by stress considerations.

These stresses are largely due to bending and centrifugal forces and are discussed in Chap. 10. It appears that the maximum height which can be used with straight parallel impulse blading is about 20 per cent of the mean blade ring diameter. Where it is necessary to exceed this ratio because of flow requirements, the blades may be tapered or twisted, thereby reducing both the bending and centrifugal stresses. With these modifications the blade height may approach about 30 per cent of the mean blade ring diameter under extremely favorable conditions.

Instead of tapering or twisting the blades, it is possible to increase the flow area through the blade passages by increasing the blade entrance and exit angles. As a consequence the nozzle angle α must also be increased. This modification results in lower efficiency since the whirl is decreased. An economic study must be made of the decreased efficiency vs. the higher cost of warped or twisted blades. The following limiting values for the blade and nozzle angles appear to give generally satisfactory results for last stage buckets:

$$\alpha = 25° \text{ to } 30°$$
$$\beta = 40° \text{ to } 45°$$
$$\gamma = 35° \text{ to } 40°$$

Another solution lies in the possibility of decreasing the rotational speed of the turbine. The mean blade speed is given by

$$U_m = \frac{\pi D_m N}{60} \qquad \text{where } N = \text{rotational speed, rpm}$$

and

$$D_m = \frac{U_m \times 60}{\pi N}$$

From this relationship it can be seen that decreasing the rotational speed for a given value of U_m increases D_m. Now the maximum blade height permitted is a direct function of D_m. Therefore if a 3600-rpm turbine is decreased to 1800 rpm, the permissible blade height is doubled for a fixed value of U. Also the area of the flow annulus is given by

$$A = \pi D_m h_b \tag{9-28}$$

From the previous example where h_b and D_m are doubled the annular area is quadrupled.

Although the foregoing consideration offers a real solution to the problem of maximum blade height, it is clear that the over-all radial dimensions of the turbine have been increased. Usually the additional weight and bulk brought about by lowering the rotational speed of large turbines are too costly to justify this approach to the problem. Furthermore, if the same annular area is to be maintained from Eq. (9-28), it is evident that the blade height of an 1800-rpm turbine is reduced to a fourth of its height in a 3600-rpm turbine. The difficulties encountered by this reduction of blade height in the high-pressure stages of high-pressure and high-temperature turbines pose another difficult problem to be solved.

If none of the solutions discussed is possible or if those possible are exploited to the fullest extent, the only choice remaining is to divide the flow in the low-pressure end of the turbine and to supply it to two low-pressure turbines. The longest blade in use at present on a 3600-rpm rotor is a 25-in. reaction steam-turbine blade on a 50-in. spindle. The tip speed of this blade is almost 1100 mph.

9-8. Blade Entrance and Exit Angles. It was stated previously that the angles β and γ of the velocity diagram represent the fluid angles and not the blade angles. Consider first the blade entrance angle, which will

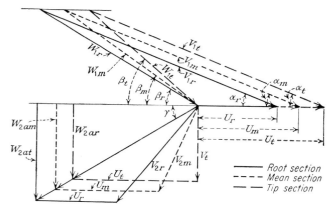

Fig. 9-14. Velocity diagrams at root, mean, and tip sections—Parallel impulse blades.

be designated as β' to distinguish it from the fluid angle β. If the flow entering a blade passage were absolutely uniform and the linear velocity of the blade U were constant at all sections along the blade, then making $\beta' = \beta$ would provide shockless and nonturbulent entrance. Now of course β is determined from the average velocity entering the blade passage, and the linear velocity of the blade increases radially. If the direction and magnitude of the absolute velocity entering the blade passage and the exit angle γ are considered fixed, Fig. 9-14 reveals the variations which take place in β at the root, mean, and tip sections of the blade. If β' is made equal to β_m, it is evident that the entering flow will strike the back of the blade at the tip section. This is an undesirable condition because a retarding force is exerted on the blade in addition to the losses incurred by turbulence due to the sharp impact of the fluid on the blade. At the root section the flow entrance angle is less than β' so that the entering fluid does not strike the back of the blade. Furthermore, the impact of the fluid on the blade is less sharp and a smaller loss due to turbulence is incurred. With these considerations in mind it is preferable that $\beta' > \beta$ at nearly all sections of the blade. If the blade is not too long, it is generally satisfactory to make $\beta' = \beta_t$.

A similar situation occurs if the speed of the turbine changes with constant mass rate of flow. If the speed is increased, then the velocity diagram drawn for the larger value of U will, when compared with the original velocity diagram, resemble the comparison between the tip- and mean-section velocity diagrams of Fig. 9-14. Therefore the flow will strike the backs of the blades with consequent loss. This condition is referred to as overspeeding. If, however, the speed of the turbine is decreased, a condition known as underspeeding, the comparison of the the new and original velocity diagrams is similar to a comparison of the root- and mean-section velocity diagrams of Fig. 9-14. It will be recalled that this latter situation is less severe than the condition of overspeeding. Therefore for a variable-speed turbine it is desirable that β' be made greater than or at least equal to the largest value of β expected so as to avoid the more severe condition of the flow striking the backs of the blades.

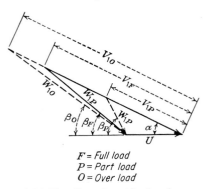

F = Full load
P = Part load
O = Over load

Fig. 9-15. The effect of part load and over-load on entrance velocity triangle at constant speed.

Another source of loss is incurred whenever the ratio $V_1/U = \nu$ changes, but little can be done about this except to design for the optimum value of ν for the conditions expected to be encountered in service. This is an important consideration in turbines intended for marine applications.

A deviation between β and β' can also exist in a constant-speed turbine operating at part load or overload. Load variation is normally accomplished by a compensating variation in mass rate of flow. Since the areas of the flow passages of a given turbine must be regarded as a fixed element and if the pressure and temperature of the fluid entering the turbine are unchanged, the specific volume of the fluid is also unchanged. From the continuity equation it is evident that if the flow is decreased the velocity of the fluid must also decrease. Similarly if the mass rate of flow is increased, the velocity increases. Figure 9-15 shows the effect of variation in mass rate of flow on the entrance velocity triangles. At part load $\beta_P > \beta_F$ while at overload $\beta_F > \beta_0$. For a turbine which must operate at part load, it is advisable that β' be made equal to β_P at some part load at which the turbine is likely to operate a great deal of the time. Then for all loads above this part load and including full load the turbine will be operating under a less severe condition analogous to underspeeding.

As for the blade exit angle γ', it is nearly always made equal to the fluid angle γ in impulse stages having small nozzle and blade heights (about $\frac{3}{4}$ in.) and in stages designed for low velocity ratios or partial admission. In other cases some reaction is usually introduced by decreasing γ' so as to reduce the flow area at blade exit. The true criterion is not the extent to which γ' is decreased but the exit flow area as determined by the product of blade height and blade exit opening. The blade height may be set at the minimum required to provide proper cover or overlap for the preceding nozzles. The flow area needed to establish the required static pressure drop across the blade is obtained by reducing the exit opening by means of decreasing γ'. Obtaining the correct flow-passage area is far more important than the exact setting of the angle. Generally no more than 5 to 10 per cent reaction is introduced in impulse blade passages.

The angle γ' is often decreased in single-stage turbines or in the last row of multistaged turbines in order to reduce the leaving loss. This is accomplished without a pressure drop in the blade passages by increasing the blade exit height a sufficient amount to offset the decrease in the blade opening caused by decreasing γ'. Obviously, decreasing γ' increases the whirl with an attendant increase in efficiency. However, the blade exit height cannot be increased much over the entrance height without the fluid losing contact with the blades near the tip. This limitation in turn places a restriction on the amount γ' may be reduced. A further limitation is imposed by the fact that losses in the blade passages due to the extreme fluid deflection angle may offset the gain resulting from an increased whirl.

9-9. Angle of Efflux. Experiment indicates that the actual angle of the fluid leaving a turbine blade will differ somewhat from the blade exit angle γ'. The difference between the two angles, $\gamma - \gamma'$, is referred to as the deviation angle and is always positive. This is an important consideration, since under some circumstances a substantially lower deflection of the fluid than anticipated can occur with a corresponding decrease in work output.

No theoretical relationships have been developed which will predict with a reasonable degree of accuracy the extent of deviation. However, the results of experiments in both this country and abroad show that Mach number, Reynolds number, and opening coefficient are important parameters. Above Re = 100,000 there is very little variation in deviation angle with Re. Since nearly all turbine stages are designed with Re in excess of 100,000, the Mach number becomes the sole parameter for a given blade configuration. The effect of the blade configuration on efflux angle has long been recognized in terms of an empirical relationship between γ and the blade opening coefficient o/t expressed as follows:

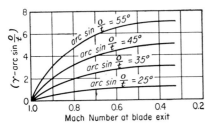

Fig. 9-16. Deviation of efflux angle from arcsin o/t for different values of M and o/t.

$$\gamma = \arcsin \frac{o}{t} \qquad (9\text{-}29)$$

This relationship is fairly accurate for most turbine blading when the Mach number at blade exit is near unity. However, at low Mach numbers and large values of γ', Eq. (9-29) is in considerable error. Figure 9-16 shows a plot of the deviation of the true efflux angle from that calculated by means of Eq. (9-29) for various values of Mach number and opening coefficient. These curves represent a summary of both published and unpublished data for conventional turbine blades. It will be noticed that at $M = 1$ the deviation is zero and therefore Eq. (9-29) applies exactly. However, the deviation becomes very pronounced at low Mach numbers, the more severe deviation being obtained with large

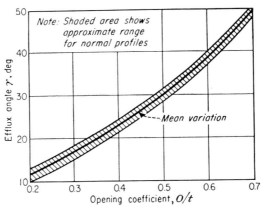

Fig. 9-17. Variation of efflux angle and opening coefficient. (*Courtesy of Allis-Chalmers Manufacturing Company.*)

values of the blade exit angle. This latter observation seems quite reasonable in view of the obvious fact that with a wider opening at exit or a larger pitch the blades are less capable of influencing flow directions.

Figure 9-17 shows the efflux angle plotted against the opening coefficient for common turbine blades within the usual range of Mach numbers encountered in practice. The curves of Fig. 9-17 should be used in preference to Eq. (9-29) since they take into account the deviation of the efflux angle from that given by arcsin o/t.

Stationary nozzles experience a deviation of efflux angle from the geometric nozzle angle γ' similar to that occurring with moving blades. For foil nozzles the relationships of Fig. 9-17 are appropriate. Similar curves for round or conical nozzles are not available. However, it is interesting to examine qualitatively some aspects of the deviation of flow direction from that given by the geometric exit angle of round nozzles.

From the geometry of the round nozzle and its setting it is evident that the outlet must be oblique, giving an oval-shaped exit passage. It has been seen that if the exit pressure is equal to or higher than the

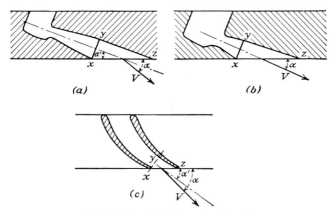

Fig. 9-18. Flow deflections at nozzle exit.

critical pressure the flow will leave the nozzle at the geometric angle γ'. However, if the exit pressure is less than critical, some expansion occurs in the zone defined by xyz of Fig. 9-18c, with the result that the issuing jet is deflected.

For a converging-diverging nozzle of the type shown in Fig. 9-18a, the correct exit area of the nozzle is at xy, the side yz being parallel to the nozzle axis. As long as the nozzle operates between the correct pressures, the efflux angle will equal the geometric angle α'. However, if the exit pressure is lower than the design value, expansion will take place in the zone xyz with deflection of the flow toward x. Figure 9-18b illustrates a nozzle in which yz is divergent and expansion takes place in the xyz zone even at design pressures. The result again is flow deflection but occurring this time under all conditions of flow.

9-10. Geometry of Impulse Blade Profiles. Impulse blade profiles are usually standardized by the manufacturer of turbines. However, Fig. 9-19 illustrates a type of profile layout often used for symmetrical impulse blades.   It will be noticed that the centers of curvature of the convex and concave sides of adjacent blades are coincident and therefore the passage width is constant.   The centers of curvature are indicated as o and o'.   Since $\beta' = \gamma'$,

$$C = ab + bd = 2r \cos \beta'$$

from which

$$r = \frac{c}{2 \cos \beta'} \qquad (9\text{-}30)$$

The other radius of curvature r' is governed by the blade pitch and the need to maintain a constant width in the passage.

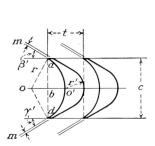

Fig. 9-19. Symmetrical impulse blade profile.

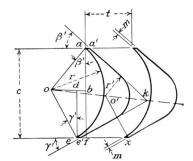

Fig. 9-20. Unsymmetrical impulse blade profile.

Figure 9-20 illustrates a type of unsymmetrical impulse blade profile. The radius of curvature is

$$r = \frac{c}{\cos \beta' + \cos \gamma'} \qquad (9\text{-}31)$$

The distance $db = r(\sin \beta - \sin \gamma')$.   Starting with point e and calculating r, the center o is easily located.   The point k locates the intersection of the lines forming the straight portion of the back of the blade.   The intersection of the perpendicular at x with ok locates the center of curvature for the back of the blade.

9-11. Losses in Impulse Blade Passages.   In Chap. 8 blade losses were taken into account by the use of a blade friction factor k_b.   Although this factor was expressed as the ratio of relative velocity leaving the blades to relative velocity entering, its magnitude is not a function of velocity in most turbine designs.   At subsonic velocities the Reynolds number is an important criterion of passage losses.   However, when the Reynolds number is in excess of 100,000, there is virtually no variation in passage efficiency with Reynolds number.   Since nearly all turbine stages are designed with Re > 100,000, it is clear that neither kinematic viscosities nor velocity changes can have much effect on the passage efficiency.

Those factors which contribute to loss in turbine passages are summarized as follows.

1. Sharp deflection of the fluid within the passage, the resulting centrifugal force causing compression near the concave surfaces and a corresponding rarefaction near the convex surfaces resulting in boundary-layer separation.

2. Deviation of blade entrance angle from the relative angle at which the fluid approaches the blade with turbulence as a consequence.

3. Narrow blades, since for given values of β and γ the curvature of the concave surface of the blades is more severe.

4. Turbulence at the outlet of the preceding row of nozzles caused by the finite thickness of the nozzle exit edges. This turbulence is usually in the form of trailing vortices which seem to disappear at high velocities. The consequence of this source of loss is a reduction of the kinetic energy delivered to the blades.

Because of the many imponderables involved in determining the magnitude of losses in turbine flow passages it is impossible to develop rational relationships which are satisfactory for design purposes. Therefore in developing design relationships it is necessary to select those factors which seem to influence the performance of the turbine so that a satisfactory correlation can be developed between predicted and test results. In general, quite satisfactory correlation has been obtained by assuming that the losses are functions of blade shape, angle of incidence, deflection angle, and the ratio of the relative velocity entering the blade passage to the relative velocity leaving the preceding row.

An interpretation and evaluation of extensive test results in comparison with design computations yield three significant coefficients. The coefficients are:

k_p = profile loss coefficient. This coefficient accounts for the losses attendant to turbulence, friction, fluid deflection within the passage, curvature of blade profile, and deviation of efflux angle from blade exit angle.

k_i = incidence loss coefficient. This coefficient accounts for losses due to turbulence introduced by the angle of incidence.

k_{co} = carry-over loss coefficient. This coefficient accounts for the loss of kinetic energy while in transit between rows.

For a row of impulse blades with no static pressure drop occurring in the passages, the relative velocity leaving the row is

$$W_2 = k_{co}k_pk_iW_1 \qquad (9\text{-}32)$$

where W_1 is equal to the relative velocity entering the row of blades. The product of k_{co}, k_p, and k_i is analogous to the factor k_b utilized for convenience in Chap. 8.

For a stationary row of nozzles in which the approach velocity is not neglected, the absolute velocity leaving the nozzle is given as

$$V_1 = k_p \sqrt{2gJ \Delta h_s + (k_i k_{co} V_0)^2} \qquad (9\text{-}33a)$$

or

$$V_1 = 223.7 k_p \sqrt{\Delta h_s + \frac{(k_i k_{co} V_0)^2}{2gJ}} \qquad (9\text{-}33b)$$

where V_0 is the approach velocity. If the approach velocity is negligible, Eq. (9-33b) reduces to

$$V_1 = 223.7 k_p \sqrt{\Delta h_s}$$

From this equation it is seen that k_p is similar to the velocity coefficient used in conjunction with nozzles in Chap. 7.

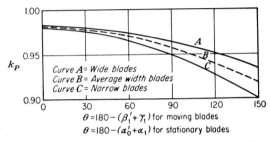

Fig. 9-21. Profile loss coefficient for blades and nozzle foils.

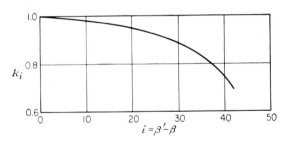

Fig. 9-22. Incidence loss coefficient for standard impulse blades.

Figure 9-21 gives values of the profile loss coefficient for turbine blades and nozzle foils as a function of profile width c and the deflection angle θ based on the geometric entrance angle and the efflux angle.

Figure 9-22 plots values of the incidence loss coefficient against i, the angle of incidence, for standard impulse blades with sharp entrances edges and of the type shown in Fig. 9-24.

Figure 9-23 plots values of the incidence loss coefficient for nozzle foils and blades with blunt entrance edges similar to the entrance edges of the foil nozzles shown in Fig. 9-24.

It is almost impossible to obtain correlation of the carry-over loss coefficient with any of the parameters related to the other loss coefficients.

The carry-over loss coefficient can vary from almost zero for the carry-over from the moving blades to a partial-admission row of nozzles, or if the rows are far apart axially, and may approach unity for reaction blading and nozzles. The carry-over loss coefficient seems to improve with taller

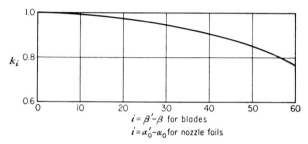

Fig. 9-23. Incidence loss coefficient for blunt-nosed blades and nozzle foils.

blades. As a first approximation it is usual to neglect the carry-over velocity to a partial-admission row of nozzles or when a row of blades is widely separated axially from the following row of nozzles. For other

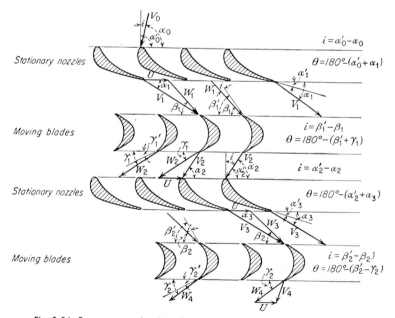

Fig. 9-24. Pressure-staged turbine showing orientation of angles and velocities.

situations k_{co} is assumed to be equal to the value of k_p for the row receiving the carry-over velocity.

The values of the loss coefficients given in Figs. 9-21 to 9-23 apply to superheated or wet steam and gases as far as calculations relating to conditions internal to a stage are concerned.   If wet steam is used as the fluid, then the stage efficiency is reduced 1 per cent for each per cent of moisture, the moisture percentage being taken as the average of the moisture contents at stage inlet and outlet.

REACTION TURBINE FLOW PASSAGES

9-12. Reaction Blade Profiles. The conventional reaction blade profile is the product of evolution brought about by experiment and the accumulation of test data over the years.   Therefore there is no rational method for laying out the profile of such conventional reaction blades. However, a few observations are of some value.

The earliest reaction blades had a pronounced sharp hook at entrance not unlike the conventional impulse blade profile.   With the knowledge that the relative entering angle of the fluid changes with load the hook-shaped blade gave way to a blade with a well-rounded or blunt entrance edge.   The modern reaction blade profile resembles an airfoil and in some instances may be adapted from an actual base airfoil, particularly in gas turbines.   Airfoil blading is discussed in some detail under Flow Passages with Radial Equilibrium.

(a)   *(b)*   *(c)*

Fig. 9-25. Conventional reaction blade profiles.

The profiles of conventional reaction blades are fairly well standardized within a particular organization, and vary slightly among different organizations.   However, all reaction blade profiles have some distinguishing characteristics.   The concave side is very nearly of constant radius, while the convex side is usually formed by faired circles in a shape that provides a passage which is always converging.   It is of particular importance that the passage never becomes divergent in order to avoid losses which accompany a diverging passage.   Normally, supersonic velocities are avoided in the flow passages, but occasionally it is necessary to introduce them in order to reduce the over-all length of the turbine and to use them where high rotational speeds are acceptable.   In such cases if the actual velocity leaving the passage does not exceed the sonic velocity by more than 20 to 30 per cent, the convergent passage may be retained with only a slight drop in efficiency.   If it is necessary to exceed these limits, then more stages must be employed.

Figure 9-25 illustrates three types of conventional reaction blade profiles.   Figure 9-25a shows the old type of profile, now obsolete, with its sharp-edged entrance.   Figure 9-25b illustrates a typical profile used when very little variation in the relative entrance angle of the fluid is expected.   If the load variations are such that a considerable change in the fluid relative entrance angle is expected, then a profile resembling that of Fig. 9-25c will involve less severe losses.

The curvature of conventional reaction blades is concentrated near the entrance of the blade. The curvature decreases until the back of the blade is practically straight before the exit edge is reached. The exit edges are made as thin as possible, consistent with strength requirements, in order to reduce trailing vortices to a minimum.

9-13. Blade Angles, Gauging, and Pitch. The entrance angle of conventional reaction blades is not clear from an examination of the profile but appears to vary from 80° to 90°. The blade entrance angle is usually made from 3° to 15° larger than the relative entrance angle of the fluid as obtained from the velocity diagram. How much $\beta' > \beta$ depends on the length of the blade and the load variations expected.

The blade exit angle may vary from 14.5° in the higher-pressure stages to a maximum of 37° in the last row of large condensing steam turbines. Normally, the blade exit angle is not expressed in degrees but in terms of gauging. The term gauging has the same significance as the opening coefficient. From Eq. (9-29),

$$\sin \gamma = \frac{o}{t} = \text{gauging}$$

Gauging is usually expressed as a percentage. Therefore for $\gamma = 14.5°$ the corresponding gauging is 25 per cent; 60 per cent gauging means that $\gamma = 37°$ approximately.

The term gauging comes from the former practice of twisting light-section blades by force to adjust the exit angle. A gauge template was used to obtain the desired opening between blades. By this method it was possible to keep several rows of blades at constant height, any required increase in exit flow area being obtained by adjusting the exit angle.

Current practice calls for machining the angle into the blade assembly. Occasionally, the blade assembly is cast by precision casting or lost-wax methods. The blade heights are increased from row to row even to the extent of putting the blades on a conical drum when necessary.

The determination of reaction blade pitch is a matter for experiment. In general, the pitch is given in terms of blade width. For a blade similar to that of Fig. 9-25b, the ratio of pitch to width t/c is usually taken to be about 0.85. Similarly for a section like that of Fig. 9-25c, $t/c = 1.125$ approximately. A more fundamental view of blade pitch is given under Flow Passages with Radial Equilibrium.

9-14. Blade Width and Height. The statements made in Sec. 9-6 relative to the width of impulse blades apply also to reaction blades. Since the blade entrance angle of reaction blading cannot be clearly defined, as pointed out in the previous section, it is necessary to determine the blade setting in terms of the gauging. Then the area for flow in a reaction stage may be given by the general expression

$$A = \lambda \pi d_m h_b$$

where A = annular area available for flow in reaction stage, sq in.

λ = gauging expressed as a decimal

h_b = blade height, in.

d_m = mean blade ring diameter, in.

Writing the equation of continuity for the stationary row of blades,

$$G = \frac{A V_1}{v} = \frac{\lambda \pi d_m h_{bs} V_1}{144 v_1}$$

Solving for h_{bs}, the stationary blade height, expressed in inches, is

$$h_{bs} = \frac{144 G v_1}{\lambda \pi d_m V_1} \tag{9-34}$$

Similarly, it can be shown that h_{bm}, the moving blade height expressed in inches, is

$$h_{bm} = \frac{144 G v_2}{\lambda \pi d_m W_2}$$

For a symmetrical stage, h_{bm} may be expressed as a function of v and U, since $V_1 = W_2$,

$$h_{bm} = \frac{144 G v_2 v}{\lambda \pi d_m U} \tag{9-35}$$

The minimum height for reaction blading should not be less than 5 per cent of the mean blade ring diameter. The maximum height should not exceed 20 per cent of the mean blade ring diameter, unless the blade is tapered, in which case as much as 30 per cent is permissible. The minimum limit of blade height is imposed because of increased energy losses with short blades while the maximum limit is dictated solely by stress considerations.

The usual arrangement of reaction stages in gas turbines and in high-pressure topping steam turbines is to allow the blade height to increase in order to provide increasing annular area for the expanding flow. The drum diameter may be kept constant if the increase in specific volume of the fluid is not so great as to require an appreciable increase in blade height. Then the assumption of constant mean blade ring diameter is reasonably accurate. If constant mean blade ring diameter is to be strictly maintained, then the drum diameter may be decreased with increasing blade height. Figure 9-26b shows an arrangement with constant drum diameter and slight increase in blade height.

In large condensing steam turbines, the drum diameter and blade heights increase with expanding flow. This arrangement permits increasing the annular area without excessive blade height where the increase in specific volume is great. With this arrangement, illustrated in Fig. 9-26a, the concept of constant mean blade ring diameter must be abandoned.

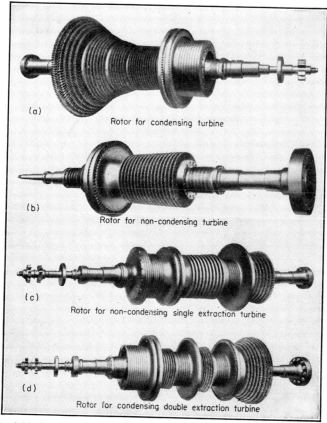

(a)

Rotor for condensing turbine

(b)

Rotor for non-condensing turbine

(c)

Rotor for non-condensing single extraction turbine

(d)

Rotor for condensing double extraction turbine

Fig. 9-26. Rotor arrangements. (*Courtesy of Westinghouse Electric Corporation.*)

Figures 9-26c and d show another possible arrangement where the reaction stages are grouped. This arrangement offers the advantage of designing groups of stages for nearly constant mean blade ring diameter.

Sometimes the specific volume of steam becomes too great at the low-pressure end of a turbine to be handled by any of the previously mentioned arrangements. The solution lies in dividing the flow near the low-pressure end and sending it through two identical stage groups arranged as shown in Fig. 1-11.

9-15. Losses in Reaction Blade Passages. The coefficients discussed in Sec. 9-10 in connection with impulse blades are applicable to reaction blades as well. The values of the coefficients given in Figs. 9-17, 9-21, and 9-23 are also applicable to reaction blades. For a stationary row of reaction blades (nozzles), Eqs. (9-33a) or (9-33b) apply. For a moving row of reaction blades, since they also form nozzles, Eq. (9-33a) may be expressed:

$$W_2 = k_p \sqrt{2gJ \; \Delta h_s + (k_i k_{co} W_1)^2} \qquad (9\text{-}36)$$

FLOW PASSAGES WITH RADIAL EQUILIBRIUM

9-16. Free Vortex. The material presented thus far has been restricted to a representative section on a turbine blade taken at the mean blade height. The linear velocity of the blade was considered to be constant for this representative section and by extension it was also taken as constant for comparatively short blades. However, it is apparent that the linear velocity of points on the blade varies directly as the radial distance from the center of rotation and for long blades the variation is considerable from root to tip. It follows that the velocity diagrams vary from root to tip also, and as a consequence, if parallel blading is retained, losses will occur from turbulence. Such a variation of the velocity diagram for an impulse blade is shown in Fig. 9-14. An examination of Fig. 9-28 indicates also that the assumption of constant ΔV_U radially is in considerable error. It is clear that one-dimensional steamline flow cannot be maintained as long as the foregoing conditions are imposed.

If a given particle of fluid is traced in its path through the turbine, it is observed that since the velocity has whirl and axial components, the path resembles that of a helix of increasing radius. Two-dimensional streamline circulatory flow was discussed in Sec. 6-16. From this the conditions necessary for streamline flow are known. Consider first the condition of free-vortex flow. It will be recalled that for two-dimensional circulatory flow V_a, the axial component of velocity is constant and the vorticity is

$$rV_U = \text{const}$$

If the free-vortex principle is applied to the fluid entering and leaving the blade row, it follows that

$$r \, \Delta V_U = \text{const}$$

Now the energy delivered to the rotor per pound per second of flow is

$$E = \frac{\omega r \, \Delta V_U}{g}$$

which compared with the preceding expression reveals constant energy delivered to the rotor at all radii since ω is constant.

An examination of the derivation of the expression $r\,\Delta V_U = $ constant, given in Sec. 6-16, reveals another relationship. The radial component of fluid velocity decreases from blade root to tip and for the condition of constant stagnation pressure it would be expected that a corresponding decrease in static pressure would occur radially toward the blade root. It would appear also that because of the static pressure difference flow would take place radially toward the blade root. However, the force due to the static pressure difference is balanced by centrifugal force and therefore radial equilibrium is attained.

9-17. Forced Vortex. If the fluid is assumed to obey the forced vortex relationships, it will be recalled from Sec. 6-16 that the fluid will rotate as a solid body, or

$$\frac{V_U}{r} = \omega$$

Now from the Bernoulli equation, since the velocity of the fluid increases radially, the static pressure must decrease radially, instituting radial flow outward. The centrifugal force augments this outward radial flow and theoretically at least radial equilibrium is not obtained. In fact, however, the flow will adjust itself so that radial equilibrium is attained as a result of the turbine boundaries, since the turbine is an axial-flow machine. If the blading is designed in accordance with the forced-vortex principle, a danger exists that the flow angles after radial equilibrium is reached will not match the blade angles and unfavorable angles of incidence may be the result. As a consequence, poorer performance may be expected and under severely adverse conditions even stalling could occur.

It is clear from the foregoing that the establishment of a design based on stable conditions of radial equilibrium is essential, and for this reason a design in accordance with the free-vortex principle is desirable.

9-18. Requirements for Radial Equilibrium. Although the free-vortex principle when coupled with constant axial velocity radially and constant energy transfer radially satisfies the conditions for radial equilibrium, it is interesting to examine other possibilities. If the absolute velocity is resolved into three components in the tangential, axial, and radial directions,

$$V^2 = V_U{}^2 + V_a{}^2 + V_R{}^2$$

Then the stagnation pressure may be written

$$P^\circ = P + \rho\,\frac{V_U{}^2}{2} + \rho\,\frac{V_a{}^2}{2} + \rho\,\frac{V_R{}^2}{2}$$

For conditions of steady flow along concentric streamlines, the velocity, static pressure, and density are constant with time and $dV_R = 0$. Let r equal the radius of any concentric streamline, and then, differentiating with respect to r,

$$\frac{dP^\circ}{dr} = \frac{dP}{dr} + \rho V_U \frac{dV_U}{dr} + \rho V_a \frac{dV_a}{dr}$$

But it was shown in Sec. 6-16 that for plane circulatory flow and for radial equilibrium,

$$\frac{dP}{dr} = \rho \frac{V_U{}^2}{r}$$

which substituted in the preceding equation yields

$$\frac{dP^\circ}{dr} = \rho \frac{V_U{}^2}{r} + \rho V_U \frac{dV_U}{dr} + \rho V_a \frac{dV_a}{dr} \qquad (9\text{-}37)$$

Now the energy transferred to the blades is at the expense of the energy in the fluid and may be expressed in terms of the stagnation enthalpy change dh°. Also the energy given up by the fluid may be expressed dynamically in terms of a change of stagnation pressure, or dP°. The change in density along concentric streamlines is considered to be constant with time as before. Taking suitable account of units, Eq. (9-37) becomes

$$\frac{dh^\circ}{dr} = \frac{1}{gJ} \left(\frac{V_U{}^2}{r} + V_U \frac{dV_U}{dr} + V_a \frac{dV_a}{dr} \right) \qquad (9\text{-}38)$$

Suppose that two variables are assumed such as degree of reaction and axial velocity. For radial equilibrium, dV_U must vary inversely as the radius. From Eq. (9-38) it is evident that the energy transfer to the rotor must also vary. However, it is conceivable that V_a and dh° could vary in such a way as to produce radial equilibrium.

Another possibility is the maintenance of constant specific mass rate of flow G/A, with either radial variation of axial velocity or static pressure. This scheme is occasionally used in the design of aircraft gas turbines, but the complicated relationships make it justifiable only when performance of the turbine is extremely critical.

A common specification is that of constant reaction radially, constant energy transfer to rotor radially, and constant axial velocity radially.

9-19. Velocity Diagrams. Some of the consequences of introducing the requirement of radial equilibrium in turbine flow passages are more easily examined with the aid of the velocity diagrams. For this purpose it is convenient to use the polar type of velocity diagrams shown in Fig. 8-11 and discussed in Sec. 8-11 in connection with impulse turbines.

Figure 9-27a shows a typical velocity diagram for a reaction section of a turbine blade in which the entrance and exit axial velocities are equal. Two velocity vectors V_m and W_m not considered heretofore are introduced. These vectors are known as the mean absolute and mean relative

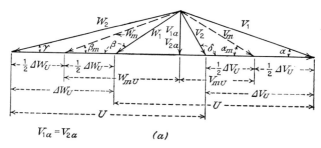

$$V_{1a} = V_{2a} \qquad (a)$$

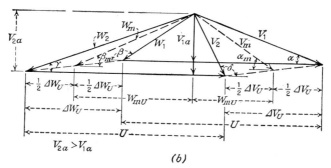

$$V_{2a} > V_{1a}$$

$$(b)$$

Fig. 9-27. Velocity diagrams.

velocity vectors, respectively, and their directions are established as follows:

$$\cot \beta_m = \tfrac{1}{2}(\cot \beta + \cot \gamma)$$
$$\cot \alpha_m = \tfrac{1}{2}(\cot \alpha + \cot \delta)$$

When $V_{1a} = V_{2a}$, the mean velocity vectors can also be defined in terms of the whirl components, or

$$V_{mU} = \tfrac{1}{2}(V_{1U} + V_{2U})$$
$$W_{mU} = \tfrac{1}{2}(W_{1U} + W_{2U})$$

In Fig. 9-27a, V_m is drawn to the mid-point of V_U, and W_m to the mid-point of W_U.

Figure 9-27b shows a velocity diagram for the case where $V_{2a} > V_{1a}$. Now W_m is drawn to the mid-point of the line joining the extremities of W_1 and W_2. V_m is drawn in a similar manner.

Figure 9-28 shows the velocity diagrams at the root, tip, and mid-sections of a turbine blade when the conditions of 50 per cent reaction at mid-section and free-vortex flow are imposed. Some other degree of reaction at the mid-section or zero reaction (pure impulse) at the root section could have been assumed. Entrance and exit axial velocities are made equal although not necessary to the maintenance of radial equilibrium.

From an examination of Fig. 9-28 the following points are clear: α, β, δ, U, W_m, and W_2 increase radially; γ, β_m, V_1, W_1, V_2, and ΔW_U decrease radially. Since β increases and γ decreases radially, it is evident that a twist must be incorporated in the blade in order that the blade angles can accommodate the flow entrance and exit angles without shock or flow

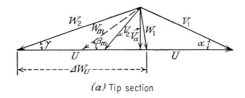

(a) Tip section

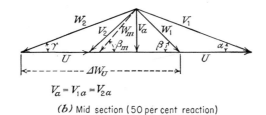

$$V_a = V_{1a} = V_{2a}$$

(b) Mid section (50 per cent reaction)

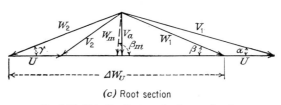

(c) Root section

Fig. 9-28. Velocity diagrams for free-vortex flow.

separation. The severity of the twist can be lessened somewhat by keeping γ constant. Also it is observed that W_2 increases and W_1 decreases radially, which means the degree of reaction must increase radially.

Figure 9-29 illustrates the velocity diagrams for constant reaction of 50 per cent radially, constant entrance and exit axial velocities and $r \Delta W_U$ constant. It will be noted that the principal advantage of this arrangement is that the variation of the angles is much less severe than when the degree of reaction is permitted to increase radially.

The requirement of maintaining radial equilibrium in turbine design removes much of the distinction between impulse and reaction blades.

In effect, blades designed in accordance with these concepts could, in an extreme case, have pure impulse at the root section but with an increasing degree of reaction radially.

The problem of satisfying the conditions for radial equilibrium is not mandatory except from the standpoint of performance. Therefore the free-vortex design is usually employed only in the last stages of large steam turbines or in gas turbines where the performance of the turbine is so essential to good over-all performance of the entire plant.

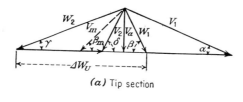

(a) Tip section

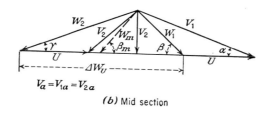

$V_a = V_{1a} = V_{2a}$

(b) Mid section

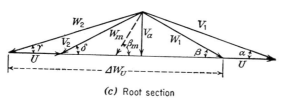

(c) Root section

Fig. 9-29. Velocity diagrams for constant 50 per cent reaction.

9-20. Elements of the Airfoil. The development of the science of gas dynamics has provided a rational approach to turbine blade design. Therefore when high efficiency is sought in the design of turbine flow passages, it is observed that the blade sections resemble airfoils or facsimiles of airfoils. To be sure, some of the conventional reaction blade sections do resemble airfoils but their determination was largely by trial and error rather than by the application of gas dynamic theory. It is well then that some attention be given to gaining a familiarity with the nomenclature and use of airfoil sections in turbine blade design.

Figure 9-30 shows sections of two airfoil blades. The distinction between these two sections lies chiefly in the curvature of the mean

camber line. Figure 9-30a has a parabolic mean camber line and Fig.
9-30b a circular arc mean camber line. The airfoil blade section is
identified by the following elements:

x_1 = camber inlet angle
x_2 = camber outlet angle
θ = camber angle
c = chord
b = maximum thickness of blade expressed as a percentage of
  chord length
l = camber expressed as a percentage of chord length
d = location of camber expressed as a percentage of chord
  length
L.E.Rad. = leading-edge radius of curvature expressed as a percentage
  of chord length

It can be seen readily from the foregoing that the chord length is an
important reference value.

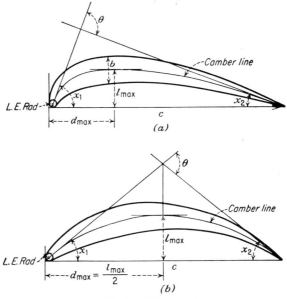

Fig. 9-30. Airfoil blade sections.

An airfoil blade section is built on a curved backbone known as the
mean camber line. The mean camber line may be simply an arc of a
circle, a combination of faired circular arcs, a parabola, or any convenient curve. The blade profile may be then developed from a standard
thickness form such as the Clark Y, Göttingen 398, RAF 0.27, a suitable

section obtained from the NACA technical reports (such as *NACA TR* 460 or *L* 560), or a specially developed thickness form applicable to turbine blades.

Figure 9-31 shows data taken from *NACA TR* 460 for the NACA 0012 airfoil. It may be noticed that this particular thickness form is symmetrical and has no camber. The first digit of the designating number 0012 refers to the maximum camber as a percentage of the chord length, the second digit to the location of the maximum camber in tenths

Station	Upper	Lower
0	0	0
1.25	1.894	− 1.894
2.5	2.615	− 2.615
5	3.555	− 3.555
7	4.200	− 4.200
10	4.683	− 4.683
15	5.345	− 5.345
20	5.738	− 5.738
25	5.941	− 5.941
30	6.002	− 6.002
40	5.803	− 5.803
50	5.294	− 5.294
60	4.563	− 4.563
70	3.664	− 3.664
80	2.623	− 2.623
90	1.448	− 1.448
95	0.807	− 0.807
100	(0.126)	(− 0.126)
100	0	0
L. E. Rad. : 1.58		

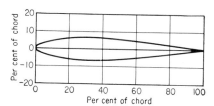

Fig. 9-31. NACA-0012 airfoil.

of the chord length from the leading edge, and the last two digits refer to the maximum thickness as a percentage of the chord length. This checks with the tabulated data and the airfoil profile for NACA 0012 given in Fig. 9-31.

To utilize the data given for an airfoil thickness form, the shape of the mean camber line and the chord length must be first determined by methods discussed in Sec. 9-21. Instead of stations being taken along the chord as shown in Fig. 9-31, they are taken along the mean camber line. The points establishing the upper and lower profile are taken normal to the mean camber line. Smooth curves drawn through these points and faired to the leading-edge curve establish the blade profile.

9-21. Single Airfoil Principle. Figure 9-32 shows the forces which act on a section of airfoil blade. The lift may be found from Eq. (6-84), substituting W_m for V_∞,

$$dL = C_L\rho \frac{W_m^2}{2} c \, dr \qquad (9\text{-}39)$$

From Eq. (6-85),

$$dD = C_D\rho \frac{W_m^2}{2} c \, dr \qquad (9\text{-}40)$$

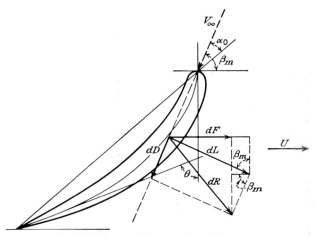

Fig. 9-32. Forces acting on turbine airfoil blade.

Since dL is perpendicular to W_m and dD is in the same direction as W_m, the force acting in the direction of blade rotation is

$$dF_U = dL \sin \beta_m - dD \cos \beta_m$$

or

$$dF_U = dL \sin \beta_m \left(1 - \frac{dD}{dL} \cot \beta_m\right)$$

As pointed out in Sec. 6-17, dD/dL is negligible and therefore the term $(dD/dL) \cot \beta_m$ may be omitted. Hence

$$dF_U = DL \sin \beta_m$$

Substituting for dL its equivalent from Eq. (9-39),

$$dF_U = C_L\rho \frac{W_m^2}{2} c \, dr \sin \beta_m \qquad (9\text{-}41)$$

Now dF_U may be also expressed

$$dF_U = \frac{G}{g} \Delta W_U = \rho A V_a \Delta W_U$$

or

$$dF_U = \rho V_a t \, dr \, \Delta W_U \qquad (9\text{-}42)$$

where t = blade pitch. Setting Eqs. (9-41) and (9-42) equal,

$$C_{L}\rho \frac{W_{m}^{2}}{2} c \, dr \sin \beta_{m} = \rho V_{a} t \, dr \, \Delta W_{U}$$

and

$$C_{L} = \frac{2V_{a}t \, \Delta W_{U}}{W_{m}^{2}c \sin \beta_{m}}$$

From Fig. 9-32 it can be seen that $v_{a}/W_{m} = \sin \beta_{m}$. Therefore

$$C_{L} = \frac{2\Delta W_{U}}{W_{m}} \frac{t}{c}$$

The ratio of blade chord to pitch c/t is designated as σ and is known as the solidity factor, so that

$$C_{L}\sigma = \frac{2\Delta W_{U}}{W_{m}} \tag{9-43}$$

Equation (9-43) may be derived directly from Eqs. (9-39) and (9-40). The circulation for one blade in an axial-flow turbine may be expressed from Eq. (8-10) in terms of t:

$$\Gamma_{b} = t \, \Delta W_{U} \tag{9-44}$$

Setting Eqs. (6-83) and (9-39) equal,

$$L' = \frac{dL}{dr} = C_{L}\rho \frac{W_{m}^{2}}{2} c = \rho W_{m}\Gamma_{b}$$

from which

$$C_{L} = \frac{2\Gamma_{b}}{W_{m}c}$$

Substituting Eq. (9-43),

$$C_{L} = \frac{2\Delta W_{U}}{W_{m}} \frac{t}{c} \qquad \text{or} \qquad C_{L}\sigma = \frac{2\Delta W_{U}}{W_{m}} \tag{9-43}$$

After the velocity diagrams are drawn for the root, tip, and mid-sections of the blades in accordance with the principles of Secs. 9-17 and 9-18, the values of ΔW_{U} and W_{m} can be found for these sections of the blade. Therefore Eq. (9-43) may be solved for $C_{L}\sigma$ immediately. The solidity factor σ is seen to depend on the chord and pitch of the blades. The pitch in turn depends on the number of blades used. The lift exerted on each blade is greater when a few blades are used. That is, the aerodynamic loading on the blades is increased with fewer blades. However, the total lift exerted on the blade assembly is a function of the product of lift per blade and the number of blades. Therefore the total lift can be expected to increase with an increase in the number of blades even though the aerodynamic loading is decreased. However, a point is reached where the product of the lift per blade and the number of blades is a maximum and any further increase in the number of blades results in a decrease in total lift.

The number of blades, which determines the pitch at all radii of the blade annulus, is also observed to be controlled by conditions at the root and tip of the blades. If the pitch is too great at the tips of the blades, the desired flow pattern may not be impressed by the blades. At the root, a physical limitation to the closeness of the blades is encountered, since the blade attachment form reduces clear flow area at this point. Too low a pitch may result in choking of the flow at the root section even if the pitch can be achieved physically. An additional complication is introduced by the fact that the taper of long blades can be quite considerable from root to tip.

Another factor which must be considered in determining the blade pitch is the aspect ratio. The aspect ratio is defined as the ratio of blade height to chord length or h_b/c for untapered blades. If the blade is tapered both in terms of chord length and thickness, a usual requirement for long blades, then the aspect ratio is defined as the ratio of h_b^2 to the projected area of the blade on the plane containing the chord of the mid-section airfoil. Secondary losses, which will be discussed in Sec. 9-24, are found to decrease with large aspect ratios.

The product $C_L\sigma$ obtained from Eq. (9-43) establishes the value of c/t which can be maintained for a given blade section. The maximum value of C_L for a turbine airfoil blade is about 1.6. The solidity factor σ ranges from 2.0 at the root to about 1.2 at the tip section. It must be remembered, however, that once the pitch is fixed at one section of the blade it is automatically determined for all other sections. Since the chord length is usually decreased to accomplish a taper, or is constant for untapered blades, it is evident that the solidity must decrease radially.

Figure 9-33 illustrates a method by which the isolated airfoil principle may be employed in design. The velocity diagram represents the condition at some particular section of the blade under consideration. The velocity vector W_2 is drawn from the extremity of W_1 parallel to its original location in the velocity diagram. The mean velocity vector W_m is extended and intersects W_2 at its extremity. The camber angle θ is seen to be equal to $180 - (\beta + \gamma)$. From Eq. (9-43), substituting the values of V_m and ΔW_U obtained from the velocity diagram, $C_L\sigma$ is found. Consideration must now be given to the solidity factor. The solidity factor may be taken to vary radially from 2.0 to 1.2, from which a suitable solidity may be determined for the section under consideration. If the pitch has been fixed for another section, then the pitch for the section under consideration is given by $2\pi r/z$, where r is the radius to the section under consideration and z is the number of blades.

However, if the pitch has not been fixed previously for another section,

then the relationship of chord to pitch must be established. The desired
axial length of the turbine, aspect ratio, and strength considerations will
govern the selection of chord length, which in turn fixes the pitch for a
given solidity. Having established the radial variation of solidity, the
value of C_L is found from Eq. (9-43).

Now C_L is associated with a definite angle of attack for a particular airfoil section. This requires that the chord be rotated clockwise from W_m
through an angle equal to the angle of attack associated with the value of
C_L. The chord length then fixes the axial width of the blade. The
camber inlet and outlet angles x_1 and x_2 are erected at the extremities of

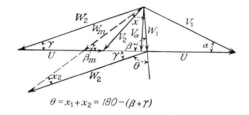

$$\theta = x_1 + x_2 = 180 - (\beta + \gamma)$$

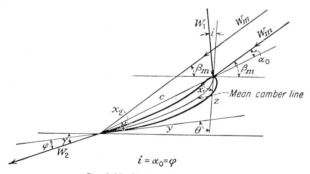

$$i = \alpha_0 = \varphi$$

Fig. 9-33. Single airfoil principle.

the chord. A suitable faired camber line is drawn tangent to the lines
y and z at the leading and trailing edges of the chord.

The angle of attack for the desired value of C_L may be obtained from
wind-tunnel tests for an isolated airfoil of similar camber such as those
published by the NACA. A basic thickness form may be adapted to the
required camber line by the methods outlined in Sec. 9-19, and wind-
tunnel tests will give the C_L and α_0 relationships for the resulting airfoil
section. It is important that the angle of attack corrected for infinite
aspect ratio be used, since this condition is very closely approximated by
turbine blades. End vortices in turbine blades are minimized due to the
fact that the root end is fixed to the rotor and the tip end is either fixed to
a shroud ring or has very little clearance.

9-22. Limitations of the Single Airfoil Principle. The single airfoil principle is very valuable in the design of fans, blowers, and compressors with low energy input per stage, since its use makes available the extensive wind-tunnel-test results for aircraft airfoil sections. Unfortunately, when the blades are too closely pitched, the single airfoil principle cannot be applied with any assurance of obtaining expected results. The reason for this lies in the fact that the interference of neighboring blades changes the local flow pattern to the extent that the results obtained for an isolated airfoil are no longer valid.

The pressure drop and consequently the work output of a row of blades depends on the magnitude of $C_L\sigma$. Therefore unless an unreasonable number of stages is to be employed, the product of $C_L\sigma$ must be large, and for the maximum lift obtainable for a given airfoil the blades must necessarily be closely pitched in a turbine. The highest value of the solidity for which the single airfoil principle is valid probably lies between 1.0 and 1.2. It follows then that for most turbine applications the single airfoil principle is valid only near the blade tips. An entirely different approach must be taken for the other sections. This approach, known as the cascade principle, is discussed in Sec. 9-23.

9-23. Cascade Principle. When the solidity exceeds about 1.2, the single airfoil principle cannot be used with any acceptable degree of accuracy. However, higher solidities can be used if the interference of neighboring blades is taken into account by testing a lattice of airfoils instead of an isolated airfoil. When the solidity exceeds about 2.0, the principle of flow in channels must be used. This latter principle formed the basis of the conventional approach taken for many years in the design of steam turbines. The channel-flow principle treats the problem as one of flow in converging and diverging passages, concerning which a wealth of experience and test data has been accumulated.

Many gas-turbine designs fall within the range of solidities for which the cascade principle is applicable. Unfortunately, very little published information is available for turbine blade cascades and that which is available is not suitable for generalization. The channel-flow principle seems in general to be the most suitable for steam turbines in view of the solidities employed.

For the design of both steam- and gas-turbine flow passages, the most satisfactory method is one which combines the knowledge of the cascade principle with that of the channel-flow principle and operating test data. This was the approach used in Sec. 9-10, the loss coefficients being determined from a combination of cascade and performance test data.

The combined channel-flow and cascade principles are applied to a turbine stage designed for radial equilibrium in the sample problem outlined at the end of the chapter. The cascade principle itself will be discussed in greater detail in the chapter covering axial-flow compressors.

9-24. Secondary-flow Losses. Whenever the direction of flow is changed, secondary flows are induced, with losses which may be quite significant in their magnitude. Figure 9-34 illustrates secondary flow in a curved passage of rectangular cross section. The boundary layer x has a lower static pressure and is almost stationary in comparison with a streamline y out in the stream. The static pressure gradient coupled with centrifugal force due to turning of the flow induces the streamline y to move to the boundary layer x. Energy is transferred from the streamline y to the boundary layer x, which moves out into the main stream. Since this process is continuous, a secondary circulatory flow pattern is established. The energy transfer occurs with an increase of entropy and therefore is a source of loss.

The loss attendant to secondary flow is minimized by a wider flow passage for a given height. If the aspect ratio has a value greater than 3 for turbine blades, the secondary-flow losses are minimized. The higher the aspect ratio, the less significant are the secondary-flow losses.

9-25. Some General Comments on the Design of Turbine Flow Passages. It is evident from a consideration of the material in the preceding sections that the design of turbine flow passages depends in large measure on the judgment of the designer. No attempt has been made to develop a design technique, for there are almost as many different techniques as there are designers.

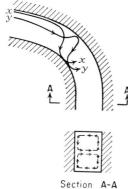

Section A-A

Fig. 9-34. Secondary flow in curved passage.

In general, the designer must consider the application of the turbine and the level of performance required. Overshadowing every design decision is the consideration of initial and operating cost, ease of manufacture, and expected life of the machine.

Small steam turbines for driving pumps, fans, blowers, and other auxiliary machinery normally are designed with parallel-section impulse blades. The level of performance required would not justify the incorporation of twisted blades designed for radial equilibrium. In other words the savings due to improved performance over the life of the turbine would not offset the increased initial cost. Usually, the blades of small steam turbines are comparatively short and very little loss is incurred by using parallel-section blades.

In the high-pressure stages of large steam turbines the blades are short enough so that the requirement of radial equilibrium can be neglected without serious loss. However, in the low-pressure stages where the blades reach a considerable height it is essential to design for radial equilibrium and to use airfoil blades. In the intermediate stages the decision to use standardized conventional reaction blades rather than the specially designed airfoil blade may be dictated by the economics of the application.

As for the gas turbine, more careful attention must be given to a consideration of radial equilibrium and airfoil blading. In general it may be said that an improvement of 1 per cent in the over-all turbine efficiency results in a corresponding increase of 4 to 5 per cent in the over-all thermal efficiency of the plant. Therefore it is not unusual to find gas turbines with airfoil blades even when designed for impulse at the blade mid-section. It is usual also to design for the optimum value of v' in gas turbines even when this means incorporating more stages. Some gas turbines designed to utilize waste gases have incorporated the standard impulse blades but their use is not common.

In the aircraft gas turbine prime consideration must be given to the military requirements in regard to performance. On the other hand the turbine must present as small a frontal area as possible and be light and compact. Hence aircraft gas turbines are designed for few stages with large output per stage. However, quite a bit of latitude may be taken in the matter of turbine speed within the requirements imposed by the compressor. Furthermore the leaving loss from the turbine is available to the jet. Thus a larger axial velocity is permissible ranging 750 to 900 fps.

9-26. Relationships between the Velocity Ratios. It is convenient for design purposes to establish a relationship between the actual and isentropic velocity ratios. For a 50 per cent reaction stage the ratio v/v' may be obtained by dividing the actual velocity ratio by the expression for the isentropic velocity ratio given in Eq. (9-2).

$$\frac{v}{v'} = \frac{223.7 \sqrt{\dfrac{(\Delta h_S)_{\text{stage}}}{2}}}{V_1} \tag{9-45}$$

or

$$\frac{v}{v'} = \sqrt{2gJ \frac{(\Delta h_S)_{\text{stage}}}{V_1^2}} \tag{9-46}$$

where V_1 is the actual absolute velocity leaving the stationary blades or entering the moving blades. From the entrancevelo city triangle and the law of cosines, $W_1^2 = V_1^2 + U^2 + 2UV_1 \cos \alpha$, where W_1 is the relative velocity entering the moving blades. Since 50 per cent reaction stage is being considered, $W_1 = V_2$. Then Eq. (9-46) may be expressed:

$$\frac{v}{v'} = \sqrt{\frac{V_2^2 + 2gJ[(\Delta h_S)_{\text{stage}}/2] - (V_1^2 + U^2 - 2UV_1 \cos \alpha)}{V_1^2}}$$

or

$$\frac{v}{v'} = \sqrt{\frac{V_2^2 + 2gJ[(\Delta h_S)_{\text{stage}}/2]}{V_1^2} - 1 - 2\frac{U}{V_1}\cos \alpha - \left(\frac{U}{V_1}\right)^2}$$

Substituting for U/V_1 the symbol ν for the actual velocity ratio,

$$\frac{\nu}{\nu'} = \sqrt{\frac{V_2{}^2 + 2gJ[(\Delta h_S)_{\text{stage}}/2]}{V_1{}^2}} - 1 - 2\nu \cos \alpha - \nu^2$$

Observing that V_2, the absolute velocity leaving the moving row, is also the approach velocity to the following stationary row, it is clear that the expression

$$\frac{V_2{}^2 + 2gJ[(\Delta h_S)_{\text{stage}}/2]}{V_1{}^2}$$

is the reciprocal of the blade efficiency. Therefore

$$\frac{\nu}{\nu'} = \sqrt{\frac{1}{\eta_b} - 1 + (2\nu \cos \alpha - \nu^2)}$$

The expression $2\nu \cos \alpha - \nu^2$ occurred frequently in the relationships previously derived. Designating this expression by the symbol ξ,

$$\frac{\nu}{\nu'} = \sqrt{\frac{1}{\eta_b} - 1 + \xi} \qquad (9\text{-}47)$$

Now the stage efficiency may be expressed as the ratio of the work done on the blades divided by the energy available to the stage on the basis of the stagnation enthalpy drop. The energy available to the stage is also the sum of the work done on the blades and the losses. The losses are found as the difference between the available energy to the stage and the work done on the blades. It can be readily seen that the following are equivalent expressions:

$$\eta_s = \frac{E}{\text{available energy}} = \frac{E}{E + \text{losses}} = \frac{E}{E + (\text{available energy} - E)}$$

From Eq. (8-39),

$$E = \frac{V_1{}^2}{gJ} (2\nu \cos \alpha - \nu^2) = \frac{V_1{}^2 \xi}{gJ}$$

Then

$$\eta_s = \frac{V_1{}^2/gJ}{\dfrac{V_1{}^2 \xi}{gJ} + \left(\dfrac{V_2{}^2}{2gJ} + \dfrac{(\Delta h_S)_{\text{stage}}}{2} - \dfrac{V_1{}^2}{2gJ}\right)2}$$

$$\eta_s = \frac{\xi}{\xi + (1/\eta_b) - 1} \qquad (9\text{-}48)$$

From Eqs. (9-46) and (9-47),

$$\frac{\nu}{\nu'} = \sqrt{\frac{\xi}{\eta_s}} \qquad (9\text{-}49)$$

Figures 9-35 through 9-39 show the velocity ratio relationships for various common values of α, η_b, and η_s for reaction stages.

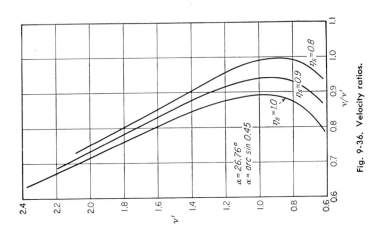

Fig. 9-36. Velocity ratios.

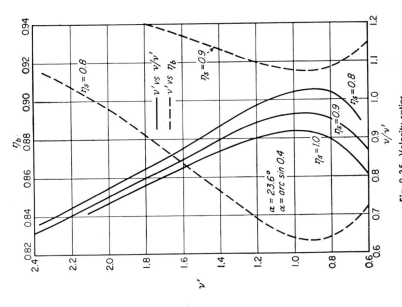

Fig. 9-35. Velocity ratios.

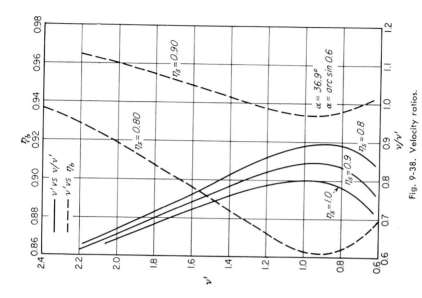

Fig. 9-38. Velocity ratios.

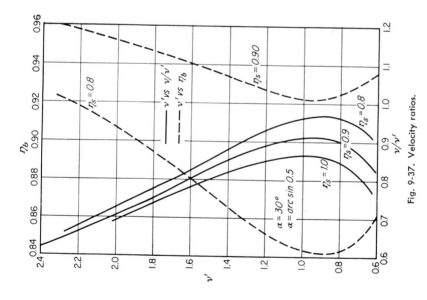

Fig. 9-37. Velocity ratios.

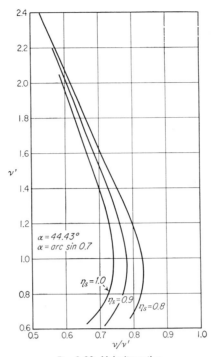

Fig. 9-39. Velocity ratios.

9-27. Design Calculations for Impulse Stage Flow Passages. The application of the principles discussed thus far may be best presented in the form of illustrative problems. The following problem is somewhat simplified because of space limitations and a desire not to obscure the main points by too much detail.

Example. A mechanical-drive turbine is to consist of a single Curtis stage with two rows of moving blades. The following data are given:

Fluid: steam
Initial temperature: 560 F
Initial pressure: 300 psia
Exhaust pressure: 100 psia
Speed: 3600 rpm
Brake output: 500 hp
Mechanical efficiency: 0.97
Parasitic losses: 3 per cent

The flow passages are to be designed to the extent of determining the following principal dimensions:

1. Number, size, and type of nozzles
2. Width, pitch, height, and angles for all blades

The steam conditions for this turbine are identical to those used for the steam nozzle of Example 1, Sec. 7-10. In Example 1 it was noted that the velocity developed is supersonic. Therefore a conical nozzle will be used and all the conditions except for the areas have already been found. Selecting an actual velocity ratio, $\nu = 0.20$ from Fig. 9-2, and noting that the actual velocity leaving the nozzles is 2180 fps,

$$U_m = 0.20 \times 2180 = 436 \text{ fps}$$
$$D_m = \frac{436 \times 60}{\pi \times 3600} = 2.32 \text{ ft}$$

To decrease this diameter, a lower value of ν or a higher rotational speed could be employed. Other alternatives are to increase the number of

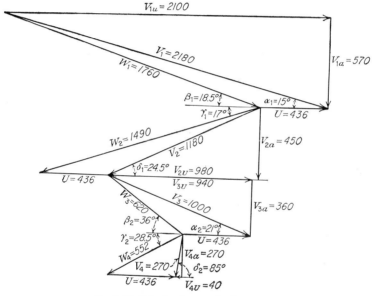

Fig. 9-40. Velocity diagram for Example 1.

rows of moving blades or adopt multistaging. The ultimate decision must be based on the economic considerations of initial cost and efficiency.

Before proceeding to the velocity diagram, a decision must be made in regard to the nozzle angle and the blade angles. A nozzle angle of $\alpha = 15°$ will be selected for high efficiency. The fluid relative exit angle will be taken as the average of the fluid relative entering angle and the nozzle angle. This results in some decrease of the fluid relative exit angle with a resulting improvement in efficiency over the symmetrical blade. If standardized blades are to be used, the angles available will govern to a large extent the flow angles adopted.

A start can be made on the velocity diagram as shown in Fig. 9-40.

The entrance velocity triangle can be drawn since α, V_1, and U are known. The value of β_1 and W_1 are scaled from the velocity triangle. Now the direction and magnitude of W_2 can be determined:

$$\gamma_1 = \frac{\alpha_2 + \beta_1}{2} = \frac{15 + 18.5}{2} = 16.75°, \text{ say } 17°$$

An incidence angle of 5° may be selected to help the situation at the blade tips and

$$\theta_1 = 180 - (\beta_1' + \gamma_1) = 180 - (23.5 + 17) = 139.5°$$

From Eq. (9-32) and Figs. 9-22 and 9-23,

$$W_2 = k_{co}k_ik_pW_1$$
$$W_2 = 0.925 \times 0.99 \times 0.925 \times 1760 = 1490$$

The exit velocity triangle now can be completed and V_2 and δ_1 are scaled.

The absolute velocity entering the guides is V_2 and its direction δ_2. This of course is the same as the absolute velocity leaving the preceding row of moving blades. The velocity V_2 then is the carry-over velocity to the guides. The direction of the absolute velocity leaving the guide blades is taken as

$$\alpha_2 = \frac{\delta_1 + \gamma_1}{2} = \frac{24.5 + 17}{2} = 20.75°, \text{ say } 21°$$

Assuming an incidence angle of 5° as before,

$$\theta_2 = 180 - (\delta_1' + \alpha_1) = 180 - (29.5 + 21) = 129.5°$$

and
$$V_3 = k_{co}k_pk_iV_2$$
$$V_3 = 0.93 \times 0.93 \times 0.99 \times 1180 = 1000 \text{ fps}$$

The velocity V_3 is the absolute velocity entering the last row of moving blades. The balance of the velocity diagram is completed by the same methods employed for the first row of moving blades:

$$\gamma_2 = \frac{\alpha_2 + \beta_2}{2} = \frac{21 + 36}{2} = 28.5°$$
$$\theta_3 = 180 - (\beta_2' + \gamma_2) = 180 - (41 + 28.5) = 110.5°$$
$$W_4 = k_{co}k_pk_iW_3$$
$$W_4 = 0.948 \times 0.948 \times 0.99 \times 620 = 552 \text{ fps}$$

Finally, the tangential and axial components of the velocities are determined by scaling the velocity diagram.

The values found graphically by drawing the velocity diagram to scale could have been found by trigonometric relationships. However, if a sufficiently large scale is selected and care is taken in laying out the velocity diagram, the graphical solution is much more convenient and accurate enough.

The net tangential velocity acting on the two moving rows of blades is

$$\Sigma \Delta V_U = (V_{1U} - V_{2U}) + (V_{3U} - V_{4U})$$
$$\Sigma \Delta V_U = (2100 + 980) + (940 + 40) = 4060 \text{ fps}$$

From Eq. (8-16),

$$E = \frac{U \Sigma \Delta V_U}{gJ} = \frac{436 \times 4060}{32.2 \times 778} = 70.9 \text{ Btu}$$

and

$$\eta_{bl} = \frac{E}{\Delta h_s} = \frac{70.9}{103} = 0.687$$

From Eq. (9-4),

$$\eta_s = (0.97)^2 (0.687)(1 - 0.03) = 0.626$$

Since this is a single-stage turbine (one pressure drop), $\eta_s = \eta_i$. The brake engine efficiency is

$$\eta_{cb} = 0.97 \times 0.626 = 0.606$$

Thus far the capacity of the turbine has not been introduced in the computations. The capacity determines the mass rate of flow. Presumably the turbine could be designed for any capacity within the geometric limitations imposed on the turbine. For the capacity specified,

$$G = \frac{500 \times 2545}{0.606 \times 103 \times 3600} = 5.67 \text{ lb per sec}$$

Referring again to Example 1, Sec. 7-10, it is noted that the actual specific volumes at the exit and throat of the nozzles are 4.57 and 3.09 cu ft per lb, respectively. The actual velocity at the throat is 1680 fps. Assuming $C_d = 0.98$ as before, the total flow areas required for the present problem are

$$A_c = \frac{5.67 \times 3.09}{0.98 \times 1680} \times 144 = 1.53 \text{ sq in.}$$

$$A_1 = \frac{5.67 \times 4.57}{0.98 \times 2180} \times 144 = 1.75 \text{ sq in.}$$

Assume 4 nozzles. Then the throat and exit areas of each nozzle are 0.383 and 0.437 sq in., respectively. The corresponding diameters are 0.68 and 0.745 in. With a step-up or cover of approximately $\frac{1}{16}$ in., the blade entrance height in the first moving row is 0.81 in., which is in excess of the minimum height of 0.75. The other blade heights are found as follows. [Refer to Eqs. (9-25), (9-26), and (9-27).]
First row:

$$h_{b1} = h_n + \frac{1}{16} = 0.745 + 0.063 = 0.808 \text{ in., say } 0.81 \text{ in.}$$

$$h_{b2} = h_n \times \frac{V_{1a}}{V_{2a}} = 0.745 \times \frac{570}{450} = 0.945 \text{ in., say } 0.95 \text{ in.}$$

Guides:

$$h_{b3} = h_{b2} + \tfrac{1}{16} = 0.945 + 0.063 = 1.01 \text{ in.}$$

$$h_{b4} = h_n \times \frac{V_{1a}}{V_{3a}} = 0.745 \times \frac{570}{360} = 1.18 \text{ in.}$$

Second row:

$$h_{b5} = h_{b4} + \tfrac{1}{16} = 1.18 + 0.063 = 1.543 \text{ in., say } 1.54 \text{ in.}$$

$$h_{b6} = h_n \times \frac{V_{1a}}{V_{4a}} = 0.745 \times \frac{570}{270} = 1.57 \text{ in.}$$

The increase in specific volume in passing through each blade was neglected in determining the blade exit heights. It is left as an exercise for the reader to determine the effect of blade reheat on the exit heights of the blades (see Sec. 9-7).

If the blade heights determined above are retained, the pitch and widths of the blades remain to be found. The pitch will be determined at the pitch circle or mean blade ring diameter taken as the locus of blade mid-heights. In Sec. 9-6 it was stated that the blade widths for a turbine of this type range from $\tfrac{5}{8}$ to 1 in. Selecting 1 in. as the width of all blades, also from Sec. 9-6,

$$\frac{t}{c} = 0.6 \qquad \text{and} \qquad t = 0.6 \text{ in.}$$

The pitch of the guides probably would be changed to avoid a resonant effect.

The effect of deflection of the steam issuing from the blades might be taken into consideration. If not, the blade angles are as follows:

$$\alpha_1' = 15°$$
$$\beta_1' = 23.5° \qquad \delta_1' = 29.5° \qquad \beta_2' = 31°$$
$$\gamma_1' = 17° \qquad \alpha_2' = 21° \qquad \gamma_2' = 28.5°$$

The reader should check the velocity diagram for the tip section of the blades to determine if the 5° angle of incidence is adequate.

Constant pitch diameter or mean blade ring diameter has been assumed in the problem. The tip and root radii of the blades can be readily determined by adding or subtracting, respectively, from D_m one-half the blade heights.

9-28. Design Calculations for Multistaged Turbine Flow Passages

Example. Design the flow passages of a reaction gas turbine for a brake output of 10,000 kw at 90 per cent brake engine efficiency. Gas enters the turbine at 1500 F and 75 psia with a velocity of 400 fps and expands to 15 psia.   Assume the gas has approximately the same thermo-dynamic properties as air.

Inlet conditions (air tables):

$$P_1 = 75 \text{ psia} \qquad T_1 = 1500 \text{ F} \qquad P_{r1} = 160.37 \qquad h_1 = 493.64$$

Final conditions (air tables):

$$P_x = 15 \text{ psia} \qquad P_{rx} = 160.37 \times {}^{15}\!/_{75} = 32.07$$
$$T_x = 815 \text{ F} \qquad h_x = 310.3$$
$$(\Delta h_s)_{\text{turbine}} = h_1 - h_x = 493.64 - 310.3 = 183.3 \text{ Btu per lb}$$

Mechanical efficiencies vary from 0.96 to 0.98.   Assume a mechanical efficiency of 98 per cent.   Then $\eta_i = 0.92$.   Restrict leaving loss to 300 fps = 1.8 Btu per lb.   (If this were an aircraft gas turbine the leaving velocity would be utilized in the jet and might be as high as 900 fps.)

$$\text{Internal work} = 0.92(310.3 - 1.8) = 167 \text{ Btu per lb}$$
$$\text{Internal output} = \frac{10,000}{0.98} = 10,200 \text{ kw}$$

Required mass rate of flow through turbine:

$$G = \frac{10,200 \times 3413}{3600 \times 167} = 59.9 \text{ lb per sec}$$

Actual conditions at turbine exhaust:

$$h'_x = 493.64 - (167 + 1.8) = 324.8 \text{ Btu per lb}$$
$$T'_x = 870.4 \text{ F} \qquad \text{(air tables)}$$
$$v'_x = \frac{RT'_x}{P_x} = \frac{53.34(870.4 + 460)}{15 \times 144} = 32.9 \text{ cu ft per lb}$$

Volume rate of flow at exhaust = $59.9 \times 32.9 = 1970$ cfs
Assume axial velocity = 275 fps

Then the required annular area for flow = ${}^{1970}\!/_{275} = 7.2$ sq ft. Allowing 15 per cent for the blades, the gross annular area is

$$7.2 \times 1.15 = 8.25 \text{ sq ft}$$

The ratio of blade height to mean blade ring diameter may vary from 0.1 to 0.3, depending on whether high or low pressure stages are being considered.   Selecting $h_b/D_m = 0.25$ for the last blade row,

$$\text{Gross annular area} = \pi D_m h_b = 0.25\pi D_m{}^2 = 8.25 \text{ sq ft}$$
$$D_m = 3.24 \text{ ft} = 38.9 \text{ in.}$$
$$h_b = 0.25 \times 38.9 = 9.75 \text{ in.}$$

Mean blade speeds used in practice vary from 800 fps to 1000 fps.   For jet applications the mean blade speed may go as high as 1200 fps.   Selecting $U_m = 800$ fps, the Btu equivalent of mean blade speed $= (800)^2/2gJ$ $= 12.8$ Btu per lb. To obtain $\eta_i = 0.92$, the stage efficiency should be about 90 per cent. Figure 9-6 indicates that for $\eta_s = 0.90$ and a pressure ratio of 7, RF_N would probably be 1.02. Assuming 50 per cent reaction at the mean blade ring diameter and vortex blading, the approximate isentropic enthalpy drop per row, from Eq. (9-6),

$$(\Delta h_S)_{\text{row}} = \sqrt{\frac{RF_N(\Delta h_S)_{\text{turbine}}}{2N}}$$

Equation (8-43) shows that stage efficiency depends on α and velocity ratio. Values of α for reaction stages vary from $20°$ to $30°$ in practice. The requirement of high stage efficiency implies a need for higher blade efficiency obtainable through the use of a high isentropic velocity ratio. Taking $\alpha = 23.6°$ from Fig. 9-1, ν' probably will be about 1.25 for $\eta_s = 0.92$. From Eq. (9-21),

$$\nu' = \sqrt{\frac{2N \times \text{Btu equivalent of mean blade speed}}{RF_N(\Delta h_S)_{\text{turbine}}}}$$

$$1.25 = \sqrt{\frac{2N \times 12.8}{1.03 \times 183.3}}$$

$$N = 11.4 \text{ stages}$$

Possibly 11 stages or 22 rows will do. For $\eta_s = 0.90$ and a pressure ratio of 7, Fig. 9-6 yields $RF_\infty = 1.024$.

$$RF_N = 1 + (1.024 + 1)[(21 - 1)/21] = 1.0228, \text{ say } 1.023$$

$$\eta_s = \frac{\eta_i}{RF_N} = \frac{0.92}{1.023} = 0.90$$

which checks with the assumed value of 0.90. Then

$$\nu' = \sqrt{\frac{22 \times 12.8}{1.023 \times 183.3}} = 1.22$$

From Fig. 9-35 with $\eta_s = 0.90$, $\alpha = 23.6°$, and $\nu' = 1.22$, the ratio $\nu/\nu' = 0.938$ and therefore $\nu = 1.145$.

$$\nu = \frac{U_m}{V_1} \qquad V_1 = \frac{U_m}{\nu} = \frac{800}{1.145} = 700 \text{ fps}$$

$$V_{1a} = V_1 \sin \alpha = 700 \times 0.4 = 280 \text{ fps}$$

which is somewhat higher than the assumed value. An adjustment could be made, but this value would be considered a close enough check.

The velocity diagram for the mean blade section now may be drawn as shown in Fig. 9-41. Before proceeding to the velocity diagrams for the other sections on the blade, the blade height must be determined. If the energy distribution is plotted on an h-S diagram, the condition of the gas may be determined at each row of blades. With this information the blade heights may be determined from the continuity relationship. However, the locus of points of blade tips forms a curved outline necessitating a curved casing. From a manufacturing standpoint this is not desirable, and it is usual, wherever possible, to substitute a straight diverging outline. The resulting outline is approximately conical with the included angle limited to about 20°.

Vortex blades are usually installed on a constant inner radius which has many advantages from a construction and performance standpoint.

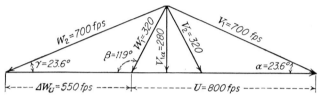

Fig. 9-41. Velocity diagram—mean section.

With a constant enthalpy drop per stage, a constant amount of reaction takes place at the inner radius, with the result that identical profiles may be used for all blades. Even identical discs may be used with this arrangement. A further advantage results from the fact that the blades of the first row are short and the degree of reaction increases slightly over the blade length. Hence a larger temperature drop occurs in the stationary blades, affording some relief from the effects of temperature on the moving blades.

For the purpose of illustration only, the exit blades will be considered. Then the required area is

$$A = \frac{Gv'_x}{0.85 V_{1a}} = \frac{59.9 \times 32.9}{0.85 \times 280} = 8.1 \text{ sq ft}$$

$$A = \pi(r_t^2 - r_r^2) = \pi\left[\left(r_m + \frac{h_b}{2}\right)^2 - \left(r_m^2 - \frac{h_b}{2}\right)^2\right]$$

$$A = 2\pi r_m h_b$$

$$h_b = \frac{A}{2\pi r_m} = \frac{8.1}{3.24\pi} = 0.795 \text{ ft} = 9.55 \text{ in.}$$

$$r_r = r_m - \frac{h_b}{2} = 19.45 - 4.78 = 14.67 \text{ in.}$$

$$r_t = r_m + \frac{h_b}{2} = 19.45 + 4.78 = 24.23 \text{ in.}$$

Tip Section. Since $rV_{1U} = \Omega = $ constant,

$$V_{1Ut} = 650 \times \frac{19.45}{24.23} = 520 \text{ fps}$$

$$\Delta V_{Ut} = 550 \times \frac{19.45}{24.23} = 440 \text{ fps}$$

The velocity diagram may now be drawn to scale noting that

$$U_t = \frac{\omega r_m}{r_m} r_t = \frac{U_m}{r_m} r_t = \frac{800}{19.45} \times 24.33 = 1000 \text{ fps}$$

Also the axial velocity entering and leaving the blades is constant radially. A convenient method for drawing the velocity diagram to scale is as follows.

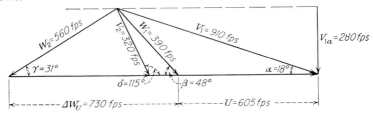

Fig. 9-42. Velocity diagram—root section.

1. Lay out U to scale.

2. Erect a perpendicular to U at its extremity and equal to the entering axial velocity V_{1a}.

3. Through a point at the extremity of V_{1a} draw a line parallel to U, and lay off a distance equal to V_{1U}.

4. V_1 now may be drawn between the extreme points of V_{1U} and U and the value of α and V_1 scaled from the diagram.

5. Closing the triangle formed by V_1 and U gives W_1, whose magnitude and direction may also be scaled.

6. To construct exit velocity diagram lay off a distance equal to ΔV_U and connect this point with the beginning of V_1 to give V_2.

7. From where V_2 intersects U lay off a distance equal to U, and connect this point with the beginning of V_1 to give W_1. All vector magnitudes and directions may be scaled from the velocity diagram.

If preferred, the magnitude and direction of all velocity vectors may be solved trigonometrically. The deflection angle for the moving blades is

$$\theta = 180 - (\beta + \gamma) = 180 - (150 + 17) = 13°$$

The deflection angle for the stationary blades is

$$\theta = 180 - (\alpha + \delta) = 180 - (27 + 105) = 48°$$

Mean Section. The velocity diagram for the mean section was drawn previously. The deflection angle for the moving blades is

$$\theta = 180 - (119 + 23.6) = 37.4°$$

and for the stationary blades

$$\theta = 180 - (23.6 + 119) = 37.4°$$

Root Section. The velocity diagram for the root section may be drawn in a manner similar to that used for the tip section.

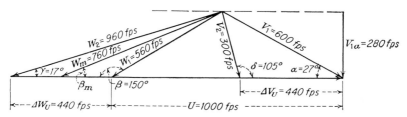

Fig. 9-43. Velocity diagram—tip section.

$$V_{1Ur} = 650 \times \frac{19.45}{14.67} = 865 \text{ fps}$$

$$\Delta V_{Ur} = 550 \times \frac{19.45}{14.67} = 730 \text{ fps}$$

$$U_r = \frac{800}{19.45} \times 14.67 = 605 \text{ fps}$$

The deflection angle for the moving blades is

$$\theta = 180 - (48 + 31) = 101°$$

and for the stationary blades

$$\theta = 180 - (18 + 115) = 47°$$

The stage efficiencies now may be checked.

Tip Section

$$\eta_s = \frac{\text{work done}}{(\Delta h_S)_{\text{stage}} + (V_2{}^2/2gJ)}$$

$$\text{Work done} = \frac{U \, \Delta W_U}{gJ} = \frac{1000 \times 440}{gJ} = 17.6 \text{ Btu per lb}$$

$$(\Delta h_S)_{\text{stage}} = \frac{RF_N (\Delta h_S)_{\text{turbine}}}{N} = \frac{1.023 \times 183.3}{11} = 17.1 \text{ Btu per lb}$$

$$\eta_s = \frac{17.6}{17.1 + [(300)^2/2gJ]} = 0.93$$

Mean Section

$$\eta_s = \frac{17.6}{17.1 + [(320)^2/2gJ]} = 0.92$$

Root Section

$$\eta_s = \frac{17.6}{17.1 + [(320)^2/2gJ]} = 0.92$$

These results give an average efficiency for the stage somewhat better than 92 per cent, comparing favorably with the assumed efficiency of 90 per cent.

It is interesting to check the velocities obtained thus far against the various loss coefficients. For the mean section the deflection angle θ for the stationary blades was found to be $37.4°$. The isentropic enthalpy drop in each row is

$$(\Delta h_S)_{\text{row}} = \frac{RF_N(\Delta h_S)_{\text{turbine}}}{2N} = \frac{1.023 \times 183.3}{22} = 8.53 \text{ Btu per lb}$$

The approach velocity to the stationary rows is, from Eq. (9-33b),

$$V_1 = 223.7 k_p \sqrt{(\Delta h_S)_{\text{row}} + \frac{(k_i k_{co} V_2)^2}{2gJ}}$$

Taking $k_{co} = k_p$ and designing for zero incidence, $k_i = 1$. From Fig. 9-21 with $\theta = 37.4$, $k_p = 0.975$ approximately. Then

$$V_1 = 223.7(0.975) \sqrt{8.53 + \frac{(0.975 \times 320)^2}{2gJ}}$$

$$V_1 = 223.7(0.975) \sqrt{10.47}$$
$$V_1 = 704 \text{ fps}$$

which is a very good check. Similarly $W_2 = 704$ fps. The rotational speed of the turbine is

$$N = \frac{U \times 60}{2\pi r_m} = \frac{800 \times 60}{2\pi \times 19.45/12} = 4700 \text{ rpm}$$

If this speed is not suitable for the particular application under consideration, an adjustment must be made in the number of stages, the velocity ratio, the mean blade diameter, and the blade angles or a distributed adjustment of all these factors must be made.

The Mach number should be checked from root to tip of blades and should not exceed a value of 0.95, values lower than 0.85 being preferable. This avoids losses due to flow separation and other losses accompanying supersonic flows.

Another point to be considered is the number of stages required. Perhaps eleven stages would be considered too many or even more stages might be used if a slower rotational speed is required. To meet this situation, Rateau stages or even a Curtis stage might be employed at the high-pressure end. Since the blades are not tall at the high-pressure end of the turbine, the vortex principle might be neglected there and parallel blades employed. This arrangement would also offer the advantage of a sharp reduction in temperature in the early stationary passages.

Continuing with the design, for the purpose of illustration consideration will be extended only to the moving blades. From Eq. (9-43) for the tip section

$$C_L \sigma = \frac{2 \times 440}{760} = 1.16$$

If a chord length of 2 in. at the root is selected, the blade pitch is about 1.1 in. Then at the root the solidity factor $\sigma = \frac{c}{t} = \frac{2}{1.1} = 1.82$ and the number of blades is 84. The solidity factor at the tip section is

$$\sigma_t = \sigma_r \frac{r_r}{r_t} = 1.82 \frac{14.67}{24.23} = 1.1$$

Hence C_L at the tip section is 1.05.

The preceding relationship makes the solidity factor decrease radially in inverse proportion to the radius. Since the pitch increases directly as the radius, the chord length must remain constant. However, if it is desirable to decrease the chord length radially, a somewhat different variation in solidity factor will take place, depending on chord-length variation radially.

For example, assume the chord length is to decrease inversely in proportion to the radius. The root pitch is 1.1 and the number of blades is

$$z = \frac{2\pi r_r}{t_r} = \frac{2\pi \times 14.67}{1.1} = 84$$

The pitch at the tip radius is

$$t_t = \frac{2\pi r_t}{z} = \frac{2\pi \times 24.23}{84} = 1.82 \text{ in.}$$

The chord length at the tip section is

$$c_t = c_r \frac{r_r}{r_t} = 2 \times \frac{14.67}{24.23} = 1.2$$

and the solidity factor at the tip section is

$$\sigma_t = \frac{c}{t} = \frac{1.2}{1.82} = 0.66$$

which gives a coefficient of lift

$$C_L = \frac{1.16}{0.66} = 1.76$$

This coefficient of lift would be impossible of achievement even with expanding flow. The chord-length variation may be taken arbitrarily as a straight-line decrease from 2 in. at root to 1.5 in. at the tip. Then

$$\sigma_t = \frac{1.5}{1.82} = 0.824$$

and
$$C_L = \frac{1.16}{0.824} = 1.41$$

which can be reached with expanding flow.

$NACA\ TR\ 460$ describes a number of thin airfoil sections which can provide a $C_L = 1.05$ or 1.41.   One such airfoil is NACA 2509 which gives $C_L = 1.05$ at $\alpha_0 = 7°$.   The direction of the chord is $\beta_m - \alpha_0$, the value of β_m being obtained from the tip-section velocity diagram shown in Fig. 9-43.

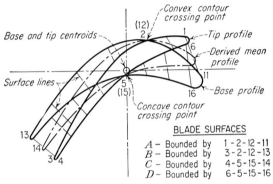

BLADE SURFACES

A – Bounded by   1 – 2 – 12 – 11
B – Bounded by   3 – 2 – 12 – 13
C – Bounded by   4 – 5 – 15 – 14
D – Bounded by   6 – 5 – 15 – 16

Fig. 9-44. Blade section orientation. (Courtesy of Allis-Chalmers Manufacturing Company.)

For the root section a faired circular arc camber line is selected with a camber angle $\theta = 101°$.   A standard thickness form is then established on this camber line by the methods described in Sec. 9-19.   The root and tip sections are oriented on the same axis in a manner similar to that shown in Fig. 9-44.   Intermediate sections are interpolated by generation of a surface of straight radial lines from root to tip sections.

An alternate method is to find directly the intermediate sections at a number of radii by the method used in determining the root section. When all the sections are oriented on the same axis, a blade profile shape is developed.

References

1. Ainley, D. G.: Performance of Axial-flow Turbines, *Proc. IME*, 1945.
2. Church, E. F.: "Steam Turbines," McGraw-Hill Book Company, Inc., New York, 1950.
3. Emmert, H. D.: Current Design Practices for Gas Turbine Power Elements, *Trans. ASME*, 1949.
4. "Gas Turbine Lectures," Westinghouse Electric Corporation, 1944.
5. Goudie, W. J.: "Steam Turbines," Longmans, Green & Co., Inc., New York, 1922.
6. Heinze, F. J.: Thermodynamics and Turbine Design, Westinghouse Lectures, 1948.

7. Jacobs, E. N., K. E. Ward, and R. M. Pinkerton: Tests in the Variable-density Wind Tunnel, *NACA TR* 460, 1933.
8. Kearton, W. J.: "Steam Turbine Theory and Practice," Pitman Publishing Corp., New York, 1948.
9. Keller, C. (translated and adapted by L. S. Marks and J. R. Weske): "Axial Flow Fans," McGraw-Hill Book Company, Inc., New York, 1937.
10. Robinson, E. L.: Report on Reheat Factors, *Mech. Eng.*, February, 1928.
11. Stodola, A., and L. C. Loewenstein: "Steam and Gas Turbines," McGraw-Hill Book Company, Inc., New York, 1927.

Problems

9-1. Steam is delivered at 450 psia and 600 F to a turbine and exhausts at 1.5 in. Hg abs. The turbine consists of one two-row Curtis control stage followed by Rateau staging. The turbine is to operate at a constant speed of 3600 rpm and it is desirable to restrict the mean blade ring diameter of this control stage to 3.5 ft. Determine for the control stage the following:

(a) The available energy in order to maintain a suitable value of ν'.

(b) The velocity diagram with unsymmetrical blades (mean blade height).

(c) The stage efficiency, assuming losses other than nozzle and blade losses to be 3 per cent of available energy.

(d) The condition of the steam leaving the control stage in terms of stagnation and static properties.

All nozzle and blade losses are to be taken into account.

9-2. Assuming standard parallel-section impulse blades, conical nozzles, and a flow of 150,000 lb per hr, find for the stage of Prob. 9-1 (a) number and size of nozzles (assume $\alpha = 15°$); (b) blade entrance and exit angles; (c) blade heights; (d) disc and blade tip diameters for constant mean blade ring diameter.

9-3. For equal energy distribution among the Rateau stages of Prob. 9-1, determine for constant disc diameter and a suitable value for the velocity ratio (a) the number of stages (neglect carry-over); (b) the velocity diagrams at mean blade height; (c) the stage efficiency assuming parasitic losses to 1.5 per cent.

9-4. It is desirable to use foil nozzles in the stages of Prob. 9-3. Calculate (a) nozzle dimensions; (b) blade angles and heights, pitch, and width; (c) tip diameter of blades.

9-5. If the turbine described in the preceding problems has a mechanical efficiency of 97 per cent, calculate the brake output. What is the static condition of the steam leaving the turbine?

9-6. A gas turbine is to be designed for a brake output of 5000 hp. The gas enters the turbine at a pressure and temperature of 65 psia and 1450 F, respectively, and leaves at 15 psia. The turbine is to be designed for 50 per cent reaction at the blade mid-height and constant mean blade ring diameter is to be maintained. Sixteen separate expansions are to be provided with equal energy distribution among these expansions. The mechanical losses for the turbine amount to 2 per cent of the available energy for the turbine and the stage parasitic losses are 1.2 per cent of the available energy for each stage. Carry-over is not to be neglected and all blade losses are to be taken into account.

(a) Determine the available energy for each stage.

(b) Draw the root, mean, and tip velocity diagrams for a representative stage (vortex blades).

(c) Determine the blade heights of the first and last rows of blades and the diameter of the drum at these locations.

(d) Lay out to scale the aerodynamic blade profiles for the root, mean, and tip sections of the last-row blades.

9-7. The Rateau stages of Prob. 9-3 are to be replaced by standard reaction blades except in the last row, where vortex blades will be used. Carry-over is not to be neglected.

(a) Find the number of stages.

(b) Draw the velocity diagrams at mean blade height and at the root and tip sections of the last row.

(c) Calculate the stage efficiencies if parasitic losses are 1 per cent.

(d) Determine blade dimensions and pitch.

(e) Draw the blade profiles for the root, mean, and tip sections of the blades in the last row.

9-8. A simple impulse turbine is to be designed as the prime mover for a 60-cycle, two-pole, d-c generator developing 30 kw at the terminals. The generator efficiency is 95 per cent. The turbine is to be gear-connected to the generator, the turbine turning at 23,000 rpm. Steam is available at 150 psia and saturation temperature and a condenser with a pressure of 2 in. Hg abs is also available for the exhaust steam. Mechanical losses in the turbine including the reduction gear are 4 per cent of the available energy.

(a) Design the turbine passages for the above conditions, establishing all principal dimensions.

(b) If gas were used in the above turbine instead of steam, what would be the principal dimensions, assuming the gas is available at 1500 F and 60 psia. The turbine exhaust pressure is 14.7 psia. How do these dimensions compare with those obtained in (a)? Discuss the reasons for the differences. What compromises are needed?

CHAPTER 10

MECHANICAL ASPECTS OF TURBINE DESIGN

10-1. Introduction. The preceding chapter was concerned primarily with the design of the internal flow passages of the turbine. However, some of the design decisions made in connection with the flow passages are influenced by the mechanical aspects of the over-all turbine design. The purpose of this chapter is to examine the parasitic losses, the stresses to which the blades are subjected, and the problems associated with the turbine shell and rotor.

PARASITIC LOSSES

10-2. Disc Friction. If a disc were to rotate in free air, a certain amount of pumping action would take place, imparting motion to the surrounding air. Because of the relative motion of the disc and the air, friction would exist between the disc and the boundary air. Both of these effects result in a degradation of energy. Kinetic energy is transferred from the disc to the air, and the friction results in a transfer of heat to the air. A situation very similar to this exists in the case of a turbine disc rotating in steam or gas. Energy which was once transferred to the disc through the blading is now returned in part to the steam or gas and consequently represents a deduction from the useful work. According to experiments performed by Stodola this loss may be reduced by one-half to three-quarters by encasing the disc, in other words by reducing the space on each side of the disc. The clearance on each side of turbine discs is extremely small so that the losses are reduced accordingly. The following formula recommended by Stodola gives satisfactory results for turbine discs without blades, provided the clearance on both sides of the disc is very small:

$$\text{hp}_{df} = K \left(\frac{U}{100} \right)^3 \left(\frac{D}{v} \right) \tag{10-1}$$

where $K = 0.0625$ for dry saturated or superheated steam
$K = 0.0608$ for air or gas
$U =$ peripheral velocity of disc, fps
$D =$ diameter of disc peripheral circle, ft
$v =$ specific volume of gas or steam surrounding disc, cu ft per lb

Disc friction is usually calculated only for impulse stages, since the drum friction in reaction stages is so small it may be neglected.

10-3. Windage Losses. When moving blades come in contact with inactive fluid, some kinetic energy is imparted to the fluid at the expense of the kinetic energy of the blades. There is also the inevitable frictional effect. This loss, known as the windage loss, is appreciable when it becomes necessary to resort to partial admission. In the high-pressure stages of an impulse turbine where the specific volume of the fluid is very

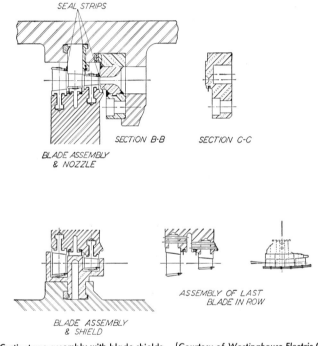

Fig. 10-1. Curtis stage assembly with blade shields. (*Courtesy of Westinghouse Electric Corporation.*)

small, the total area required to pass the fluid may not be large. In such a situation, placing nozzles around the full periphery of the nozzle ring results in exceedingly short nozzles which are undesirable from an efficiency standpoint. In order to maintain reasonable nozzle heights, the number of nozzles is reduced, and they are placed in blocks symmetrically arranged around the nozzle ring. This arrangement results in partial admission of the fluid as opposed to full peripheral admission. Since there are areas around the nozzle ring which do not admit fluid, it follows that corresponding areas in the blade ring receive no active fluid. These blind areas in the blade passages are only partially filled with inactive fluid. It is the action of the moving blades on the inactive fluid in the blind passages that causes the major source of loss.   Shielding blind passages (see Fig. 10-1) tends to reduce the loss.

Since reaction turbines are designed for full peripheral admission the windage loss as well as the disc friction can be neglected.   It is convenient then to use a single expression for windage and disc friction loss for application to impulse stages.   The combined loss may be found from Kerr's formula:

$$\text{hp}_r = [K_1 D + n K_2 (1 - \epsilon) h_b{}^{1.5}] \left(\frac{U}{100} \right) \left(\frac{D_m}{v} \right) \qquad (10\text{-}2)$$

where hp_r = power loss due to windage and disc friction, hp
 D_m = mean blade ring diameter, ft
 h_b = effective blade height, in.
 U = mean blade velocity, fps
 v = specific volume of fluid, cu ft per lb
 ϵ = fraction of nozzle ring which is active
 n = 1 for one row of blades, 1.23 for two rows of blades, and 1.8 for three rows of blades
 K_1 = 0.0608 and K_2 = 0.458 for air and gas
It is suggested that values of K_1 = 0.0625 and K_2 = 0.232 be used for dry steam.   If the fluid is wet steam, then the results obtained from Eq. (10-2) should be multiplied by the following constant suggested by Moyer:

$$K_3 = 1 + \frac{1}{4} \left(\frac{v}{100} \right)^2 \qquad (10\text{-}3)$$

where y = per cent of moisture in steam.

10-4. Leakage.   The leakage of working fluid in turbines occurs between stages, past the shaft, and around the balance piston.   In general, leakage is considered a loss in so far as the leakage fluid may be ineffective in doing work on the blading, cause local disturbances or turbulence, or represent a material loss of the working fluid itself.

Interstage leakage is composed of diaphragm leakage and blade tip leakage.   Diaphragm leakage takes place in both impulse and reaction stages through the radial clearance between the stationary nozzle diaphragm and the shaft or drum.   Tip leakage occurs in reaction stages through the clearance between the outer periphery of the moving blades and the casing because of the pressure differential which exists across the blades.

Tip leakage is not considered for impulse blades since the pressure differential is at most very small.   Even when impulse blades are designed for some reaction, the holes which are normally drilled in the disc prevent any appreciable pressure difference.   Diaphragm and tip leakage represents a deduction from the mass rate of flow effective in doing work on the blades and consequently is a loss. Tip leakage is even more serious because the local disturbances it creates contribute to further loss. These disturbances are caused by the difference in flow direction of the leakage fluid and the fluid passing through the blades, the tip leakage flowing axially while the flow through the blades conforms in general to the blade profile.

Interstage leakage becomes increasingly less toward the low-pressure stages. This can be seen if it is granted that clearances are substantially constant in all stages. Then with increasing specific volume and decreasing pressure, the mass rate of flow must decrease.

Shaft leakage occurs through the radial clearance between the shaft and casing at both the high- and low-pressure ends of turbines. Normally, fluid leaks to the atmosphere at the high-pressure end of turbines because of the positive pressure inside the casing. This condition is also true at the low-pressure end of gas turbines and noncondensing steam turbines. Since a vacuum exists inside the casing at the low-pressure end of condensing steam turbines, atmospheric air leaks into the turbine. Air leakage may also occur at the high-pressure end of all turbines during the starting period or at conditions of extremely low load. The shaft leakage of working fluid represents a loss of the fluid and its associated energy. Air leakage imposes an additional burden on the condenser air ejectors and tends also to decrease the vacuum with an attendant decrease in available energy.

Balance-piston leakage occurs between the balance piston and the casing. This leakage, however, is not a complete loss, since it is usually bled off and introduced in a lower-pressure stage where it may be effective in doing work. When balance-piston leakage is handled in this manner, only a very small amount of high-pressure shaft leakage is possible.

10-5. Preventive Measures to Reduce Leakage. An obvious means of minimizing leakage is to reduce clearances as much as possible after providing for expansion of turbine parts so as to avoid rubbing or metal-to-metal contact. When this has been done, it is necessary to use seals or packing to further reduce the leakage flow. These seals usually take the form of labyrinths, carbon rings, water, steam or air seals, or gland leak-off. Labyrinths are commonly used for balance piston and interstage leakage. For shaft leakage, labyrinths may be used with carbon rings and gland leak-off. Very small turbines may use carbon rings alone for shaft leakage. Water or steam seals are used to prevent air leakage. Air seals are used in gas turbines to prevent shaft leakage.

10-6. Labyrinth Seals. Labyrinth seals consist of a series of thin strips fixed to the casing or other stationary member and arranged so as

to maintain the smallest possible clearance with the shaft. The small
constrictions increase the velocity
of the leakage fluid only to have it
dissipated in the pockets, thus
effectively throttling the fluid.
Figure 10-2 shows a stepped labyrinth. The tips of the strips are
made extremely thin so that if
rubbing occurs the tips will wear
away without damaging or distort-
ing the shaft. Figure 10-3 shows
some labyrinth arrangements.

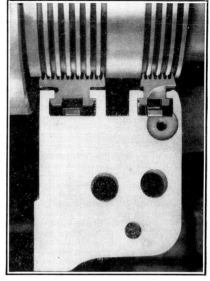

It must be borne in mind that
labyrinth seals do not prevent
entirely the leakage of fluid but are
effective only in reducing the leakage to a tolerable quantity. The
effectiveness of the labyrinth seal
is a function of the number of labyrinths employed for a particular
pressure drop. Enough labyrinths

Fig. 10-2. Stepped labyrinth. (Courtesy of
General Electric Company.)

should be used to throttle the leakage flow to a pressure approaching
that existing in the area into which the leakage is discharged.

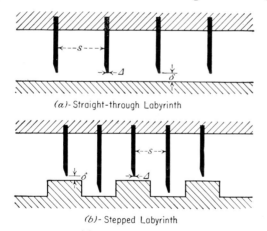

(a)-Straight-through Labyrinth

(b)- Stepped Labyrinth

Fig. 10-3. Labyrinth seals: (a) straight-through labyrinth; (b) stepped labyrinth.

The following equation derived by Egli and confirmed by his experiments gives generally satisfactory results:

$$G_L = \frac{\pi D \delta f_c f_{pr} \phi}{144} \sqrt{g \frac{P}{v_0}} \qquad (10\text{-}4)$$

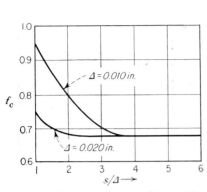

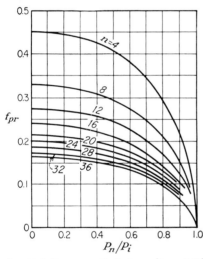

Fig. 10-4. Contraction factors. (*From Egli.*[5])

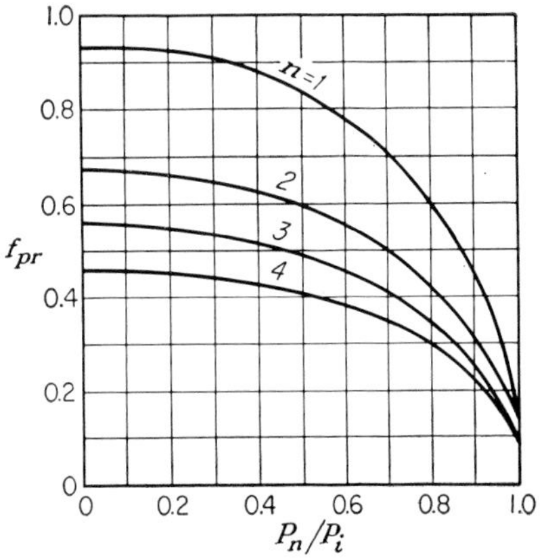

Fig. 10-5. Pressure ratio factors. (*From Egli.*[5])

Fig. 10-6. Pressure ratio factors. (*From Egli.*[5])

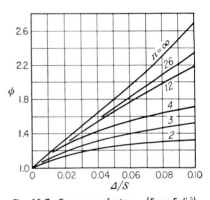

Fig. 10-7. Carry-over factors. (*From Egli.*[5])

where G_L = leakage, lb per sec

δ = radial clearance, in.

D = clearance diameter, in.

f_c = contraction factor for throttling from Fig. 10-4

f_{pr} = pressure-ratio factor for labyrinth from Fig. 10-5 or Fig. 10-6

ϕ = carry-over factor from Fig. 10-7

ϕ = 1 for stepped labyrinths

g = acceleration due to gravity, ft per sec^2

P_0 = pressure entering labyrinth, psf abs

P_n = pressure leaving labyrinth, psf abs

Δ = thickness at tip of strip, in.

v_0 = specific volume entering labyrinth, cu ft per lb
s = pitch of strips

Equation (10-4) may be used for steam or gas.

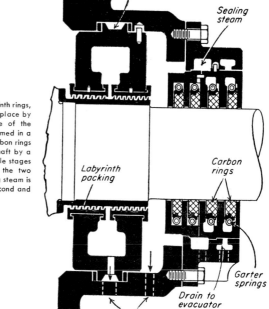

The labyrinth seal consists of two labyrinth rings, each made of four segments and held in place by a split retaining ring. Fins on the face of the labyrinth rings mesh between the fins formed in a sleeve on the shaft. Each of the four carbon rings is made of four segments held to the shaft by a garter spring. Steam leak-offs to suitable stages in the turbine are provided between the two labyrinth and carbon-ring seals. Sealing steam is supplied at low pressure between the second and third carbon rings.

Fig. 10-8. Combination labyrinth and carbon-ring shaft seals. (*Courtesy of Socony Vacuum Oil Company.*)

Fig. 10-9. Carbon packing rings. (*Courtesy of Worthington Corporation.*)

10-7. Carbon-ring Seals. Carbon rings present an effective seal against shaft leakage in small turbines and are used extensively in conjunction with labyrinth and water seals for shaft leakage in larger turbines. In multistaged turbines carbon rings are used with labyrinths to minimize stage leakage. Carbon-ring seals, as the name implies, consist of a ring of carbon rectangular in cross section and usually divided into four segments.   The rings fit snugly into a recess in the casing and are kept tight against the shaft by means of a garter spring.   Since there is actual contact between the carbon ring and the shaft, a certain amount of wear is unavoidable, making it necessary to replace the rings periodically.   Figures 10-8 to 10-10 show carbon rings used as a shaft seals.

10-8. Water, Steam, and Air Seals.   The water seal is essentially a centrifugal pump runner or impeller placed on the turbine shaft.   The runner maintains the water in a high-pressure ring at its periphery, thus providing an effective seal.   Condensate or clean water is supplied to the runner.   Since the water seal is not fully effective at less than operat-

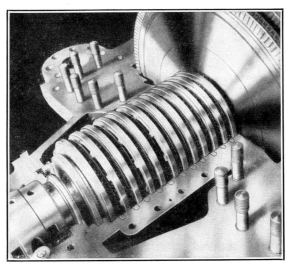

Fig. 10-10. Assembled carbon packing gland.   (*Courtesy of Worthington Corporation.*)

ing speed, it is always supplemented by labyrinths.   Figures 10-11 and 10-12 show a water seal and labyrinth combination.

The power required by the water-seal runner represents a deduction from the useful work done by the turbine.   The loss per runner may be obtained from Martin's formula:

$$\mathrm{hp}_{ws} = 0.25 \left[2 \left(\frac{D_i}{10} \right)^5 - \left(\frac{D_a}{10} \right)^5 - \left(\frac{D_b}{10} \right)^5 \right] \left(\frac{N}{1000} \right)^3 \qquad (10\text{-}5)$$

where hp_{ws} = power loss per runner, hp

   D_i = peripheral diameter of runner, in.

D_a and D_i = inside diameter rotating rings of water on each side of impeller

   N = speed of shaft, rpm

The diameters D_a, D_b, and D_i are a function of the pressure differential inside and outside the turbine casing.

Steam and air seals operate on the same principle, the only difference being the fluid used.   Air is used for gas turbines, and steam is used as the sealing fluid in steam turbines.   In low-pressure steam seals, leak-off steam from the high-pressure seals may be used to create a positive pressure and thus prevent the leakage of air into the turbine.   Some of the sealing steam leaks into the turbine with no serious loss, while the rest leaks out against the incoming air and is drained off.   Sealing steam is sometimes bled from an intermediate stage or from a steam supply line.   Figure 10-8 shows steam seals used in combination with other seals.

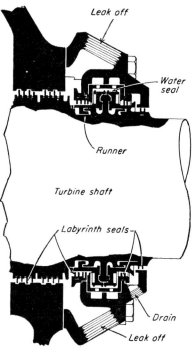

The runner acts like the impeller of a centrifugal pump, building up a pressure in the water and holding it away from the shaft.   For leakage to occur, steam passing the labyrinth seal must flow through the water.   This it cannot do as long as the pressure built up in the water is greater than the pressure of the steam reaching the water seal. The water supply to the seal must be adjusted so that neither leakage of water nor steam occurs.   The water supplied to this type gland should be free from scale-forming impurities.   Foreign substances impair the seal and may cause water to flow along the shaft into the adjacent bearing, thus contaminating the oil.   All drains should be kept open at all times.

Fig. 10-11. Combination water seal and labyrinth seal. (*Courtesy of Socony Vacuum Oil Company.*)

In the gas turbine, air seals may be used at both the high- and low-pressure ends of the turbine.   The air is not only effective in reducing the leakage of gas but is also an aid to cooling the shaft ends before entering the bearings.   Cool air at a pressure somewhat higher than that of the gas inside the casing is introduced to the labyrinth seals.   After being introduced to the labyrinth seals, the air flows into the turbine, preventing leakage of hot gases while some of the air flows outward and is returned at a point in the air circuit of the gas-turbine power plant so that its pressure fluctuates directly with the load.   Figure 10-13 shows an air sealing arrangement.

10-9. Special Sealing Devices. A number of different types of sealing arrangements have been developed for reaction blading.   One method called tip profiling is used for unshrouded blades. The blade tip is beveled to a thin edge and sloped so that a small clearance may be maintained without a danger of serious damage in the event of rubbing. Clearances vary from 0.025 to 0.100 in.

Figures 10-14 and 10-15 show two methods for sealing shrouded blades. Figure 10-15 illustrates the end tightening method which consists of sharp tongues raised on the shroud ring to reduce both the radial

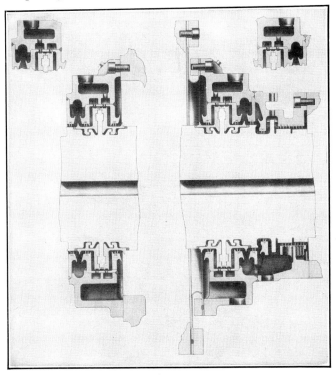

Fig. 10-12. Water seals and labyrinths. (*Courtesy of Westinghouse Electric Corporation.*)

and axial clearances. Another method is shown in Fig. 10-14 in which two radial sealing strips are used to reduce the clearance. Clearances vary from 0.015 to 0.070 in. Any of the methods shown in Figs. 10-14 and 10-15 is much more efficient than tip profiling. In gas turbines, however, it is necessary to omit the shroud band in the low-pressure stages where the tip velocities are high in order to reduce the centrifugal stress at the blade root. Fortunately, with long blades the tip leakage can be kept small.

10-10. Leakage Efficiency, η_l. The leakage efficiency may be found from the following expression:

$$\eta_l = \frac{G - G_L}{G} \tag{10-6}$$

where G = total mass rate of flow, lb per sec
     G_L = leakage mass rate of flow, lb per sec
Equation (10-4) gives the value of G_L for labyrinths. For tip and diaphragm leakage when the special sealing devices described in Sec. 10-9 are used, G_L may be computed approximately from the continuity rela-

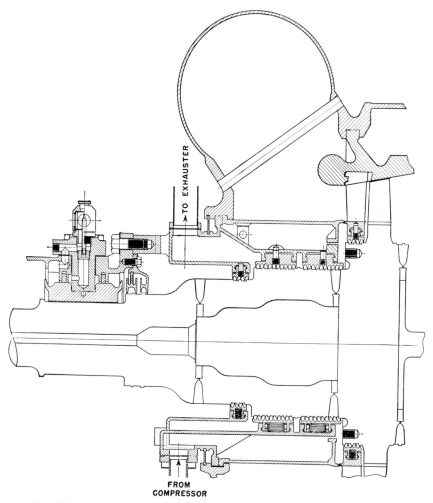

Fig. 10-13. Gas-turbine air seal. (*Courtesy of Allis-Chalmers Manufacturing Company.*)

tion. For tip leakage, a rule of thumb is to decrease the leakage efficiency 2 per cent for each 1 per cent of leakage area. The per cent of leakage area is obtained by dividing the clearance area by the sum of the clearance area and the blade passage area. Carbon-ring-seal leakage may also be approximated from the continuity equation.

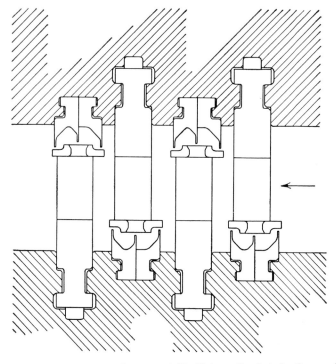

Fig. 10-14. End tightening. *(Courtesy of Allis-Chalmers Manufacturing Company.)*

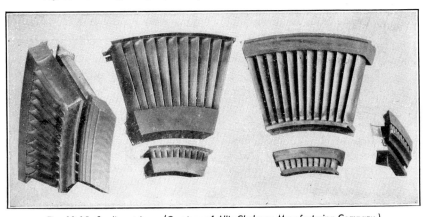

Fig. 10-15. Sealing strips. *(Courtesy of Allis-Chalmers Manufacturing Company.)*

10-11. Bearing Losses. The losses which occur in bearings depend on the type of bearing, load, oil viscosity, speed of shaft, bearing surface area, and film thickness. For design purposes, it is satisfactory to assume a loss of 1 per cent of the turbine internal output for each bearing, including thrust bearings.

10-12. Radiation Losses. Radiation losses in steam turbines are usually very small and can be neglected. Since the high-temperature steam is confined to the smallest part of the casing and large temperature drops take place in the high-pressure Curtis stages, the radiation losses are correspondingly small. Lagging reduces the radiation loss to a negligible quantity.

In gas turbines radiation losses may be much more significant if adequate insulation is not provided. In fact, all pipes carrying the hot gases, as well as the turbine itself, must be well insulated.

10-13. Miscellaneous Losses. Care must be taken to avoid significant pressure drops in turbine inlet and outlet passages. This is particularly true of the gas turbine. High velocities, abrupt changes in flow direction, and obstructions must be carefully avoided. In steam turbines some pressure losses are unavoidable, such as those which occur in the steam strainer, governor valve, and throttling valve. These losses range from 5 per cent of the pressure on the boiler side of the throttle valve for stationary steam turbines and may be as high as 15 psi in marine steam turbines with involved throttling systems.

10-14. Stage Output and Efficiency. In computing the stage output, account must be taken of the nozzle and blade losses, parasitic losses, interstage leakage losses, and carry-over. The stage efficiency is the output of the stage divided by the available energy of the stage. The output of an impulse stage operating with full peripheral admission and carry-over is given by the expression

$$E_{\text{stage}} = G \left[\frac{2gJ(\Delta h_S) + V_1^2}{550 \times 2g} \right] U \eta_n \eta_b \eta_l - \text{hp}_{df} \qquad (10\text{-}7)$$

where E_{stage} = output of stage, hp
Δh_S = isentropic enthalpy drop in stage, Btu per lb
V_1 = carry-over velocity, fps
G = mass rate of flow, lb per sec
η_n = nozzle efficiency
η_b = blading efficiency
η_l = leakage efficiency for stage
hp_{df} = disc friction losses, hp

For an impulse stage with partial admission, Eq. (10-7) becomes

$$E_{\text{stage}} = G \left(\frac{J(\Delta h_S)_{\text{stage}}}{550} \right) U \eta_n \eta_b \eta_l - \text{hp}_r \qquad (10\text{-}8)$$

where hp_r = friction and windage loss in horsepower. For a reaction stage of two rows,

$$E_{\text{stage}} = G \eta_s \left[\frac{2gJ(\Delta h_S)_{\text{stage}} + V_1^2}{500 \times 2g} \right] U \eta_s \eta_l \qquad (10\text{-}9)$$

where η_l = leakage efficiency for stage, including diaphragm and tip leakage.

The stage efficiency η_s may be computed simply by dividing the appropriate equation for stage output expressed in Btu per pound per second of flow of fluid by the available energy of the stage $(\Delta h_S)_{stage}$, expressed in the same units.

10-15. Turbine Output. The internal output of the turbine is equivalent to the sum of the outputs of the individual stages less the over-all internal losses, such as shaft leakage, radiation, dummy leakage, and water-, steam-, or air-seal losses but not including the bearing and governor and pump losses. The shaft output is equal to the internal output less the bearing, pump, and governor losses.

TURBINE ROTOR

10-16. Blade Stresses. The determination of the blade stresses is a critical factor regardless of the type of blades being designed. Gas-turbine blading is particularly important from the stress standpoint because of the high temperatures encountered. The severest stresses are imposed by the centrifugal forces due to high rotational speeds. Bending stresses are also imposed by centrifugal force, fluid-pressure differences, and vibration. Provision must be made in the blade design to withstand all these stresses encountered in operation.

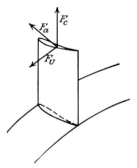

Fig. 10-16. Centrifugal and bending forces on a turbine blade.

10-17. Centrifugal Stresses. Centrifugal stresses are a function of the mass of material in the blade, blade length, and rotational speed. It is the component of centrifugal force acting radially outward which is of concern here. This force exerts a tensile stress at the blade root which tends to pull the blade away from the disc or rotor. Obviously sufficient cross-sectional area must be provided in the blade at the root and a material capable of withstanding the stress without fatigue must also be provided.

Consider a single blade fixed to a disc as shown in Fig. 10-16. Designating the area of the blade section as a, in square inches, and the specific weight of the blade material as γ, in pounds per square inch, then

$$dF = \frac{\gamma a \, dr}{12g} \, \omega^2 r \tag{10-10}$$

where dF is the centrifugal force on an element of blade dr located at a radius r. The total centrifugal force exerted at the blade root due to the mass of the entire blade is obtained by integrating Eq. (10-10) between the limits r_r and r_t.

$$F_c = \int_{r_r}^{r_t} \frac{\gamma a \, dr \, \omega^2 r}{12g}$$

and

$$F_c = \frac{\gamma a \omega^2}{12g} \left(\frac{r_t^2}{2} - \frac{r_r^2}{2} \right)$$

or

$$F_c = \frac{\gamma a \omega^2}{24g\pi} A = \frac{\gamma a A}{24g\pi} \left(\frac{2\pi N}{60} \right)^2 \tag{10-11}$$

where A = annular area, sq in.

N = rotational speed, rpm

The centrifugal stress at the blade root is the centrifugal force divided by the area of the blade section, assuming a constant-section blade,

$$S_c = 4.52 \gamma A \left(\frac{N}{1000} \right)^2 \tag{10-12}$$

where S_c = tensile stress due to centrifugal force, lb per sq in.

N = rotational speed, rpm

If the blade is tapered, the mass of material is reduced, thereby reducing the centrifugal stress. Since the stress exerted at any section of the blading decreases radially, reaching a minimum near the tip, a constant cross-sectional area is not required for strength. Hence where the centrifugal stresses are severe the blade is tapered by decreasing both its thickness and width. If a tapered blade is used, Eq. (10-12) is modified by the taper factor f_t.

$$S_c = 4.52 \gamma f_t A \left(\frac{N}{1000} \right)^2 \tag{10-13}$$

Values of the taper factor may be found from Fig. 10-17 where they are given as a function of area ratio and type of taper. A taper somewhere between a linear and conical taper appears to be most practical.

10-18. Bending Stresses. Impulse blades are subject to bending from centrifugal stress and the tangential force exerted by the fluid. Reaction blades have an additional bending stress due to large axial thrust because of the pressure drop which occurs in the blades. All turbine blades may be subjected to bending because of vibration. Consider first the bending due to axial thrust. The axial force exerted on an element of blade (Fig. 10-16) is

$$dF_a = \Delta P \frac{2\pi}{z} r \, dr \tag{10-14}$$

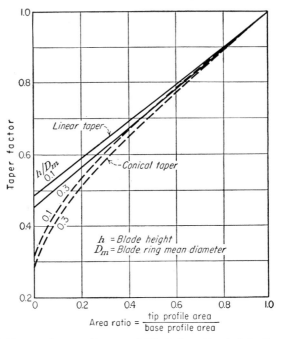

Fig. 10-17. Taper factors. *(Courtesy of Allis-Chalmers Manufacturing Company.)*

where F_a = axial force, lb

ΔP = pressure drop across blades, psi

z = number of blades in row

r = radial distance, in.

The moment of the axial bending force about the blade root,

$$dM_a = \Delta P \frac{2\pi}{z} (r - r_r)r \, dr$$

Integrating with ΔP constant everywhere along the blade height,

$$M_a = \frac{\Delta P 2\pi}{z} \int_{r_r}^{r_t} (r - r_r)r \, dr$$

$$M_a = \frac{\Delta P \pi}{3z} (r_r^3 - 3r_r r_t^2 + 2r_t^3)$$

or $$M_a = \frac{\Delta P \pi h_b^2}{3z} (r_r + 2r_t) \qquad \text{lb-ft} \qquad (10\text{-}15)$$

The bending force due to tangential thrust on an element of blade is

$$dF_U = \frac{2\pi}{z} (dm_1 V_{1U} - dm_2 V_{2U})r \, dr \qquad m = \text{mass, slugs}$$

or $$dF_U = \frac{2\pi}{gz} \left(\frac{V_{1a}V_{1U}}{v_1} - \frac{V_{2a}V_{2U}}{v_2} \right) r \, dr$$

The bending moment taken around the blade root

$$dM_U = \frac{2\pi}{gz} \left(\frac{V_{1a}V_{1U}}{v_1} - \frac{V_{2a}V_{2U}}{v_2} \right) (r - r_r)r \, dr$$

or

$$M_U = \frac{2\pi}{gz} \int_{r_r}^{r_t} \left(\frac{V_{1a}V_{1U}}{v_1} - \frac{V_{2a}V_{2U}}{v_2} \right) (r - r_r)r \, dr \qquad (10\text{-}16)$$

If the ratio of V_a/v can be regarded as being constant without serious error and if free-vortex flow is assumed, Eq. (10-16) can be put in a form which is easily integrated:

$$M_U = \frac{2\pi}{gz} \frac{V_a}{v} \int_{r_r}^{r_t} \left(\frac{r_m}{r} V_{1Um} - \frac{r_m}{r} V_{2Um} \right) (r - r_r) \, dr$$

or

$$M_U = \frac{2\pi}{gz} \frac{V_a}{v} r_m \int_{r_r}^{r_t} \Delta V_U (r - r_r) \, dr$$

and

$$M_U = \frac{\Delta V_U \, \pi r_m h_b{}^2 V_a}{gzv} \qquad (10\text{-}17)$$

If free-vortex flow is not applicable, then Eq. (10-16) must be integrated graphically. All the values in Eq. (10-16) will be known for every section on the blade in an actual case.

Normally, the blade outline is obtained by laying out the blade sections at their several radii so that the locus of their centroids forms a straight radial line. The blade surfaces are generated by a series of straight lines in order to simplify the forging or casting problems. However, if the centroids are put out of alignment due to fluid bending moments, then there results an opposing bending moment from the centrifugal force. It is usual to neglect the bending moment resulting from centrifugal force, since this procedure is on the safe side and a very tedious computation is eliminated.

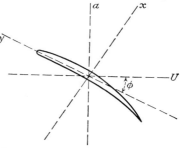

Fig. 10-18. Principal axis for turbine blade.

The bending moments M_a and M_c are referred to the axial and tangential axes, respectively, and must be transferred to the principal axes of inertia x and y, as shown in Fig. 10-18, in order to determine the stresses. A method for finding the principal axes of inertia may be obtained from any standard text on strength of materials. Similarly the methods for obtaining the moments of inertia about these axes may be reviewed.

For the entrance or leading edge of the blade the stress is

$$S_{bl} = \frac{M_x C_{xl}}{I_{xl}} + \frac{M_y C_{yl}}{I_{yl}} \qquad (10\text{-}18)$$

and for the exit edge

$$S_{be} = \frac{M_x C_{xe}}{I_{xe}} - \frac{M_y C_{ye}}{I_{ye}} \qquad (10\text{-}19)$$

and for a point located at the intersection of the y axis and the back of the blade which of course is subjected to compression stress

$$S_b = -\frac{M_x C_b}{I_t} \qquad (10\text{-}20)$$

It is to be noted that the positive sign stands for tension and the negative sign for compression.

The total stress at a given point on a turbine blade may be found by adding the centrifugal stress at that point to the bending stress. It is clear that since the entrance edge of the blade is in tension from the bending forces and the centrifugal stress is tensile, the maximum stress will be found at the entrance edge.

Sometimes for turbine blades of the vortex type the centroids of the sections at the various radii are lined up so that the blade leans in the direction of rotation. This arrangement results in a bending component of the centrifugal force which is counter to the fluid bending forces, thus reducing to some extent the total bending stress on the blade. In these cases the bending moments due to centrifugal force must be calculated.

10-19. Vibrations. An examination of the theory of vibration in turbine blades and discs is not within the scope of this book. However, it is desirable to present some of the pertinent facts.

Turbine blades are subject to resonant vibrations induced by irregularities in the fluid flow path resulting from such obstructions as struts, the nonsymmetry of stationary passages, disturbances in the wake of stationary blades, nonsymmetry of radial-pressure distribution, shock, and partial admission. Although partial admission is rarely used in gas turbines, a similar effect is introduced by separate combustion chambers. If the blades are fixed to a disc, the vibrations may be transmitted to the disc, the blades and disc vibrating as though they constituted a continuous disc. Blades fixed to a drum in common with the blades of other stages generally do not transmit vibrations to the drum. The reason for this appears to be in the damping mass and stiffness of the drum. Where blade failures have occurred, many times the failure cracks have extended to the discs, but where a drum was used, the failure was confined to the blades alone.

The frequency of vibration is seen to depend on the stiffness and mass of the blades. Lashing or lacing wires and shrouds add stiffness to the blades and in some measure can be used to dampen or increase the frequency of vibrations. Some blade materials exhibit better damping characteristics than others; a 12 per cent chrome steel is excellent for this purpose.

When the blade and disc assembly is considered as a unit along with shrouding and lacing wires, or if the blades are unsymmetrical, as is particularly the case with free-vortex blades, then an analytical determination of vibration frequency is not too fruitful because of the many variables which have to be taken into account. Although a few empirical relationships have been advanced, the only safe procedure is to test the assembly, making suitable modifications to increase or decrease the vibration frequency. Slackening the lacing wires or shroud and removing metal from the blade near the root will lower the frequency. Stiffening the shroud or lacing wires and removing metal near the blade tips will have the opposite effect. This process is referred to as tuning.

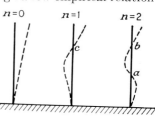

a, b and *c* are nodes
n = Number of nodes

Fig. 10-19. Modes of vibration for turbine blades.

Figure 10-19 illustrates in principle the modes of vibration of turbine blades. Here an unshrouded and unlaced turbine blade is approximated by a uniformly loaded cantilever beam. The mode of vibration is identified in terms of the number of nodes. The fundamental or first mode of vibration corresponds to $n = 0$, the second mode to $n = 1$, the third to $n = 2$, etc. For a uniformly loaded cantilever beam, the transverse or bending vibration frequency is given by the general expression

$$f_t = \frac{\psi_n}{2\pi} \sqrt{\frac{EIg}{wh^4}} \qquad (10\text{-}21)$$

where f_t = frequency, cycles per sec
ψ_n = constant depending on the mode of vibration or number of nodes
E = modulus of elasticity, psi
I = moment of inertia of section, in.^{4}
w = weight per unit length, lb
h = length of beam, in.

The values of the constant ψ_n are as follows:

$$n = 0 \qquad \psi_0 = 3.52$$
$$n = 1 \qquad \psi_1 = 22.4$$
$$n = 2 \qquad \psi_2 = 61.7$$

For a tapered blade, Eq. (10-21) is modified by an experimentally determined frequency factor k_f, which may be obtained from Fig. 10-20. Equation (10-21) thus modified may be rewritten to yield the frequency of the fundamental mode of transverse vibration.

$$f_t = \frac{3.52}{2\pi} k_f \sqrt{\frac{EIg}{Wh_b^3}}$$
(10-22)

where E = modulus of elasticity at operating temperature of the blade
  I = moment of inertia of root section of blade, in.[4]
  W = weight of blade, lb
  h_b = blade height, in.
  k_f = frequency factor

In general, destructive vibratory stresses can be avoided if the frequency of the blade, as determined from Eq. (10-22), is at least 5 per cent

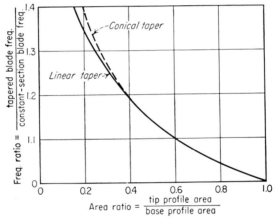

Fig. 10-20. Frequency factors. (*Courtesy of Allis-Chalmers Manufacturing Company.*)

higher than four times the maximum speed at which the turbine is expected to operate.

Centrifugal force causes a stiffening of the blades with a resulting increase in frequency. This effect is not usually very large and can be estimated from the following expression proposed by Campbell:

$$f_r = \sqrt{f_t^2 + B\left(\frac{N}{60}\right)^2}$$

where f_r = combined frequency, cycles per sec
  B = rotation coefficient
  N = speed of rotation, rpm

Figure 10-21 gives practical values of B for the usual blade constructions.

10-20. Disc Stresses. In the standard steam impulse stage the turbine blades are usually carried on discs which are integral with the shaft. In smaller turbines or low-temperature turbines the disc may be shrunk and keyed to the shaft. A few small gas turbines consisting of one or two stages are equipped in the same way.

For higher-speed impulse turbines (3600 rpm or higher) such as in the control or high-pressure stage of large turbines, the shaft and disc are machined from one solid forging.

Reaction blades are usually fixed to a center-bored forged rotor consisting of one piece. Under some circumstances a hollow forging or drum is used to carry reaction blades.

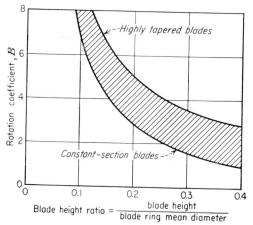

Fig. 10-21. Rotation coefficients. (*Courtesy of Allis-Chalmers Manufacturing Company.*)

The analysis of the stresses in these rotors is similar, no matter which type is used. The stresses involved are both tangential and radial. If a solid flat disc rotating at high speed is considered, it is known from elastic theory that the radial and tangential stresses are a maximum at the center. Now if a hole is center bored in the disc, the tangential stress at the periphery of the hole is doubled while the radial stress becomes zero. If the hole is enlarged, the tangential stress at its periphery is increased, as is the tangential stress at the outer periphery of the disc. The tangential stress at the periphery of the hole is greater than that at the periphery of the disc, a stress gradient existing which drops rapidly at first and then slowly until the outer periphery of the disc is reached. The radial stress reaches a maximum somewhere between the limits of zero at the periphery of the hole and zero at the outer periphery of the disc. Under all circumstances the tangential stress is greater than the radial stress and is of prime concern.

The higher tangential stress at the periphery of the hole has been found experimentally to be a local stress concentration which is apparently relieved by plastic flow when the elastic limit is reached. As far as the ability of the disc to carry blades is concerned, there is little effect from centering boring.

An accurate or precise determination of the stresses in a disc may be desirable for certain purposes, but the relationships are too involved to be included here. If it is assumed that the cross-sectional area of the disc is uniformly loaded as far as centrifugal load is concerned, then the average tangential stress across the radial cross section of the disc provides an important stress parameter.

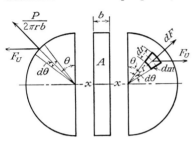

Consider a disc of uniform thickness uniformly loaded centrifugally, as described in the preceding paragraph.

Fig. 10-22. Tangential stress in constant-thickness disc.

Consider first the disc without the load. Then the tangential force exerted on the disc half section due to an element of mass on the rotating disc is (see Fig. 10-22)

$$dF_U = (dm\ \omega^2 r) \sin \theta$$

or

$$dF_U = 2mr(2\pi N)^2 \sin \theta \tag{10-23}$$

But

$$dm = \rho\, dA\ b = \rho r\, d\theta\, dr\, b$$

where ρ = mass density, slugs per cu ft

A = area of disc half section

Substituting in Eq. (10-23) and integrating,

$$F_U = (2\pi N)^2 \rho b \int_0^r \int_0^\pi \sin \theta\, d\theta\ r^2\, dr \tag{10-24}$$

or

$$F_U = (2\pi N)^2 \rho b\, \frac{2r^3}{3}$$

Since $br^3/3 = I$ for the disc half section, Eq. (10-24) may be expressed

$$F_U = (2\pi N)^2 2\rho I \tag{10-25}$$

Then the uniform load carried by the disc at its outer periphery is applied to the disc half section and the tangential stress is

$$F_U = \int_0^\pi \frac{P}{2\pi r b} \sin \theta\, d\theta\ b$$

$$F_U = \frac{P}{\pi} \tag{10-26}$$

The average tangential stress over the disc cross-sectional area may be obtained by dividing the sum of Eqs. (10-25) and (10-26) by $2A$, the disc cross-sectional area, or

$$S_{DU} = \frac{(2\pi N)^2 2\rho I + \dfrac{P}{\pi}}{2A}$$

or

$$S_{DU} = 28.4\gamma \left(\frac{N}{1000}\right)^2 \left(\frac{I}{A}\right) + \frac{P}{2\pi A} \qquad (10\text{-}27)$$

where S_{DU} = average tangential stress of disc, psi
γ = specific weight of disc, lb per cu in.
I = moment of inertia of disc half section about xx
N = speed of disc, rpm
A = area of disc half section, sq in.
P = total peripheral load, lb

The limit of the permissible average tangential stress obtained from Eq. (10-27) is one-third the yield strength of the material used taken at the normal speed. Another consideration of particular importance in

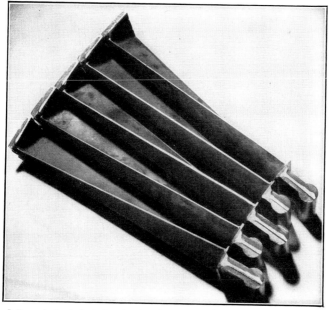

Fig. 10-23. Bulb and shank fastening for impulse blade. (*Courtesy of De Laval Steam Turbine Company.*)

high-temperature gas turbines is the permissible creep during the anticipated life of the turbine.

10-21. Blade Fastenings. There are a number of different methods for fixing turbine blades to the disc or drum, depending on the conditions of service. The type of fastening selected must be adequate to resist the centrifugal and bending forces to which the blades may be subjected. Blades which are loosely fastened to the disc or drum will amplify any vibrations induced in the blades, causing fatigue failure. It must be remembered that the failure of one blade may lead to the destruction of the entire turbine.

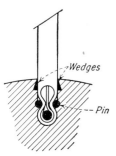

Figure 10-23 shows the bulb and shank type of fastening which is suitable for low-pressure impulse steam turbines. This type of fastening is slipped axially into similarly shaped slots on the disc. The fastening is then tightened in place by the insertion of two wedges. The bulb and shank type of fastening has been used in European gas turbines. Figure 10-24 illustrates a type of bulb and shank attachment used by the Germans for hollow blades in the BMW 003 turbine.

Fig. 10-24. Fastening for BMW 003 turbine blade.

Figure 10-25 illustrates another type of fastening known as the straddle-T which is widely used on low-pressure impulse steam turbines. A modification of the straddle-T fastening known simply as a straddle

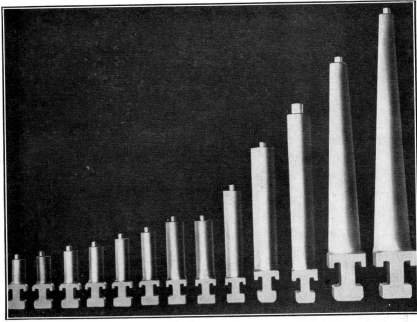

Fig. 10-25. Straddle-T fastenings. (*Courtesy of Westinghouse Electric Corporation.*)

fastening is shown in Fig. 10-26. This type of fastening is used for the long low-pressure blades of large steam turbines. The straddle fastening is slipped radially into the slot provided on the disc or drum at a

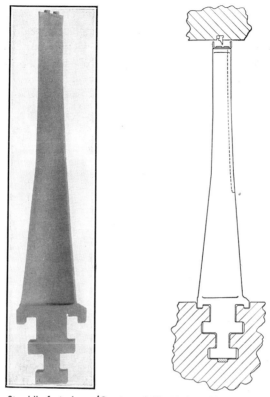

Fig. 10-26. Straddle fastening. (*Courtesy of Allis-Chalmers Manufacturing Company.*)

point that is widened for this purpose. The blades are then pushed along in the slot until the last blade is inserted, whereupon a special stop piece is put in place. Usually two diametrically opposed entrance points are provided in the slot in order to preserve symmetry.

Figure 10-27 shows a T-shaped attachment which is used in the high-pressure impulse stages of large steam turbines and in some gas turbines. This type of fastening is inserted radially in the manner described for the straddle-T fastening.

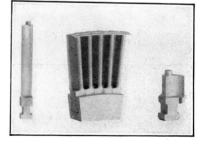

Fig. 10-27. T-shaped fastening. (*Courtesy of Allis-Chalmers Manufacturing Company.*)

Figure 10-28 illustrates the Christmas-tree or fir-tree attachment. This type of fastening which is inserted on the disc axially is the most satisfactory for Rateau control stages, long free-vortex blades, and gas-turbine blades. The Christmas-tree fastening is obviously inserted on the disc axially and therefore cannot be used on a drum except in the very last row.   In order to avoid the large axial clearance required for insertion of this fastening, the discs must be stepped.   This type of fastening is advantageous in that it provides a wide axial dimension and sufficiently large area of contact to handle heavy centrifugal forces.

Gas-turbine blades are sometimes welded in place, a scheme which appears to be very desirable from a production point of view.   Although

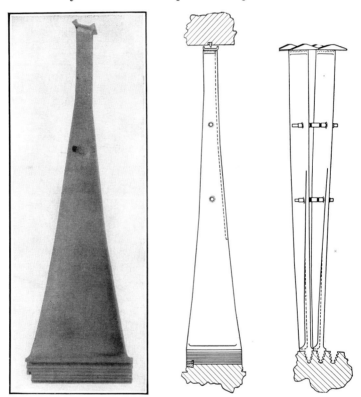

Fig. 10-28. Christmas-tree or fir-tree fastening.   (*Courtesy of Allis-Chalmers Manufacturing Company.*)

welding has met with wide acceptance in short-life turbines in this country, particularly in aircraft gas turbines, there is the ever-present likelihood of distortion, imperfect welds, or serious stress concentrations. Therefore in the long-life plants used in stationary practice the blades are generally not welded to the disc or drum.

10-22. Shrouding.   The shroud is a band placed around the periphery of the blade tips in order to stiffen the blades and prevent spillage of the fluid over the blade tips.   This is particularly important in reaction turbines where a pressure gradient exists across the moving blades although formerly reaction blades were unshrouded.   In high-pressure impulse blades where partial admission is employed, the shroud is beneficial in stiffening the blades which are subjected to vibration.

Shrouds may be continuous or in segments integral with one or more blades, as shown in Figs. 10-15 and 10-23. The continuous shroud is usually attached to the blades by means of tenons cast or forged integral with the blade. The tenons fit through holes in the shroud and are riveted into smooth spherical surfaces. Tenons are shown on the blades of Fig. 10-25. Often the so-called continuous shroud is not continuous at all but is broken between groups of blades with a space of 0.03 in. allowed for expansion. The truly continuous shroud has a tendency to distort under the influence of high temperatures and may break away from the tenon, causing eventual blade failure. This aspect of shrouding is particularly important in gas turbines since blade materials are usually 50 per cent austenitic and considerable flexibility must be incorporated in the design to take care of expansion.

The weight of the shroud adds considerably to the centrifugal stresses at the blade root. This consideration is of particular importance in gas turbines where stresses are a major concern. Fortunately, with the longer gas turbine blades where centrifugal stresses are most critical the leakage losses over the blade tips can be kept small within the limits of safe operating clearances. In such cases the shroud is omitted. In shorter blades the shroud must be used to give more effective control of both leakage and bending stresses.

10-23. Lacing Wires. One of the reasons for using a shroud on turbine blading is to hold the blades in their correct position under the influence of bending forces. If shrouding is not used in long blades, then lacing or lashing wires must be used to keep the blades in alignment and to add stiffness. In very long blades both the shroud and lacing wires must be used. Figure 1-11 shows the lacing wires used with the long low-pressure reaction blades of a large steam turbine.

Formerly the lacing wire was strung through bossed holes machined in the blade. The wires were then silver-soldered or brazed to the blades. This method usually resulted in local stress concentrations which were often a cause for blade failure. It is the practice at present to weld short pieces of lacing wire of airfoil-shaped cross section to each side of the blade. When the blade has been finish-machined and stress relieved, the sections of lacing wire touch each other and may be joined by welding or by a welded sleeve. A disadvantage of the lacing wire lies in the fact that it disturbs flow patterns and contributes to vibration tendencies. This is one of the reasons an airfoil cross section is used for the lacing wire.

10-24. Cooling of Gas-turbine Blades. The advantage of high turbine inlet temperature has been mentioned many times in connection with the gas turbine. Cooling gas-turbine blades, whereby the temperature of the metal is kept several hundred degrees lower than the gas temperature, permits the employment of correspondingly higher turbine inlet temperatures with the metals available at present. Another advantage is greater power output for a given size compressor.

The two principal methods of cooling blades are water cooling and air cooling. It would appear that water should be a superior cooling medium because of its comparatively higher specific heat and the possibility of evaporative cooling. However, the difficulties encountered in maintaining a leakproof and simple system coupled with the corrosive and scaling effects of water make it a less desirable coolant. Most of the investigations undertaken up until now have been sponsored by groups primarily interested in the aircraft gas turbine where the advantages of air as a coolant are obvious.

Air cooling may be accomplished by blowing a thin film of cold air through slits pointed rearward along the blade surface. The cold boundary layer thus formed is an effective insulator for the blade. Another method is to inject cold air into hollow blades provided with inserts to distribute the air or into blades provided with cooling holes running radially from root to tip. Laboratory investigations of air-cooled blades have established that gas temperatures about 600 F higher than for uncooled blades are possible. However, the danger of clogged cooling passages, corrosion, and coolant failure are ever present.

The problem of blade cooling is primarily a problem in heat transfer. The question is largely that of attempting to maintain uniform cooling of the blade either by employing air as an insulator as in film cooling or as a conductor in the case of internal cooling.

METALLURGICAL CONSIDERATIONS

10-25 Properties of Metals. The employment of high-temperature steam or gas reduces the allowable stresses for a given material, not to mention the thermal stresses which may be incurred. This is a particularly critical consideration in the gas turbine where the cycle efficiency is extremely sensitive to turbine inlet temperature. In fact, the feasibility of the gas turbine is dependent almost entirely on the availability of high-temperature superalloys.

In considering the suitability of an alloy for a specific application in the turbine, attention must be directed to the temperature expected to be encountered, the maximum stresses and their character, the growth or deformation of the alloy under operating temperatures and stresses, the adaptability of the alloy to manufacturing processes, the expected or desired life of the turbine, and the cost and availability of the alloy.

Some of the more important characteristics of the metals used in steam and gas turbines are reviewed here briefly. More detailed information is best obtained from a standard work devoted entirely to metallurgy.

10-26. Creep. It is observed that a metal subjected to constant stress at constant temperature below the elastic limit undergoes elongation or deformation with time. Creep is the result of slippage along the crystallographic planes of the individual crystals combined with a certain amount of flow of the grain boundary material so that the metal behaves like a plastic substance. When the stress is removed and the metal cooled, only slight recovery takes place with time.

Creep is a matter of serious concern in turbines where close clearances must be maintained and the danger of rubbing of moving parts such as blades can be disastrous. Creep is also an important consideration for bolts and other connecting devices necessary to maintaining tight joints.

Three important tests are performed to determine the creep characteristics of a given material, namely, the creep-rupture test, long-term creep test, and creep-relaxation test.

In the creep-rupture test the metal is subjected to constant stress at constant temperature over the required period of time for failure or fracture.

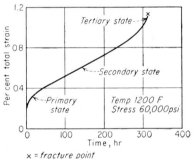

Fig. 10-29. Creep-rupture curve (K-42-B forged).

The stress selected is usually such that failure occurs within 2000 hr. Figure 10-29 shows the results of a typical creep-rupture test for K-42-B alloy at 1200 F and 60,000 psi. This alloy has 20 per cent Cr, 41 per cent Ni, and 22 per cent Co. An examination of Fig. 10-29 reveals that the strain increases at a decreasing rate (slope of curve decreasing) until about 30 hr. This is the primary state in which a combination of elastic and plastic deformation takes place. In the secondary state the slope of the curve is constant, indicating that a steady rate of deformation takes place. The secondary state is also known as the continuous-flow state. In the tertiary state the slope increases rapidly until the material is fractured.

Occasionally structural changes or surface instability may occur, changing the metallurgical condition of the alloy during creep tests. This effect can be readily checked by means of plotting the stress vs. rupture-time relationship on log-log paper. The result is normally a straight line. If the slope of the line changes, some structural or surface instability has occurred which may or may not be important depending on the cause.

In most instances the creep test is conducted as far as the secondary state and the probable deformation of the material is estimated by extrapolation for the life of the machine at the stresses and temperatures expected in service. This type of test is referred to as a long-term creep test. The results of a typical creep test for Timken 16-25-6 alloy are shown in Fig. 10-30.

The ductility of the material before failure takes place is of importance. In the tertiary state most alloys which possess high creep-rupture strength will fracture with low yield or deformation. This is an undesirable characteristic since very little warning is given of an imminent failure. In

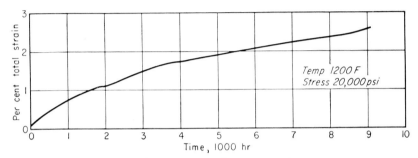

Fig. 10-30. Creep test (Timken 16-25-6).

effect, the material behaves as though it were more or less brittle in the tertiary state.

10-27. Endurance. Materials used in turbines are subjected to the effects of repeated stresses and often fatigue failure is a result. Fatigue failure appears to be caused by rupturing of the atomic bonds resulting from local fragmentation of the crystals. Tiny cracks which cannot be observed by a microscope are formed at first and gradually grow worse until they are visible.

Fatigue failure is of serious concern since it can occur with great suddenness and without warning. The incipient cracks which are at first invisible grow at a very slow rate and if careful periodic examination is made by some special means such as the magnaflux method they may be detected in time.

TABLE 10-1. ENDURANCE STRENGTHS

Material	Stress,* psi
K 42 B	30,000
Nimonic 80	29,000
Cast Hirsch Vitallium	40,000
Timken 16-25-6	20,000

* 1500 F; 120 cycles per sec; 10^8 cycles.

Fortunately, in the turbine, reversal stresses are not dominant. However, this may not be true in a Rateau control stage of a steam turbine operating with partial admission.

In determining the endurance of a material against fatigue failure, the material is subjected to alternating positive and negative stresses at a series of different stress values. By reducing the stress levels, a stress is ultimately determined at which fatigue failure does not occur. This stress is known as the endurance limit. For the alloys usually employed in turbine design there is no clear indication of the endurance limit even after sustaining stress reversals hundreds of millions of times. Each stress reversal sustained is referred to as a cycle and it is usual to report the stress values and number of cycles sustained by the alloy as well as the temperature. Table 10-1 gives the endurance strengths for some superalloys at 10^8 cycles at a standard frequency of 120 cycles per second and at 1500 F.

10-28. Damping. The damping capacity of a material is the amount of internal friction and energy dissipation per unit volume of the material for one cycle of stress. There is no apparent relationship between the damping capacity and any of the other mechanical properties of a material except for the general observation that damping capacity seems to decrease with higher tensile strength. It is certain that the damping capacity bears no relation to the endurance characteristics of the material.

High damping capacity of the material is of importance in blades and discs subject to vibration if fatigue failure is to be avoided. For this purpose it has been found that high chrome-content alloys are very satisfactory. Chrome alloys with 13 per cent of chrome or more are generally in use for both steam and gas-turbine blades subjected to high stresses at high temperature.

10-29. Corrosion; Oxidation. Hot turbine parts operate in an oxidizing atmosphere and therefore the materials used must be resistant to corrosion. In steam turbines, dissolved or free oxygen and carbon dioxide in the steam and salt deposits left by the steam are causes of corrosion and oxidation and may result in eventual failure from fatigue if corrosion-resistant materials are not used. The problem is even more severe in gas turbines which are exposed to highly corrosive and oxidizing combustion gases. The fact that a material has excellent strength properties is a secondary consideration, since the loss of metal by scaling, spalling, and chemical attack on its constituents by corrosion can cause rapid failure. However, it is a fortunate coincidence that most of the alloys used because of other desirable properties are highly resistant to corrosion and oxidation. The constituents of these alloys, notably chromium, place them among the stainless types.

TABLE 10-2. CHEMICAL COMPOSITION AND PROPERTIES OF SOME ALLOYS

Material	Chemical composition										Stress to rupture, 1000 hr, 1000 psi	Endurance strength[c] at 1500 F	Uses
	C	Mn	Si	Cr	Co	W	Mo	Cb	Ti	Al			
Cyclops 17-A	0.40	0.65	1.1	7.5	...	...	...	...	...	...	......	44,000[a]	Steam-turbine blades
Cyclops 17-W	0.46	0.58	0.43	13	...	...	...	...	...	...	19,000[a]	37,000[d]	Steam-turbine blades Gas-turbine discs
S-816	0.40	0.75	0.75	20	42	4	4	4	...	...	18,000[b]	33,000	Gas-turbine blades
S-590	0.40	0.50	0.50	20	20	4	4	4	...	...	15,000[b]	......	Gas-turbine blades and spindles
Vitallium	0.25	0.60	0.60	27	63	...	5.5	...	...	...	14,200[b]	41,000	Gas-turbine blades
K-42-B	...	0.60	0.90	18	23	...	...	...	2.2	0.75	11,000[b]	30,000	Gas-turbine discs
25 Cr-20 Ni	0.23	1.03	1.80	25	...	...	...	...	...	...	4,600[b]	29,000[d]	Flame tubes
19-9-DL	0.30	1.00	0.60	19	...	1	1	0.30	0.30	...	10,000[b]	17,000	Bolts

[a] At 1000 F.
[b] At 1500 F.
[c] 10^8 cycles at 120 cycles per sec.
[d] At 1200 F.

10-30. Workability. The blades and other parts of the turbine exposed to high temperatures may be manufactured by one of the following methods:

1. Machine from bar stock
2. Forge to finish size
3. Rough-forge and machine
4. Precision cast by the lost-wax method

Steam-turbine blades are generally made by method (1). Gas-turbine blades may be made by any of the methods listed, depending on the workability of the material used. Some of the materials used in gas turbines can be forged or cast while others are suitable for only one process. A major factor in selecting an alloy is the cost of manufacture by the method imposed by the workability characteristics of the material.

10-31. Characteristics and Properties of Some Alloys. Table 10-2 shows a few typical alloys used in steam- and gas-turbine construction. Many others are available and are used, but the few given are a representative sample.

10-32. Materials Other than Steel. There are two classes of materials which give promise of success in gas turbines at high temperatures. The cemented hard carbides comprise one class while ceramics comprise the other.

Cemented carbides are produced by the methods of powder metallurgy and consist of finely divided carbide particles immersed in a matrix of soft ductile metal. The carbide is formed at temperatures in excess of 2500 F by a reaction between carbon and a metal. The carbide is then ground to a fine particle size, mixed with a binder, pressed into shape, and sintered at a temperature in excess of 2500 F. The product is dense, nonporous, and hard, possesses a uniform grain size, and is strong.

Carbides of tungsten, zirconium, molybdenum, tantalum, and titanium are available with cobalt as the matrix. A particularly interesting cemented carbide is that of titanium with cobalt. It has the desirable characteristics of lightness and high degree of hardness at high temperatures; is corrosion and oxidation resistant at high temperatures; is resistant to thermal shock and maintains its tensile and compressive strengths at high temperatures. Laboratory tests indicate this carbide is suitable for gas turbines at 1800 F or higher. So far as is known no gas turbine has been built with any of the parts made of cemented carbides but considerable effort is being directed toward developing the use of this material. One serious deterrent is the very high cost of the material at present.

Various ceramic materials have been proposed or are under investigation. Some of these are silicon carbide with iron and carbon, porcelain, fused quartz, and sintered aluminum oxide with iron. Although the ceramic materials are of interest in so far as they are able to withstand high temperatures, they do offer some other difficulties. Among these difficulties are brittleness, low endurance limit, low resistance to thermal shock, and severe sensitivity to slight cracks or flaws. Furthermore, no suitable method has been developed for attaching ceramic blades to a metallic disc.

Probably the most promising material is a combination of ceramics and metals such as bonding alumina to steel for turbine blades or silicon carbide with iron and sintered aluminum oxide.

TURBINE CASING AND ACCESSORIES

10-33. Steam-turbine Casings. The turbine casing carries the stationary blade and nozzle blocks, confines the steam to the flow passages, and provides a structural frame. The casing must be strong and rigid under all conditions of operation. In a large steam turbine the casing may be subjected to pressures in excess of 2000 psia at the high-pressure end ranging down to atmospheric pressure or lower at the exhaust end. The casing is subjected to a similar temperature gradient in an axial direction.

Flanges and ribs must be kept very small and not too deep in order to minimize the possibility of distortion when the massive casing is subjected to such wide temperature differentials. When internal braces and ribs must be provided to stiffen the casing, it is inevitable that they will cause flow disturbances which become even more pronounced at off-design operating conditions. The consequences of these flow disturbances are resonant vibrations and loss of available energy in the steam. Distortions of the casing under temperature change can result in rubs resulting from twisting of diaphragms and shrouds as well as failure to maintain operating clearances.

Another important consideration in the design of the casing is expansion and contraction under the influence of temperature changes. The mass of the casing is great, and when subjected to a large temperature change, the expansion is considerable and can amount to as much as an inch or more. Since expansion cannot be eliminated, it must be controlled if proper alignment is to be maintained. Figure 10-31 illustrates a scheme to provide for expansion or contraction of the turbine casing. The flanges of the horizontal casing joint are extended to rest on a ball-seated supporting block which is so tilted that the supporting surface lies on a sloping plane with respect to the plane of the axial center line of the turbine. Thus when the casing expands or contracts, the vertical expansion is compensated by the axial expansion with the result that the casing slides up or down on the sloping plane of the support.

In condensing turbines it is usual to anchor the low-pressure end of the casing so that the condenser does not have to move with expansion and contraction of the casing. The turbine as a whole expands axially toward the high-pressure end in keyways provided in the foundation. Radial expansion is free to take place in all directions from the axial center line of the turbine. The turbine shaft is keyed to the casing by means of the thrust bearing at the high-pressure end so that the rotor is pulled toward the high-pressure end with the expansion of the casing. As long as the casing and rotor expand at the same rate, correct axial alignment will always be maintained. However, in starting from a cold

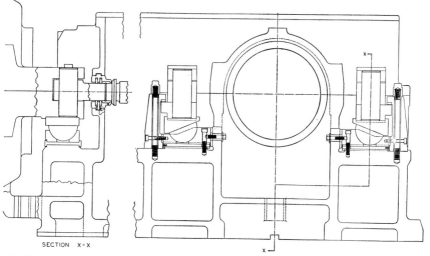

SECTION X-X

Fig. 10-31. Design of temperature-compensated support for high-temperature end of steam-turbine casings. (*Courtesy of Allis-Chalmers Manufacturing Company.*)

stop, the rotor expands at a somewhat faster rate than the casing, and a suitable adjustment must be made to provide for axial clearance between rotor and stator elements.

The casings of large steam turbines are normally split horizontally. In this way the upper half can be removed to provide convenient access to the internals for repairs or inspection. The casings of low-pressure and low-temperature units are usually made of cast iron, while at high pressures (in excess of 1200 psig) the casings are sometimes made of forgings. For high pressures and temperatures, between 450 F and 800 F, the casings are often made of cast carbon steel, while the low-pressure casings of large central station units are very often manufactured from rolled flat steel plate. For temperatures between 800 F and 1000 F, cast carbon-molybdenum or forged nickel-chromium-molybdenum steels are used. For temperatures in excess of 1000 F, 18-8 stainless steel is satisfactory.

The thickness of the material in the casing may be calculated from the thin cylinder formula given as follows:

$$m = \frac{Pd}{2f}$$

where m = thickness, in.

P = internal pressure, psig

d = internal diameter, in.

f = permissible stress, psi

For steam temperatures above 1000 F, which are usually accompanied by high pressures, a double casing is widely used. The use of a double casing makes possible the division of the high pressure between the two casings. This is accomplished by admitting to the space between the casings steam at a pressure intermediate between the high-pressure steam and atmospheric pressure. In this manner the effect of the high-pressure steam is divided between the inner and outer casings so that each casing needs only to contain one half of the initial high pressure.

10-34. Gas-turbine Casings. The problems associated with steam-turbine casings are also found in the gas-turbine casing, only they are greatly accentuated because of the higher temperatures involved. However, the pressures to which gas-turbine casing are subjected are very low in comparison to the steam turbine.

The casing for stationary units may be fabricated from alloy plates similar in composition to 19-9-DL (19 Cr, 9 Ni). The casing may be horizontally or vertically split. For high-temperature operation a double casing may be used with insulating material provided between the inner and outer casings.

The problem of expansion and growth in gas-turbine casings is acute, particularly in regard to differential rates of expansion of the rotor and casing. Usually the cold machine is set out of alignment so that at operating temperatures it will be in alignment. Compressor and turbine shafts are joined by a splined coupling so that a certain amount of misalignment can be tolerated and provision can be made for axial expansion. The axial position of the rotor relative to the casing is maintained by steel rods on each side of the thrust bearing which transmit movement of the casing to the thrust bearing.

10-35. Joints. The joint formed by the flanges of the two halves of the turbine casing can be particularly troublesome especially in the case of gas turbines. The trouble lies in the fact that the bolts creep and relax under the influence of steady high temperature. The bolt threads, which are actually crack starters, present another difficulty. However, making the shank thinner than the thread end makes for a strong bolt since it removes stress concentrations from the weakest part of the bolt, permitting uniform stretching.

The flange bolts are normally placed on the flange as close as possible to the casing proper yet leaving sufficient metal between the bolthole and the casing proper. The bolts are closely spaced and the flange is wide. Sometimes the seats on the boltheads and nuts are spherical. Many other provisions are made such as tapered threads so that there is an even bearing on all threads when the bolt stretches. Flange faces are often undercut at the bolt diameter, thereby increasing the moment of the outer section. Normally, the bolts are of hollow construction and are set up tight after electric heating to a specified elongation.

Any of several alloys of chrome-molybdenum-vanadium are used for the bolts for steam-turbine casing flanges. For gas turbines 19-9-DL seems to be in general use.

References

1. Barrett, C. S.: "Structure of Metals," McGraw-Hill Book Company, Inc., New York, 1952.
2. Carlson, J. R.: Another Step in Turbine Blade Evolution, *Westinghouse Engineer*, May, 1952.
3. Church, E. F.: "Steam Turbines," McGraw-Hill Book Company, Inc., New York, 1950.
4. Den Hartog, J. P.: "Mechanical Vibrations," McGraw-Hill Book Company, Inc., New York, 1947.
5. Egli, A.: The Leakage of Steam through Labyrinth Seals, *Trans. ASME*, 1945.
6. Emmert, H. D.: Current Design Practices for Gas Turbine Power Elements, *Trans. ASME*, 1949.
7. Evans, C. T.: Materials for Power Gas Turbines, *Trans. ASME*, 1947.
8. Evans, C. T.: High Temperature Alloys for Dynamic Loading, *Iron Age*, June, 1944.
9. "Gas Turbine Lectures," Westinghouse Electric Corporation, 1944.
10. Heinze, F. J.: Thermodynamics and Turbine Design, Westinghouse Lectures, 1948.
11. Kearton, W. J.: "Steam Turbine Theory and Practice," Pitman Publishing Corp., New York, 1948.
12. Kroon, R. P.: Turbine Blade Fatigue Testing, *Mech. Eng.*, July, 1940.
13. Kroon, R. P.: Influence of Lashing and Centrifugal Force on Turbine Blade Stresses, *Trans. ASME*, 1934.
14. Martin, H. M.: "Design and Construction of Steam Turbines," Longmans, Green & Co., Inc., New York, 1913.
15. "Stationary Steam Turbines," Socony Vacuum Oil Company, 1949.
16. Stodola, A., and L. C. Loewenstein: "Steam and Gas Turbines," McGraw-Hill Book Company, Inc., New York, 1927.
17. Wilson, C. D.: Present-day Concepts in Steam Turbine Design, *Trans. Pennsylvania Electric Association*, 1952.

Problems

10-1. The disc of a simple impulse turbine has a peripheral velocity of 1200 fps when rotating at 24,000 rpm. Steam is at a pressure and temperature of 40 psia and 300 F.

(a) Calculate disc friction loss in horsepower.

(b) If the same peripheral velocity is retained and the speed of rotation is decreased to 12,000 rpm, what is the disc friction loss? (Same steam conditions.)

(c) Calculate the disc friction loss for the peripheral and rotational speeds of (a) and (b) if the steam condition is 30 psia and 150 F.

10-2. The control stage of a large turbine is a De Laval stage operating with partial admission. About 60 per cent of the mean blade ring circumference is active. The mean blade ring diameter is 3 ft and the blade height is 1.5 in. The rotational speed is 3600 rpm. The steam condition is 900 psia and 1000 F. (a) Calculate disc friction loss in horsepower; (b) calculate windage loss in horsepower.

10-3. Solve Prob. 10-1 if gas at 1500 F and 60 psia is used in parts (a) and (b). Solve part (c) for gas at 1200 F and 80 psia.

10-4. The following data apply to a labyrinth used to seal steam at 150 psia and 360 F where the low-pressure side is at atmospheric pressure:

Clearance: 0.015 in.
Clearance diameter: 12 in.
Thickness of strips at tips: 0.02 in.
Pitch of strips: $\frac{3}{8}$ in.
Number of strips: 12
Type of labyrinth: straight-through

(a) Find leakage for above conditions.
(b) Find leakage if the fluid is gas at 18 psia and 900 F and the labyrinth is stepped.

10-5. The following information relative to a turbine blade is given:

$$\gamma = 0.3 \text{ psi}$$
$$a_r = 0.16 \text{ sq in.}$$
$$a_t = 0.08 \text{ sq in.}$$
$$r_r = 14 \text{ in.}$$
$$r_t = 26 \text{ in.}$$
$$N = 6000 \text{ rpm}$$
$$V_a = 260 \text{ fps}$$
$$\Delta V_{Um} = 380 \text{ fps}$$
$$\Delta P = 10 \text{ psi}$$
$$z = 80 \text{ blades}$$

$$\beta_m = 70°; \beta = 45°; \alpha_0 = 5°$$
$$\left(\frac{I_{xl}}{C_{xl}}\right)_{root} = 0.0045 \text{ in.}$$
$$\left(\frac{I_{yl}}{C_{yl}}\right)_{root} = 0.03 \text{ in.}$$
$$\left(\frac{I_{xe}}{C_{xe}}\right)_{root} = 0.004 \text{ in.}$$
$$\left(\frac{I_{ye}}{C_{ye}}\right)_{root} = 0.02 \text{ in.}$$
Free-vortex stage

Calculate for root section:
(a) Centrifugal stress in pounds per square inch
(b) Axial and tangential bending moments
(c) Leading and exit-edge bending stresses in pounds per square inch
(d) Maximum stress

10-6. Determine the running frequency of vibration for the blade of Prob. 10-5 if the following additional data are applicable: $E = 26 \times 10^6$ psi, $W = 8$ lb, $I = 200$ in.^{4}

10-7. What is the average tangential stress in a disc of 16 in. diameter and 1.5 in. thickness? Assume that disc thickness is uniform, $N = 8000$ rpm, $P = 90,000$ lb, and $\gamma = 0.3$ lb per cu in. What would be the average tangential stress if instead of $P = 90,000$ lb the centrifugal force of the blades of Prob. 10-5 were used?

CHAPTER 11

STEAM-TURBINE CONTROL AND PERFORMANCE

11-1. Introduction. The purpose of this chapter is to establish a familiarity with the various means available to control the speed and output of steam turbines. Closely associated with the control of a turbine is the effect of such control on performance. In Chap. 4 the thermodynamic aspects of turbine performance were considered with special reference to the design or most efficient load on the turbine. However, it is a rare turbine indeed which operates at constant load and it must be expected that operation at other than design conditions will be accompanied by decreased efficiency. The system of control utilized introduces its own irreversibilities which must be taken into account in estimating the performance of a turbine under all conditions of service.

CONTROL

11-2. Control and Supervisory Instruments. It is necessary to provide certain control and supervisory instruments for the safe and effective operation of a turbine. The number and type of instruments and controls used depend somewhat on the size and application of the turbine. For large central station turbines, the control and supervisory instruments are located for convenience on the turbine control board as far as practicable.

Some of the types of controls and instruments employed for large steam turbines are listed with their functions.

1. Pressure gauges are provided which indicate or record the oil pressure to the bearings and the governor mechanism, the pressure of steam or water to the gland seals, the steam pressure at the stop valve, in the steam chest, at all stages receiving or delivering steam, and in any case at the first stage and exhaust. For a condensing turbine a vacuum gauge and a barometer are provided to permit computation of the absolute pressure at turbine exhaust.

2. Thermometers are provided which indicate or record steam temperatures at the locations listed under (1) where steam pressures are

taken. In addition the oil temperatures entering and leaving the bearings are taken.

3. A speed and camshaft-position recorder is required to indicate and record the speed of the turbine in rpm during starting and shutdown periods and the rotation of the camshaft in per cent while the turbine is in operation. During operation (other than starting or shutting down) the turbine speed is obtained from the generator frequency recorder, thereby permitting the speed recorder to be used to record the camshaft position instead. The opening of the valves and therefore the load on the turbine are functions of the camshaft position.

The equipment normally consists of two detectors mounted on the turbine, the power unit and recorder being located on the turbine control board. One detector produces voltage in proportion to the speed of the turbine. The other detector supplies voltage in proportion to the rotation of the camshaft. A relay in the power unit makes the selection between the two detectors. The relay is energized through an interlock or switch operated from the generator line breaker. Finally, the power unit rectifies the selected detector signal putting it on the recorder.

4. An eccentricity recorder is provided to indicate and record the eccentricity of the shaft at the high-pressure end of the turbine. The components of this instrument consist of a detector coil located at the low-pressure end of the shaft, a transfer switch on the turning gear, and a power unit and recorder located on the turbine control board. The eccentricity of the shaft causes the air space between the shaft and the coil detector to vary, thereby changing the current flowing through the coil. The power unit circuit supplies the coil current, separates its variations, and puts a signal on the recorder in accordance with the eccentricity of the shaft. The eccentricity is recorded in mils.

5. A vibration amplitude recorder is provided which indicates and records the horizontal vibration (sometimes the vertical vibration as well) occurring at each main bearing of the turbine and generator. The vibration is read in mils.

The instrument consists of a detector at each bearing and a power unit and recorder located on the turbine control board. The detector voltages which are in proportion to the bearing vibrations are supplied in sequence to the recorder circuit by a cyclic time switch. The power unit integrates the vibration-velocity signal, amplifies it, and moves the recorder in accordance with the displacement of the vibration in mils.

6. An expansion indicator is provided on the turbine control board to show the axial expansion of the turbine casing. Normally, a point is selected on the casing and its movement relative to a point on the foundation is indicated and may even be recorded. The expansion of the casing should be steady, any unsteadiness being a warning that the turbine sup-

ports are probably not moving properly in the keyways provided for them on the turbine foundation.

7. A noise meter is mounted either on the turbine control board or near the turbine. The purpose of this instrument is to pick up and amplify the noise made by various moving parts of the turbine. This instrument may be regarded as the engineer's stethoscope by means of which he may detect any unusual sounds caused by threatened failure of a turbine part.

8. Flowmeters are mounted on the turbine control board to indicate, record, and integrate the mass rate of flow to the turbine, the steam extracted at the various extraction points, and the flow to the condenser.

9. Wattmeters, voltmeters, and ammeters are also provided on the turbine control board which in conjunction with the flowmeters provide a means for determining the steam rate and heat rate of the unit.

10. Handwheels for operating the various drain valves may be located at the turbine or on the turbine gauge board. When the turbine is shut down, it is desirable to drain the casing, valves, and other places, such as in pipe bends, where condensate may collect.

11. Governor controls are located at the turbine or on the turbine control board to provide regulation and control of governor valves.

12. Manual controls are provided at the turbine or on the turbine control board for regulation and by-passing of sealing steam for the gland seals.

13. A trip lock lever for testing the overspeed trip is usually mounted on the turbine control board.

11-3. Principles of Governing. In order to control and regulate the output of a turbine in accordance with the variable demands met in service, it is necessary to maintain accurate and positive control of speed, pressure, and flow. To accomplish these ends, all steam turbines are provided with a main or operating governor. The main governor serves to keep speed constant in cases where the turbine is used as the prime mover for a generator, since the frequency depends on the speed of a generator for a given number of poles. In other applications a variable speed may be desirable, and the governor must provide for the several speeds required. If the turbine is of the mixed-pressure, back-pressure, or extraction types, the governor must regulate the flow under the influence of a combination of speed and one or more pressures.

In addition to the main governor each turbine is provided with an overspeed governor or emergency trip whose function is to protect the turbine against destructive overspeeding brought about by some cause such as sudden loss of load.

Governing is accomplished by regulating the mass rate of flow through a single admission valve or through a bank of admission valves supplying individual nozzles or groups of nozzles. The former method is known as throttle governing and the latter as nozzle governing. In nozzle governing the opening or closing of the admission valves is actuated by a camshaft under the influence of the governing mechanism.

Before the steam reaches the admission or governing valves it passes through a stop valve. This valve is either wide open or shut tight with no intermediate position possible and is used only when starting or shutting down the turbine. It is interesting to note that the stop valve is sometimes erroneously referred to as a throttle valve even though it is apparent that no throttling process can occur other than that due to the normal pressure drop when the valve is wide open.

Governors may be classified according to their function, *i.e.*, speed or pressure governors. Each classification then may be further identified by its structural arrangement such as mechanical, hydraulic, or electrical.

11-4. Direct-acting Speed-responsive Governors. If the condition of the steam entering a turbine and the mass rate of flow are held constant, the consequence of a decrease in load is a corresponding increase in speed of the turbine. Conversely, an increase in load causes a decrease in turbine speed. The speed-responsive governor takes advantage of this relationship to regulate the mass rate of flow to the turbine to compensate for the change in load.

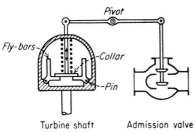

Fig. 11-1. Simple direct-connected centrifugal flyball governor.

A speed-governing system consists of the speed governor or speed-sensitive element, the speed-control mechanism, and the governor-controlled valves. The design features of this system vary considerably depending on the manufacturer.

Probably the most rudimentary speed-sensitive element is the centrifugal flyball type directly mounted on the turbine shaft and governing the admission valve opening through a simple lever-and-fulcrum linkage mechanism. Figure 11-1 illustrates such a simple governor. Fly bars are used instead of flyballs but this type of governor is nevertheless called a flyball governor inasmuch as its forerunner actually employed flyballs. It can be seen from the figure that the greater centrifugal force attendant to higher speed of the governor spindle causes the flybars to move outward. This action in turn causes a force to be exerted on a collar against the force of a spring. Movement of the collar up or down on the governor spindle actuates the linkage mechanism, thereby controlling the opening of the admission valve.

Consider two positions of the fly bars. When the fly bars are at the "in" position and the turbine is operating at the load and speed corresponding to this position, the centrifugal and spring forces are in equilibrium. Now suppose the load is decreased and the turbine speeds up. The centrifugal force increases, compressing the spring until the spring force again balances the new centrifugal force. In the meantime the collar has moved up, partially closing the admission valve to reduce the mass rate of steam flow to the appropriate value for the new load condition. Thus it is seen that the turbine operates at a different speed corresponding to each load.

Examining Fig. 11-1, it is evident that the centrifugal force depends on the diameter of the circular path of rotation of the fly bars as well as turbine speed. The spring force against which centrifugal force acts is a function of the dimensions of the spring and the extent to which it is compressed. It is clear that the increase in centrifugal force brought about by a change of speed must be sufficiently great to overcome the resistance of the spring as well as the friction and inertia of the system in order to open or close the admission valve. This operating force can be increased only by making the governor larger, a fact which places a very definite limitation on the use of this type of governor for any but very small units.

Since the friction and inertia of the governing system must be overcome in addition to the spring force before action is brought about to compensate the admission valve opening, this type of governor is not sensitive in its response to speed changes. Then summarizing the limitations of the direct-connected centrifugal governor the following are apparent:

1. It lacks sensitivity to speed change.

2. The operating force developed is a function of governor size as well as speed.

3. A different speed accompanies each load on the turbine.

In small mechanical-drive turbines none of these limitations is serious, and therefore this type of governor may be used because of its simplicity and rugged construction.

Figure 11-2 shows an actual direct-connected centrifugal governor used on a small mechanical-drive turbine. The components and action may be readily identified by comparison with Fig. 11-1.

11-5. Characteristics of the Simple Speed-responsive Governor. When it is desirable to adhere to some constant speed, the speed governor mechanism of Figs. 11-1 and 11-2 are modified to include a speed changer. The speed changer may be a simple spring known as a secondary spring and used as illustrated in Figs. 11-3 and 11-4. This spring may be adjusted manually to change the force of the governor spring in order to alter the relationship of speed-load changes. In this way the original speed can be restored after a load change has taken place. At a given speed the fly bars take up a different position for each load. Because of this characteristic the governor is sometimes called a travel governor.

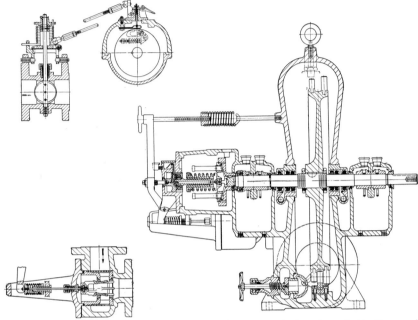

Fig. 11-2. Direct-acting centrifugal flyball governor. (*Courtesy of the Terry Steam Turbine Company.*)

A slightly more complex but more desirable arrangement may be obtained by utilizing a speed changer which positions the admission valve lever arm about the governor collar as a fulcrum. The desirable feature of this scheme is that the fly-bar position is the same at all loads for a given speed, resulting in what is known as a nontraveling governor.

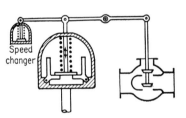

Fig. 11-3. Direct-connected centrifugal flyball governor with speed changer.

The two extremes of turbine operation are, of course, full load and no load. (Overload will not be considered here.) A governor spring can be selected and correlated with valve opening so that a predetermined variation in speed will occur from no load to full load. The centrifugal force of the fly bars may be expressed as a function of speed and travel of the governor. Usually speed change from full load to no load is limited to 3 or 4 per cent of the speed at rated load. For example, if rated speed is 3600 rpm, the speed at full load would be limited to 3528 rpm and at no load to 3672 rpm. If centrifugal force at these speeds is plotted against governor travel, the result is as shown in Fig. 11-5. The spring-force characteristic curve shows the force the spring must develop to balance centrifugal force developed by the fly bars for each speed from full

Fig. 11-4. Direct-connected centrifugal flyball governor with secondary-spring speed changer. (*Courtesy of De Laval Steam Turbine Company.*)

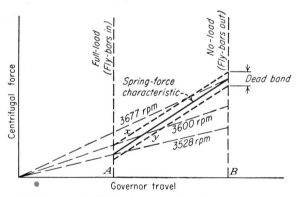

A – B represents limits of governor travel

Fig. 11-5. Spring-force characteristic for direct-acting centrifugal flyball governor.

load to no load as well as the position of the collar on the governor spindle. The variation in speed from 3528 rpm at full load to 3672 rpm at no load divided into the rated speed of 3600 rpm is called the regulation or speed droop of the governor. For this case the regulation is 4 per cent.   If the governor is to be regulated for a certain amount of overload, the per cent regulation is expressed in terms of the rated load and rated speed, or

$$R_s = \left(\frac{N_0 - N}{N_r}\right) 100 \qquad (11\text{-}1)$$

where R_s = steady-state speed regulation (at rated load and rated speed), per cent

N_0 = speed at no load, rpm

N = speed at rated load, rpm

N_r = rated speed, rpm

The dotted lines parallel to the spring-force characteristic curve of Fig. 11-5 represent the effect of the inertia and friction of the governing system.   In going from full load to no load, the dotted line x gives the successive positions of the governor collar at various speeds.   For load change in the reverse direction, line y is appropriate.   The deviation represented by x and y from the spring-force characteristic curve results from the fact that the centrifugal force must overcome the friction and inertia forces as well as the spring force before a change of valve opening is accomplished.   The vertical distance between x and y is called the dead band since it is a zone in which a change of speed does not cause a change of governor position.   The dead band is an indication of the sensitivity of the governor and is defined as the speed change necessary to effect a change of admission valve opening, expressed as a per cent of rated speed.

To reduce the effect of friction and inertia in the governing system, it is usual to provide ball bearings or knife-edges and even mechanical oscillators in order to keep the system in motion.   The permissible limit of the dead band of a governing system depends on the size and type of turbine and may be found from the AIEE-ASME Recommended Specification for Speed-governing of Steam Turbines.[7]   In general, the maximum values of dead band permitted range from 0.06 to 0.20 per cent of rated speed.

11-6. Speed-responsive Governors with Servomotors.   Methods for correcting two of the inherent limitations of the simple speed-responsive governor were discussed in the preceding section, namely, speed variation with load and lack of sensitivity.   The third limitation lies in the need to make the governor of considerable size in order to develop sufficient operating force for the valves of larger turbines.

Figures 11-6 and 11-7 illustrate the incorporation of an oil relay in a speed-responsive governing system.   Movement of the governor operates an oil relay or pilot valve which controls the flow of oil into or out of a power cylinder.   The power cylinder is operated by oil supplied from a

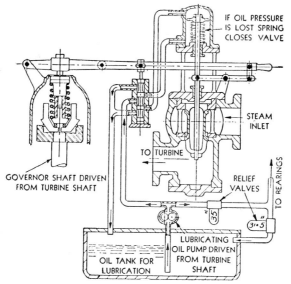

Fig. 11-6. Diagrammatic arrangement of centrifugal speed-responsive oil-relay governor. (*Courtesy of Worthington Corporation.*)

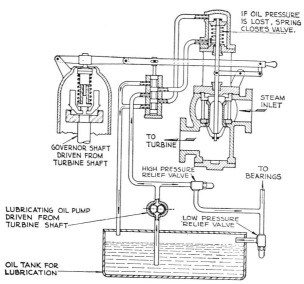

Fig. 11-7. Diagrammatic arrangement of centrifugal speed-responsive oil-relay governor with speed changer. (*Courtesy of Worthington Corporation.*)

positive displacement gear pump driven by the governor spindle. In this way the small force developed by the governor is amplified by the power cylinder so that the admission valve is manipulated without difficulty and the sensitivity of the governing system is greatly improved.

As stated previously, small turbines are governed through a single admission valve. However, individual manually operated nozzle valves are sometimes provided in order to improve performance during long periods at part load. The nozzle valves may admit steam to one or more nozzles and offer the opportunity to cut out those nozzles not

Fig. 11-8. Manually operated nozzle cutout valves. (*Courtesy of De Laval Steam Turbine Company.*)

required at reduced mass rate of flow. Figure 11-8 shows manually operated nozzle valves in addition to the admission or governor valve.

Automatic nozzle governing is employed in larger turbines provided with a Curtis or Rateau control stage. The governing system for nozzle governing requires considerable operating force to function, and it is usually necessary to employ more than one servomotor or power cylinder to amplify the operating force developed by the governor.

Figure 11-9 illustrates a bar-lift valve gear for nozzle governing. The six valves shown on the bar control the flow of steam to the six corresponding nozzle groups. The valves can be adjusted on the bar by means of the lock nuts or the stem lengths to provide any desired sequence of opening or closing of the valves when the bar is lifted or lowered. The movement of the bar is accomplished by the main servomotor or power

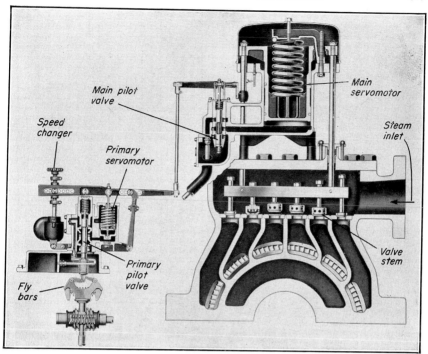

Fig. 11-9. Bar-lift valve gear with governor and servomotors. (Courtesy of General Electric Company.)

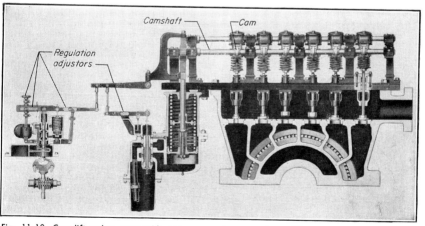

Fig. 11-10. Cam-lift valve gear with governor and servomotors. (Courtesy of General Electric Company.)

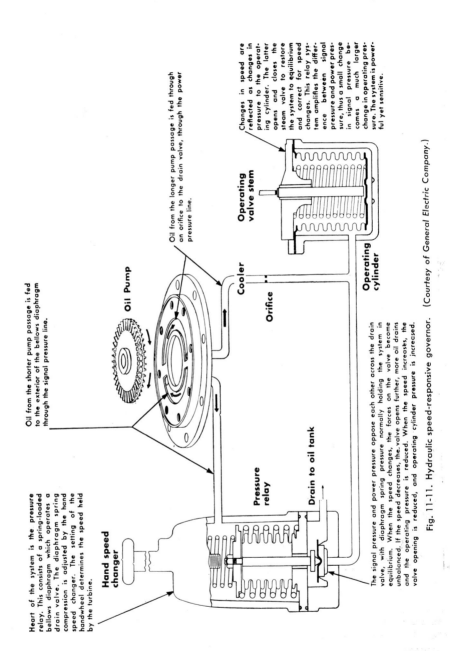

Oil from the shorter pump passage is fed to the exterior of the bellows diaphragm through the signal pressure line.

Oil from the longer pump passage is fed through an orifice to the drain valve, through the power pressure line.

Changes in speed are reflected as changes in pressure to the operating cylinder. The latter opens and closes the steam valve to restore the system to equilibrium and correct for speed changes. This relay system amplifies the difference between signal pressure and power pressure, thus a small change in signal pressure becomes a much larger change in operating pressure. The system is powerful yet sensitive.

Heart of the system is the pressure relay. This consists of a spring-loaded bellows diaphragm which operates a drain valve. The diaphragm spring compression is adjusted by the hand speed changer. The setting of the handwheel determines the speed held by the turbine.

The signal pressure and power pressure oppose each other across the drain valve, with diaphragm spring pressure normally holding the system in equilibrium. When the speed changes, the forces on the valve become unbalanced. If the speed decreases, the valve opens further, more oil drains and the operating pressure is reduced. When the speed increases, the valve opening is reduced, and operating cylinder pressure is increased.

Oil Pump

Cooler

Orifice

Operating valve stem

Operating cylinder

Pressure relay

Drain to oil tank

Hand speed changer

Fig. 11-11. Hydraulic speed-responsive governor.   (Courtesy of General Electric Company.)

cylinder which is in turn controlled by the main pilot valve or relay. The primary servomotor actuates the main pilot valve and is itself actuated by the primary pilot valve under the influence of the speed-responsive governor. The primary and main servomotors effect a series amplification of the operating force developed by the governor.

Figure 11-10 illustrates the cam-lift valve gear. The governor mechanism is similar to that of Fig. 11-9. The vertical movement of the main servomotor piston rod causes the camshaft to rotate by means of a rack-and-pinion arrangement. Each cam raises a valve against the force of a spring through the action of a rocker. The setting of the cams can be adjusted to afford any desired sequence of valve opening.

11-7. Hydraulic Speed-responsive Governor. Thus far only the centrifugal type of speed-responsive governor has been considered. The hydraulic governor is a type which depends for its operation on the change in oil pressure brought about by a centrifugal pump mounted on the turbine shaft. The oil pressure varies very nearly as the square of the turbine speed.

Figure 11-11 illustrates and explains the operation of a hydraulic speed-responsive governing system. More elaborate systems are available for large installations, but the principle of operation is very similar to that of Fig. 11-11.

11-8. Pressure Regulators. Pressure regulators or pressure-responsive governors are used to control and regulate the pressures of inlet and extraction steam as well as the pressure of exhaust steam from back-pressure or topping units. The pressure regulator is a simple device and is usually arranged for coordination with the speed governor.

Consider first the back-pressure governor. The back-pressure turbine, it may be recalled, either delivers steam at a particular pressure for some industrial process or it is used as a topping unit delivering steam at an appropriate pressure to a low-pressure turbine. In each case the back-pressure turbine functions as a pressure reducer. Under these circumstances it is desirable to maintain control over the exhaust pressure.

A typical pressure-responsive governor is shown in Fig. 11-12. The governor is connected to the region where pressure is to be controlled. A change in steam pressure actuates the bellows diaphragm A which causes a lever to move about a fulcrum. Movement of the lever controls the setting of an oil relay, varying the pressure on the bellows B, which in turn moves the linkage to the governor control valve. At the same time the compression is altered in the linkage spring. A slower moving bellows C is also actuated by oil pressure, regulated by means of a needle valve, and serves to compensate for the compression of the linkage spring bringing the steam pressure back to the value for which the governor is set.

The pressure-responsive governor discussed in the preceding paragraph can be used to control and regulate not only the exhaust pressure of a back-pressure turbine but also inlet or extraction pressures as well. When it is desired to regulate the pressure of extracted steam at all conditions of flow and load, a grid valve gear may be used to regulate the flow beyond the extraction point in the turbine. Such a grid valve is illus-

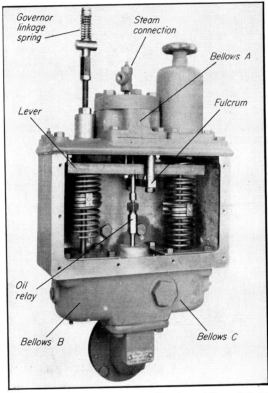

Fig. 11-12. Pressure-responsive governor. (*Courtesy of General Electric Company.*)

trated in Fig. 11-13. Instead of a grid valve it is more usual to use a poppet-valve arrangement not unlike the bar-lift mechanism of Fig. 11-9 for high-pressure extraction. Whichever type is used, the valve is located in the turbine and not in the extraction line.

If the oil relays and servomotors are not considered, in order to simplify the representation of the system, Fig. 11-14 shows a single three-arm lever interconnecting mechanism for coordinating the action of the speed-responsive governor and a pressure-responsive governor controlling a single-extraction pressure. Assuming constant extraction flow, an increase in load on the turbine requires the flow of more steam throughout

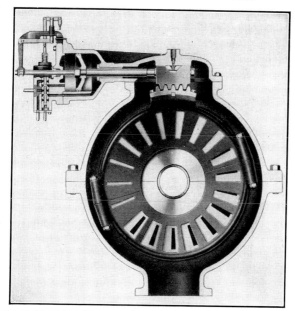

Fig. 11-13. Grid valve gear. (*Courtesy of General Electric Company.*)

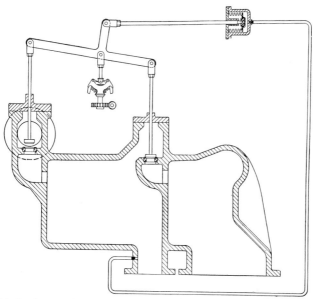

Fig. 11-14. Single extraction pressure governing. (*Courtesy of General Electric Company.*)

the turbine to the exhaust.   In response to the speed governor, the three-arm lever opens both the admission and grid valve.   However, an increased demand for extraction steam with constant load requires that more steam be admitted to the turbine and less exhausted.   Now the three-arm lever responds to the pressure governor opening the admission valve and closing the grid valve.   Whether it is desired to maintain constant load and change the extraction flow, or vice versa, the action of both the admission and grid valves is simultaneous and related in such a

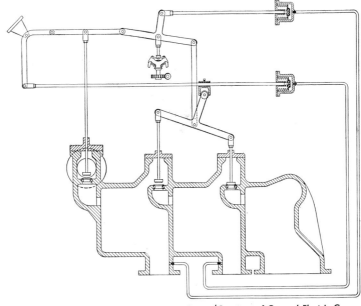

Fig. 11-15. Double extraction pressure governing.   (*Courtesy of General Electric Company.*)

way that the proper relationship between load and extracted steam is maintained.

Figure 11-15 shows a double three-arm lever mechanism for coordinating a speed governor with two pressure governors.

11-9. Speed Regulation and Parallel Operation.   The speed regulation of the simple speed-responsive governor was discussed in Sec. 11-5 for a nonextraction unit.   Equation 11-1 gives the speed regulation or speed droop for any nonextraction turbine, regardless of the type of governor employed.   When an extraction turbine is involved, the speed regulation is defined by the following expression from the recommended specification of the AIEE-ASME Joint Committee:

$$R_s = \frac{(N_m - N)}{N_r} \times \frac{P_r}{(P_r - P_m)} \times 100 \qquad (11\text{-}2)$$

where R_s = steady-state speed regulation, per cent of rated speed

N = speed at rated power output with rated extraction pressures and zero extraction flows, rpm

N_m = speed at minimum load at which rated extraction pressures with zero extraction flows can be obtained, rpm

N_r = rated speed, rpm

P_r = rated load, kw

P_m = minimum power output at which extraction pressures with zero extraction flow are permitted, kw

Figure 11-16 shows speed-changer setting plotted against per cent of rated speed for various loads on a turbine. From the curves it can be

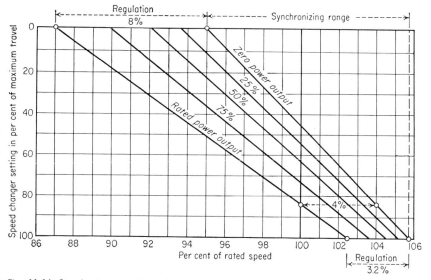

Fig. 11-16. Steady-state speed regulation having different values for different speed-changer settings. (*AIEE-ASME Joint Committee Recommended Specification 600, May, 1949.*)

seen that rated speed can be obtained at any load by adjusting the speed-changer setting. Now suppose that two or more turbines are to operate in parallel. One of three possibilities can exist if the turbines have the same ratings:

1. The speed regulation is the same.
2. The speed regulation is different.
3. One governor is isochronous (zero regulation or zero droop) and the other has some speed regulation.

With reference to Fig. 11-17, the curve identified by the numbers (1) and (2) refers to two units having the same value for the speed regulation and operating in parallel. Each unit is at half load and at rated speed. If full load is carried by each unit, the speed is 98 per cent of rated speed.

The combined load is shared equally between the two units at all magnitudes of the combined load within the capabilities of the machines. When both units are operating at full load and 98 per cent of rated speed, it is necessary to adjust the speed changers of both governors to obtain rated speed.

With further reference to Fig. 11-17, consider the curves (1) and (3), which are for different values of speed regulation. The setting of the speed changers is such that each unit is at 50 per cent load at rated speed. If the combined load is increased it is seen that when unit 1 is at full load unit 3 is at 75 per cent of full load and the synchronous speed is 99 per cent of rated speed. When unit 3 is at no load, unit 1 is at 25 per cent of

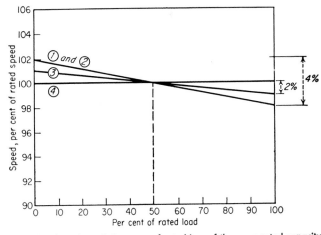

Fig. 11-17. Speed-regulation curves for turbines of the same rated capacity.

full load. Also it will be noted that when unit 1 with 4 per cent regulation goes to full load, an increase of 50 per cent of full load, unit 2 with 2 per cent regulation goes to three-quarters load, an increase of 25 per cent of full load. The same relationship holds for all increases or decreases of combined load; therefore it may be concluded that load additions to units of the same rated capacity but different speed regulations are divided in inverse proportion to the speed regulations.

Comparing either curve 1 or curve 3 with curve 4 in Fig. 11-17, it can be seen that any load additions or subtractions are taken by unit 4, which has an isochronous governor. As before, it is assumed that the speed changers have been set so that each unit is initially at half load and rated speed.

Figure 11-18 illustrates the division of loads when units of different rated capacity and different speed regulation are operated in parallel. Unit A is rated at 15,000 kw, 3600 rpm, and has 4 per cent regulation, while unit B is rated at 10,000 kw, 3600 rpm, and has 2 per cent regulation.

If the speed-changer setting is not changed and the units are in parallel operation at rated speed, the load division is 7400 kw for unit A and 4800 kw for unit B making a combined load of 12,200 kw. With the speed-changer setting unchanged, an increase in load causes a decrease in speed of both units. For example, if the combined load is increased to 19,000 kw without adjusting the speed changer, unit A takes 10,400 kw and unit

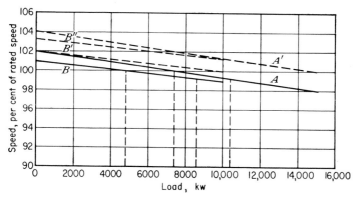

Fig. 11-18. Regulation of speed-droop curves for parallel operation.

B 8600 kw, each unit running at a speed equal to 99.2 per cent of rated speed.

If a combined load of 25,000 kw is to be held at rated speed, then the speed of both machines must be adjusted. If A is adjusted to A' and B to B' in order to have full load at rated speed for each unit, the full combined load of 25,000 kw is taken. If a combined load is to be equally divided between the two units, it is seen that B can be adjusted to B'',

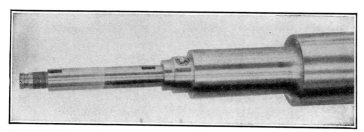

Fig. 11-19. Overspeed pin in turbine shaft. (*Courtesy of Worthington Corporation.*)

keeping A' at its new setting, the results being a combined load of 20,000 kw at 101.2 per cent of rated speed each unit taking 10,000 kw. If rated speed is desired and equal division of load, B may be adjusted until it intersects A at rated speed (not shown in figure). The result is 7400 kw load on each machine. Another possibility is to adjust B to B', keeping the original setting A for the other unit. Now, unit A takes a load of

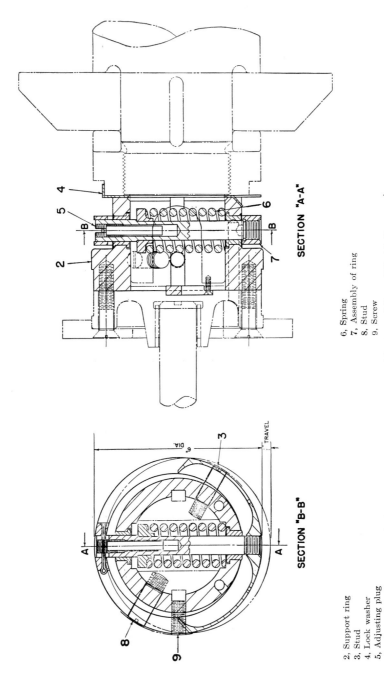

SECTION "A-A"

SECTION "B-B"

Fig. 11-20. Eccentric ring.   (Courtesy of General Electric Company.)

2, Support ring
3, Stud
4, Lock washer
5, Adjusting plug

6, Spring
7, Assembly of ring
8, Stud
9, Screw

7400 kw at rated speed, and unit B at setting B' and rated speed takes its full load at 10,000 kw.

Thus it is evident that any speed and load division may be obtained for units operating in parallel within the limits of their capacities and governor ranges by manipulating the speed changer of one or both machines.

11-10. Emergency Governors. Every turbine is provided with some form of emergency governor to protect the machine against overspeeding, low vacuum, low oil pressure, and excessive load. The first of these gov-

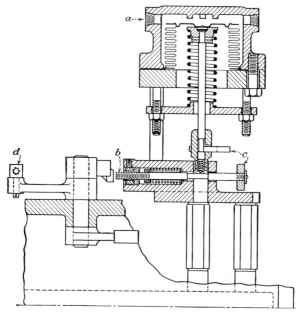

Fig. 11-21. Low-oil-pressure trip mechanism. (*Courtesy of Worthington Corporation.*)

ernors, known as the overspeed trip, acts to shut off the supply of steam by closing the stop valve in the event turbine speed exceeds 9 or 10 per cent above normal.

One common type of overspeed trip design employs a pin or weight on the turbine shaft as shown in Fig. 11-19. Centrifugal force acting on the pin is opposed by a spring until about 10 per cent overspeed is reached, whereupon the centrifugal force overcomes spring force and the pin flies out, striking a trigger. The trigger may release a spring which immediately closes the stop valve. In larger machines the trigger actuates an oil relay which in turn operates a servomotor to close the stop valve.

Another type of overspeed trip incorporates an eccentric ring on either the main shaft or the governor spindle. The eccentric ring is actuated by centrifugal force against the force of a spring when the turbine overspeeds. This results in the ring being placed in an eccentric position so that it strikes the trigger of the overspeed trip, thereby closing the stop valve. The eccentric ring type of emergency governor usually operates through an oil relay and servomotor arrangement in larger turbines. An eccentric ring is illustrated in Fig. 11-20.

Whichever type of emergency overspeed governor is used, it can be reset after the turbine has attained normal speed without serious further drop in rotor speed.

Figure 11-21 illustrates one form of low oil-pressure trip mechanism which actuates an oil relay to close the stop valve in the event lubricating oil pressure is lost. Lubricating oil under system pressure is admitted at a, balancing the force exerted by a spring bellows. When oil pressure fails, the spring forces the bellows up, releasing the pin b which strikes a trigger actuating a linkage mechanism to an oil relay connected at d. When normal oil pressure is resumed, the pin and bellows spring are reset by means of the handles at c.

PERFORMANCE

11-11. Introduction. The various efficiencies, heat rate, and steam rate for steam turbines and their cycles were defined in Chap. 4, and no further comment need be made here. The primary purpose of this division of the subject matter is to develop some qualitative relationships which in some measure permit forecasting the ultimate performance of the turbine, thus making it possible to arrive at a more judicious design. Where possible, quantitative relationships among the performance parameters are developed in order that a reasonably accurate prediction of performance can be made before the turbine is completely designed, constructed, and tested.

11-12. Effect of Throttle Governing. When throttle governing is used as the method for controlling the output of a turbine, the primary aim is to reduce the mass rate of flow. Ideally, the available energy per pound of steam flow remains constant, the reduced output being accomplished by a reduction of total available energy by reason of fewer pounds of steam being admitted to the turbine per unit time. Incidental to reducing the mass rate of flow the steam experiences an increasing pressure drop across the governing valve as the valve is closed against flow. Consequently, a throttling or constant enthalpy process occurs across the valve with an increase in entropy and a corresponding decrease in the availability of energy per pound of steam flow. Furthermore, the state of the steam entering the first stage of the turbine is changed and, a priori, the condition or expansion line for the turbine is different for each load.

Even when the governor valve is wide open, a pressure drop occurs and hence throttling is evident at all loads on the turbine. Usually the governor valve is sized to handle the flow at the predominant load with the valve wide open.

Figure 11-22 shows the effect of throttle governing on the condition line. Point x indicates the condition of the steam in the main steam line before entering the governor valve. Point a is the condition of the steam when the governor valve is wide open, xa indicating the throttling process. The available energy per pound of steam is indicated by the constant entropy expansion ad. When the mass rate of flow is reduced by partially closing the governing valve, further throttling occurs to some point such as b or c, depending on how much the valve is closed. It is observed that the available energy as shown by bf and ch is reduced in direct proportion to the amount of throttling or reduction in mass rate of flow.

Figure 11-22 also indicates that when throttle governing is employed, the pressure drops per turbine stage must decrease. Since the nozzle flow areas in each stage are a fixed element at all loads, it follows that with reduced mass rate of flow lower velocities are developed. Therefore smaller enthalpy drops per stage occur and consequently smaller pressure drops. Of course the nozzle and blade losses increase since the nozzles

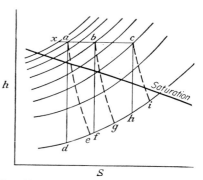

Fig. 11-22. Effect of throttle governing on condition line.

are overexpanding and the blades are subjected to a condition analogous to underspeeding. This latter condition occurs because the blade speed is constant, or nearly so, when the governor is regulated for rated rpm, with the result the velocity ratio ν increases.

Some of the losses incurred because of throttle governing are tempered by an increase in stage efficiency owing to the fact that with increased throttling more of the expansion occurs in the superheated region, as evidenced in Fig. 11-22.

Figure 11-23a shows a plot of steam flow in pounds per hour vs. turbine output or load expressed in kilowatts. When throttle governing at constant rpm is employed, the resulting curve, known as the Willans line, is very nearly a straight line between no load and most efficient load. Hence if the steam flows at any two loads between no load and most efficient load are known or calculated, the steam flows at all points along BC can be found. The points B and C represent no load and most efficient load, respectively. The intercept ob represents the steam flow required to keep the turbine turning over at rated speed and no load. The intercept *oa* represents the energy input in kilowatts to the turbine from an outside source to maintain rated speed at no load and zero steam flow. The portion of the Willans line between *C* and *D* represents the increase in mass rate of flow for loads greater than the most efficient load. The steeper slope of the Willans line above most efficient load is accounted for by the fact the increased output is accomplished by means of by-passing high-pressure steam to the lower-pressure stages. Of course the flow passages in the lower-pressure stages are not designed for high-pressure steam and consequently a marked drop in efficiency occurs, followed in this case by an increase in steam flow.

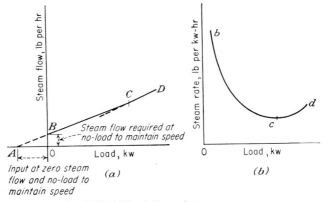

Fig. 11-23. Willans's line and steam-rate curves.

The steam rate may be obtained from the Willans line at various loads by dividing the steam flow by the corresponding load. The result can be plotted as steam rate vs. load, as shown in Fig. 11-23*b*.

11-13. Effect of Initial Pressure and Temperature Changes. Reference was made in Chap. 4 to the effect of higher turbine inlet temperature on the thermal efficiency of the cycle in which the flow through the turbine is the expansion process. Figures 11-24 through 11-27 have been plotted for various inlet temperatures and pressures for an ideal turbine operating with a constant exhaust pressure of 1 in. Hg abs. The curves are contours of constant pressure on the surface of the pressure-temperature plane, pressure and temperature being the independent variables.

Figure 11-24 shows the influence of pressure and temperature on steam rate. At high temperatures, say 1100 F or 1200 F, there is in general a reduction of steam rate at higher pressures. However, for temperatures in the approximate range of 600 to 800 F steam rate decreases with increased pressure until above about 1000 psia where a further increase in pressure is accompanied by an increase in steam rate. Although the steam rate is not an absolute indication of the efficiency of the energy conversion, it is an important parameter in determining the size of the machine.

Figure 11-25 shows that heat rate is improved at higher temperatures and pressures with the exception of a temperature range between approximately 650 F and 750 F and pressures in excess of about 2200 psia. It should be noted that the peak of the warped surface for heat rate is not at all as pronounced as that for steam rate. Another important observation is the relative improvement in heat rate for the same incremental increase of temperature or pressure at different locations on the curves.

Figures 11-26 and 11-27 show the effect of inlet pressures and temperatures on exhaust volume in cubic feet per kilowatt-minute output and moisture content of exhaust steam, respectively. In general the observations made in reference to Figs. 11-24 and 11-25 are true for Fig. 11-26. The exhaust volume per unit output is important because it is one of the limiting factors in the last stage. Economic considerations may dictate a different inlet pressure and temperature to avoid a divided flow turbine for a given output.

Figure 11-27 shows that the moisture content of the exhaust steam increases with higher inlet pressure and decreases with higher inlet temperature. A moisture content in excess of 15 per cent cannot be tolerated in the last stage even when moisture catchers are used because of the severe erosive effects. Figure 11-27 seems to indicate a very restricted range of turbine inlet pressures and temperatures in consideration of this aspect of the problem. However, it must be remembered that the curves are for an ideal turbine. The inefficiency of a real turbine results in an increase of entropy with a movement of the state point to the right on the h-s diagram, with a consequent decrease in the moisture fraction. Figure 11-27 can be replotted, taking into account the expected internal engine efficiency of the turbine and a range of suitable inlet temperatures and pressures can be determined.

The effects of changing condition of the steam entering a turbine as a result of throttle governing can be studied by means of Figs. 11-24 through 11-27.

11-14. Effect of Nozzle Governing. If it were feasible to provide nozzle governing for all nozzles in each and every stage in a turbine, an ideal situation would exist in which the areas of the turbine flow passages would conform to the mass rate of flow at all loads. For such ideal governing, the pressures, velocities, and nozzle and blade efficiencies would be constant with load. The Willans line for such a turbine would be a straight line as indicated for the throttle-governed turbine. However, the mass rate of flow and steam rates for the ideally governed turbine would be considerably less than for the throttle-governed turbine at part loads as illustrated in Fig. 11-28.

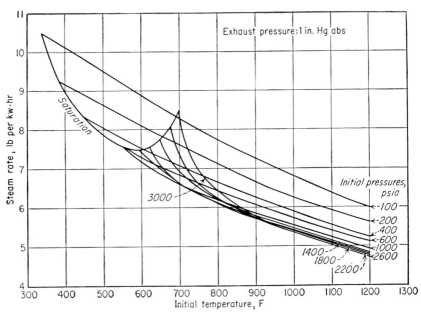

Fig. 11-24. Steam rates for an ideal turbine with variable inlet temperature and pressure and constant exhaust pressure.

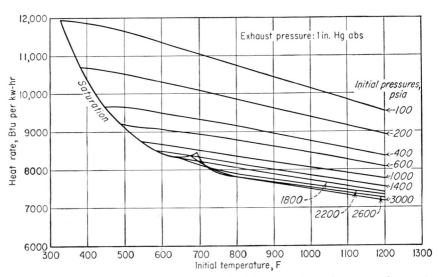

Fig. 11-25. Heat rates for an ideal turbine with variable inlet temperature and pressure and constant exhaust pressure.

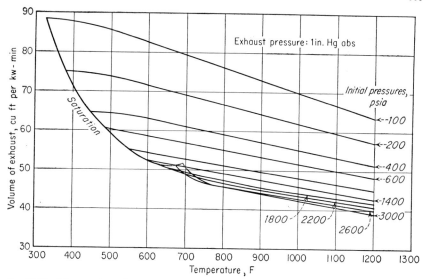

Fig. 11-26. Exhaust volume for an ideal turbine with variable inlet temperature and pressure and constant exhaust pressure.

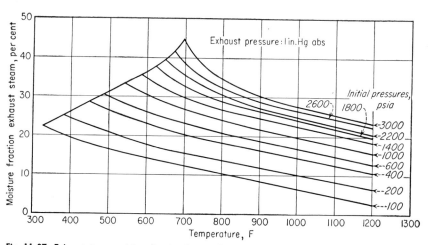

Fig. 11-27. Exhaust-steam moisture fraction for an ideal turbine with variable inlet temperature and pressure and constant exhaust pressure.

In an actual turbine, nozzle governing must be restricted to the first-stage nozzles, as described in Sec. 11-6. Even here each nozzle is not governed but rather groups of nozzles, the number of groups usually being restricted to six or eight. When nozzle governing is employed, the

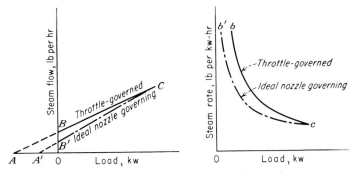

Fig. 11-28. Ideal nozzle governing vs. throttle governing.

pressure and temperature of the steam entering the first-stage nozzles are constant with load. Referring to the condition line of Fig. 11-29, P_1 is the pressure at the exit of the first stage at most efficient load with all nozzles passing the full flow of steam for which they were designed. Now suppose some of the nozzle-governing valves are closed. The entering condition of the steam is unchanged, as stated before, but the mass rate of flow is decreased. Since nozzle governing is confined to the first stage and the nozzle areas of succeeding stages are a fixed element, it follows that the absolute pressure of the steam entering the second-stage nozzles is in direct proportion to the mass rate of flow through the turbine, assuming that the efficiency of the first stage does not vary markedly.

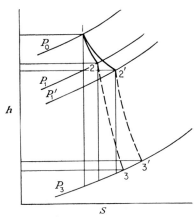

Fig. 11-29. Effect of nozzle governing on condition line.

Actually the efficiency of the first stage suffers somewhat at reduced load, primarily because of increased windage losses and the higher velocities developed incident to the increased pressure drop. Returning to Fig. 11-29, if some of the first-stage nozzles are closed in order to reduce load, then the pressure entering the second-stage nozzles drops to P_1'. The condition of the steam leaving the first stage is given at (2') to indicate the decreased efficiency attendant to windage and lower value of v due to increased steam velocity. It is clear that the available energy for the remaining stages of the turbine has been decreased. The situation there is analogous to that of the throttle-governed turbine. That is to say, the pressure drops per stage for the remaining stages decrease with a consequent increase in v. The type of losses described in Sec. 11-12, as applicable to the throttle-governed turbine, are incurred.

The significant feature of nozzle governing is that considerably less throttling of the steam occurs than if a single valve were used. Therefore the decrease in availability of energy to the whole turbine is much less severe. The fact that an increase in pressure drop occurs in the first-stage nozzles is not too serious since the effect of the larger pressure drop is largely recovered as increased output in the first stage.

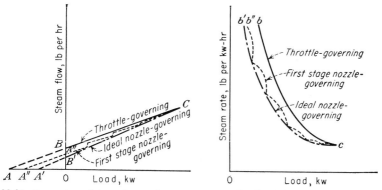

Fig. 11-30. Comparison of steam flow and steam rates at various loads for throttle governing, ideal governing, and first-stage nozzle governing.

The presence of some throttling even with nozzle governing is evident when it is realized that, at most, eight nozzle-governing valves are in current use. To avoid throttling completely, an infinite number of nozzles and governing valves are required. As it is, throttling must occur when some nozzle valves are necessarily partially closed to give close regulation of mass rate of flow. However, as pointed out before, the amount of throttling is small in comparison to that obtained with the single valve used in throttle governing.

Figure 11-30 compares the flow-vs.-output and steam-rate-vs.-output curves for throttle governing, ideal nozzle governing, and first-stage nozzle governing with six nozzle valves. The scalloped or humped steam-rate curve is characteristic of nozzle governing.

11-15. Parsons Number and Quality Factor. The performance and geometry of a multistaged turbine may be expressed in terms of general relationships which are of considerable interest and importance to the designer.

One of these relationships is the Parsons number, which is defined as the sum of the products of the root mean square of the diameters expressed in inches and the square of the rotational speeds in rpm divided by the constant 1000^2, or

$$\lambda = \sum_{0}^{n} \left(\frac{DN}{1000} \right)^2 \tag{11-3}$$

where λ = Parsons number
D = root mean square of stage diameter, in.
N = rotational speed, rpm
For constant mean diameter Eq. (11-3) may be expressed

$$\lambda = n \left(\frac{DN}{1000} \right)^2 \tag{11-4}$$

Substituting $U = \pi DN/12 \times 60$ in Eq. (11-3), the Parsons number becomes

$$\lambda = 0.05253 \ \Sigma U^2 \tag{11-5}$$

where U = mean blade velocity in fps.

From the definition of velocity ratio the average velocity ratio for the turbine may be expressed

$$\nu_t^2 = \frac{\Sigma \pi^2 D^2 N^2}{(12 \times 60)^2 2gJ \ \Sigma (\Delta h_S)_{\text{stage}}} \tag{11-5a}$$

$$\nu_t^2 = \frac{1}{2633 \ \Sigma (\Delta h_S)_{\text{stage}}} \sum \left(\frac{DN}{1000} \right)^2$$

or
$$\lambda = 2633 \nu_t^2 \ \Sigma (\Delta h_S)_{\text{stage}} \tag{11-6}$$

Equation (11-6) relates the physical dimensions of the turbine to the sum of the available energies of the stages for a given value of ν. Of course the most advantageous value of ν is selected for the type of stage under consideration. Conversely, the average value of ν for the turbine can be computed if $\Sigma (\Delta h_S)_{\text{stage}}$ and the stage mean diameters are known.

From Eq. (9-5) the following may be substituted in Eq. (11-5a):

$$\text{RF}_N (\Delta h_S)_{\text{turbine}} = \Sigma (\Delta h_S)_{\text{stage}}$$

to yield
$$\nu_t^2 = \frac{\lambda}{(12 \times 60)^2 2gJ \ RF_N (\Delta h_S)_{\text{turbine}}} \tag{11-7}$$

Substituting from Eq. (11-5) in Eq. (11-7) and rearranging,

$$\frac{\Sigma U^2}{(\Delta h_S)_{\text{turbine}}} = \nu_t^2 2gJ \ RF_N \tag{11-8}$$

The expression $\Sigma U^2/(\Delta h_S)_{\text{turbine}}$ is known as the quality factor for the turbine and is a criterion of its performance. Figure 11-31 shows a plot of brake engine efficiency vs. quality factor based on values suggested by Kraft. It is clear that the value of the quality factor must be higher for a reaction turbine than is the case with an impulse turbine because of the difference in the velocity ratios. Therefore Eq. (11-8) is not only an index of performance of turbines of the same type but of different turbines as well, while Eq. (11-5) is an index of size and performance.

11-16. Performance of Automatic Extraction Turbines. Where process steam is required, some means must be provided to reduce the pressure of the steam from boiler pressure to the desired pressures for the processes involved. Of course the pressure could be reduced by means of pressure-

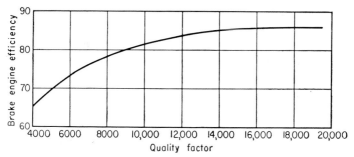

Fig. 11-31. Quality factor as a performance parameter.

reducing valves but the throttling process obviously would be extremely wasteful. The use of an automatic extraction turbine permits full utilization of the energy which would be degraded by throttling, to do useful work in the form of turbine output. The steam delivered to the turbine must meet the variable needs in terms of turbine output and extraction steam while close control of extraction steam pressure is normally required.

Automatic extraction turbines may be designed for either condensing or noncondensing operation and may provide one or two extraction points. A single extraction noncondensing turbine may therefore provide steam at two pressures for process work and similarly a double-extraction noncondensing turbine may provide steam at three pressures. The complications involved in the governing system have discouraged the employment of more than two extraction points.

Consider first the single-extraction turbine operating condensing or noncondensing. It is convenient to think of the turbine as consisting of two separate units, one before the extraction point and the other after the extraction point. Usually the section after the extraction point, referred to as the low-pressure section, is designed to handle full flow when operating straight condensing or noncondensing as the case may be. The section before extraction, called the high-pressure section, is designed for the maximum flow required to permit extraction of the specified amount of steam and at the same time provide the required turbine output corresponding to this condition. The high-pressure section is normally provided with first-stage nozzle governing. In order to avoid a pressure drop at the extraction point and to minimize throttling losses when passing less than full-load steam flow to the low-pressure section, it is necessary to provide some means for varying the nozzle area in the stage immediately following extraction. The area variation may be accomplished by means of a grid valve, discussed in Sec. 11-8 and illustrated in Fig. 11-13. However, the use of the grid valve is limited to pressures and temperatures below 165 psia and 575 F because of the sliding contact between the oscillating and stationary rings and because of the type of materials used. If higher extraction pressures and temperatures are required, it is usual to provide a steam chest with poppet-type extraction valves similar to the main nozzle governing system.

The stages in the high-pressure section may consist of a single Curtis stage or an arrangement of Curtis-reaction or Curtis-Rateau stages, depending on the magnitude of the available energy. The governing stage is usually a Curtis stage. In the low-pressure section the arrangement may consist of all Rateau stages or a Rateau stage followed by reaction stages. A Curtis control stage may be used after the extraction point if the extraction pressure exceeds about 80 psia.

Now the performance of the high-pressure section is quite similar to that of a straight noncondensing turbine and may be expressed in the same manner. However, this is not true of the low-pressure section, since for any given flow at turbine inlet any number of different extraction flows may prevail. The low-pressure section obviously receives a flow equal to the difference between turbine inlet flow and extraction flow. With a highly variable flow to the low-pressure section, a similar variation will exist in the enthalpy of the steam entering this section of the turbine. Hence an expression of the performance characteristics of the low-pressure section must be based on some average enthalpy entering the section, with the result the performance data are not precise. The average enthalpy is obtained by subtracting the average output of the high pressure section in Btu per pound from the enthalpy entering the turbine.

To construct the Willans line for the entire turbine, it is first necessary to construct the Willans line for each section for different turbine inlet flows and extraction flows. For example, the output of the high-pressure section can be computed on the basis of calculated or observed data for a sufficient number of turbine inlet flows to establish the Willans line for this section of the turbine. Then a constant extraction flow at controlled pressure is selected and the flows to the low-pressure section are obtained by subtracting the constant extraction flow from the turbine inlet flows taken in determining the Willans line of the high-pressure section. The output of the low-pressure section is calculated for these flows and thus the Willans line is established for the section. Now it is clear that for a given turbine inlet flow and constant extraction flow the total output of the turbine is fixed at the sum of the outputs deter-

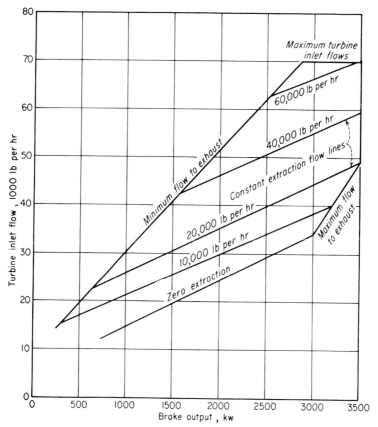

Fig. 11-32. Turbine inlet flow vs. brake output for single automatic extraction turbine.

mined from the two Willans lines. The total output is plotted against turbine inlet flow at various constant extraction flows to give a diagram similar to Fig. 11-32. This diagram is for an automatic single extraction condensing turbine rated at 3000 kw and capable of an overload to 3500 kw on a brake output basis. The extraction pressure is 45 psia. The initial pressure and temperature are 415 psia and 600 F. Condenser pressure is 2 in. Hg abs.

Several features of Fig. 11-32 merit discussion. The maximum turbine inlet flow represents the limit imposed by the passages of the high-pressure section of the turbine. Corresponding to this for the low-pressure section is the maximum flow to exhaust. This limit can be exceeded only by raising the pressure of the extracted steam. Another limiting line on the diagram is the minimum flow to exhaust. The significance of this line is that turbine output is produced substantially in the high-pressure section, a minimum flow passing to the low-pressure section. Thus the line representing the minimum flow to exhaust is also the maximum extraction limit for a given turbine inlet flow or output. The minimum flow to the exhaust can never be zero since some steam must be supplied to the low-pressure section to carry away the heat generated by windage friction. If cooling steam were not provided, it is entirely possible that the blades might even approach the melting point, resulting in failure or at least permanent distortion.

By means of a chart similar to Fig. 11-32 it is possible to determine the output or turbine inlet flow required for a given amount of extraction.

The performance curves for an automatic double extraction turbine are obtained in a manner similar to that followed for the single extraction turbine. The essential difference is that the turbine is now considered to consist of three sections operating in series. To establish the performance curves, the following points must be considered:

1. The quantities of extraction steam, the extraction pressures, and the maximum output are specified by the particular application intended.

2. The flow to the high-pressure section is dictated by the flow required at turbine inlet to maintain full load while providing the full required extraction flow at both extraction points.

3. The flow to the intermediate section (between extraction points) is fixed at the rate of flow required to maintain full load with no extraction from the high-pressure extraction point and the maximum required extraction flow from the low-pressure point.

4. The flow to the low-pressure section is determined as the flow required to maintain full load when extracting no steam at all.

The Willans line is constructed for the three sections in the manner described for the single extraction turbine, with the foregoing points kept in mind. Figure 11-33 illustrates the performance curves for a 7500-kw automatic double extraction condensing turbine operating between 415 psia and 700 F and an exhaust pressure of 2 in. Hg abs. The extraction pressures are indicated in the figure. The section of the chart to the left is applicable when high-pressure extraction takes place. The section of the chart to the right applies to low-pressure extraction. Thus if there is no high-pressure extraction, the section of the chart to the right is interpreted as if the turbine were a single extraction turbine and the section of the chart to the left is ignored. If both high- and low-pressure extraction takes place, the combined chart is read as indicated by the dotted lines. Note that the high-pressure zero extraction line is used as a reference line in going from the left to right sections of the chart, or vice versa.

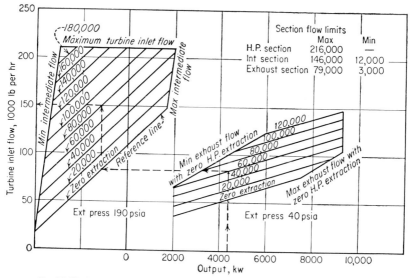

Fig. 11-33. Turbine inlet flow vs. output for double automatic extraction turbine.

11-17. Performance of the Mixed-pressure Turbine.

The mixed-pressure turbine utilizes low-pressure steam discharged from industrial processes in addition to a higher pressure turbine inlet steam. The low-pressure steam is admitted to the turbine at some intermediate stage. The mixed-pressure turbine may operate under any of the following conditions:

1. Steam is admitted to the turbine inlet and induction point simultaneously.
2. Steam is admitted to the induction point only.
3. Steam is admitted to the turbine inlet only.
4. Steam is admitted to the turbine inlet and extracted from the induction point. In this way the mixed-pressure turbine is used as an extraction turbine.

The mixed-pressure turbine like the single extraction turbine may be considered to consist of two turbine sections. The low-pressure section is designed to handle the required flow for maximum output with no work being done by the high-pressure section. A minimum flow of cooling steam must be provided for the high-pressure section under this condition of operation.

The turbine inlet flow vs. output curves for the mixed-pressure turbine resemble those of the automatic single extraction turbine. Figure 11-34 shows such a family of curves for a mixed-pressure turbine which at times is used as a single extraction turbine. It will be noted that a new limiting line is added for the minimum turbine inlet flow.

11-18. A-C Generator. It is not within the scope of this book to discuss the generator in detail. However, a few salient performance factors are presented because of their relationship to the turbogenerator output.

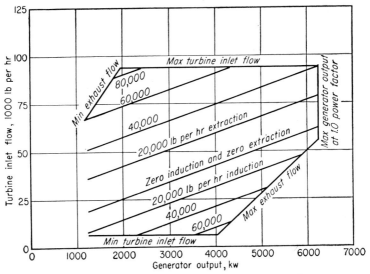

Fig. 11-34. Turbine inlet flow vs. output for mixed-pressure turbine.

The rotational speed of the generator and therefore of its prime mover, if not geared, is

$$N = \frac{120f}{n}$$

where N = speed, rpm

f = frequency, cycles per sec

n = number of poles

Since 60-cycle frequency is in general use in this country, the maximum rotational speed of the generator is 3600 rpm for the minimum number of poles, which is two.

The power factor is the cosine of the phase angle. Turbogenerator output is normally rated at 0.80 or 0.85 power factor. In the standardized units discussed in the next section, the rated output is always given at 0.85 power factor. The generator itself is rated in kilovolt-amperes (kva) and thus the turbogenerator output which is given in kilowatts is obtained by multiplying the kilovolt-ampere rating of the generator by the power factor.

The generator is cooled by air or hydrogen, the latter being used for generators rated in excess of 15,000 kw at 0.85 power factor. The use of hydrogen is effective in reducing the rotational losses of the generator about 10 per cent when the hydrogen pressure is at 0.5 psig. The gen-

TABLE 11-1. EFFECT OF HYDROGEN PRESSURES ON GENERATOR, kva

Generator rating*	20,000	30,000	40,000	60,000
Generator kva:				
0.5 psig hydrogen	23,529	35,294	47,058	70,588
15 psig hydrogen	27,058	40,588	54,117	81,176

* 3600 rpm, 60 cycles, three-phase, 0.85 pf, 0.8 short-circuit ratio.

TABLE 11-2. STANDARDIZED TURBOGENERATORS*

	Single-casing single-flow turbine				Tandem-compound double-flow turbine	
	Air-cooled generator	Hydrogen-cooled generator				
	11,500 kw	15,000 kw	20,000 kw	30,000 kw	40,000 kw	60,000 kw
Throttle pressure, psig	600	850	850	850	850 | 1250	850 | 1250
Throttle temperature, °F	825	900	900	900	900 | 950	900 | 950
Exhaust pressure, in. Hg abs	1.5	1.5	1.5	1.5	1.5	1.5
Turbine capability, kw	12,650	16,500	22,000	33,000	44,000	66,000
Number of extraction openings	4	4	4	5	5	5
Saturation temperature at 1st	175	175	175	175	175	175
openings at turbine-gen- 2d	235	235	235	235	235	235
erator ratings with all 3d	285	285	285	285	285	285
extraction openings in 4th	350	350	350	350	350	350
service, °F 5th				410	410	410
Generator kva:						
Air-cooled generator	13,529					
Hydrogen-cooled generator						
0.5 lb hydrogen pressure		17,647	23,529	35,294	47,058	70,588
15.0 lb hydrogen pressure		20,294	27,028	40,588	54,117	81,176
Power factor	0.85	0.85	0.85	0.85	0.85	0.85
Short-circuit ratio	0.8	0.8	0.8	0.8	0.8	0.8

* Data from General Electric Company.

erator kva may be increased by further reducing generator losses through using hydrogen at higher pressures, up to 15 psig. Table 11-1 shows the increase in generator kva when using hydrogen at 0.5 psig and 15 psig.

11-19. AIEE-ASME Preferred Standard Turbine. The large turbogenerators (15,000 to 60,000 kw) currently being installed in central

TABLE 11-3. PERFORMANCE DATA*

30,000-kw units, 850 psig, 900 F

Exhaust pressure, in. Hg abs	Per cent of rated load	Straight condensing steam rate, lb/(kw)(hr)	Extraction performance 5 heaters				Extraction performance 4 heaters			
			Heat rate, Btu/(kw)(hr)	Feed-water temp °F	Throttle steam rate, lb/(kw)(hr)	Condenser steam rate, lb/(kw)(hr)	Heat rate, Btu/(kw)(hr)	Feed-water temp. F	Throttle steam rate, lb/(kw)(hr)	Condenser steam rate, lb/(kw)(hr)
1	25	8.39	10,716	296	9.02	7.31	10,854	253	8.81	7.44
	50	7.76	9,770	342	8.57	6.60	9,892	293	8.31	6.73
	75	7.63	9,435	375	8.54	6.32	9,542	321	8.21	6.43
	100	7.65	9,408	403	8.76	6.31	9,497	345	8.36	6.38
	110	7.72	9,438	414	8.88	6.31	9,521	354	8.45	6.39
1½	25	8.70	11,101	298	9.36	7.66	11,244	255	9.15	7.81
	50	7.93	9,970	343	8.76	6.81	10,095	295	8.49	6.95
	75	7.71	9,543	376	8.64	6.48	9,651	321	8.31	6.59
	100	7.68	9,462	404	8.81	6.40	9,552	346	8.41	6.49
	110	7.73	9,479	415	8.92	6.42	9,562	354	8.49	6.50
2	25	8.99	11,484	301	9.71	7.99	11,632	257	9.48	8.15
	50	8.12	10,199	345	8.97	7.03	10,327	296	8.69	6.17
	75	7.83	9,691	377	8.79	6.65	9,801	323	8.45	6.75
	100	7.76	9,561	405	8.91	6.53	9,652	347	8.50	6.62
	110	7.79	9,560	416	9.01	6.53	9,644	355	8.57	6.61
2½	25	9.30	11,841	302	10.03	8.30	11,994	259	9.79	8.47
	50	8.32	10,409	347	9.17	7.23	10,540	298	8.89	7.37
	75	7.97	9,850	379	8.95	6.80	9,962	324	8.60	6.91
	100	7.85	9,678	407	9.04	6.66	9,770	348	8.62	6.75
	110	7.88	9,661	417	9.12	6.65	9,746	356	8.67	6.73

* Data from General Electric Company.

TABLE 11-4. REPRESENTATIVE CENTRAL STATION STEAM-TURBINE PERFORMANCE*
AIEE-ASME Preferred Standard

Extraction Performance—Five-stage Feedwater Heating

Load, kw	Straight condensing steam rate, lb/kwhr	Steam flow to throttle, 1000 lb/hr	Steam flow to condenser, 100 lb/hr	Temp. feedwater leaving last heater, °F	Turbine heat rate,† Btu/kwhr	Station heat rate,‡ Btu/kwhr
	30,000-kw Single-case Turbine Generator Unit Steam conditions: 850 psig, 900F, 1.5 in. Hg abs					
7500	8.70	70.2	57.5	298	11,100	13620
15000	7.93	131.4	102.2	344	9,970	12235
22500	7.71	194.4	148.5	375	9,545	11710
30000	7.68	264.3	192.0	404	9,460	11610
33000	7.73	294.4	211.9	414	9,480	11630
	60,000-kw Tandem-compound Turbine Generator Unit Steam conditions: 850 psig, 900F, 1.5 in. Hg abs					
15000	8.45	136.5	111.6	297	10,800	13250
30000	7.75	256.5	199.5	343	9,740	11950
45000	7.56	382.5	286.7	375	9,390	11520
60000	7.55	519.6	376.8	403	9,305	11420
66000	7.60	578.2	415.1	414	9,310	11425
	60,000-kw Tandem-compound Turbine Generator Unit Steam conditions: 1250 psig, 950F, 1.5 in. Hg abs					
15000	8.15	129.8	106.1	293	10,435	12870
30000	7.43	242.7	188.4	338	9,375	11565
45000	7.21	359.1	269.6	369	8,985	11085
60000	7.19	488.4	355.2	395	8,940	11030
66000	7.23	543.8	392.7	406	8,955	11045

* Data from Westinghouse Electric Corporation.

† Turbine heat rate = $\dfrac{\text{throttle flow (throttle enthalpy-enthalpy feed leaving last heater)}}{\text{net generator output, kw}}$

‡ Station heat rate = $\dfrac{\text{turbine heat rate}}{\text{(boiler efficiency)} \times (1\% - \text{auxiliary loss}) \times \text{(operating ratio)}}$

Assumed efficiencies for station heat rate:

	1250 psig inlet, %	850 psig inlet, %
Boiler efficiency................	88	88
Auxiliary loss..................	6	5.5
Station operating ratio..........	98	98

Auxiliary loss is made up of the following items: boiler feed pump power, forced and induced draft fan power, firing equipment power, circulating and condensate pump power, etc.

Station operating ratio is a factor to allow for operation at other than most efficient design point.

stations conform with few exceptions to the joint AIEE-ASME preferred standards for large turbogenerators. The standardization applies to dimensions, number, and location of extraction points for feedwater heating, steam conditions, and the specifications for reporting capacity and performance. Of course performance itself is not standardized, since obviously it would be undesirable. However, the performance of standardized machines as manufactured by the major companies differs only slightly. The essential features of the standardized units are given in Table 11-2. Space does not permit the listing of performance data for all of the standardized units. However, Table 11-3 for a 30,000-kw unit is representative.

For performance characteristics at other than the stated conditions, it is necessary to apply correction factors obtained from curves furnished by the manufacturer. The performance of the regenerative cycle requires a heat balance taking into consideration the losses involved not only in the turbine and generator but the boiler, heaters, pumps, and other station auxiliaries. Table 11-4 gives some representative performance data for central stations using standardized turbines.

References

1. Caughey, R. J.: Recent Developments in Turbine Governing to Meet Special Conditions, *Combustion*, June, 1940.
2. Kearton, W. J.: "Steam Turbine Theory and Practice," Pitman Publishing Corp., New York, 1948.
3. Kraft, H.: The Modern Steam Turbine, *VDI*, 1930.
4. Newman, L. E., J. M. Lyons, and L. B. Wales: "Modern Turbines," John Wiley & Sons, Inc., New York, 1944.
5. Newman, L. E.: Modern Extraction Turbines, *Power Plant Eng.*, January, February, March, and April, 1945.
6. Pollard, E. V.: How to Estimate Turbine Performance with Uncontrolled Extraction, *Power Plant Eng.*, April, 1947.
7. Recommended Specification for Speed-governing of Steam Turbines Intended to Drive Electric Generators Rated 500 kw and Up, AIEE-ASME Joint Committee, *AIEE* 600, May, 1949.
8. Salisbury, J. K.: "Steam Turbines and Their Cycles," John Wiley & Sons, Inc., New York, 1950.
9. Salisbury, J. K.: Steam Turbine Flow-pressure Characteristics, *Gen. Elec. Rev.*, March and April, 1950.
10. Skrotzki, B. G. A., and W. A. Vopat: "Steam and Gas Turbines," McGraw-Hill Book Company, Inc., New York, 1950.
11. Steam Turbines, *Power*, December, 1945.
12. Warren, G. B., and P. H. Knowlton: Relative Engine Efficiencies Realizable from Large Modern Steam-turbine Generator Sets, *Trans. ASME*, 1941.

CHAPTER 12

THE CENTRIFUGAL COMPRESSOR

12-1. Introduction. The air compressor occupies a position of importance in the gas-turbine power plant equal in every respect to that of the turbine. When it is recalled that the net useful output of the plant is the difference between turbine output and compressor input, it is clear that the gain from a highly efficient turbine can be largely nullified by an inefficient compressor. Furthermore, for efficient over-all performance it is essential that the turbine characteristics match those of the compressor.

There are many similarities between the compressor and turbine in so far as the principles of operation are concerned. However, the design application of these principles for the compressor is much more severely restricted because the compressor carries out a diffusion process. This chapter is concerned with an examination of the theory of operation and the application of this theory in the design of centrifugal air compressors.

The centrifugal compressor is advantageous when a single-stage compressor operating with a pressure ratio not exceeding 4:1 is required. While a pressure ratio of 4:1 can be achieved in a single-stage centrifugal compressor, a multistaged axial-flow compressor would be required so that the advantage of the centrifugal compressor in this range of pressure ratio is obvious. Another advantage of the single-stage centrifugal compressor is its ability to operate more efficiently over a wider range of mass rate of flow than a comparable axial-flow compressor. The centrifugal compressor is rugged in construction and is less susceptible to the effects of deposits left on the flow passages by the air. It is used principally in superchargers and jet-aircraft power plants operating at lower pressure ratios and handling smaller quantities of air.

When a multistaged air compressor handling large quantities of air is required, the axial-flow air compressor is advantageous. A multistaged axial-flow compressor has a higher efficiency level, smaller frontal area, and a larger capacity for a given frontal area and is lighter and less bulky than a comparable multistage centrifugal compressor. However, the efficiency of the axial-flow compressor is more adversely affected by

349

deposits settling on the blades, wear, and flow changes than the centrifugal compressor. The axial-flow compressor is used in aircraft gas-turbine power plants and almost exclusively in stationary plants.

The positive displacement rotary compressor has not been used extensively. The only important application is the Lysholm compressor in the marine gas-turbine power plant built by the Elliott Company. A phantom view of the Lysholm compressor is shown in Fig. 2-16. The principle advantage of this compressor is its wider range of stable flow.

12-2. Description and Operation. The principal components of the centrifugal compressor are the impeller and the diffuser. The impeller rotates with the shaft at high speed and imparts kinetic energy to the air with some static pressure rise. The air is accelerated by centrifugal force

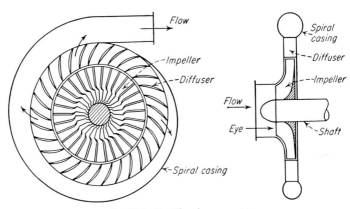

Fig. 12-1. Centrifugal compressor.

in the impeller. The diffuser is stationary and converts the kinetic energy of the air leaving the impeller into static pressure. Thus it is seen that the compression of the air is accomplished essentially in two steps.

Figure 12-1 shows the principal parts of the centrifugal compressor. When the impeller is rotating at high speed, air is drawn in through the eye of the impeller. The absolute velocity of the inflow is axial. The direction and magnitude of the entering relative velocity depend on the linear velocity of the impeller at the radial position of the eye considered, as well as the magnitude and direction of the entering absolute velocity. The impeller vanes at the eye are bent to provide shockless entrance for the entering flow at its relative entrance angle. The air then flows radially through the impeller passages due to centrifugal force. Although some static pressure rise occurs in the impeller passages, the work done on the air manifests itself principally in the form of kinetic energy. Therefore it is necessary to provide a diffusing passage to accomplish the purpose of the compressor, which is to raise the static pressure of the air.

The flow from the diffusers is collected in a spiral passage from which it is discharged from the compressor. It is clear from Fig. 12-1 that the area available for inflow is the annular area represented by the eye of the impeller. The area for the outflow from the impeller is equal to the outer perimeter of the impeller times the depth of the impeller vanes at exit.

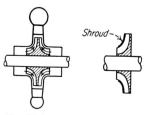

Fig. 12-2. Double impeller and shrouds.

A single impeller without shrouds is illustrated in Fig. 12-1. A double impeller is often used when larger flows are to be handled. The principle of operation is the same as for the single impeller. In order to reduce leakage between the impeller and the casing a shroud is sometimes provided. However, the shroud is not usual because of the fabrication difficulties involved. Very rarely are back-swept or forward-swept impeller vanes used, the normal construction being the straight radial vane illustrated. Figure 12-2 illustrates the double-impeller centrifugal compressor and the impeller shroud.

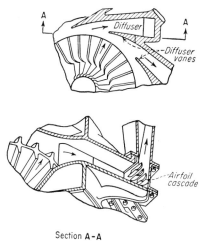

Section A-A

Fig. 12-3. Diffuser arrangement for multi-burner aircraft gas turbine. (After Caughey.[1])

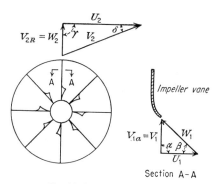

Section A-A

Fig. 12-4. Velocity diagrams.

Figure 12-3 illustrates a diffuser arrangement generally employed in aircraft gas-turbine installations where a number of burners are used in parallel. Diffusing outlets are provided equal in number to the burners employed. Some diffusion occurs in the vaneless space between the impeller and the inlet to the diffuser vanes. Of course diffusion takes place in the vaned passages followed by more diffusion in an axial direction after the passage takes a right-angled turn. It should be observed

that an airfoil cascade is provided to minimize possible shock and turbulence losses occasioned by the abrupt turn.

The velocity diagrams for the centrifugal compressor are similar in
principle to those drawn for the turbine. Figure 12-4 shows the inflow
and outflow velocity diagrams for a radial-flow impeller. The velocity
vector V_1 represents the absolute velocity entering the impeller eye, its
direction being axial as shown. The vector U_1 is the mean linear
velocity of the impeller vane at the eye and W_1 is the relative velocity
entering the eye. The vector W_2 is the relative velocity shown leaving
the impeller in a radial direction since a radial vane is under consideration.
It is noted that U_2, the linear velocity of the impeller tip, is greater than
U_1 because of the radial distance between the eye and tip. The direction
and magnitude of the absolute velocity leaving the impeller are V_2. An
examination of the velocity triangles reveals that V_1 has no tangential
component and the tangential component of V_2 must always be equal to
U_2.

12-3. Energy Transfers and Relations. If the ideal conditions for
streamline flow listed in Sec. 8-3 are applied to the centrifugal compressor
the energy transferred to the air in the form of work per pound per second
flow is given by Eq. (8-7):

$$E = \frac{1}{g}\,(U_1 V_{1U} - U_2 V_{2U}) \qquad (8\text{-}7)$$

But it was noted in Sec. 12-2 that the velocity of the flow entering the
impeller eye is axial and therefore it has no whirl component. If the subscript 1 in Eq. (8-7) refers to the flow entering the impeller eye and the
subscript 2 refers to the flow leaving the impeller tip, then Eq. (8-7) can
be written

$$E = -\frac{U_2 V_{2U}}{g} \qquad (12\text{-}1)$$

The negative sign indicates that work is done on the fluid. Now it was
also pointed out in the last section that $U_2 = V_{2U}$ for radial vanes. Equation (12-1) under these conditions becomes

$$E = -\frac{U_2{}^2}{g} \qquad (12\text{-}2)$$

It is seen from Eq. (12-2) that the work done on the air is independent
of the entering velocity and a priori is also independent of the dimensions
of the eye. Equation (12-2) also shows that the maximum work done on
the air by a given impeller depends on the speed and tip diameter of the
impeller. This is an important observation, for in order to maintain a
given frontal area increased pressure rise can be achieved only by increasing the rotational speed. Vice versa, if a limit is placed on the rotational

speed, an increase in pressure rise can be accomplished solely by increasing the tip diameter of the impeller. The only other alternative is to adopt multistaging, which has its drawbacks, as pointed out before.

The heat transfer in the compression process under consideration is negligible and the energy equation may be written

$$h_2^o - h_1^o = - \frac{W}{J} \tag{12-3}$$

If the preceding equation is written for the entrance and exit of the compressor, the absolute velocities at these points will be very nearly the same in most designs and the work done on the air may be expressed by the static enthalpy increase:

$$h_2 - h_1 = - \frac{W}{J} \tag{12-4}$$

Equation (12-4) can be expressed in terms of the mean value of C_p, or

$$W = -JC_p(T_2 - T_1) = - \frac{U_2^2}{g} \tag{12-5}$$

Since the compression is isentropic,

$$T_2 = T_1 \left(\frac{P_2}{P_1} \right)^{(k-1)/k}$$

and

$$JC_pT_1 \left[\left(\frac{P_2}{P_1} \right)^{(k-1)/k} - 1 \right] = \frac{U_2^2}{g} \tag{12-6}$$

from which

$$\frac{P_2}{P_1} = \left[\frac{U_2^2}{gJC_pT_1} + 1 \right]^{k/(k-1)} \tag{12-7}$$

Similarly

$$\frac{P_2^o}{P_1^o} = \left[\frac{U_2^2}{gJC_pT_1^o} + 1 \right]^{k/(k-1)} \tag{12-8}$$

Equations (12-7) and (12-8) show that the pressure ratio achieved in an ideal compressor with radial-vaned impeller depends on the linear velocity of the impeller tip and the temperature of the air entering the impeller.

12-4. Losses. It is inevitable that losses must occur in any machine and of course the centrifugal compressor is no exception. The internal losses sustained in a compressor are manifested by an increase of the enthalpy of the air. Very little energy is lost from the system. With an increase in entropy the required static pressure is achieved by doing more work on the air to offset the effect of the irreversibilities and it is clear that the temperature of the air leaving the compressor must be higher than if an isentropic compression occurred. While it is true that the higher-temperature air is of some benefit as far as heat addition in the combustor is concerned, it must be remembered that the work input to the compressor has been purchased from the turbine at the expense of the turbine irreversibilities and the limitation of the second law imposed on the turbine.

Among the internal losses which occur in the compressor are (1) friction between air and walls of the flow passages; (2) disc friction; (3) leakage between impeller and casing; (4) turbulence; (5) shock. In addition to the internal losses the compressor sustains an external loss in the form of bearing friction.

12-5. Adiabatic Efficiency. The adiabatic efficiency is defined as the ratio of work input to the compressor for isentropic compression between specified pressure limits to the adiabatic (and nonisentropic) work for compression between the same pressure limits, considering internal losses. Thus it is seen that the adiabatic efficiency of a compressor is analogous to the internal engine efficiency of a turbine.

With reference to Eq. (12-5), the adiabatic efficiency may be written

$$\eta_{ad} = \frac{T_2 - T_1}{T_{2'} - T_1} \tag{12-9}$$

where $T_{2'}$ is the actual temperature of the air leaving the compressor.

Also, from Eq. (12-6), if the polytropic path exponent n is used for the actual compression process,

$$\eta_{ad} = \frac{(P_2/P_1)^{(k-1)/k} - 1}{(P_2/P_1)^{(n-1)/n} - 1} \tag{12-10}$$

The mechanical efficiency of the compressor is the index of the external losses. These losses are confined principally to the bearings and are very small. The over-all efficiency of the compressor is

$$\eta_{\text{over-all}} = \eta_{ad}\eta_m \tag{12-11}$$

12-6. Effect of Compressibility. Shock and flow separation were discussed in Sec. 6-18 as a distinct possibility even when the Mach number based on the mean velocity of the flow passage is less than unity. It was pointed out that the local velocity near a surface may reach the velocity of sound because of local accelerations. A subsequent deceleration could result in a standing shock wave with flow separation behind the wave front. Such an occurrence takes place with an increase in entropy, and therefore some of the work done on the air is used to raise the temperature of the air. Since the purpose of the air compressor is to raise the static pressure of the air, and not its temperature, shock and flow separation must be regarded as losses.

Consider the specific problem at the impeller eye. It is noted that the impeller vanes are bent at the eye in order to provide shockless entrance for the flow at its relative entrance angle. The absolute velocity of the air entering the flow annulus of the impeller eye varies from a minimum near the inner and outer radii to a maximum somewhere near the mean radius. The linear velocity of the impeller at the eye varies from a minimum at the inner radius to a maximum at the outer radius. Therefore the relative entering velocity increases radially over the eye flow annulus, reaching a maximum value at the outer radius. The Mach number of the entering flow relative to the impeller is

$$M_1 = \frac{W_1}{\sqrt{gkRT_1}}$$

From the foregoing observations it is seen that the Mach number of the entering flow given by the preceding expression is a maximum at the outer radius of the impeller eye. Also the entering Mach number is increased for lower absolute temperatures of the entering air.

The Mach number at the outer radius of the impeller eye based on the relative entering velocity is regarded as the flow inlet Mach number for design purposes. Even when the inlet Mach number is less than unity, it is likely that supersonic local velocities can be reached when the flow is deflected through the entering relative angle and when passing from the axial to the radial flow passages of the impeller. As a consequence a situation similar to that shown in Fig. 6-31 can occur. If the flow inlet Mach number is kept below 0.9 (preferably 0.85) experience indicates local accelerations to sonic or supersonic velocities are not likely to occur.

The velocities reached in the radial portion of the impeller are usually low enough so that the Mach number of the stream is well below 0.9. It is necessary sometimes to thicken the impeller vanes to reduce the effects of vibrations. The reduced passage area resulting from thickening the vanes may cause local accelerations to the velocity of sound. However, this is a problem which rarely occurs and can be avoided by careful attention to the Mach numbers.

The Mach number of the air flow will reach its maximum value at the impeller tip and may under some circumstances equal or exceed unity. Since the purpose of the diffusers is to decelerate the flow with a corresponding increase in static pressure, careful attention must be given the design of this part of the compressor to avoid serious shock and flow separation losses. Figure 12-3 shows that a considerable amount of space is provided between the impeller and the diffuser vanes. Fortunately, a vortex appears to exist in this vaneless space, and deceleration occurs at constant angular momentum without the formation of shock waves. By the time the flow reaches the entrance edges of the diffuser vanes, the Mach number is below 0.9 and further deceleration can occur in the vaned portion of the diffuser without shock. Of course it is essential that sufficient vaneless space be provided in the design of the compressor so that a satisfactory Mach number is reached before entering the diffuser vanes. This space requirement can be easily determined by consideration of the relationships of Sec. 6-16. If the flow Mach number is below 0.9 at the impeller tip, only a small clearance space need be provided before entering the diffuser vanes, as shown in Fig. 12-1.

12-7. The Diffuser. The difficulties encountered in attempting to provide for an efficient diffusion process were discussed in Sec. 6-8. Since a pressure gradient exists in a direction opposite to that of the flow, it is to be expected that the flow streamlines will tend to break away from the diverging passage walls, reversing their direction in order to flow with the pressure gradient. The result is turbulence. This situation is aggravated if the divergence angle of the diffuser passage is too great. About 12° is accepted as the maximum included angle of divergence for satisfactory diffusion.

The cross-sectional view of the centrifugal compressor of Fig. 12-1 shows that the depth of the diffuser vanes is constant. The divergence of the diffuser passages occurs solely in the width. The entrance angle of the diffuser vane must coincide with the angle of the absolute velocity entering the diffuser. This angle will be different from the angle of the absolute velocity leaving the impeller because of the free-vortex flow which occurs in the radial space between impeller tip and diffuser vanes. From the previous discussion of free-vortex flow in the axial clearance between rows of turbine blades it is clear that the tangential component of velocity decreases from impeller tip to diffuser vane inlet. Furthermore, the radial component of velocity must decrease radially in the clearance space in keeping with continuity of flow, since the space is of constant depth and flow area increases directly as the radius. Therefore the absolute velocity itself must decrease radially in the clearance space and, as a consequence, the entrance angle to the diffuser vanes is changed. Also it is evident that since the variation of the radial component of velocity depends on the continuity relationship, the angle of entering absolute velocity to the diffuser vanes will change with mass rate of flow and pressure ratio. The pressure ratio is an influence since the specific volume term in the continuity equation depends on pressure and temperature.

From the foregoing it is apparent that the diffuser losses must increase at reduced flow or changed pressure ratio. Compressors have been built for stationary installations with movable diffuser vanes in order to adjust the vane inlet angles for other than design operating conditions. Figure 12-5 shows the effect of off-design operating conditions for a fixed-vane impeller. Not more than a few degrees deviation between vane inlet angle and flow entrance angle need exist before a serious drop in diffuser efficiency is experienced.

As for the vane shape itself, consideration must be given to the flow pattern. In the previous discussion it was ascertained that the flow in a vaneless diffuser followed the principle of constant angular momentum. If it is assumed that the specific volume of the air remains constant, then the radial and tangential components of the absolute velocity vary inversely as the radius from the center of the impeller. Therefore the absolute velocity itself varies inversely as the radial distance from the center of the impeller. If in addition the angle between the absolute velocity vector and its tangential component is constant radially, then all the conditions for a logarithmic spiral are fulfilled. Now the specific volume of the air is not constant as assumed, and consequently the radial component of velocity does not vary inversely as the radius from the center of the impeller. Consequently, the actual path of the flow in the diffuser is not a logarithmic spiral but some

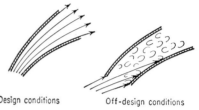

Design conditions   Off-design conditions

Fig. 12-5. The effect of off-design conditions on diffuser-vane flow.

modification of the logarithmic spiral. Sometimes the diffuser vanes are shaped in accordance with a logarithmic spiral but more often a modified form is used, the modifications being dictated by the continuity equation for compressible flow.

12-8. Prewhirl. Mention was made before of the necessity of keeping the Mach number of the flow entering the impeller eye below the value of 0.9. When the absolute velocity of approach is high enough or the static absolute temperature of the entering air is low enough to make the Mach number exceed 0.9, then prewhirl offers an opportunity to reduce the relative velocity entering the impeller eye. Prewhirl is also of value when the shape of the leading edge is difficult to obtain by bending because of a small relative entering angle.

Prewhirl is obtained by means of intake guide vanes, as illustrated in Fig. 12-6. Figure 12-7 shows the effect of prewhirl on the inlet velocity triangle. The entering absolute velocity now has a tangential component, but the magnitude of the relative velocity is reduced and the flow enters with a larger relative angle. Thus the magnitude of the flow inlet Mach number is lower than if prewhirl had not been used.

Equation (8-7) indicates that since the absolute velocity entering the impeller eye has a tangential component, the work done on the air must be greater for the same compressor inlet and outlet conditions. Therefore before a decision is made to incorporate prewhirl the gain from reducing shock and flow separation losses must be measured against the increased work input required. On this basis there appears to be little justification for prewhirl vanes except in centrifugal compressors subjected to the severe conditions of altitude and speed changes met in jet aircraft.

Fig. 12-6. Centrifugal compressor with prewhirl vanes. *(Courtesy of General Electric Company.)*

12-9. Performance Characteristics. The performance of a compressor has been seen to depend on a number of variables such as P_1, P_2, T_1, T_2, G, v_1, v_2, k, D_t, and N. To express the performance of a compressor in terms of all these variables would require a formidable number of tests and test curves. The results would be involved and confused. Dimensional analysis provides a means by which performance characteristics may be evaluated in terms of a concise representation of a convenient number of parameters. These parameters are dimensionless groups.

Consider the static pressure at compressor outlet designated as P_3. Then

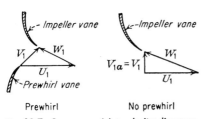

Fig. 12-7. Compressor inlet velocity diagrams showing effect of prewhirl.

$$P_3 = f_1(P_1, T_1, D, G, N) \qquad (12\text{-}12)$$

Since the only gas under consideration is air, it is not necessary to include the ratio of the specific heats. The specific volume is omitted, since it is specified by P_1 and T_1 through the equation of state. The variable

D is a characteristic dimension of the compressor. The following dimensions are chosen:

M = mass
L = length
t = time

Therefore

$$P = M^1L^{-1}t^{-1} \quad \text{psf}$$
$$T = L^2t^{-2} \quad \text{°R}$$
$$D = L \quad \text{ft}$$
$$G = M^1t^{-1} \quad \text{lb per sec}$$
$$N = t^{-1} \quad \text{rpm}$$

From Buckingham's π theorem it is known that three dimensionless groups are possible. There are six variables and three basic dimensions, the difference being the number of dimensionless groups. The three dimensionless groups are found by combining P_1, T_1, and D with each of the remaining variables so that

$$\pi_1 = P_1{}^aT_1{}^bD^cP_3 \tag{12-13}$$
$$\pi_2 = P_1{}^{a_1}T_1{}^{b_1}D^{c_1}G \tag{12-14}$$
$$\pi_3 = P_1{}^{a_2}T_1{}^{b_2}D^{c_2}N \tag{12-15}$$

Substituting the basic dimensions for the variables in π_1,

$$\pi_1 = (M^1L^{-1}t^{-2})^a(L^2t^{-2})^bL^c(M^1L^{-1}t^{-2})^1$$
$$M \quad 0 = a + 1$$
$$L \quad 0 = -a + 2b + c - 1$$
$$t \quad 0 = -2a - 2b - 2$$

from which $a = -1$, $b = 0$, $c = 0$. Substituting these values for the exponents in Eq. (12-13),

$$\pi_1 = P_1{}^{-1}T_1{}^0D^0P_3{}^1 = \frac{P_3}{P_1}$$

Similarly π_2 in Eq. (12-14) becomes

$$\pi_2 = P_1{}^{-1}T_1{}^{0.5}D^{-2}G^1 = \frac{G\sqrt{T_1}}{P_1D^2}$$

and π_3 in Eq. (12-15) is

$$\pi_3 = P_1{}^0T_1{}^{0.5}D^1N = \frac{DN}{\sqrt{T_1}}$$

Now the various values of π may be written

$$\pi_1 = f_1(\pi_2,\pi_3)$$

or

$$\frac{P_3}{P_1} = f_2\left(\frac{G\sqrt{T_1}}{P_1D^2}, \frac{DN}{\sqrt{T_1}}\right) \tag{12-16}$$

If a given compressor is under consideration, D will be constant and Eq. (12-16) may be simplified to read

$$\frac{P_3}{P_1} = f_3\left(\frac{G\sqrt{T_1}}{P_1}, \frac{N}{\sqrt{T_1}}\right) \tag{12-17}$$

If a comparable analysis is made with T_3, the compressor outlet temperature taken as a function of the variables, the ratio of T_3/T_1 will be found to be a function of the dimensionless groups of Eqs. (12-16) and (12-17). Likewise if stagnation temperatures and pressures are considered, Eqs. (12-16) and (12-17) again will be the result except that stagnation temperatures and pressures are substituted for their static counterparts in the equations.

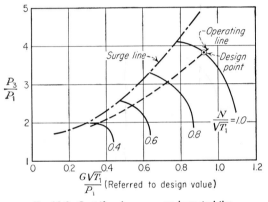

Fig. 12-8. Centrifugal compressor characteristics.

With the aid of Eqs. (12-16) and (12-17), written for stagnation or static conditions, the performance of a given compressor or geometrically similar compressors can be plotted in terms of three dimensionless parameters, provided dynamic similarity is maintained. It will be noted that viscosity was omitted as a variable. If it had been introduced, a fourth dimensionless group, the Reynolds number, would have been produced. However, experiment indicates that the Reynolds number has very little influence on pressure ratio in a high-speed compressor, undoubtedly because of the highly turbulent condition of the flow.

Figure 12-8 shows a plot of $G\sqrt{T_1}/P_1$ referred to its design value against P_3/P_1 and $N/\sqrt{T_1}$ also referred to their design values. The operating line is the locus of points of maximum efficiency at various values of $N/\sqrt{T_1}$. The surge line represents the limit of stable operation, the region to the right of the surge line being for stable conditions. A plot of compressor characteristics such as shown in Fig. 12-8 may be obtained from one series of tests, the performance at other operating conditions being obtained from the relationships among the dimensionless parameters.

12-10. Pressure Coefficient and Slip Factor. The pressure coefficient is defined as the adiabatic work required to raise the static pressure of the air to the actual level achieved in the compressor divided by the adiabatic work required to raise the static pressure of the air to the maximum level prescribed by the impeller tip speed. Equation (12-6) gives the adiabatic work required to raise the static pressure of the air to the maximum value within the limitation of impeller tip speed. This maximum value of the pressure will be designated as $P_{2,\max}$. Then

$$-W_{\max} = JC_pT_1\left[\left(\frac{P_{2,\max}}{P_1}\right)^{(k-1)/k} - 1\right] = \frac{U_2{}^2}{g}$$

Designating the actual pressure achieved by the compressor as simply P_2, the corresponding adiabatic work is

$$-W = JC_pT_1\left[\left(\frac{P_2}{P_1}\right)^{(k-1)/k} - 1\right]$$

Then the pressure coefficient ϕ_p is

$$\phi_p = \frac{JC_pT_1[(P_2/P_1)^{(k-1)/k} - 1]}{JC_pT_1[(P_{2,\max}/P_1)^{(k-1)/k} - 1]}$$

or

$$\phi_p = \frac{JC_pT_1g[(P_2/P_1)^{(k-1)/k} - 1]}{U_2{}^2} \tag{12-18}$$

From Eqs. (12-5) and (12-9) the actual static temperature rise accompanying the actual static pressure rise is

$$-W = JC_p(T_2 - T_1) = JC_p(T_{2'} - T_1)\eta_{ad}$$

and

$$-W = JC_pT_1\left[\left(\frac{P_2}{P_1}\right)^{(k-1)/k} - 1\right] = JC_p(T_{2'} - T_1)\eta_{ad}$$

or

$$T_{2'} - T_1 = \frac{T_1[(P_2/P_1)^{(k-1)/k} - 1]}{\eta_{ad}} \tag{12-19}$$

Substituting from Eq. (12-18),

$$T_{2'} - T_1 = \frac{\phi_p}{\eta_{ad}}\frac{U_2{}^2}{gJC_p} \tag{12-20}$$

Thus far it has been assumed that the tangential velocity of the air leaving the impeller is equal in magnitude to the impeller-tip linear velocity. Unfortunately, this condition cannot be achieved in a real compressor since secondary flow effects cause the air to leave the impeller at a tangential velocity somewhat lower in magnitude than the impeller-tip velocity. A quantitative evaluation of the influence of secondary flow is difficult to make, and the predicted results are rarely substantiated on test. It is customary therefore to assess this aspect of the flow problem in terms of a slip factor defined as follows:

$$\phi_s = \frac{V_{2U,\text{actual}}}{U_2}$$

The pressure coefficient, adiabatic efficiency, and slip factor are related by another factor termed the work input factor.

$$\phi_w = \frac{\phi_p}{\eta_{ad}\phi_s} \tag{12-21}$$

Values of the work input factor are determined experimentally and are found to range from 1.035 to 1.04 for most compressors used in gas-turbine installations. If Eq. (12-21) is substituted in Eq. (12-20), the following expression which is useful in design is the result:

$$T_{2'} - T_1 = \frac{\phi_s \phi_w U_2{}^2}{gJC_p} \tag{12-22}$$

The work input factor and the adiabatic efficiency take into account that portion of the work done on the air which does not manifest itself as a static pressure rise. This portion of the work is in a sense regarded as a loss since it does not accomplish the intended purpose. However, the total work done on the air is manifested in other forms of energy in keeping with the first law. In contrast, the slip factor limits the amount of work which can be done on the air by a given compressor even if the compression process were isentropic.

Taking the pressure coefficient, slip factor, and adiabatic efficiency into account, Eqs. (12-7) and (12-8) may be expressed.

$$\frac{P_2}{P_1} = \left[\frac{U_2{}^2\phi_p}{gJC_pT_1} + 1\right]^{k/(k-1)} = \left[\frac{U_2{}^2\phi_s\phi_w\eta_{ad}}{gJC_pT_1} + 1\right]^{k/(k-1)} \tag{12-23}$$

and $$\frac{P_2^{\circ}}{P_1^{\circ}} = \left[\frac{U^2\phi_p}{gJC_pT_1^{\circ}} + 1\right]^{k/(k-1)} = \left[\frac{U^2\phi_s\phi_w\eta_{ad}}{gJC_pT_1^{\circ}} + 1\right]^{k/(k-1)} \tag{12-24}$$

Increasing the number of vanes increases the value of the slip factor. Unfortunately too many vanes may increase unduly the frictional losses. For this reason a compromise must be reached, the optimum number of vanes giving a slip factor about 0.9. The pressure coefficient must be determined experimentally. Values of 0.63 to 0.67 for small compressors used for superchargers and 0.70 to 0.77 for larger centrifugal compressors are common.

12-11. Surging. Surging was referred to briefly in Sec. 12-9. Figure 12-9 shows P_2/P_1 plotted against $G\sqrt{T_1}/P_1$ for fixed values of N, T_1, and P_1. Therefore the curve represents a plot of compressor outlet pressure vs. mass rate of flow.

Suppose that the compressor is provided with a valve in the discharge

line. When the valve is fully closed, the mass rate of flow of course is
zero and the static pressure developed is that delivered by the impeller
to the air trapped in the compressor. This condition is shown at a in Fig.
12-9. Opening the valve permits flow to take place, and consequently
the diffuser becomes effective in increasing the static pressure as shown
at b and c. Point c represents the maximum pressure ratio and is therefore the most efficient point for the given values of N, P_1, and T_1. As the
valve is opened still further and the mass rate of flow increases beyond c,
the efficiency of the compressor declines with a corresponding decrease in
pressure ratio. When the design mass rate of flow is greatly exceeded,
the incidence between the vane and air
angles becomes so large that flow separation and shock occur, accompanied by a
rapid decrease in efficiency.

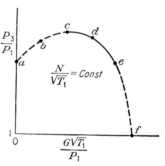

Fig. 12-9. Compressor surging.

Suppose the compressor is operating to
the left of c at some point b. A decrease
in mass rate of flow is accompanied by a
decrease in the pressure developed by the
compressor. Now if the static pressure of
the air at compressor outlet does not decrease as rapidly as the developed pressure, there is a natural tendency for the air
to flow back into the compressor in the
direction of the pressure gradient. When the pressure of the air at the
compressor outlet drops, the pressure gradient is reversed and so is the
direction of the flow. An unstable condition exists in which a cyclic
reversal of flow takes place at extremely high frequency. By keeping to
the right of c a decrease in mass rate of flow is accompanied by an
increase of pressure ratio and stability is maintained.

The point b was selected arbitrarily. The point to the left of c where
surging begins is a function of the ability of the flow passages downstream
of the compressor to swallow the flow. Therefore for stable compressor
operation, consideration must be extended to the burners, the regenerators, and in particular the turbine in their relation to the compressor.
This aspect of the problem is discussed further in Chap. 16.

12-12. Centrifugal Compressor Design Calculations. Although theoretical relations may be developed for the design parameters of the centrifugal compressor unsatisfactory correlation is obtained on test. The
actual design procedure employed is guided by the designer's experience
and empirical modifications of the theoretical relationships. No attempt
is made here to lay down a specific design technique but rather to apply
the fundamental relations discussed in the preceding sections. This purpose is best accomplished by means of an illustrative problem.

368

THEORY AND DESIGN OF STEAM AND GAS TURBINES

Example. The following data are given for a centrifugal compressor, and it is required to establish the principal dimensions and design characteristics.

$N = 15,000$ rpm
$G = 50$ lb per sec
Ambient temperature $= 70$ F
Atmosphere pressure $= 14.7$ psia
$V_{1a} = V_{3a} = 450$ fps
Pressure ratio $= 4$
Hub diameter at eye $= 6$ in.
Adiabatic efficiency $= 0.76$
Double-sided impeller

The pressure leaving the compressor is $4 \times 14.7 = 58.8$ psia. The stagnation temperature rise may be obtained from Eq. (12-19):

$$T^0_{3'} - T^0_1 = T_1\left[\left(\frac{P^0_3}{P^0_1}\right)^{(k-1)/k} - 1\right] = \frac{530}{0.76}[4^{0.286} - 1]$$

$$T^0_{3'} - T^0_1 = 336 \text{ F}$$
$$T^0_3 - T^0_1 = 0.76 \times 336 = 255.4 \text{ F}$$
$$T^0_{3'} = 336 + 530 = 866 \text{ R} = 406 \text{ F}$$
$$T^0_3 = 325.4 \text{ F} = 785.4 \text{ R}$$

The tip speed of the impeller is obtained from Eq. (12-22) introducing the slip factor in place of η_{ad}. The slip factor and the work input factor are assumed to be 0.9 and 1.04, respectively.

$$U_2 = \sqrt{\frac{(T^0_{3'} - T^0_1)gJC_p}{\phi_w\phi_s}}$$
$$U_2 = \sqrt{\frac{336 \times 32.2 \times 778 \times 0.24}{1.04 \times 0.9}}$$
$$U_2 = 1470 \text{ fps}$$

The tip speed also could be found from Eq. (12-20) by taking $\phi_p = 0.71$. The pressure coefficient is in general about five points lower than η_{ad}.

$$U_2 = \sqrt{\frac{(T^0_{3'} - T^0_1)gJC_p\eta_{ad}}{\phi_p}}$$
$$U_2 = \sqrt{\frac{336 \times 32.2 \times 778 \times 0.24 \times 0.76}{0.71}}$$
$$U_2 = 1470 \text{ fps}$$

Such a close check is not always obtained because of the latitude in selecting values of ϕ_w, ϕ_s, and ϕ_p. However, the acceptable latitudes are not wide and a reasonably close correlation can be expected. The impeller tip diameter now may be found.

$$D_2 = \frac{60 U_2}{\pi N} = \frac{60 \times 1470 \times 12}{15,000 \times 3.14} = 22.4$$

For the present it will be assumed that prewhirl is not needed. The intake air is accelerated to an axial velocity of 300 fps, which means that the air must be cooled below the ambient temperature and a suction exists. The dynamic temperature of the air is

$$\frac{V_{1a}^2}{2gJC_p} = \frac{(450)^2}{64.4 \times 778 \times 0.24} = 16.85 \text{ F}$$

The stagnation temperature of the impeller eye is of course equal to the ambient temperature given as 70 F. Therefore

$$T_e = T_1^\circ - \frac{V_{1a}^2}{2gJC_p} = 70 - 16.85 = 53.15 \text{ F, say } 53.2 \text{ F}$$

$$P_e = P_1^\circ \left(\frac{T_e}{T_1^\circ}\right)^{k/(k-1)} = 14.7 \left(\frac{513.2}{530}\right)^{3.5} = 13.2 \text{ psia}$$

$$v_1 = \frac{RT_e}{P_e} = \frac{53.34 \times 513.2}{13.2 \times 144} = 14.4 \text{ cu ft per lb}$$

The annular area required at the impeller eye is

$$A_1 = \frac{Gv}{V_{1a}} = \frac{50 \times 14.4 \times 144}{450 \times 2} = 115 \text{ sq in. each side}$$

Let D_e = eye tip diameter and D_h = eye hub diameter. Then

$$A_1 = \frac{\pi}{4}(D_e^2 - D_h^2) = 115 \text{ sq in.}$$

and

$$D_e = \sqrt{\frac{4}{\pi} A_1 + D_h^2} = \sqrt{\frac{4}{\pi} 115 + 6^2} = 13.5 \text{ in.}$$

The Mach number at the eye tip diameter now can be checked:

$$U_e = \frac{\pi D_e N}{60} = \frac{3.14 \times 13.5 \times 15,000}{60 \times 12} = 885 \text{ fps}$$

The relative velocity of the air at the impeller-eye tip with no prewhirl is

$$W_e = \sqrt{V_{1a}^2 + U_e^2} = \sqrt{(450)^2 + (885)^2} = 990 \text{ fps}$$

The velocity of sound in the air at this point is

$$a = \sqrt{gkRT_e} = \sqrt{32.2 \times 1.41 \times 53.34 \times 513.2} = 1115 \text{ fps}$$

$$M_e = \frac{W_e}{a} = \frac{990}{1115} = 0.89$$

The Mach number is lower than the maximum allowable value of 0.9 and is therefore acceptable. If the Mach number had been greater than 0.9, it would have been necessary to introduce prewhirl. Prewhirl would necessitate increasing V_{2U} in order to offset the V_{1U} introduced. Consequently the impeller tip diameter would have to be increased. Stress considerations limit the maximum impeller tip speed to about 1500 fps. Since the impeller tip speed is already 1470 fps, there would be very little leeway for adjustment and it might have been necessary to revise the design completely.

The diameter ratio should be checked.

$$D_r = \frac{D_2}{D_e} = \frac{22.4}{13.5} = 1.66$$

The absolute minimum acceptable value of D_r is 1.5 with values near 2.0 being preferable for high efficiency. The value of D_r obtained in this problem is regarded as satisfactory. The reason a small value of D_r is not tolerated is that the flow may not be accelerated to the impeller tip speed in such a short passage before leaving the impeller.

The bending angles for the impeller vanes at the eye now can be established. This will be done for the hub, mid, and eye tip diameters.

D	U	$\tan \beta = \dfrac{V_{1a}}{U}$	β, degrees
6.0	394	1.14	54.5
9.75	640	0.704	35.1
13.5	885	0.51	27

Before proceeding to the impeller, it should be remarked that the thickness of the impeller vanes was neglected in calculating the annulus area at the eye. Normally, the area would be increased about 5 per cent to allow for the vane thickness.

Since this is a radial impeller, the vane exit angle γ will be equal to 90°. Because of slip, $V_{2U} = \phi_s U_2$ which with the magnitude of the radial velocity V_{2R} will determine the direction and magnitude of the absolute exit velocity V_2. The direction of the absolute exit velocity δ is normally between 12° and 24°. Too low a value of δ results in excess diffusion rates which cannot be maintained with good efficiency. Too high a value of δ causes high Mach numbers relative to the diffuser vanes which may result in shock and flow separation or flow restriction.

The total area available for flow at the impeller tip, neglecting the thickness of the vanes, is

$$A_2 = \frac{Gv_2}{V_{2R}} = \frac{Gv_2}{V_{2U} \tan \delta} = \frac{Gv_2}{\phi_s U_2 \tan \delta}$$

The angle δ will be assumed to be $16°$

and
$$V_2 = \frac{V_{2U}}{\cos \delta} = \frac{\phi_s U_2}{\cos \delta} = \frac{0.9 \times 1470}{0.961} = 1375 \text{ fps}$$

To find $v_{2'}$, it is necessary first to find P_2 and $T_{2'}$. In a straight or radial-vaned impeller it is usual to assume that one-half the static pressure rise occurs in the impeller passages and the other half in the diffuser passages. The over-all static pressure rise is $P_3 - P_1$ and the static pressure rise in the impeller is $58.8 - 14.7/2 = 22$ psia.

$$P_2 = 14.7 + 22 = 36.7$$

The corresponding isentropic static temperature rise is

$$T_2 = T_1 \left(\frac{P_2}{P_1}\right)^{(k-1)/k} = 530 \left(\frac{36.7}{14.7}\right)^{0.286} = 690 \text{ } R = 230 \text{ F}$$

$$T_{3'} - T_3 = 406 - 325.4 = 80.6 \text{ F}$$

Assigning half the losses to the impeller,

$$T_{2'} = 230 + 80.6 = 310.6 \text{ F} = 770.6 \text{ R}$$
$$v_{2'} = \frac{RT_{2'}}{P_2} = \frac{53.34 \times 770.6}{36.7 \times 144} = 7.8 \text{ cu ft per lb}$$
$$A_2 = \frac{50 \times 7.8 \times 144}{0.9 \times 1470 \times 0.287} = 147.5 \text{ sq in.}$$

The theoretical axial width of the impeller at the tip is

$$b_2 = \frac{A_2}{\pi D_2} = \frac{147.5}{3.14 \times 22.4} = 2.1 \text{ in.}$$

Since this is a double-sided impeller about $\frac{1}{8}$ to $\frac{1}{4}$ in. must be provided in the width to allow for the thickness of the impeller disc. If $\frac{1}{4}$ in. is assumed, b_2 will be 2.35 in.

The Mach number of the air leaving the impeller based on the absolute velocity V_2 should be checked

$$a = \sqrt{gkRT_{2'}} = \sqrt{32.2 \times 1.41 \times 53.34 \times 770.6}$$
$$a = 1370 \text{ fps}$$
$$M = \frac{V_2}{a} = \frac{1375}{1370} = 1$$

The air must be decelerated in a vaneless space between impeller and diffusers by taking advantage of the constant angular-momentum principle to avoid shock at entry to the diffuser vanes. To accomplish this, the Mach number should be brought below 0.9. It should be borne in mind that the static pressure of the air leaving the impeller was estimated and hence the Mach number may be in error significantly one way or the other.

The ratio of the diameter of the circle formed by the locus of points of the diffuser-vane entrance edges to the impeller tip diameter is normally kept between the limits of 1.1 to 1.4. Thus the radial clearance between impeller tip and diffuser vanes is set within a rather restricted range. It will be assumed that a ratio of 1.2 is satisfactory for the present design. Then

$$D_d = 1.2 D_2 = 1.2 \times 22.4 = 26.9 \text{ in.}$$

The radial clearance is 2.25 in.

Applying the constant angular-momentum principle,

$$V_{dU} = \frac{V_{2U} r_2}{r_d} = \frac{0.9 \times 1470 \times 11.2}{13.5} = 1100 \text{ fps}$$

The flow is radial and therefore depends on the radial cross-sectional area and the radial velocity. The specific volume of the air in turn depends on the radial velocity and the static pressure. The passage area beyond the impeller tip will increase at least by the amount of area occupied by the impeller vanes and disc. It is also usual to increase the axial width by a taper up to an included angle of about 10° or 12°. It is obvious that the area increases radially even if the axial width is kept constant. Since the radial velocity must decrease from impeller tip to diffuser-vane inlet because of the increasing flow area, the static pressure must increase.

The stagnation temperature after the impeller is constant since no energy transfers take place between the air and surroundings.

$$T_{2'}^{\circ} = T_{2'} + \frac{V_2^2}{2gJC_p} = 310.6 + \frac{(1375)^2}{2gJC_p} = 467.6 \text{ F}$$

$$T_{2'}^{\circ} = T_d^{\circ} = 467.6 \text{ F}$$

$$T_d = T_{2'}^{\circ} - \frac{V_2^2}{2gJC_p}$$

It is necessary to arrive at the value of the radial velocity V_{dR} by trial and error. Usually a number of trials are needed. Only the successful trial is shown here. Assuming $V_{dR} = 250$ fps,

$$\frac{V_{dR}^2}{2gJC_p} = \frac{(250)^2}{2gJC_p} = 5.2 \text{ F}$$

$$\frac{V_{dU}^2}{2gJC_p} = \frac{(1100)^2}{2gJC_p} = 101 \text{ F}$$

$$\frac{V_d^2}{2gJC_p} = \frac{V_{dR}^2 + V_{dU}^2}{2gJC_p} = 106.2 \text{ F}$$

$$T_{d'} = 467.6 - 106.2 = 361.4 \text{ F} = 821.4 \text{ R}$$

$$P_d = P_2 \left(\frac{T_d}{T_{2'}}\right)^{k/(k-1)} = 36.7 \left(\frac{821.4}{770.6}\right)^{3.5} = 45 \text{ psia}$$

$$v_d = \frac{RT_d}{P_d} = \frac{53.34 \times 819}{45 \times 144} = 6.75 \text{ cu ft per lb}$$

$$A_d = \frac{\pi \times 26.9 \times 2.35}{144} = 1.38 \text{ sq ft}$$

$$V_{dR} = \frac{50 \times 6.75}{1.38} = 245 \text{ fps}$$

This is a close enough check with the assumed value of 250 fps.

The angle of entrance at the diffuser-vane leading edge is

$$\alpha_d = \arctan {}^{245}\!/_{1100} = 12.6°$$

A check of the Mach number at entrance to the diffuser vanes may be made now:

$$V_d^2 = \sqrt{V_{dR}^2 + V_{dU}^2} = \sqrt{(245)^2 + (1100)^2}$$
$$V_d = 1130 \text{ fps}$$
$$a = \sqrt{32.2 \times 1.41 \times 53.34 \times 821.44}$$
$$a = 1410 \text{ fps}$$
$$M = {}^{1130}\!/_{1410} = 0.8$$

Attention is directed to the vaned diffusers which follow the vaneless space which is itself a diffuser. A few degrees incidence would be added to the entrance angle found before. The outer diameter of the diffuser is kept within a ratio of $1.4D_2$ to $1.8D_2$, depending on the application and whether or not an elbow diffuser is used similar to that shown in Fig. 12-3. The smaller ratio applies to aircraft compressors which are usually provided with some form of elbow diffuser.

The number of diffuser vanes selected is determined by the number of burners for installations where burners in parallel are used. For other installations, a number of diffuser vanes is selected which is prime to the number of impeller vanes in order to avoid a resonant effect. In some designs the number of diffuser vanes is about a third of the number of impeller vanes.

The velocities and exit angle at the diffuser-vane tips may be found by methods similar to those used in finding the conditions entering the diffuser vanes.

Before leaving the problem it is desirable to compute the power input required for compressor:

$$E = C_p(T_{3'}^° - T_1^°) = 0.24(336) = 81 \text{ Btu per lb}$$

Assuming a mechanical efficiency of 0.98,

$$\text{hp} = \frac{81}{0.98} \times \frac{778}{550} \times 50 = 5850$$

References

1. Cheshire, L. J.: The Design and Development of Centrifugal Compressors for Aircraft Gas Turbines, *IME War Emergency Issue* 12, *ASME Reprint*, 1947.
2. Church, A. H.: "Centrifugal Pumps and Blowers," John Wiley & Sons, Inc., New York, 1944.
3. Kearton, W. J.: "Turbo-blowers and Compressors," Sir Isaac Pitman & Sons, Ltd., London, 1926.
4. Wislicenus, G. F.: "Fluid Mechanics of Turbo-machinery," McGraw-Hill Book Company, Inc., New York, 1947.

Problems

12-1. Establish the principal dimensions and design characteristics of a centrifugal compressor for the following conditions:

N = 12,000 rpm
G = 60 lb per sec
Ambient temperature = 60 F
Atmospheric pressure = 14.5 psia
$V_{1a} = V_{3a}$ = 450 fps
Pressure ratio = 3.5
Hub diameter at eye = 5 in.
Adiabatic efficiency = 0.74
Double-sided impeller

12-2. If the compressor of Prob. 12-1 is to have a single-sided impeller and the Mach number at inlet is to be kept at a minimum, what adjustment or adjustments must be made?

12-3. Design the compressor of Prob. 12-1 for a total pressure ratio of 6.0 taken in two stages. Neglect losses between stages.

CHAPTER 13

THE AXIAL-FLOW AIR COMPRESSOR

13-1. Introduction. The axial-flow air compressor is often described as a reversed reaction turbine. There would appear to be some merit to such a description from a cursory examination of the axial-flow air compressor and the fact the energy transfer in the compressor is the reverse of that in the turbine. It is also recognized that the axial-flow air compressor generally consists of a series of bladed diffusing passages as opposed to the series of expanding passages found in the turbine. Nevertheless, a closer examination of the compressor blade profiles and their orientation reveals many significant differences when compared with their counterparts in the turbine. The subsequent discussion will highlight some of these differences and the reasons for their existence.

It was demonstrated in Sec. 6-8 that although considerable latitude can be taken in shaping a flow passage for accelerating flow, rather strict compliance with aerodynamic principles must be met in designing the flow passage for decelerating or diffusing flow, if serious shock losses are to be avoided. Hence more severe limitations must be imposed on the solidity factors, lift coefficients, deflection angles, incidence angles, and the liberties taken with the correct aerodynamic shape of the blades. Consequently, the flow passages of the axial-flow air compressor are found to consist of a far greater number of stages with more sparsely bladed rows than the reaction turbine. Blade profiles are definite airfoils of low camber instead of the facsimile airfoils of faired circular arcs designed for large deflection angles, characteristic of turbine blade profiles. Figure 13-1 shows the rotor of an axial-flow air compressor for the purpose of comparison with the turbine rotor.

From the foregoing it is understandable that a reaction turbine which serves efficiently in its intended role would undoubtedly show very poor performance if reversed to serve as an air compressor. Early attempts to adapt the reaction turbine to serve as an axial-flow air compressor met with very poor results. It was not until the development of the science of aerodynamics that the reason for this poor performance was fully understood and a rational basis could be evolved for the design of the modern axial-flow air compressor of high efficiency.

Some of the fundamental energy-transfer relationships for the axial-flow air compressor were developed in Sec. 8-24 and will not be repeated here. Attention is also directed to the airfoil-lift relationships of Sec. 9-20 which are applicable to the blades of the axial-flow air compressor. The purpose of this chapter is to develop some further relationships which are useful in understanding the theory of the axial-flow air compressor and the application of these relationships in design.

13-2. Stage Characteristics. It is desirable to group the different types of compressor stages according to some broad classification in order to facilitate a discussion of the relative merits of the various arrangements

Fig. 13-1. Axial-flow compressor spindle. (Courtesy of Westinghouse Electric Corporation.)

available. A number of classifications are in use but only the one most commonly used is treated here.

Before attempting to classify the compressor stages, it is well to define what is meant by "degree of reaction" when applied to the compressor stage. The degree of reaction is defined as the ratio of the static enthalpy rise in the rotor to that in the stage. If the specific heat can be regarded as being constant, this is the same as the ratio of the static temperature rise in the rotor to that in the stage. If further, the compression process is assumed to be isentropic, the corresponding static pressure rises satisfactorily fulfill the definition.

The different types of compressor stages may be classified generally as symmetric, nonsymmetric axial-inflow, and nonsymmetric axial-outflow.

The symmetric stage, sometimes referred to as a 50 per cent reaction stage, is illustrated in Fig. 13-2. The static pressure rises in this type of stage are equal for both the stationary and moving rows of blades. Therefore a symmetric velocity diagram results. The blades and their orientation in the stator and rotor are reflected images of each other. In the velocity diagram of Fig. 13-2, V_1 and W_1 represent, respectively, the absolute and relative velocities entering the moving blades. Similarly V_2 and W_2 are, respectively, the absolute and relative velocities leaving the moving blades. Therefore V_2 is the absolute velocity entering the stationary blades and V_1 the absolute velocity leaving the stationary blades. Consequently, the first stage of the compressor must be preceded by prewhirl vanes to provide the velocity vector V_1 if the stage is symmetric. The prewhirl thus attained, and maintained by the succeeding stationary rows of blades, is advantageous in that for a given blade speed

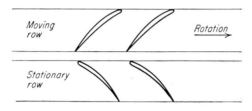

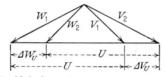

Fig. 13-2. Symmetric compressor stage.

and axial velocity component, the magnitude of W_1 is thereby decreased. Thus higher blade speeds and axial velocity components are possible without exceeding the limiting value of 0.70 to 0.75 for the inlet Mach number. Higher blade speeds result in a compressor of smaller diameter and less weight.

A further advantage of the symmetric stage arises from the equality of static pressure rises in the stationary and moving blades which results in maximum static pressure rise for the stage. Therefore a given pressure ratio can be achieved with the minimum number of stages, a contributing factor to the lightness of this type of compressor. The most serious disadvantage of the symmetric stage is the higher leaving loss resulting from the high axial velocity components which are employed. Nevertheless the advantages enumerated are of such obvious importance in aircraft applications that the symmetric-staged compressor is used. In stationary installations where weight and frontal area are of lesser importance one of the other types of stages are normally employed.

The nonsymmetric stage with axial inflow is illustrated in Fig. 13-3. The term nonsymmetric is applied because the inequality of pressure rises in the stationary and moving rows of blades results in a nonsymmetrical velocity diagram. The specification of axial inflow is in actuality a special case of the nonsymmetric stage. It is noted from the velocity diagram of Fig. 13-3 that the absolute velocity V_1, entering the moving blades, or leaving the stationary blades, is axial in direction. Therefore the term "axial inflow" refers to the direction of the flow entering the moving blades. The moving blades impart a whirl component to the velocity of the leaving flow which is removed in the following row of stationary blades. It is evident from this and from the velocity diagram that the major part of the stage pressure rise occurs in the moving row of

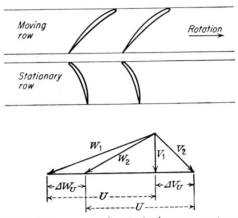

Fig. 13-3. Nonsymmetric (axial-inflow) compressor stage.

blades, the degree of reaction varying from 60 to 90 per cent. Normally the stage is designed for constant energy transfer and axial velocity at all radii so the condition of vortex flow is maintained in the spaces between rows of blades.

The principal advantage of the nonsymmetric axial-inflow stage is the low leaving loss resulting from lower axial velocity and blade speeds. Because of the small static pressure rise in the stationary blades certain simplifications can be introduced such as constant-section stationary blades and the elimination of interstage seals. Higher actual efficiencies have been achieved in this type of stage than with the symmetric stage primarily because of the reduced leaving loss. It will be shown later that the maximum theoretical efficiency would be expected from the symmetric stage. The major disadvantages stem from the low static pressure rise in the stationary blades which necessitates a greater number of stages to achieve a given pressure ratio and thus contribute to a heavier compressor. The lower axial velocities and blade speeds, necessary to keep within the inlet Mach number limitations, result in a larger diameter and also a heavier machine. In stationary applications where the increased weight and frontal area are not of great importance it is usual to employ this type of stage in order to take advantage of the higher efficiency. However, the nonsymmetric stage has been used in a few aircraft applications.

The nonsymmetric axial-outflow stage is shown in Fig. 13-4. The distinguishing characteristics of this type of stage are the axial direction of the absolute velocity V_2 leaving the moving blades and the fact that the static pressure rise occurs entirely in the moving row of blades. Actually a static pressure drop occurs in the stationary blades with an increase in absolute velocity as evidenced by the velocity diagram of Fig. 13-4.

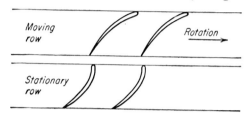

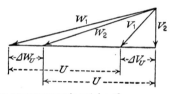

Fig. 13-4. Vortex or nonsymmetric axial-outflow compressor stage.

Hence the degree of reaction is in excess of 100 per cent. The absolute velocity V_1 leaving the stationary blades, or entering the moving blades, has a tangential component opposite in direction to that of the blade velocity. This tangential component is removed in the moving blades which reestablish axial flow before entering the stationary blades. The axial-outflow stage is also designed for constant axial velocity and energy transfer radially, thus satisfying the conditions for vortex flow in the spaces between the rows of blades.

The principal advantages of the axial-outflow stage are found in the lowest axial velocities and blade speeds attainable with any type of staging resulting in the lowest possible leaving loss. Although these characteristics are advantageous when viewed from the standpoint of leaving loss, they do result in a heavy machine of many stages and of large diameter. The whirl component entering the moving blades in a direction opposed to that of the blade velocity tends to produce a high relative velocity entering the moving blades. In order to keep within the allowable limit of the inlet Mach number, extremely low values must be accepted for the blade velocity and axial velocity. The axial-outflow stage is capable of the highest actual efficiency because of the extremely low leaving loss and the beneficial effects of designing for free-vortex flow. This type of compressor is particularly well suited for closed-cycle plants where smaller quantities of air are introduced to the compressor at elevated static pressures.

The foregoing stage classifications do not imply that the type of velocity diagram adopted at one radius must be employed at all radii. The designer has considerable freedom, within the limitations of maintaining radial equilibrium, or constant reaction, to adopt any combination of velocity diagrams radially which suits best the purpose of the design. Furthermore, there is no necessity for keeping the same type of velocity diagram in all stages. In fact, it is found desirable in many instances, because of changed volume and temperature, to change the type of velocity diagram part way through the compressor. The classifications given here are analogous to the classifications of impulse and reaction applied to turbine stages.

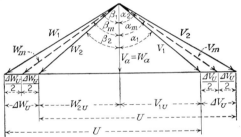

Fig. 13-5. Compressor-stage velocity diagram.

13-3. Blading Efficiency.

The efficiency of the blades in a compressor stage may be defined as the ratio of the energy transferred to the air by the blades to the energy input to the stage, or

$$\eta_{bl} = \frac{\text{energy transferred to air}}{\text{energy input}}$$

Considering the profile losses of the blades,

$$\eta_{bl} = \frac{E_i - E_l}{E_i} = 1 - \frac{E_l}{E_i} \tag{13-1}$$

where E_i = energy input, ft-lb

E_l = energy loss, ft-lb

It is convenient to consider the losses in the stator and rotor blades separately; therefore Eq. (13-1) may be expressed

$$\eta_{bl} = 1 - \frac{E_{lr} + E_{ls}}{E_i} \tag{13-2}$$

From Fig. 13-5,

$$E_{lr} = \frac{W_m}{g} D_r = \frac{W_m}{g} \frac{D_r}{L_r} L_r = \epsilon L_r \frac{W_m}{g} \tag{13-3}$$

where D = drag, lb
L = lift, lb
$\epsilon = \dfrac{D}{L}$

Also from Fig. 13-5,

$$E_i = \frac{U}{g} F_{Ur} = \frac{U}{g} (L_r \cos \beta_m + D_r \sin \beta_m) \tag{13-4}$$

or

$$E_i = L_r \frac{U}{g} (\cos \beta_m + \epsilon \sin \beta_m) \tag{13-5}$$

From the geometry of Fig. 13-5,

$$E_i = L_r \frac{U}{gW_m} \left[V_a + \left(W_{2U} + \frac{\Delta W_U}{2} \right) \right] \tag{13-6}$$

Dividing Eq. (13-3) by Eq. (13-6),

$$\frac{E_{lr}}{E_i} = \frac{\epsilon W_m{}^2}{U \left[V_a + \epsilon \left(W_{2U} + \dfrac{\Delta W_U}{2} \right) \right]} \tag{13-7}$$

Again from the geometry of Fig. 13-5,

$$\frac{E_{lr}}{E_i} = \frac{\epsilon \left[\left(W_{2U} + \dfrac{\Delta W_U}{2} \right)^2 + V_a{}^2 \right]}{U \left[V_a + \epsilon \left(W_{2U} + \dfrac{W_U}{2} \right) \right]}$$

and

$$\frac{E_{lr}}{E_i} = \frac{\epsilon \left[\left(W_{2U} + \dfrac{\Delta W_U}{2} \right)^2 + V_a{}^2 \right]}{U^2 \left[\dfrac{V_a}{U} + \epsilon \left(\dfrac{W_{2U} + \dfrac{\Delta W_U}{2}}{U} \right) \right]} \tag{13-8}$$

Designating the flow coefficient $\phi = V_a/U$ and the degree of reaction, $R = \left(W_{2U} + \dfrac{\Delta W_U}{2} \right) \Big/ U$. Substituting in Eq. (13-8),

$$\frac{E_{lr}}{E_i} = \frac{\epsilon(\phi^2 + R^2)}{\phi + \epsilon R} \tag{13-9}$$

Similarly, the ratio of the energy loss in the stator blades to the stage energy input may be expressed

$$\frac{E_{ls}}{E_i} = \frac{\epsilon[\phi^2 + (1 - R)^2]}{\phi + \epsilon(1 - R)} \tag{13-10}$$

The values of ϵ for the rotor and stator blades are usually so nearly equal that the difference is neglected. Then adding Eqs. (13-9) and (13-10),

$$\frac{E_{ls} + E_{lr}}{E_i} = \epsilon \left[\frac{\phi^2 + R^2}{\phi + \epsilon R} + \frac{\phi^2 + (1 - R)^2}{\phi + \epsilon(1 - R)} \right] \tag{13-11}$$

Substituting in Eq. (13-2),

$$\eta_{bl} = 1 - \epsilon \left[\frac{\phi^2 + R^2}{\phi + \epsilon R} + \frac{\phi^2 + (1 - R)^2}{\phi + (1 - R)} \right] \tag{13-12}$$

Equation (13-12) shows that high blade efficiency depends on the flow coefficient, the degree of reaction, and, as would be expected, a low value of ϵ.

In order to find the optimum values of ϕ and R for maximum η_{bl}, it is convenient to make the simplification of eliminating the drag from consideration in developing Eq. (13-6). If this is done, Eq. (13-12) simplifies to

$$\eta_{bl} = 1 - \epsilon \left\{ 2\phi + \frac{1}{\phi} [R^2 + (1 - R)^2] \right\} \tag{13-13}$$

To find the maximum value of ϕ,

$$\frac{d\eta_{bl}}{d\phi} = \frac{d}{d\phi} \left(1 - \epsilon \left\{ 2\phi + \frac{1}{\phi} \left[R^2 + (1 - R)^2 \right] \right\} \right) = 0 \tag{13-14}$$

$$2 - \frac{1}{\phi^2} [R^2 + (1 - R)^2] = 0$$

and
$$\phi = 0.5 \tag{13-15}$$

To find the optimum value of R,

$$\frac{d\eta_{bl}}{dR} = \frac{d}{dR} \left(1 - \epsilon \left\{ 2\phi + \frac{1}{\phi} [R^2 + (1 - R)^2] \right\} \right) = 0 \tag{13-16}$$

$$2R - 2(1 - R) = 0$$

and
$$R = 0.5 \tag{13-17}$$

Thus it is seen that the maximum theoretical blading efficiency is obtained with a 50 per cent reaction stage operating with a flow coefficient of 0.5. This may seem to contradict the statements made in Sec. 13-2 which indicated the symmetric stage to be the least efficient of the types discussed. Equations (13-12) and (13-13) refer to the basic blading efficiency and do not take into account stage parasitic and leaving losses. Now Eq. (13-15) indicates that a high axial velocity is required for the symmetric stage, and hence the leaving loss is great. Therefore, although the theoretical blade efficiency for the symmetric stage is high, the other losses not contemplated by Eqs. (13-12) and (13-13) are greater and the result is a lower actual compressor efficiency on test.

The blade losses may be expressed in terms of the air angles and a drag coefficient. The static pressure rise across a row of blades is written

$$\Delta P = \left(P_2^o - \rho \frac{W_2^2}{2}\right) - \left(P_1^o - \rho \frac{W_1^2}{2}\right)$$

$$\Delta P = \frac{\rho}{2}(W_1^2 - W_2^2) - (P_1^o - P_2^o) \tag{13-18}$$

From Fig. 13-5,

$$\Delta P = \rho \frac{W_a^2}{2}(\tan^2 \beta_1 - \tan^2 \beta_2) - (P_1^o - P_2^o) \tag{13-19}$$

$$\Delta P = \rho \frac{W_a^2}{2}(\sec^2 \beta_1 - \sec^2 \beta_2) - (P_1^o - P_2^o) \tag{13-20}$$

The ideal static pressure rise is found from Eq. (13-19) or Eq. (13-20) by eliminating $(P_1^o - P_2^o)$ which represents the losses, or

$$\Delta P_{\text{ideal}} = \rho \frac{W_a^2}{2}(\sec^2 \beta_1 - \sec^2 \beta_2)$$

whence

$$\frac{\Delta P_{\text{ideal}}}{\rho \frac{W_1^2}{2}} = 1 - \frac{\cos^2 \beta_1}{\cos^2 \beta_2} \tag{13-21}$$

A similar expression may be written for the stationary row.

Returning to Eq. (13-18) and taking $W_{1a} = W_{2a}$, the equation may be expressed

$$\Delta P = \frac{\rho}{2}[W_{1U}^2 - W_{2U}^2] - (P_1^o - P_2^o) \tag{13-22}$$

Owing to the static pressure rise, a force is exerted on the blade in an upstream direction. This force may be expressed in terms of Eq. (13-22) as follows:

$$F_a = \Delta P_a \, th_b = [\tfrac{1}{2}\rho(W_{1U}^2 - W_{2U}^2) - (P_1^o - P_2^o)]th_b \tag{13-23}$$

The drag force is equal to the difference between the components of the tangential force F_U and F_a in the direction of the mean velocity vector V_m, or

$$D = F_U \sin \beta_m - F_a \cos \beta_m \tag{13-24}$$

Substituting for F_U its equivalent from Eq. (9-42) and for F_a its equivalent from Eq. (13-23) in Eq. (13-24),

$$D = \rho W_a th_b(W_{1U} - W_{2U}) \sin \beta_m - [\tfrac{1}{2}\rho(W_{1U}^2 - W_{2U}^2)$$
$$- (P_1^o - P_2^o)]th_b \cos \beta_m \tag{13-25}$$
$$D = \rho W_a th_b(W_{1U} - W_{2U}) \sin \beta_m - \tfrac{1}{2}(W_{1U} + W_{2U})(W_{1U} - W_{2U})th_b$$
$$\cos \beta_m + (P_1^o - P_2^o)th_b \cos \beta_m$$

Factoring $\rho th_b(W_{1U} - W_{2U})$ from the first two terms and noting that $W_a \sin \beta_m = \frac{1}{2}(W_{1U} + W_{2U}) \cos \beta_m$,

$$D = \rho th_b(W_{1U} - W_{2U})[W_a \sin \beta_m - \frac{1}{2}(W_{1U} + W_{2U}) \cos \beta_m]$$
$$+ (P_1^\circ - P_2^\circ)th_b \cos \beta_m$$
$$D = (P_1^\circ - P_2^\circ)th_b \cos \beta_m \qquad (13\text{-}26)$$

But, from Eq. (9-40),

$$D = C_D\rho \frac{W_m^2}{2} ch_b$$

Substituting from Eq. (13-26),

$$C_D\sigma = \frac{(P_1^\circ - P_2^\circ) \cos \beta_m}{\rho(W_m^2/2)} \qquad (13\text{-}27)$$

Now

$$W_m \cos \beta_m = W_1 \cos \beta_1 = W_a$$

or

$$W_m = W_1 \frac{\cos \beta_1}{\cos \beta_m}$$

and

$$C_D\sigma = \frac{(P_1^\circ - P_2^\circ) \cos^3 \beta_m}{\rho(W_1^2/2) \cos^2 \beta_1} \qquad (13\text{-}28)$$

The expression $\dfrac{P_1^\circ - P_2^\circ}{\rho(W_1^2/2)} = \dfrac{\Delta P^\circ}{\rho(W_1^2/2)}$ is called the total or stagnation

pressure loss coefficient.

The efficiency of the blade row may be defined as the ratio of the ideal static pressure rise, less losses to the ideal static pressure rise, or

$$\eta_{bl} = \frac{\Delta P_{\text{ideal}} - \Delta P^\circ}{\Delta P_{\text{ideal}}}$$

Expressed in terms of the total pressure loss coefficient, the blading efficiency is

$$\eta_{bl} = 1 - \frac{\Delta P^\circ/\frac{1}{2}\rho W_1^2}{\Delta P_{\text{ideal}}/\frac{1}{2}\rho W_1^2} \qquad (13\text{-}29)$$

13-4. Design Coefficients. Many variables which influence the effectiveness of the design of an axial-flow compressor may be associated as ratios to serve as convenient guideposts for the designer and at the same time simplify the evaluation of a given design.

The flow coefficient was introduced in Sec. 13-3 and in Sec. 8-24. This coefficient is closely akin to the velocity ratio used in turbine design and has a similar significance. However, it should be noted that the flow coefficient, often called the compressor-velocity ratio, is defined as the ratio of the axial velocity to the blade linear velocity. Defined in this way the flow coefficient possesses a further significance not apparent in the turbine-velocity ratio. In Sec. 8-24 the flow coefficient was related to the air angles and indeed this relation is evident from the velocity diagram. Assuming that the blade speed is held constant, it is clear that an increase in ϕ results in an increase in α_1, the air entrance angle. A similar effect is obtained when the axial velocity is held constant and the blade speed decreased. Therefore it may be concluded that the flow coefficient is sensitive to changes in the angle of incidence. Furthermore, the flow coefficient is a useful parameter for representing the stalling characteristics of the compressor in that it affects the magnitude of the angle of attack and vice versa.

Another useful parameter is the pressure coefficient, which is defined as the ratio of the actual enthalpy rise in the stage to the dynamic pressure equivalent of the blade velocity:

$$\psi = \frac{\Delta h}{U^2/2gJ} \tag{13-30}$$

The actual enthalpy rise may be expressed

$$E = \Delta h = \frac{U}{gJ}\Delta V_U = \frac{U}{gJ}\Delta W_U$$

Substituting in Eq. (13-30),

$$\psi = \frac{2\Delta W_U}{U} = \frac{2\Delta V_U}{U} \tag{13-31}$$

If the static pressure rise in the stage is small enough so that the air can be regarded as being incompressible, the pressure coefficient may be expressed in terms of the stagnation pressure rise in the stage, or

$$\psi = \frac{\Delta P^\circ}{\rho(V^2/2)} \tag{13-32}$$

The pressure coefficient is a criterion of the limitations imposed by blade velocity on the work done on the air in a stage. The usefulness of this factor will be made more apparent in Sec. 13-5.

The work coefficient is a useful criterion of the limitations imposed by excessive Mach number brought about by high air relative velocities. Often this limitation, rather than blade velocity, governs the work which can be done in a stage. The work coefficient is defined basically as the ratio of the actual enthalpy rise in the stage to the dynamic pressure equivalent of the highest value of the air relative velocity reached in the stage. More often the tip velocity of the blade is used instead of the highest air relative velocity.

$$\Omega = \frac{\Delta h}{U_t/2gJ} \tag{13-33}$$

Substituting for Δh its equivalent in terms of the whirl components as before,

$$\Omega = \frac{2\Delta W_U}{U}\left(\frac{U}{U_t}\right)^2 = \frac{2\Delta V_U}{U}\left(\frac{U}{U_t}\right)^2 \tag{13-34}$$

Substituting from Eq. (13-31),

$$\Omega = \psi\left(\frac{U}{U_t}\right)^2 \tag{13-35}$$

13-5. Blade Loading. The forces which act on a compressor blade were discussed in Sec. 6-17 which covers elementary airfoil theory and in Sec. 9-20 in connection with turbine blading. The principles examined in those sections are directly applicable to the compressor blade. However, the axial orientation of the air and blade angles in the compressor must be kept in mind.

The tangential force exerted on the moving blades in the compressor stage is given as follows with reference to the velocity diagram of Fig. 13-5:

$$F_U = L \cos \beta_m + D \sin \beta_m$$
$$F_U = L(\cos \beta_m + \epsilon \sin \beta_m)$$

Solving for the lift on the blade,

$$L = \frac{F_U}{\cos \beta_m + \epsilon \sin \beta_m} \tag{13-36}$$

From Eq. (9-39) the lift L may be also written

$$L = C_L\rho \frac{W_m{}^2}{2} c \tag{13-37}$$

Also from Eq. (9-42),

$$F_U = \rho V_a t \, \Delta W_U \tag{13-38}$$

Substituting Eqs. (13-37) and (13-38) in Eq. (13-36),

$$C_L\sigma = \frac{2\Delta W_U V_a}{W_m{}^2(\cos \beta_m + \epsilon \sin \beta_m)} \tag{13-39}$$

Now from the geometry of the velocity diagram the following relations are apparent:

$$\sin \beta_m = \frac{W_{2u} + (\Delta W_u/2)}{W_m}$$

$$\cos \beta_m = \frac{V_a}{W_m}$$

$$W_m = \sqrt{[W_{2u} + (\Delta W_u/2)]^2 + V_a{}^2}$$

Substituting in Eq. (13-39),

$$C_L\sigma = \frac{2\Delta W_u V_a}{\left[V_a + \epsilon\left(W_{2u} + \dfrac{\Delta W_u}{2}\right)\right]\left[\sqrt{\left(W_{2u} + \dfrac{\Delta W_u}{2}\right)^2 + V_a{}^2}\right]} \tag{13-40}$$

Substituting $\qquad \phi = \dfrac{V_a}{U}, \qquad R = \dfrac{W_{2u} + (\Delta W_u/2)}{U}$

and Eq. (13-31) in Eq. (13-40),

$$C_L\sigma = \frac{\phi\psi}{(\phi + \epsilon R)\sqrt{R^2 + \phi^2}} \tag{13-41}$$

Similarly for the stationary blades,

$$C_L\sigma = \frac{\phi\psi}{[\phi + \epsilon(1 - R)]\sqrt{(1 - R)^2 + \phi^2}} \tag{13-42}$$

It is common practice to neglect the drag force in the expression for the tangential force. This was done, it will be recalled, in the derivation of Eq. (9-43). Equations (13-41) and (13-42), respectively, may be then simplified to

$$C_L\sigma = \frac{\psi}{\sqrt{R^2 + \phi^2}} = \frac{\psi/\phi}{\sqrt{(R^2/\phi) + 1}} \tag{13-43}$$

and for the stationary blades,

$$C_L\sigma = \frac{\psi}{\sqrt{(1 - R)^2 + \phi^2}} \frac{\psi/\phi}{\sqrt{[(1 - R)/\phi]^2 + 1}} \tag{13-44}$$

Neglecting the drag force merely means that a few more blades will be used than are required. Since this is on the conservative side the simplification is a welcome one.

Equations (13-41) through (13-44) show clearly that the aerodynamic loading of the compressor blades is a function of the flow coefficient, the pressure coefficient, and the degree of reaction. Figure 13-6 shows a plot of $C_L\sigma$ vs. ψ/ϕ for various values of R/ϕ obtained from Eq. (13-43). The curves are general in that they apply to any stage and may be used for the stationary blades by substituting $1 - R$ for R. In aircraft and transport applications, size and weight considerations fix the degree of reaction incorporated in the design. In stationary applications, the highest attainable efficiency level may be the governing consideration. When these primary considerations have been met, the flow coefficient may be determined as a function of the degree of reaction adopted, or vice versa. Limitations on the flow inlet Mach number as evidenced by the work coefficient may modify to some extent the degree of reaction and flow coefficient initially adopted. However, it may be stated that the degree of reaction adopted, to a large extent, determines the velocity ratio. Thus for a given application it is clear from Fig. 13-6 that as the pressure coefficient increases, the aerodynamic loading on the blades also increases.

Figure 13-7 shows the variation of blade loading as a function of pressure coefficient for typical types of compressor stages, the optimum value of ϕ corresponding to the degree of reaction being used. The values of

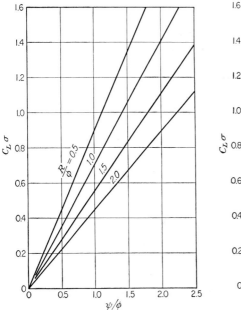

Fig. 13-6. Blade loading parameters.

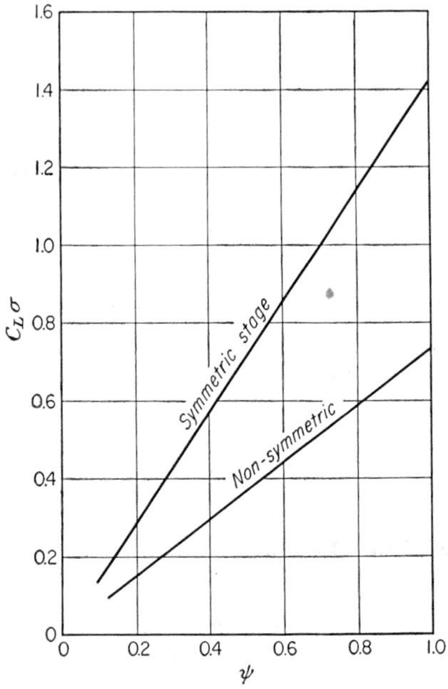

Fig. 13-7. Variation of blade loading with pressure coefficient for typical stages.

the pressure coefficients used in practice range from 0.4 to 0.7, although values as high as 0.9 to 1.0 have been used occasionally.

Equation (13-43) may be expressed in terms of the air angles obtained from the velocity diagram by noting the following equivalents:

$$\tan \beta_m = \frac{W_{2U} + (\Delta W_U/2)}{V_a} = \frac{[W_{2U} + (\Delta W_U/2)]/U}{V_a/U} = \frac{R}{\phi} = \frac{\tan \beta_1 + \tan \beta_2}{2}$$

$$(\tan \beta_1 - \tan \beta_2) = \frac{W_{2U} + \Delta W_U}{V_a} - \frac{V_{2U}}{V_a} = \frac{\Delta W_U}{V_a} = \frac{U \Delta W_U}{U \Delta V_a}$$

$$2(\tan \beta_1 - \tan \beta_2) = \frac{\psi}{\phi} = \frac{2\Delta W_U}{V_a}$$

Substituting in Eq. (13-43),

$$C_L \sigma = \frac{2(\tan \beta_1 - \tan \beta_2)}{\sqrt{\left(\dfrac{\tan \beta_1 + \tan \beta_2}{2}\right)^2 + 1}} \qquad (13\text{-}45)$$

Equation (13-45) may be also expressed in terms of β_m by substituting

$$\tan \beta_m = \frac{\tan \beta_1 + \tan \beta_2}{2}$$

$$C_L\sigma = \frac{2(\tan \beta_1 - \tan \beta_2)}{\sqrt{\tan^2 \beta_m + 1}}$$

$$C_L\sigma = 2(\tan \beta_1 - \tan \beta_2) \cos \beta_m \qquad (13\text{-}46)$$

Equation (13-46) shows that the blade loading is a function of the air deflection angle $\beta_1 - \beta_2$ and the values of β_1 and β_2. As stated before, the allowable deflection in a diffusion process is rather restricted. The flow coefficients selected for a given stage fall within a limited range and thus the air entrance angle is fixed by this consideration, assuming that suitable inlet Mach numbers are obtained. It is interesting in such situations to investigate the influence of the air exit angle on the blade loading. Figure 13-8 shows this influence for a typical range of β_1 and $\beta_1 - \beta_2$.

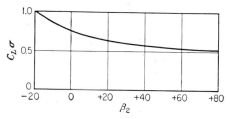

Fig. 13-8. Blading loading as a function of air exit angle.

13-6. Lift Coefficient and Solidity.

The preceding section was devoted to an examination of the factors influencing the blade loading. It is necessary now to examine the attainable values of C_L and σ. Compressor blades are designed according to the single airfoil principle or on the basis of accumulated cascade-test data. The procedure is quite similar to that employed in Secs. 9-20 to 9-22 for turbine blades except that more severe limitations must be imposed on the values of C_L and σ because of the diffusing flow encountered in the air compressor.

NACA TR 460 and NACA Rept. L-560 include a number of airfoil profiles which on the basis of isolated airfoil tests indicate that a value of $C_L = 1.4$ can be achieved without much difficulty. Design experience indicates that values of C_L in the range of 0.75 to 0.85 at the mean diameter for nonsymmetric or vortex stages and perhaps as high as 1.0 for the symmetric stage are more reasonable. At very low inlet Mach numbers there is reason to believe a value of $C_L = 1.2$ at the mean diameter could be achieved. As far as the stationary blades are concerned, a value of $C_L = 2.0$ at the root decreasing to $C_L = 1.0$ at the tip is quite satisfactory.

At present the only workable means of determining the suitable range of lift coefficients for compressor stages designed for comparatively high static pressure rises is the cascade test. Unfortunately, the published results of such tests are insufficient for the purpose of developing rational general relationships which may exist between airfoil profiles in cascade and the achievable lift coefficients.

For solidity factors below 0.8, it appears that the single airfoil principle may be used with reasonable correlation between predicted and test results. Of course, it is desirable to use the single airfoil principle whenever possible because of the wealth of test data available for single airfoils. Again, it is unfortunate that most designs require solidity factors

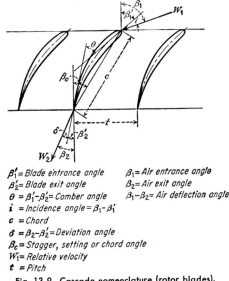

$\beta_1' =$ Blade entrance angle $\qquad \beta_1 =$ Air entrance angle
$\beta_2' =$ Blade exit angle $\qquad\qquad \beta_2 =$ Air exit angle
$\theta = \beta_1' - \beta_2' =$ Camber angle $\qquad \beta_1 - \beta_2 =$ Air deflection angle
$i =$ Incidence angle $= \beta_1 - \beta_1'$
$c =$ Chord
$\delta = \beta_2 - \beta_2' =$ Deviation angle
$\beta_c =$ Stagger, setting or chord angle
$W_1 =$ Relative velocity
$t =$ Pitch

Fig. 13-9. Cascade nomenclature (rotor blades).

in excess of 0.8. Cascade information available, in general, indicates a maximum blade loading of $C_L \sigma = 1.3$ with a corresponding value of $\sigma = 1.5$. The most commonly used range of solidity factors lies between 1.0 and 1.5, although values ranging from 0.65 to 2.0 have been used successfully in some instances.

One factor which influences the value of the solidity chosen is the aspect ratio h_b/c. The aspect ratio may be as high as 3.0 in the early stages, reducing to about 1.0 in the last stages.

13-7. Cascade Characteristics. Wind-tunnel tests of compressor blades in cascade are conducted to determine the performance characteristics in terms of certain variables related to the blades themselves. In addition the effect of Mach number and Reynolds number are investigated. Figure 13-9 gives the notation for a cascade in terms of the moving blades. A similar notation is used for the stationary blades except, of course, the absolute velocities and angles are substituted for the relative velocities and angles given in Fig. 13-9.

The test results of a given cascade are applicable, in a strict sense, only to that cascade. However, some important inferences can be drawn from a number of tests on different cascades which can be of value in preliminary design. With this in view some typical cascade test results are described, based largely on the publications of A. R. Howell (see references at end of chapter).

Figure 13-10 shows the air deflection angle and C_L plotted against incidence angle. It is noted that the two curves have very similar characteristics. As the incidence angle $\beta_1 - \beta_1'$ increases, it is accompanied by a corresponding but much smaller change in the air exit angle β_2. Therefore the air deflection angle $\beta_1 - \beta_2$ increases with an increase in the incidence angle. It is evident that the coefficient of lift C_L must also increase with an increase in the incidence angle.

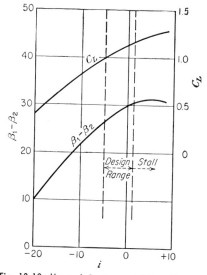

Fig. 13-10. Mean deflection and lift coefficient for a typical cascade.

However, the maximum air deflection angle and coefficient of lift are limited by the condition of stalling described in Sec. 6-18.

The effect of incidence angle, and in particular the stalling condition,

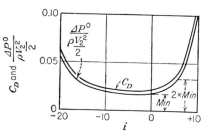

Fig. 13-11. Mean stagnation pressure loss and coefficient of drag.

on the profile drag coefficient and the stagnation pressure loss is shown in Fig. 13-11. The stagnation pressure loss is expressed as a proportion of the dynamic pressure equivalent of the absolute velocity entering the cascade. It will be noted the drag coefficient and the stagnation pressure loss curves exhibit very similar characteristics, the minimum values being reached at an incidence angle very near zero. A stalling point occurs at some positive value of the incidence angle. The exact location of this point is very difficult to specify and as a general rule is assumed to occur when the stagnation pressure loss equals twice its minimum value. Stalling can occur with too large a value of negative or positive incidence angles. Between these two extremes lies a range of incidence angles where the drag coefficient and stagnation pressure loss are fairly constant. For design purposes it is essential to select an incidence angle which will result in a minimum loss in stagnation pressure and at the same time provide a maximum value for the air deflection angle or coefficient of lift. This means the air deflection angle selected will be very close to the maximum point on the curve (see Fig. 13-10). However, care must be taken to avoid the condition of stalling within a suitable variation of load. For this reason a nominal value of the air deflection angle is selected at 0.8 times the stalling value.

An examination of cascade-test data for a considerable number of different cascades reveals that the nominal air deflection angle, for the range

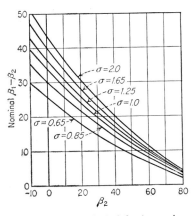

Fig. 13-12. Nominal air deflection angles.

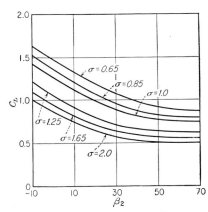

Fig. 13-13. Nominal lift coefficients.

of incidence angles generally used, depends chiefly on the solidity factor and the air exit angle β_2. While it is true that the blade profile and blade camber angle have some influence on the air deflection angle, the effect is small. Therefore the tests results may be effectively represented as in Fig. 13-12. With the aid of Eq. (13-46) and Fig. 13-12 the coefficient of lift C_L may be plotted against the air exit angle for various values of the solidity factor as shown in Fig. 13-13.

13-8. Blade Angles. Sections 9-8 and 9-9 are devoted to a discussion of the departure of the fluid entrance and exit angles from the corresponding geometric angles of the turbine blades. A similar departure exists with compressor blades for the very same reasons found to be true of turbine blades. However, the relationship between the air exit angle as a function of arcsin o/t, although applicable in most cases, is rather awkward to use. A more convenient relationship is the empirical formulation for the deviation angle:

$$\delta = \beta_2 - \beta_2' = \frac{m\theta}{\sqrt{\sigma}} \tag{13-47}$$

where $\theta = \beta_1' - \beta_2'$. Howell gives the following value for m within a range of β_2' between $-10°$ and $50°$:

$$m = 0.23\left(\frac{2a}{c}\right)^2 + 0.1\left(\frac{\beta_2'}{50}\right)$$

where a = distance of maximum camber from leading edge of blade
  c = chord length

The blade entrance angle is $\beta_1' = \beta_1 - i$, and for the optimum value of the nominal air deflection angle, i has a range from $-5°$ to $+5°$. A

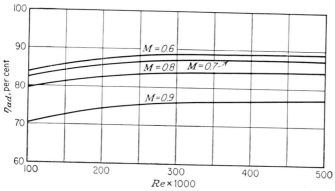

Fig. 13-14. Mach and Reynolds numbers effect on compressor adiabatic efficiency.

higher positive incidence angle can be used at higher values of the solidity factor as shown approximately for the following solidity factors:

σ	i
2	$+5°$ to $0°$
1	$0°$ to $-2.5°$
0.65	$-5°$ to $-2.5°$

13-9. Mach Number and Reynolds Number. Nearly all axial-flow air compressors operate with Reynolds number in excess of 200,000. Some compressors operate at Reynolds numbers as high as 1,000,000, or even higher. The blade chord is taken as the characteristic dimension for the Reynolds number. Figure 13-14 shows a plot of compressor adiabatic efficiency vs. Reynolds number for various values of entering flow Mach number. In general, it is noted that when the Reynolds number goes below 400,000, the adiabatic efficiency drops slightly at first, followed by a more rapid drop below 300,000 and a very severe drop below 200,000 and 100,000.

A high Reynolds number is conducive to higher efficiency; yet it is seen that a high Mach number is not. Again it will be noted from Fig. 13-14 that the same incremental increase of Mach number causes a more severe drop in efficiency in the high ranges of the Mach number. In the design of an axial-flow air compressor care must be taken to provide conditions that make possible a Reynolds number in excess of 250,000 and a Mach number below the limit of 0.70 to 0.75.

13-10. Three-dimensional Flow Considerations. The single-airfoil or cascade wind-tunnel tests are based on two-dimensional flow. Therefore test results must be modified to take into account the finite length of the blades. The development of three-dimensional-flow theory has not reached the point where an entirely rational approach can be taken. Furthermore, the complexity of the three-dimensional relationships coupled with the need to adopt convenient and economical design and manufacturing procedures encourage the use of empirical correction factors.

Cascade tests give results for conditions at the mean blade diameter and allowance must be made for blade clearance, end losses, the radial variation in linear velocity of the blade, radial variation of blade angles, and turbulence. The flow condition in the compressor is that of vortex flow with the most common design assumptions being those of free vortex or constant reaction. Free-vortex flow, of course, satisfies the condition of radial equilibrium. However, constant-reaction flow does not satisfy this condition. Nevertheless constant-reaction design is widely used because the blade angles do not vary radially nearly so severely as with the free-vortex design. A severe variation in blade angles results in a blade of considerable twist which poses manufacturing difficulties. A more important characteristic of blading designed for free-vortex flow is the radial increase of the entering relative velocity of the air with a corresponding increase in the Mach number. If the limiting Mach number is exceeded with free-vortex blading and it is not possible to lower the rotational speed or the axial velocity, then constant-reaction blading must be adopted. There is one compensating factor in that the sonic velocity increases with increasing static temperature and therefore the Mach number decreases as the flow proceeds through the compressor. Under some conditions it may be necessary to adopt constant reaction for the early stages where the static temperature is low with the later stages designed for free-vortex flow.

The predicted performance of a row of compressor blades is predicated on conditions obtained at the mean diameter. Equation (8-50) is an expression for the energy transfer to the air, based on the air angles at the mean diameter. This equation may be rewritten in terms of angle notation adopted in this chapter as follows:

$$E = \frac{U}{g} [U - V_{1a}(\tan \beta_1 + \tan \beta_2)] \qquad (13\text{-}48)$$

It is seen from this expression that an increase in axial velocity, or the angles β_1 and β_2, results in a decrease in the energy transfer to the air. Now if the flow through the compressor annulus is traversed, it will be found that the axial velocity profile would resemble the curves shown in Fig. 13-15. In the earlier stages the velocity profile is rather flat, becoming more peaked in the later stages. After the fourth or fifth stage the profile appears not to change appreciably. If it is assumed the stages are designed for constant axial velocity radially, it is clear that an increase in axial velocity at the mean diameter must be accompanied by a decrease in axial velocity at the ends of the blades since the mass rate of flow of air will be constant at all stages in the compressor. It would seem that the reduction of axial velocity at the blade ends would compensate for the increase in axial velocity at the mean diameter. However, the influence of tip clearance and boundary layer intervenes and the net effect is a decrease in the energy transfer to the air. To account for this decrease in the energy

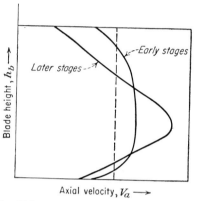

Fig. 13-15. Axial velocity distribution in compressor stages.

transfer, an empirical correction factor, known as the work-done factor, is applied to Eq. (13-48) or Eq. (8-50). From an analysis of test results Howell concludes that the mean value of the work-done factor is about 0.86.

It must be emphasized that the work-done factor is not an efficiency but simply a limitation on the maximum energy transfer to the air.

The reduction in efficiency is accounted for by means of an over-all drag coefficient. The profile drag coefficient was discussed earlier. To the profile drag coefficient must be added coefficients which take into account friction on the walls of the annulus and secondary losses such as trailing vortices, tip clearance, etc. The total drag coefficient is expressed

$$C_{DT} = C_{DP} + C_{DA} + C_{DS} \qquad (13\text{-}49)$$

where C_{DT} = over-all drag coefficient
$\qquad C_{DP}$ = profile drag coefficient obtained from wind-tunnel tests of single airfoils or cascades
$\qquad C_{DA}$ = annulus drag coefficient = $0.02t/h_b$, where t = blade pitch and h_b = blade height
$\qquad C_{DS}$ = secondary drag coefficient = $0.018C_L{}^2$

The profile drag coefficient may be taken at a constant mean value of 0.018 for design calculations.

13-11. Supersonic Axial-flow Air Compressor. Much has been said thus far about keeping the Mach number of the flow entering a compressor stage below a limiting value in order to avoid local acceleration to the velocity of sound with consequent shock and possible choking of the flow. In effect, consideration was limited to subsonic air compressors. It is clear from Eq. (6-27) that the restriction to subsonic compressors places a corresponding restriction on the maximum pressure rise which can be achieved in a given stage. In supersonic compressors, higher pressure ratios and somewhat higher mass rates of flow could be expected. Thus if diffusion through the sonic velocity could be achieved efficiently, a considerable reduction in weight and size of the compressor would result.

In Sec. 6-8 in connection with Fig. 6-10b there was described the condition of strong oblique shock in an extended wave pattern. Such shock is of course accompanied by a marked increase in entropy. However, the flow considered was that past a single surface, thus permitting an extended wave pattern. In tests on cascades of suitably shaped airfoils, it has been demonstrated that the waves originating at one airfoil are canceled at the neighboring airfoil, thus eliminating the possibility of an extended wave pattern. Thus the cause of the high increase in entropy can be avoided.

It is too early in the development of the supersonic air compressor to draw any conclusions as to a design approach. Much more experimentation is needed on supersonic cascades. At present it appears that the blade airfoils probably will be diamond-shaped in cross section. In general, two types of design are receiving attention. One is called the shock-in-rotor type and the other the shock-in-stator type. The shock-in-rotor type seems to be favored as the simpler arrangement. The velocity of the blades is high enough so that the air which enters the moving blades axially has a supersonic velocity relative to the blades. The flow is diffused to a subsonic velocity so that the Mach number entering the following stationary row of blades is below the limiting value of 0.70 to 0.75. The stationary row of blades is a conventional subsonic cascade. If the shock-in-stator type of arrangement is used, the complication of closely pitched prewhirl vanes must be introduced in order to keep the Mach number entering the first row of blades below the limiting value.

It appears to be desirable to limit the axial velocities to subsonic values. If supersonic axial velocities are used, it is necessary when starting the compressor to form a normal shock ahead of the compressor, moving it downstream into the moving blade rows. This undesirable condition

can be avoided by using only subsonic axial velocities since there seems
to be no particular advantage in supersonic axial velocities.

13-12. Performance Characteristics. The performance characteristics of the axial-flow air compressor are expressed in terms of dimensionless parameters identical to those derived for the centrifugal compressor in Sec. 12-8. Figure 13-16 shows the performance characteristics
of an axial-flow air compressor which should be compared with the characteristics shown in Fig. 12-8 for the centrifugal compressor. It should
be noted especially that at constant values of $N/\sqrt{T_1}$ there is a considerably narrower range of mass rates of flow, $G\sqrt{T_1}/P_1$, than in the

centrifugal compressor. Surging
and choking are the limitations at
either end of the $N/\sqrt{T_1}$ curves in
both the centrifugal and axial-flow
compressors. However, the surge
point is reached in the axial-flow
compressor much before the maximum pressure ratio for a given
value of $N/\sqrt{T_1}$. Since the design
usually calls for the operating line
to be near the maximum point on
the $N/\sqrt{T_1}$ curves, it follows that
the operating line for the axial-flow
compressor must be very near the
surge line, thus narrowing the range
of stable operation. Extremely

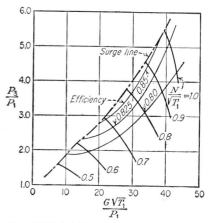

Fig. 13-16. Axial-flow compressor characteristics.

careful attention must be given to matching the components, particularly
the turbine, in a gas-turbine power plant incorporating an axial-flow
compressor.

The condition of surging is very difficult to distinguish from that of
stalling, and one condition may very well be the cause of the other.
Many explanations for the phenomenon of surging have been advanced
but as yet it is not entirely understood.

In general, it may be said that surging is brought on by a decrease in
mass rate of flow. Consequently, a decrease in axial velocity takes place
followed by an increase in the incidence angle. When the incidence
angle becomes excessive, the blade is stalled and the flow breaks down.
A reduction in the mass rate of flow through the compressor may be
brought about by the choking effect of the initial ignition of fuel in the
combustion chamber when starting up or by a choking condition being
reached in the turbine.

In the centrifugal compressor surging can be eliminated by a slight
decrease in rotational speed. However, this is not true of the axial-flow

compressor, particularly if surging is incurred at high rotational speed. In order to remove the surging condition, the compressor may need to be brought to idling speed or, worse still, stopped completely.

13-13. Axial-flow Compressor Computations

Example. An axial-flow air compressor is to be designed to deliver 40 lb per sec of air. The required pressure rise is 4 to 1. The static pressure and temperature at compressor inlet are 14.7 psia and 70 F. The mean blade radius is to be 8 in. and the axial velocity is to be kept at about 400 fps. The design adopted will be for constant 50 per cent reaction at all radii.

Since symmetric staging is specified at the mean diameter, the flow coefficient at this point will be near 0.5, from Eq. (13-15). Assuming $\phi = 0.5$,

$$U = \frac{V_a}{0.5} = \frac{400}{0.5} = 800 \text{ fps}$$

The rotational speed is

$$N = \frac{U \times 60}{2\pi r_m} = \frac{800 \times 60 \times 12}{2 \times 3.14 \times 8} = 11{,}500 \text{ rpm}$$

The specific volume of the air at entrance is

$$v_1 = \frac{RT_1}{P_1} = \frac{53.34 \times 530}{14.7 \times 14.4} = 13.35 \text{ cu ft per lb}$$

The annular area available for flow is given as $A = 2\pi r_m h_b$ and from the continuity relationship

$$A = \frac{Wv_1}{V_a}$$

and

$$h_b = \frac{Wv_1}{2\pi r_m V_a} = \frac{40 \times 13.35 \times 144}{2 \times \pi \times 8 \times 400} = 3.82 \text{ in.}$$

The ratio of the blade root diameter to tip diameter should be checked. In general, values of the ratio below 0.6 indicate that the Mach number and speeds will be unreasonable. In this instance the diameter ratio is in excess of 0.6.

Referring to Fig. 13-5, it is seen that

$$U = V_{1U} + W_{2U} + \Delta W_U$$

and

$$W_{mU} = W_{2U} + \frac{\Delta W_U}{2}$$

Also

$$V_{1U} = W_{2U}$$

Therefore

$$U = 2W_{2U} + \Delta W_U = 2W_{mU}$$

or

$$W_{mU} = \frac{U}{2}$$

With this relationship, W_m may be expressed as follows:

$$W_m = \sqrt{V_a{}^2 + \left(\frac{U}{2}\right)^2}$$

$$W_m = \sqrt{(400)^2 + ({}^{809}\!/_2)^2} = 565 \text{ fps}$$

$$\cos \beta_m = \frac{V_a}{W_m} = \frac{400}{565} = 0.71$$

It is reasonable to expect that a blade loading of $C_{l}\sigma = 1.0$ could be attained at the mean diameter of a symmetric stage. From Fig. 13-7 or Eq. (13-43), a value for the pressure coefficient $\psi = 0.7$ is indicated. Now $2(\tan \beta_1 - \tan \beta_2) = \dfrac{\psi}{\phi} = \dfrac{0.7}{0.5}$ from which $\tan \beta_1 - \tan \beta_2 = 0.7$. Or, substituting in Eq. (13-46),

$$\tan \beta_1 - \tan \beta_2 = \frac{1}{2 \times 0.71} = 0.704$$

also

$$\tan \beta_1 + \tan \beta_2 = \frac{2R}{\phi} = \frac{2 \times 0.5}{0.5} = 2$$

solving for β_1 and β_2,

$$\tan \beta_1 + \tan \beta_2 = 2.00$$
$$\tan \beta_1 - \tan \beta_2 = 0.70$$
$$\tan \beta_1 = 1.35$$
$$\beta_1 = 53.5°$$
$$\tan \beta_2 = 0.65$$
$$\beta_2 = 33°$$

Since the diagram at the mean section is symmetric,

$$\alpha_2 = \beta_1 = 53.5°$$
$$\alpha_1 = \beta_2 = 33°$$

The net whirl component is given by

$$\tan \beta_1 - \tan \beta_2 = \frac{\Delta W_U}{2} = 0.70$$
$$\Delta W_U = 0.70 \times 400 = 280 \text{ fps}$$

The air velocities and their components may be now obtained from the trigonometric relationships or the velocity diagram may be drawn to scale. Figure 13-17 shows the velocity diagram for the mean section. The blade tip and root radii are

$$r_t = 9.75 \text{ in.}$$
$$r_r = 6.27 \text{ in.}$$

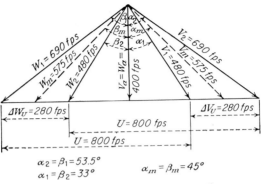

$$\alpha_2 = \beta_1 = 53.5°$$
$$\alpha_1 = \beta_2 = 33°$$
$$\alpha_m = \beta_m = 45°$$

Fig. 13-17. Velocity diagram—mean section.

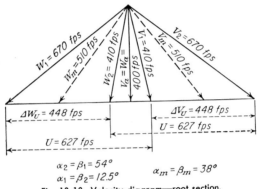

$$\alpha_2 = \beta_1 = 54°$$
$$\alpha_1 = \beta_2 = 12.5°$$
$$\alpha_m = \beta_m = 38°$$

Fig. 13-18. Velocity diagram—root section.

The axial velocities will be kept constant radially and for the condition of constant 50 per cent reaction the following may be written:

$$\Delta V_{Um} U_m = \Delta V_{Ur} U_r = \Delta V_{Ut} U_t$$

Now

$$\frac{U_m}{r_m} = \frac{U_r}{r_r} = \frac{U_t}{r_t}$$

$$U_r = \frac{800 \times 6.27}{8} = 627 \text{ fps} \quad \text{and} \quad U_t = \frac{800 \times 9.75}{8} = 975 \text{ fps}$$

and
$$\Delta V_{Ur} = 280 \times {}^{800}\!/_{500} = 448 \text{ fps}$$
and
$$\Delta V_{Ut} = 280 \times {}^{800}\!/_{975} = 230 \text{ fps}$$

The velocity diagrams for the root and tip sections may be now drawn and are as shown in Figs. 13-18 and 13-19. It is suggested the reader draw the velocity diagrams on the basis of free-vortex flow and compare the radial variation of air angles with that of the constant degree-of-action diagrams.

The Mach number at the tip section should be checked. To do this, it is necessary to know the static temperature of the air entering the first row of moving blades.

$$T_1 = T_a - \frac{V_1{}^2}{2gJC_P}$$

$$T_1 = 530 - \frac{(560)^2}{2gJC_P} = 503.9 \text{ F, say } 504 \text{ R}$$

$$a = \sqrt{gkRT} = \sqrt{32.2 \times 1.41 \times 53.3 \times 504}$$

$$a = 1220 \text{ fps}$$

$$M = \frac{W_{1t}}{a} = \frac{730}{1220} = 0.6$$

This is well below the limiting value of 0.7 to 0.75.

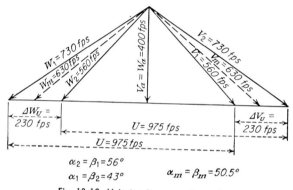

$$\alpha_2 = \beta_1 = 56°$$
$$\alpha_1 = \beta_2 = 43°$$
$$\alpha_m = \beta_m = 50.5°$$

Fig. 13-19. Velocity diagram—tip section.

The velocity diagrams give the air angles and it is necessary to determine the actual blade angles. This is done for the section at the mean blade height, the blade angles at the other sections being found in the same way. At the design point, the incidence angle is usually taken as zero so that $\beta_1' = \beta_1$. To find β_2', it is necessary to refer to Eq. (13-47). If a circular-arc camber line is assumed, $2a/c = 1$ and Eq. (13-47) is greatly simplified.

$$\delta = \frac{[0.23 + 0.1(^{33}\!/_{50})]\theta}{\sqrt{1}}$$

$$\delta = 0.296\theta$$

Now $\theta = \beta_1' - \beta_2'$

Also $\delta = \beta_2 - \beta_2'$

Therefore $\beta_2 - \delta = \beta_1' - \theta$

or $\beta_2 - 0.296\theta = \beta_1 - \theta$

and $0.704\theta = \beta_1 - \beta_2 = 53.5 - 33 = 20.5°$

$$\theta = 29.2°$$

from which $\delta = \beta_2 - \beta_2' = 0.296 \times 29.2$

and $\beta_2' = 24.35°$

Since a symmetrical stage is under consideration the angles for stationary and moving blades are the same.

The solidity factor must be resolved into the separate values of pitch and chord length. The aspect ratio governs to a large extent the chord length chosen. Selecting the high aspect ratio of 3 in order to reduce annulus drag losses,

$$c = \frac{h_b}{3} = \frac{3.82}{3} \ 1.275 \text{ in.}$$

The pitch is given by

$$t = \frac{c}{\sigma}$$

and

$$t = 1.275 \text{ in.}$$

The number of blades is

$$n = \frac{2\pi r_m}{t} = \frac{2\pi \times 8}{1.275} = 40$$

The blade losses may be determined from the total drag coefficient obtained from Eq. (13-49):

$$C_{DT} = 0.018 + 0.02 \ \frac{1.275}{3.82} + 0.018(1)^2$$

$$C_{DT} = 0.0427$$

Substituting C_{DT} in Eq. (13-28),

$$\frac{\Delta P^\circ}{\frac{1}{2}\rho W_1{}^2} = C_{D}\sigma \ \frac{\cos^2 \beta_1}{\cos^3 \beta_m} = 0.0427 \ \frac{(0.595)^2}{(0.707)^3}$$

$$\frac{\Delta P^\circ}{\frac{1}{2}\rho W_1{}^2} = 0.0425$$

Also from Eq. (13-21),

$$\frac{\Delta P_{ideal}}{\frac{1}{2}\rho W_1{}^2} = 1 - \frac{\cos^2 \beta_1}{\cos^2 \beta_2} = 1 - \frac{(0.595)^2}{(0.839)^2}$$

$$\frac{\Delta P_{ideal}}{\frac{1}{2}\rho W_1{}^2} = 0.445$$

and, from Eq. (13-29),

$$\eta_{bl} = 1 - \frac{0.0425}{0.445} = 0.904$$

Since the stage is symmetrical, the efficiencies of the stationary and moving blade rows are the same; the blade efficiency is the stage efficiency.

The static temperature rise in the stage is given by Eq. (8-51) multiplied by the work-done factor of 0.86:

$$\Delta T = \frac{800 \times 400}{32.2 \times 778 \times 0.24} \times 0.7 \times 0.86 = 32 \text{ F}$$

The pressure ratio across the stage is

$$\frac{P_2}{P_1} = \left(\frac{T_2}{T_1}\right)^{k/(k-1)} = \left(\frac{T_1 + \Delta T}{T_1}\right)^{k/(k-1)} = \left(1 + \frac{\Delta T}{T_1}\right)^{k/(k-1}$$

The actual static temperature rise is $\eta_{bl} \Delta T$ and

$$\frac{P_2}{P_1} = \left(1 + \frac{0.904 \times 32}{504}\right)^{1.4/(1.4-1)} = 1.216$$

The static pressure is obtained as follows,

$$P_1 = P_a - \frac{V_1^2}{2 \times g \times v_1 \times 144}$$

$$P_1 = 14.7 - \frac{(560)^2}{2g \times 13.35 \times 144} = 14.5 \text{ psia}$$

$$P_2 = 1.216 \times 14.5 = 17.6 \text{ psia}$$

A stage-by-stage calculation is necessary to determine the number of stages. The effect of reheat would have to be taken into consideration and it is probable that about 12 stages may be required.

References

1. Brunner, M. J., and R. E. McNair: Blading for Axial-flow Compressors, *ASME Paper* 50-A-113, 1950.
2. Davis, H.: A New Method for the Aerodynamic Design of Multi-stage Axial-flow Compressors, *J. Aeronaut. Sci.*, January, 1948.
3. Howell, A. R.: Fluid Dynamics of Axial-flow Compressors, *Proc. IME, WEP* 12, 1945.
4. Howell, A. R.: Design of Axial-flow Compressors, *Proc. IME, WEP* 12, 1945.
5. Howell, A. R., and R. P. Bonham: Overall and Stage Characteristics of Axial-flow Compressors, *Proc. IME, WEP* 60, 1950.
6. Howell, A. R.: The Present Basis of Axial-flow Compressor Design, Aeronautic Research Council (England), *R and M* 2095, 1942.
7. Kantrowitz, A.: The Supersonic Axial-flow Compressor, *NACA Rept.* 974, 1950.
8. Keller, C., and L. S. Marks: "The Theory and Performance of Axial-flow Fans," McGraw-Hill Book Company, Inc., New York, 1937.

Problems

13-1. It is required to design an axial-flow air compressor for the following conditions:

$G = 60$ lb per sec
Pressure ratio $= 3.5$
Atmospheric pressure $= 14.3$ psia
Ambient temperature $= 40$ F
$V_a = 350$ fps
Constant 50 per cent reaction at all radii

13-2. Plot the performance characteristics at overload and part loads for the compressor of Prob. 13-1, assuming the design performance has been substantiated on test.

13-3. Calculate the pressure ratio for an axial-flow air compressor with symmetric blades under the following conditions:

$V_a = 450$ fps
$V_m = 650$ fps
Ambient temperature $= 70$ F
Atmospheric pressure $= 14.7$ psia
$\sigma = 1$ (moving blades)
$C_L = 0.8$ (moving blades)
$D/L = 0.045$

Calculate the pressure ratio for nonsymmetric blading and compare with the pressure ratio obtained for symmetric blading.

13-4. A 12-stage axial-flow air compressor has been observed to handle 80 lb per sec of air when operating at a speed of 9000 rpm. The power supplied is 9800 hp and the stage efficiency is found to be 0.92 for all stages. The mean blade ring diameter is 26 in., and equal work is done in each stage. The axial velocity component is 350 fps and the stages are designed for constant 50 per cent reaction. Compressor inlet temperature and pressure are 60 F and 14.7 psia, respectively. Determine (a) the pressure ratio in the first stage; (b) blade entrance and exit angles.

CHAPTER 14

COMBUSTION

14-1. Introduction. The combustion process is of critical importance to the gas-turbine cycle because it is in this process that energy, which is later converted into work by the turbine, is supplied. Therefore any losses incurred in the combustion process have a direct effect on the thermal efficiency of the cycle.

Despite the importance of the combustion process, normally it receives less attention than the expansion, compression, and heat-transfer processes. Owing to its extreme complication, the process is not completely understood, and no rigorous analysis has been made. An empirical or trial-and-error approach is therefore adopted instead. Furthermore, it is not too difficult to achieve a combustion efficiency of 98 per cent with a static pressure loss of less than 5 per cent. This, of course, raises the question of the efficacy of attempts at further improvement. However, there is a real need for reducing the size of combustors, increasing their life and reliability, and providing a direct approach to design planning that is both economical of time and materials. This last need is especially evident in view of the diverse design procedures for combustors in current use.

It is beyond the scope of this book to examine in detail the existing theory of combustion and the reader is referred to some excellent references on the subject listed at the end of this chapter. The purpose of this chapter is to establish a general familiarity with some of the simpler chemical reactions of which the combustion process is a special case, to describe the mechanism of the combustion process used in gas-turbine plants, and to examine some of the design features of the combustor itself.

THE THERMOCHEMISTRY OF COMBUSTION

14-2. Combustion Equations. Consider a familiar equation for the reaction of hydrogen and oxygen to form water:

$$H_2 + \tfrac{1}{2}O_2 \rightarrow H_2O \tag{14-1}$$

Stated in words this equation says that 1 molecule of hydrogen combines with $\frac{1}{2}$ molecule of oxygen to form 1 molecule of water. The substances involved in the reaction are called the constituents, the reactants H_2 and O_2 combining to form the product H_2O. The reaction of Eq. (14-1) is indicated as proceeding to the right but under favorable circumstances could proceed from right to left. This latter reaction is referred to as dissociation. Equation (14-1) states the correct combining proportions of H_2 and O_2 for complete oxidation to H_2O. Hence the number of molecules preceding each of the constituents are called the stoichiometric coefficients. The stoichiometric coefficients for H_2 and H_2O are understood to be unity. Thus the stoichiometric coefficients for the reaction of carbon and oxygen to form carbon dioxide are unity in the case of each constituent:

$$C + O_2 \rightarrow CO_2 \qquad (14\text{-}2)$$

An oxidation reaction which occurs with high speed is referred to as a combustion reaction.

The molecular weights of the constituents in a reaction equation are proportional to their relative masses. If the pound is selected as the unit mass, Eq. (14-2) may be written as a mass equation as follows, after noting the molecular weights of $C = 12$, $O_2 = 32$, and $CO_2 = 44$:

$$12 \text{ lb } C + 32 \text{ lb } O_2 = 44 \text{ lb } CO_2 \qquad (14\text{-}3)$$

Each mass of constituent is defined as a mole and since the pound has been selected as the unit of mass, the mole may be further defined as a pound mole to distinguish it from moles based on some other unit of mass. Accordingly Eq. (14-2) is written

$$1 \text{ mole } C + 1 \text{ mole } O_2 \rightarrow 1 \text{ mole } CO_2 \qquad (14\text{-}4)$$

Similarly

$$1 \text{ mole } H_2 + \tfrac{1}{2} \text{ mole } O_2 \rightarrow 1 \text{ mole } H_2O \qquad (14\text{-}5)$$

Comparing Eqs. (14-1) and (14-5) and Eqs. (14-2) and (14-4) it is seen that the stoichiometric coefficients are proportional to the number of moles which change during reaction. Therefore, for example, 0.5 mole of O_2 combines with 0.5 mole of C to form 0.5 mole of CO_2. Similarly 2 moles of H_2 combine with 1 mole of O_2 to form 2 moles of H_2O.

If it is assumed that the reaction takes place at sufficiently low pressure and that all the constituents exist in the gaseous phase, they may be regarded as being ideal gases. If further it is specified that all constituents are at the same pressure and temperature, with the use of Avagadro's hypothesis, Eqs. (14-4) and (14-5) may be written as follows:

$$1 \text{ volume } C + 1 \text{ volume } O_2 \rightarrow 1 \text{ volume } CO_2 \qquad (14\text{-}6)$$
$$1 \text{ volume } H_2 + \tfrac{1}{2} \text{ volume } O_2 \rightarrow 1 \text{ volume } H_2O \qquad (14\text{-}7)$$

It is interesting to note that the stoichiometric coefficients, moles, and volumes in the preceding equations do not balance for the two sides of the equations. However, the mass equation [Eq. (14-3)] requires a balance in accordance with the law of conservation of mass.

In real combustion reactions it is rare indeed that pure oxygen is available to support combustion. More often used is atmospheric air which consists of a mixture of O_2, N_2, and other inert gases, and water vapor. For most practical applications, dry air may be taken as composed of 21 per cent O_2 and 79 per cent "N_2" by volume, where "N_2" represents all the inert gases. Therefore there are 3.76 parts of N_2 to 1 part O_2 by volume at standard conditions of pressure and temperature. The reaction for C with air then may be written on a molal basis as follows:

$$C + O_2 + 3.76\text{``}N_2\text{''} \rightarrow CO_2 + 3.76\text{``}N_2\text{''} \qquad (14\text{-}8)$$

It will be noted that the inert constituents grouped as "N_2" do not take part in the reaction, and hence the molal quantity 3.76 remains unchanged. Noting the molecular weight of "N_2" = 28.2, a mass equation may be written:

$$12C + 32O_2 + 106\text{``}N_2\text{''} = 44CO_2 + 106\text{``}N_2\text{''} \qquad (14\text{-}9)$$

When the combustion reaction for an actual fuel is written, other reactants besides carbon are introduced, such as H_2 and S, as well as inert matter.

14-3. Laws of Gas Mixtures. Dalton's law applies to a mixture of ideal gases, and accordingly

$$P = P_1 + P_2 + P_3 + \cdots = \sum_i P_i \qquad (14\text{-}10)$$

That is, the total pressure P of the mixture is equal to the sum of the partial pressures of the component gases in the mixture. From this relationship and the equation of state,

$$P_1 : P_2 : P_3 : \cdots = v_1 : v_2 : v_3 : \cdots \qquad (14\text{-}11)$$

and if n is equal to the number of moles of each component gas in the mixture,

$$P_1 : P_2 : P_3 : \cdots = n_1 : n_2 : n_3 : \cdots \qquad (14\text{-}12)$$

Therefore

$$P_1 = \frac{n_1}{n_1 + n_2 + n_3 + \cdots} P \text{ etc.}$$

or

$$P_i = \frac{n_i}{\sum_i n_i} P \qquad (14\text{-}13)$$

The expression $n_i / \sum_i n_i$ is called the mole fraction, or concentration, and gives the ratio of the number of moles of a given component gas to the number of moles of mixture. This ratio will be designated by the symbol x_i.

14-4. Entropy of a Mixture of Ideal Gases. To determine the entropy of a mixture of ideal gases, it is necessary to separate the individual gases by some reversible means. Such a means can be conceived in terms of Fig. 14-1, where for simplicity a mixture of two ideal gases is considered. The walls X and X' are fixed. The walls Y and Y' move together in such a manner that the distance between Y and Y' is always

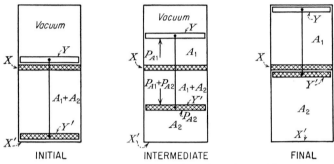

Fig. 14-1. Separation of ideal gases by isothermal reversible process.

equal to the distance between X and X'. Furthermore, X is a semipermeable membrane which is permeable to gas A_1 but impermeable to gas A_2. Similarly Y' is permeable to gas A_2 and impermeable to gas A_1.

In the initial state X and Y are together and consequently X' and Y' are in contact. Also in the initial state a vacuum exists above Y. The movement of the system YY' is assumed to be frictionless and infinitely slow so that thermal and pressure equilibrium exist at all times. Now the pressure of the gas mixture $A_1 + A_2$ is equal to the sum of the partial pressures of A_1 and A_2 alone. The vessel is of constant cross-sectional area. Therefore the force exerted on Y is due to the partial pressure of A in the space XY, while the force on Y' is due to the partial pressure of A_2 and the pressure of the gas mixture $A_1 + A_2$. From the intermediate position of Fig. 14-1 it is seen that the net force on the coupled walls, Y and Y', is zero and hence the external work is zero.

A further condition is that the entire vessel be perfectly insulated from its surroundings. The heat transfer $dQ = 0$, and since $dW = 0$, it follows from Eq. (3-12) that $dU = 0$. Then, for the ideal gases under consideration, temperature equilibrium exists and the process is isothermal. Letting S equal the entropy of the gas mixture in the initial state and

$\sum_i n_i S_i$ equal the sum of the entropies of the individual gases after separation, the following relation holds:

$$dQ = T \left(\sum_i n_i S_i - S \right) = 0 \qquad (14\text{-}14)$$

and, since T has some positive value,

$$S = \sum n_i S_i \qquad (14\text{-}15)$$

Noting that $\Sigma n_i S_i$ is the sum of the entropies of the two separated gases each at the same temperature and each at the same volume occupied by the mixture of the two gases, the partial entropy of any one of the gases in the mixture may be defined as the entropy of the gas were it to occupy alone the entire volume of the mixture at the same temperature. As a consequence of the foregoing relationships and definition, the total entropy of a mixture of ideal gases is equal to the sum of the partial entropies, a concept known as Gibbs theorem. This theorem will be useful in the work which follows.

14-5. Chemical Equilibrium. The change in partial molal entropy may be expressed in terms of the temperature and the partial pressure. [See Eq. (3-91).]

$$dS_i = C_{pi} \frac{dT}{T} - R \frac{dP_i}{P_i} \qquad (14\text{-}16)$$

where R and T are the universal gas constant and absolute temperature, respectively. Equation (14-16) may be integrated but an arbitrary constant must be introduced. It will be remembered that only changes in entropy can be measured, and the value of the constant therefore depends on the selected reference state from which entropy changes are measured. Accordingly Eq. (14-16) becomes

$$S_i = \int C_{pi} \frac{dT}{T} - R \ln P_i + S_0 \qquad (14\text{-}17)$$

Now the sum of the partial pressures of the gases in the mixture is equal to the total pressure of the mixture. In turn the ratio of the partial pressures is proportional to the number of moles of the gases present in the mixture. The partial pressure of a gas in the mixture is

$$P_i = x_i P$$

where $x_i = n_i / \Sigma n_i$ is the mole fraction. Substituting in Eq. (14-17),

$$S_i = \int C_{pi} \frac{dT}{T} - R \ln P x_i + S_0 \qquad (14\text{-}18)$$

If Eq. (14-18) is substituted in Eq. (14-15), the result is

$$S = \sum_i n_i \left(\int C_{pi} \frac{dT}{T} - R \ln Px_i + S_0 \right) \qquad (14\text{-}19)$$

The Gibbs function is given by Eq. (3-52) as

$$G = U - TS + Pv \qquad (14\text{-}20)$$

The internal energy of a mixture of ideal gases is given by the following expression, noting that the internal energy of an ideal gas is a function of temperature only:

$$U = \sum_i n_i \left(\int C_{vi} \, dT + U_0 \right) \qquad (14\text{-}21)$$

Again the arbitrary constant U_0 depends on the reference state from which changes in internal energy are measured. The volume of the mixture of gases is given by the equation of state

$$V = \sum_i n_i \frac{RT}{P} \qquad (14\text{-}22)$$

Substituting Eqs. (14-21) and (14-22) in Eq. (14-20),

$$G = \sum_i n_i \left(\int C_{vi} \, dT + U_0 - T \int C_{pi} \frac{dT}{T} + RT \ln Px_i - TS_0 + RT \right) \qquad (14\text{-}23)$$

and noting that

$$C_{vi} = C_{pi} - R$$

$$G = \sum_i n_i \left(\int C_{pi} \, dT + T \int C_{pi} \frac{dT}{T} + RT \ln P + U_0 - TS_0 \right)$$

$$+ \sum_i n_i RT \ln x_i \qquad (14\text{-}24)$$

Now the Gibbs function may be also expressed

$$G = h - TS$$

which makes it clear that the parenthetical expression in Eq. (14-24) is the Gibbs function of a mole of one gas in the mixture in terms of the temperature and total pressure of the mixture. Designating this expression as G_i,

$$G = \sum_i n_i(G_i + RT \ln x_i) \qquad (14\text{-}25)$$

Consider a mixture of gases which are chemically reactive and suppose the mixture to be contained in a vessel at constant temperature and constant pressure. The Gibbs function permits a determination of the conditions necessary for equilibrium in the mixture. From Eq. (3-55), the change in the Gibbs function is

$$dG = v\,dP - S\,dT$$

and since $dP = 0$ and $dT = 0$, the condition for equilibrium is

$$dG = 0 \qquad (14\text{-}26)$$

Suppose that the system is disturbed slightly, a chemical reaction ensuing to some extent, so that the number of moles of each gas in the mixture changes by the amount dn_i. With the aid of Eqs. (14-25) and (14-26),

$$dG = \sum_i (G_i + RT \ln x_i)\,dn_i + \sum_i n_i\,d(G_i + RT \ln x_i) = 0 \qquad (14\text{-}27)$$

which is the condition for equilibrium. But $dG_i = 0$ for equilibrium and $\sum_i n_i\,d \ln x_i$ can be shown to be equal to zero as follows:

$$\sum_i n_i\,d \ln x_i = \sum \frac{n_i}{x_i}\,dx_i$$

Now $\Sigma x_i = 1$ and therefore $\Sigma\,dx_i = 0$, so that $\Sigma n_i\,d \ln x_i = 0$. Hence Eq. (14-27) becomes

$$dG = \sum_i (G_i\,RT \ln x_i)\,dn_i = 0 \qquad (14\text{-}28)$$

Suppose for generality that a reactive mixture composed of four constituents is contained in a vessel, the reactants being designated as A_1 and A_2 and the products as A_3 and A_4. The appropriate stoichiometric coefficients are a_1, a_2, a_3, and a_4, respectively. Then the reaction may be written

$$a_1A_1 + a_2A_2 \rightarrow a_3A_3 + a_4A_4 \qquad (14\text{-}29)$$

or

$$-a_1A_1 - a_2A_2 + a_3A_3 + a_4A_4 = 0$$

Any value of a in the preceding equation is positive if the constituent is formed in the reaction and negative if the constituent disappears. Since the stoichiometric coefficients are proportional to the number of moles which change during reaction,

$$dn_1:dn_2:dn_3:dn_4 = -a_1:-a_2:a_3:a_4 \qquad (14\text{-}30)$$

Substituting Eq. (14-30) in Eq. (14-28),

$$\sum_i a_i(G_i + RT \ln x_i) = 0 \qquad (14\text{-}31)$$

and
$$\sum_i a_i \ln x_i = - \sum_i \frac{a_i G_i}{RT} \qquad (14\text{-}32)$$

For the specification of constant temperature and constant pressure, the right-hand side of Eq. (14-32) is a constant. Designating this constant as $\ln K_c$, Eq. (14-32) may be expressed

$$\sum_i a_i \ln x_i = \ln K_c \qquad (14\text{-}33)$$

where
$$\ln K_c = - \sum_i \frac{a_i G_i}{RT} \qquad (14\text{-}34)$$

or Eq. (14-33) may be expressed

$$K_c = \frac{X_3{}^{a_3} \cdot X_4{}^{a_4}}{X_1{}^{a_1} \cdot X_2{}^{a_2}} \qquad (14\text{-}35)$$

This equation is a statement of the law of mass action. The value of K_c, known as the reaction constant, can be determined for a given reaction at a specified temperature and pressure in terms of the mole fractions. The value of K_c thus obtained can be used to calculate the mole fractions of all reactants after reaction, provided they are returned to equilibrium at the initial temperature and pressure.

The equilibrium conditions may be more conveniently expressed in terms of the partial pressures. Since $x_i = P_i/P$, Eq. (14-35) may be written

$$K_p = P^{\Delta a_i} K_c = \frac{P_3{}^{a_3} \cdot P_4{}^{a_4}}{P_1{}^{a_1} \cdot P_2{}^{a_2}} \qquad (14\text{-}36)$$

where K_p is called the equilibrium constant.

14-6. Heat of Reaction. Whenever a change occurs in a system, such as a chemical reaction, the energy absorbed or liberated from the system may be expressed in terms of the heat transfer dQ. In accordance with the first law of thermodynamics [Eq. (3-12)],

$$dU = dQ - dW \qquad (14\text{-}37)$$

For a reaction which occurs at constant volume with no energy transfer across the boundary of the system,

$$dU = dQ$$

If further, the reaction takes place at constant temperature, the heat transfer is equal to the change in internal energy, where the internal energy is understood to include chemical energy. Accordingly,

$$\Delta U = U_{\text{products}} - U_{\text{reactants}} \qquad (14\text{-}38)$$

It is emphasized that although the temperatures before and after the reaction are the same, the internal energies are not equal since chemical energy is included. The change in internal energy ΔU is referred to as the heat of reaction at constant volume.

A more important reaction, as far as gas-turbine combustion processes are concerned, is a reaction at constant temperature and pressure. Referring again to Eq. (3-12), the energy equation may be written

$$dU = dQ - P \, dv \qquad (14\text{-}39)$$

Work is done in the displacement of the boundary due to a change in volume which occurs during the reaction. Therefore the heat transfer is equal to $\Delta U + P \, \Delta v$. Designating the heat transfer as ΔH, the heat of reaction at constant temperature and pressure is

$$\Delta H = \Delta U + P \, \Delta v = H_{\text{products}} - H_{\text{reactants}} \qquad (14\text{-}40)$$

Again the internal energy term U includes chemical energy.

Referring to Eq. (14-39), for a constant-pressure and constant-temperature reaction the heat of reaction may be expressed

$$dQ = \sum_i \left(\int C_{vi} \, dT + U_0 + RT \right) dn_i = \sum_i \left(\int C_{pi} \, dT + U_0 \right) dn_i \qquad (14\text{-}41)$$

Substituting from Eq. (14-30) and noting that dQ is negative for a reaction in which heat is liberated from the system,

$$-\Delta H = \sum_i a_i \left(\int C_{pi} \, dT + U_0 \right) \qquad (14\text{-}42)$$

The heat of reaction ΔH is negative if the reaction proceeds to the right as indicated in Eq. (14-29). The opposite is true when the reaction proceeds to the left.

The relationship between the heats of reaction at constant pressure and constant volume may be shown in the following manner:

$$-\Delta H = \Delta U + Pv$$

$$-\Delta H = \Delta U + RT \sum_i dn_i$$

Substituting from Eq. (14-30),

$$-\Delta H = \Delta U + RT \sum_i a_i \qquad (14\text{-}43)$$

The effect of temperature change on the constant-pressure heat of reaction may be shown through Eq. (14-42):

$$\Delta H_{T_2} - \Delta H_{T_1} = - \Sigma a_i \int_{T_1}^{T_2} C_{P_i} \, dT \qquad (14\text{-}44)$$

14-7. The Le Châtelier Principle. Differentiating Eq. (14-34) with respect to temperature and holding the pressure constant, the effect of a change in temperature on the reaction constant K_c is obtained.

$$\left(\frac{\partial \ln K_c}{\partial T}\right)_P = \frac{1}{RT^2} \sum_i a_i G_i - \frac{1}{RT} \sum_i a_i \frac{\partial G_i}{\partial T} \qquad (14\text{-}45)$$

Substituting the value of G_i as given in the parenthetical expression of Eq. (14-24),

$$\left(\frac{\partial \ln K_c}{\partial T}\right)_P = \frac{1}{RT^2} \sum_i a_i \left(\int C_{P_i}\, dT + U_0\right) \qquad (14\text{-}46)$$

Substituting from Eq. (14-42),

$$\left(\frac{\partial \ln K_c}{\partial T}\right)_P = \frac{-\Delta H}{RT^2} \qquad (14\text{-}47)$$

or

$$\frac{dK_c}{K_c} = \frac{-\Delta H}{RT}\frac{dT}{T} \qquad (14\text{-}48)$$

This is the van't Hoff equation.

Similarly if Eq. (14-34) is differentiated with respect to pressure, the temperature being held constant, the following expression is obtained:

$$\left(\frac{\partial \ln K_c}{\partial P}\right)_T = -\frac{1}{RT} \sum_i a_i \left(\frac{\partial G_i}{\partial P}\right)_T \qquad (14\text{-}49)$$

Substituting for G_i its value as found in the parenthetical expression of Eq. (14-24) and differentiating $(\partial G_i / \partial P)_T$,

$$\left(\frac{\partial \ln K_c}{\partial P}\right)_T = -\frac{\Delta v}{RT} \qquad (14\text{-}50)$$

If Eq. (14-36) is differentiated with respect to temperature at constant pressure, it can be shown that

$$\left(\frac{\partial \ln K_P}{\partial T}\right)_P = \left(\frac{\partial \ln K_c}{\partial T}\right)_P = \frac{-\Delta H}{RT^2} \qquad (14\text{-}51)$$

From Eqs. (14-34), (14-47), and (14-51) it is observed that when a reaction proceeds so that heat is liberated, that is, $-\Delta H$, if the temperature is raised the reaction proceeds in a direction consistent with a decrease in K_c and as a result the reaction is retarded. However, Eq. (14-50) indicates that if the reaction takes place with a decrease in pressure the reaction proceeds in the direction of increasing volume. These observations are generalized in the Le Châtelier principle which states that if one of the factors of equilibrium is changed so as to disturb the equilibrium of a system a counterchange takes place within the system tending to nullify the effect of the original change and restore equilibrium.

14-8. Reactions Involving Solids and Liquids. If solids and liquids are present in equilibrium with gases, the vapors of the solids and liquids must be in equilibrium. Since the vapor pressures of solids and liquids are functions of temperature only, they remain constant during reaction. Designating the vapor pressures or partial pressures of those constituents existing in the solid or liquid phase by the symbol π, the equilibrium constant may be expressed

$$K_p = \frac{P_3{}^{a_3} \cdot P_4{}^{a_4} \pi_y{}^{a_y}}{P_1{}^{a_1} \cdot P_2{}^{a_2} \pi_x{}^{a_x}} \tag{14-52}$$

and since the values of all the π's are constant, an application of the law of mass action requires consideration of only those constituents existing in the gaseous phase.

14-9. The Third Law of Thermodynamics. Several equations for the entropy of gases considered in Sec. 14-5, for example Eq. (14-17), are referred to some arbitrary datum where the entropy is equal to S_0. The absolute entropy can be computed only if a state is known where the entropy is zero. The third law of thermodynamics defines such a state as existing at the absolute zero of temperature. Therefore Eq. (14-17) can be evaluated in terms of the properties of the gas. Since test temperatures cannot reach absolute zero, experimental data must be extrapolated. Fortunately, this extrapolation can be accomplished with little difficulty and with high accuracy.

14-10. Heats of Reaction and Heats of Combustion—the Reference State. The heat of reaction was defined in Sec. 14-6. The heat of combustion is defined as the heat of reaction when one of the reactants is oxygen and the reaction proceeds rapidly to completion.

The heat of reaction, or heat of combustion as the case may be, is determined for a reaction taking place at some condition of temperature and pressure known as the reference state. Usually 77 F (25 C) and a pressure of 1 atm is selected for the reference state, although other temperatures have been used as, for example, 20 C and 18 C. The specification of pressure for the reference state is not of great importance if constituents are essentially incompressible or closely approximate an ideal gas.

For example the combustion equation for CO to CO_2 is as follows:

$$CO + \tfrac{1}{2}O_2 \rightarrow CO_2 \tag{14-53}$$

The constant-pressure heat of reaction in the reference state (77 F) is $-\Delta H = 121{,}721$ Btu per mole. All the constituents are in the gaseous

TABLE 14-1. HEATS OF REACTION
(For gaseous fuels)

Fuel	Symbol	Reaction	Latent heat, Btu per mole at 77 F	Heat of reaction, Btu per mole at 77 F (water formed is condensed)	
				ΔH (const. pr.)	ΔU (const. vol.)
Oxygen	O	$O_2 = 2O$	. . . . .	$+211,800^e$	$-121,365$
Hydroxide	OH	$H_2 + O_2 = 2OH$	. . . . .	$+12,840^e$	$-121,188$
Hydrogen	H	$H_2 = 2H$	. . . . .	$+164,640^e$	$-380,891$
	H_2	$H_2 + 0.5O_2 = H_2O$	. . . . .	$-122,963^f$	$-604,973$
Carbon monoxide	CO	$CO + 0.5O_2 = CO_2$	. . . . .	$-121,721^g$	$-668,394$
Methane	CH_4	$CH_4 + 2O_2 = CO_2 + 2H_2O$	. . . . .	$-383,022^a$	$-604,072$
Ethylene	C_2H_4	$C_2H_4 + 3O_2 = 2CO_2 + cH_2O$	. . . . .	$-607,104^h$	$-327,045$
Ethane	C_2H_6	$C_2H_6 + 3.5O_2 = 2CO_2 + 3H_2O$	. . . . .	$-671,058^i$	$-1,414,377$
Ethyl alcohol	C_2H_5OH	$C_2H_5OH + 3O_2 = 2CO_2 + 3H_2O$	$18,216^a$	$-606,204^a$	$-2,080,421$
Methyl alcohol	CH_3OH	$CH_3OH + 1.5O_2 = CO_2 + 2H_2O$	$16,092^a$	$-328,644^a$	$-2,362,226$
Benzene	C_6H_6	$C_6H_6 + 7.5O_2 = 6CO_2 + 3H_2O$	$14,495^b$	$-1,417,041^j$	$-3,490,664$
n-heptane	C_7H_{16}	$C_7H_{16} + 11O_2 = 7CO_2 + 8H_2O$	$15,750^c$	$-2,085,751^k$	
n-octane	C_8H_{18}	$C_8H_{18} + 12.5O_2 = 8CO_2 + 9H_2O$	$17,730^c$	$-2,368,089^k$	
n-dodecane	$C_{12}H_{26}$	$C_{12}H_{26} + 18.5O_2 = 12CO_2 + 13H_2O$	$23,000^d$	$-3,498,659^k$	

[a] J. Research Natl. Bur. Standards, Vol. 13, p. 189, 1934.
[b] J. Research Natl. Bur. Standards, Vol. 6, p. 881, 1931.
[c] J. Research Natl. Bur. Standards, Vol. 13, p. 21, 1934.
[d] Natl. Bur. Standards Misc. Publ., Vol. 97, 1929.
[e] Chemical Review, Vol. 27, p. 39, 1940.
[f] J. Research Natl. Bur. Standards, Vol. 6, p. 1, 1931.
[g] J. Research Natl. Bur. Standards, Vol. 6, p. 37, 1931.
[h] J. Research Natl. Bur. Standards, Vol. 18, p. 249, 1937.
[i] J. Research Natl. Bur. Standards, Vol. 12, p. 735, 1933.
[j] J. Research Natl. Bur. Standards, Vol. 2, p. 375, 1929.
[k] J. Research Natl. Bur. Standards, Vol. 18, p. 115, 1937.

For hydrocarbon compounds:

$$Q_v = 13,500C + 60,890H \text{ Btu};$$ C and H are weights in pounds in amount of fuel considered.

phase. Now the combustion equation for solid carbon to CO is

$$C(s) + \tfrac{1}{2}O_2(g) \rightarrow CO(g) \qquad (14\text{-}54)$$

and $-\Delta H = 47{,}461$ Btu per mole. If Eqs. (14-53) and (14-54) are added, and also their respective heats of reaction, the result is

$$C(s) + O_2(g) \rightarrow CO_2(g)$$

for which $-\Delta H = 169{,}182$ Btu per mole. The advantage of the reference state is clearly demonstrated since it is possible to calculate the heats of reaction for certain reactions in terms of reactions for which the heats of reaction have been determined experimentally. This is possible because the properties of h and U are determined by the state of the system and are therefore independent of the path taken during the combustion process.

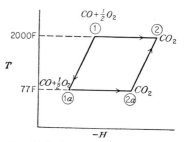

Fig. 14-2. Constant-pressure heat of reaction at other than reference state temperature.

Table 14-1 gives the heats of reaction at constant pressure and at constant volume for a number of common reactions at the reference-state conditions of 77 F and 1 atm. Suppose, for example, that a constant-pressure reaction is initiated at some temperature higher than 77 F, say 1000 F. From Eq. (14-51), it is clear that the heat of reaction is dependent on temperature and therefore the value achieved at 77 F would not be applicable at 1000 F. The procedure necessary in using the reference-state heat of reaction is to cool the system (reactants) from 1000 F to 77 F, initiate the reaction at 77 F, and heat the products to 1000 F. This procedure is illustrated in the following example.

Example 1. Compute the constant-pressure heat of reaction for the reaction $CO + \tfrac{1}{2}O_2 \rightarrow CO_2$ at 2000 F.

Figure 14-2 shows a temperature-enthalpy diagram to illustrate the procedure. Table 14-2 gives the enthalpies and internal energies of gases and vapors. The enthalpy of CO at 2000 F is 15,250 Btu per lb mole and at 77 F the enthalpy is 539 Btu per lb mole. Therefore 14,711 Btu per lb mole must be removed to cool CO from 2000 F to 77 F. Similarly O_2 has an enthalpy of 15,930 at 2000 F and 539 at 77 F, making it necessary to remove 15,391 Btu per lb mole to cool O_2 to 77 F. To cool the reactants $(CO + \tfrac{1}{2}O_2)$ from 2000 F to 77 F, a total of 22,406 Btu per lb mole must be removed. The reaction is now initiated at 77 F with

$$\Delta H = -121{,}721 \text{ Btu per lb mole}$$

To heat the product of the reaction (CO_2) from 77 F to 2000 F, a total of $23{,}910 - 670 = 23{,}240$ Btu per lb mole is required. Consequently, the

TABLE 14-2. ENTHALPY AND INTERNAL ENERGY OF GASES AND VAPORS*
Btu/lb mole vs. Temperature °F (not absolute)

t	Water vapor h	C_p	Air h	C_p	Atmospheric "nitrogen" h	C_p	Nitrogen h	C_p	Oxygen h	C_p	h − u
0	19100	8.0	0	6.9	0	6.9	0	7.0	0	7.0	910
100	19900	8.0	690	7.0	690	7.0	700	6.9	700	7.1	1110
200	20700	8.1	1390	7.0	1390	7.0	1390	7.0	1410	7.2	1310
300	21510	8.3	2090	7.1	2090	7.0	2090	7.1	2130	7.3	1510
400	22340	8.4	2800	7.1	2790	7.0	2800	7.0	2860	7.4	1710
500	23180	8.5	3510	7.3	3490	7.2	3500	7.2	3600	7.6	1910
600	24030	8.6	4240	7.3	4210	7.2	4220	7.2	4360	7.7	2100
700	24890	8.9	4970	7.4	4930	7.3	4940	7.4	5130	7.9	2300
800	25780	9.0	5710	7.5	5660	7.3	5680	7.4	5920	7.9	2500
900	26680	9.1	6460	7.6	6390	7.5	6420	7.5	6710	7.0	2700
1000	27590	9.3	7220	7.7	7140	7.5	7170	7.5	7510	8.1	2900
1100	28520	9.5	7990	7.7	7890	7.7	7920	7.7	8330	8.2	3100
1200	29470	9.6	8760	7.8	8660	7.7	8690	7.8	9150	8.3	3300
1300	30430	9.8	9540	7.9	9430	7.8	9470	7.8	9980	8.3	3500
1400	31410	10.0	10330	8.0	10210	7.8	10250	7.9	10810	8.4	3690
1500	32410	10.1	11130	8.1	10990	8.0	11040	8.0	11650	8.5	3890
1600	33420	10.3	11940	8.1	11790	8.0	11840	8.0	12500	8.5	4090
1700	34450	10.5	12750	8.1	12590	8.0	12640	8.1	13350	8.6	4290
1800	35500	10.7	13560	8.2	13390	8.1	13450	8.1	14210	8.6	4490
1900	36570	10.8	14380	8.3	14200	8.2	14260	8.2	15070	8.6	4690
2000	37650	10.9	15210	8.3	15020	8.2	15080	8.3	15930	8.7	4890
2100	38740	11.1	16040	8.4	15840	8.3	15910	8.3	16800	8.7	5080
2200	39850	11.1	16880	8.4	16670	8.3	16740	8.3	17670	8.7	5280
2300	40960	11.3	17720	8.4	17500	8.3	17570	8.4	18540	8.8	5480
2400	42090	11.3	18560	8.5	18330	8.4	18410	8.4	19420	8.8	5680
2500	43220	11.5	19410	8.5	19170	8.4	19250	8.5	20300	8.9	5880
2600	44370	11.6	20260	8.5	20010	8.4	20100	8.4	21190	8.9	6080
2700	45530	11.6	21110	8.5	20850	8.5	20940	8.5	22080	8.9	6280
2800	46690	11.8	21960	8.6	21700	8.5	21790	8.6	22970	8.9	6470
2900	47870	11.8	22820	8.6	22550	8.5	22650	8.5	23860	9.0	6670
3000	49050	11.9	23680	8.7	23400	8.5	23500	8.6	24760	9.9	6870
3100	50240	12.0	24550	8.6	24250	8.6	24360	8.7	25660	9.1	7070
3200	51440	12.1	25410	8.7	25110	8.6	25230	8.6	26570	9.0	7270
3300	52650	12.2	26280	8.7	25970	8.6	26090	8.6	27470	9.1	7470
3400	53870	12.2	27150	8.8	26830	8.6	26950	8.7	28380	9.2	7670
3500	55090	12.3	28030	8.7	27690	8.6	28720	8.7	29300	9.1	7860
3600	56320	12.4	28900	8.8	28550	8.7	28690	8.7	30210	9.2	8060
3700	57560	12.4	29780	8.8	29420	8.7	29560	8.7	31130	9.3	8260
3800	58800	12.5	30660	8.8	30290	8.7	30430	8.8	32060	9.2	8460
3900	60050	12.6	31540	8.8	31160	8.7	31310	8.7	32980	9.3	8660
4000	61310	12.6	32420	8.9	32030	8.7	32180	8.8	33910	9.3	8860
4100	62570	12.7	33310	8.8	32900	8.7	33060	8.7	34840	9.4	9060
4200	63840	12.8	34190	8.9	33770	8.8	33930	8.8	35780	9.4	9250
4300	65120	12.8	35080	8.9	34650	8.7	34810	8.8	36720	9.4	9450
4400	66400	12.8	35970	8.9	35520	8.8	35690	8.9	37660	9.4	9650
4500	67680	12.9	36860	8.9	36400	8.7	36580	8.8	38600	9.4	9850
4600	69870	13.0	37750	8.9	37270	8.8	37460	8.8	39540	9.5	10050
4700	70270	13.1	38640	9.0	38150	8.8	38340	8.9	40490	9.5	10250
4800	71580	13.1	39540	8.9	39030	8.8	39230	8.8	41440	9.5	10450
4900	72890	13.1	40430	9.0	39910	8.8	40110	8.9	42390	9.6	10640
5000	74200		41330		40800		41000		43550		10840

TABLE 14-2. ENTHALPY AND INTERNAL ENERGY OF GASES AND VAPORS*—(Continued)

t	Hydrogen h	C_p	Carbon dioxide h	C_p	Carbon monoxide h	C_p	Methane h	C_p	Ethylene h	C_p	h − u	Ethane h	C_p	Benzene h	C_p	Octane h	C_p	Dodecane h	C_p	h − u
0	0	6.9	0	8.7	0	7.0	0	8.4	0	10.0	910	0	12.4	0	21.2	0	38.6	0	54.0	910
100	690	6.9	870	9.3	700	6.9	840	9.0	1000	11.2	1110	1240	13.9	2120	24.2	3860	44.5	5400	62.9	1110
200	1380	7.1	1800	9.9	1390	7.1	1740	9.7	2120	12.6	1310	2630	15.7	4540	27.0	8310	50.6	11690	71.8	1310
300	2090	7.0	2790	10.3	2100	7.0	2710	10.4	3380	13.8	1510	4200	17.2	7240	29.9	13370	56.6	18870	80.6	1510
400	2790	7.0	3820	10.7	2800	7.1	3750	11.2	4760	15.0	1710	5920	18.7	10230	32.8	19030	62.6	26930	89.6	1710
500	3490	7.0	4890	11.0	3510	7.3	4870	11.9	6260	16.0	1910	7790	20.1	13510	35.6	25290	68.2	35890	100.3	1910
600	4190	7.0	5990	11.5	4240	7.3	6060	12.8	7860	17.1	2100	9800	21.4	17070	38.6	32110	73.5	45920	108.4	2100
700	4890	7.0	7140	11.7	4970	7.4	7340	13.3	9570	18.0	2300	11940	22.7	20930		39460	78.9	56760	116.4	2300
800	5590	7.1	8310	12.0	5710	7.5	8680	14.2	11370	18.9	2500	14210	24.1			47350	84.2	68400	124.4	2500
900	6300	7.0	9510	12.2	6460	7.6	10100	14.9	13260	19.8	2700	16620	25.4			55770	89.5	80840	132.3	2700
1000	7000	7.1	10730	12.5	7220	7.8	11590	15.7	15240	20.5	2900	19160				64720		94070		2900
1100	7710	7.2	11980	12.6	8000	7.7	13160	16.2	17290	21.2	3100									
1200	8430	7.2	13240	12.9	8770	7.9	14780	16.9	19410	21.8	3300									
1300	9150	7.2	14530	13.0	9560	8.0	16470	17.5	21590	22.4	3500									
1400	9870	7.3	15830	13.1	10360	8.0	18220	18.0	23830	23.0	3690									
1500	10600	7.3	17140	13.4	11160	8.0	20020	18.4	26130	23.5	3890									
1600	11330	7.4	18480	13.4	11960	8.2	21860	18.9	28480	24.0	4090									
1700	12070	7.4	19820	13.5	12780	8.2	23750	19.2	30880	24.4	4290									
1800	12810	7.5	21170	13.7	13600	8.2	25670	19.6	33320	24.8	4490									
1900	13560	7.6	22540	13.7	14420	8.3	27630	19.9	35800	25.3	4690									
2000	14320	7.6	23910	13.9	15250	8.4	29620	20.2	38330	25.5	4890									
2100	15080	7.7	25300	13.9	16090	8.4	31640	20.5	40880	26.0	5080									
2200	15850	7.7	26690	14.0	16930	8.4	33690	20.8	43480	26.2	5280									
2300	16620	7.8	28090	14.1	17770	8.5	35770	21.0	46100	26.5	5480									
2400	17400	7.8	29500	14.2	18620	8.5	37870	21.2	48750	26.8	5680									
2500	18180	7.9	30920	14.2	19470	8.5	39990	21.5	51430	27.1	5880									
2600	18970	7.9	32340	14.2	20320	8.5	42140	21.7	54140	27.3	6080									
2700	19760	8.0	33760	14.4	21170	8.6	44310	21.8	56870	27.6	6280									
2800	20560	8.1	35200	14.4	22030	8.6	46490	22.1	59630	27.8	6470									
2900	21370	8.1	36640	14.4	22890	8.7	48700	22.2	62410	27.9	6670									
3000	22180	8.1	38080	14.5	23760	8.6	50920	22.5	65200	28.2	6870									
3100	22990	8.2	39530	14.4	24620	8.7	53170	22.6	68020	28.3	7070									
3200	23810	8.3	40970	14.6	25490	8.7	55430	22.7	70850		7270									
3300	24640	8.2	42430	14.6	26360	8.7	57700	22.9			7470									
3400	25460	8.3	43890	14.6	27230	8.7	59990	23.0			7670									
3500	26290	8.4	45350	14.7	28100	8.8	62290	23.2			7860									
3600	27130	8.4	46820	14.6	28908	8.7	64610	23.8			8060									
3700	29790	8.4	48280	14.8	29850	8.7	66940	23.3			8260									
3800	28810	8.5	49760	14.7	30730	8.8	69270	23.5			8460									
3900	29660	8.5	51230	14.8	31610	8.8	71620	23.5			8660									
4000	30510	8.5	52710	14.8	32490	8.8	73970	23.7			8860									
4100	31360	8.6	54190	14.8	33370	8.8	76340	23.6			9060									
4200	32220	8.6	55670	14.9	34250	8.9	78700	23.8			9250									
4300	33080	8.6	57160	14.9	35140	8.9	81080	23.8			9450									
4400	33940	8.6	58650	14.9	36020	8.9	83460	23.8			9650									
4500	34800	8.7	60140	14.9	36910	8.8	85840	23.9			9850									
4600	35670	8.8	61630	15.0	37790	8.9	88230	24.0			10050									
4700	36550	8.7	63130	15.0	38680	8.9	90630	24.0			10250									
4800	37420	8.8	64630	14.9	39570	8.9	93030	24.1			10450									
4900	38300	8.8	66120	15.1	40460	8.9	95440	24.3			10640									
5000	39180		67630		41350		97870				10840									

Enthalpy is given to the nearest 10 Btu per mole, corresponding approximately to temperature measured to the nearest degree F.

Tabular differences divided by 100 are approximate values of C_p midway in each interval.

Enthalpy minus internal energy equals RT, given as $h - u$ in the right-hand columns.

For liquid water, $h - u$ is negligible (about 0.8 Btu per mole for $p = 15$ psia).

$C_p - C_v = R = 1.986$ Btu/(mole)(°F).

Enthalpy of water liquid and vapor is measured above saturated liquid at 32 F.

All other enthalpies are measured above gas or vapor at zero F.

Atmospheric "nitrogen" = 78 moles nitrogen + 1 mole argon. C_p for argon taken as 5.

*Table courtesy of Professor C. H. Berry. Data from Ellenwood, Kulik, and Gay, Cornell Univ. Eng. Expt. Sta. Bull. 30, and Marks' "Handbook," p. 301. Water to 1600 F from Keenan and Keyes steam tables.

constant-pressure heat of reaction at 2000 F is

$$\Delta H = -121,721 - 22,406 + 23,240 = -120,887 \text{ Btu per lb mole}$$

Often a combustion reaction will involve the uniting of oxygen and hydrogen to form steam as one of the products. If the steam so formed is condensed to the state of liquid water at the saturation temperature, then the latent heat of vaporization is released as part of the heat of reaction. It follows, therefore, that two heats of reaction are possible, depending on whether the product H_2O exists as steam or liquid water. When H_2O exists as steam the lower heat of reaction is commonly called the lower heating value. Similarly, if the steam produced by the reaction is condensed, the higher heat of reaction thus obtained is called the higher heating value. Of course the heating value or heat of reaction is still subject to the qualification of "constant pressure" or "constant volume." An example will illustrate the differences in the heats of reaction just discussed.

Example 2. Calculate the higher and lower heats of reaction at constant pressure and at 1000 F for the following combustion reaction. (Assume octane to be in vapor state.)

$$C_8H_{18} + 19O_2 + 71.5\text{"}N_2\text{"} \rightarrow 8CO_2 + 9H_2O + 6.5O_2 + 71.5\text{"}N_2\text{"}$$

C_8H_{18} (from Table 14-2):

$$h_{1000 \text{ F}} = 64,720$$
$$h_{77 \text{ F}} = 38.6 \times 177 = 2,970$$
$$\Delta h = \overline{61,750} \text{ Btu per lb mole}$$

O_2:

$$h_{1000 \text{ F}} = 7,510$$
$$h_{77 \text{ F}} = 7 \times 77 = 539$$
$$\Delta h = \overline{6,971} \times 12.5 = 87,200 \text{ Btu}$$

The total decrease of enthalpy to cool the reactants, $C_8H_{18} + 19O_2$, from 1000 F to 77 F is $61,750 + 87,200 = 148,950$ Btu. The atmospheric nitrogen "N_2" is not considered since it is inert.

For the products,

CO_2:

$$h_{1000 \text{ F}} = 10,730$$
$$h_{77 \text{ F}} = 8.7 \times 77 = 670$$
$$\Delta h = \overline{10,060} \times 8 = 80,480 \text{ Btu}$$

H_2O:

$$h_{1000 \text{ F}} = 27,590 \text{ (vapor)}$$
$$h_{77 \text{ F}} = 19,100 + 8 \times 77 = 19,716$$
$$\Delta h = \overline{7,874} \times 9 = 70,800 \text{ Btu}$$

The total increase of enthalpy to heat the reactants to 1000 F is

$$80,480 + 70,800 = 151,280 \text{ Btu}$$

The constant-pressure heat of reaction with H_2O existing in vapor state is

$$\Delta H_{1000 \text{ F}} = -2,368,089 + 9(18)(1050.4) - 148,950 + 151,280$$
$$= -2,195,795 \text{ Btu}$$

and in the liquid state is

$$\Delta H_{77 \text{ F}} = -2,368,089 - 148,950 + 151,280 = -2,365,795 \text{ Btu}$$

14-11. Flame Temperatures. In Sec. 14-10 attention was directed to the effect of the temperature at which a reaction is initiated on the value of the heat of reaction. In determining the heat of reaction, the products are taken to be at the temperature at which the reaction was initiated. It must be remembered, however, that the heat released (heat of reaction) for an adiabatic reaction must increase the internal energy of the products and therefore increase the temperature of the products. The temperature achieved by the products after adiabatic and complete combustion is called the theoretical flame temperature. According to the first law of thermodynamics, for a constant-pressure reaction,

$$dh = dQ - dW$$

If no external work is done and the reaction is adiabatic, $dQ = 0$ and $dW = 0$. Therefore $dh = 0$, and

$$h_{\text{reactants at } T_i} = h_{\text{products at } T_f} \tag{14-55}$$

where T_i and T_f are the temperatures before and after reaction. Now the heat of reaction at constant pressure from Eq. (14-40) is

$$\Delta H = h_{\text{reactants at } T_i} - h_{\text{products at } T_i} \tag{14-56}$$

Substituting Eq. (14-55) in Eq. (14-56), the result is

$$\Delta H = h_{\text{products at } T_f} - h_{\text{products at } T_i} \tag{14-57}$$

similarly for a constant-volume reaction

$$\Delta U = U_{\text{products at } T_f} - U_{\text{products at } T_i} \tag{14-58}$$

An example will serve to illustrate how Eq. (14-57) or (14-58) may be used to determine the theoretical flame temperature.

Example. For the constant-pressure combustion reaction for octane at 1000 F given in the example of Sec. 14-10, determine the theoretical flame temperature.

The lower heating value of 2,195,795 Btu must be used since all the products will exist as gases. From Eq. (14-57),

$$h_{\text{products at } T_f} = -\Delta H + h_{\text{products at } T_i}$$

$$h_{\text{products at } T_f} = 2,195,795 + 8(10,730) + 9(27,590) + 6.5(7,510) + 71.5(7,140)$$

$$h_{\text{products at } T_f} = 3,091,415 \text{ Btu per lb mole}$$

It is necessary to consider the excess oxygen and the inert gases since these constituents will be raised to the final or flame temperature at the expense of the heat of reaction. To find the flame temperature, it is necessary to assume some temperatures and compare with the previously calculated value for the enthalpy of the products.

Assume 3600 F:

$$h_{\text{products at } T_f} = 8(46,820) + 9(56,320) + 6.5(30,120) + 71.5(28,550)$$
$$= 3,119,130 \text{ Btu per lb mole}$$

Assume 3400 F:

$$h_{\text{products at } T_f} = 8(43,890) + 9(53,870) + 6.5(28,380) + 71.5(26,830)$$
$$= 2,938,765 \text{ Btu per lb mole}$$

Upon interpolation:

$$T_f = 3512 \text{ F}$$

14-12. Dissociation. The theoretical flame temperatures discussed in Sec. 14-11 cannot be achieved when dissociation occurs. Consider the reaction

$$CO + \tfrac{1}{2}O_2 \rightarrow CO_2$$

which takes place with a release of energy, and as a consequence, the temperature of the product CO_2 is raised. At high temperatures CO_2 will dissociate,

$$CO_2 \rightarrow CO + \tfrac{1}{2}O_2$$

with an absorption of energy thereby decreasing the temperature of the products. Stated another way, a limiting temperature is achieved where the reaction may proceed in either direction at the same rate. Thus the reaction is in chemical equilibrium:

$$CO + \tfrac{1}{2}O_2 \leftrightarrows CO_2$$

The proportion of CO_2 in the equilibrium mixture at low temperatures is high, whereas at high temperatures the proportion of CO_2 is small. It is clear, therefore, that complete combustion of CO to CO_2 cannot be achieved under adiabatic conditions because of the phenomenon of dissociation.

Although the dissociation of CO_2 has been discussed, other products of combustion may dissociate also, for example,

$$H_2O \rightleftharpoons H_2 + \tfrac{1}{2}O_2$$
$$O_2 \rightleftharpoons 2O$$
$$H_2 \rightleftharpoons 2H$$

Example. Calculate the flame temperature of the products of combustion for the reaction

$$CO + \tfrac{1}{2}O_2 \rightarrow CO_2$$

if the process is at a constant pressure of 6 atm and is adiabatic. Assume for simplicity that the reactants are initially at 77 F.

Let x = the amount of dissociation of 1 lb mole of CO_2.

Then the reaction may be written

$$2CO + O_2 \rightarrow 2xCO + 2(1-x)CO_2 + xO_2$$

The total number of moles of products is $2x + 2(1-x) + x = 2 + x$. The partial pressure of each of the products may be obtained as follows:

$$P_{CO} = \frac{(2x)6}{x+2}$$
$$P_{CO_2} = \frac{2(1-x)6}{x+2}$$
$$P_{O_2} = \frac{6x}{x+2}$$

The equilibrium constant is

$$K_p = \frac{\left[\dfrac{12(1-x)}{x+2}\right]^2}{\left(\dfrac{12x}{x+2}\right)^2 \left(\dfrac{6x}{x+2}\right)} = \frac{(1-x)^2(x+2)}{6x^3}$$

Now the value of K_p also depends on the temperature and thus the preceding equation involves two unknowns, x and T_f. The energy equation for the reaction also involves the two unknowns, x and T_f. Writing the energy equation from Eq. (14-57),

$$-\Delta H_{T_i}(1-x) + (h_{CO} + \tfrac{1}{2}h_{O_2})_{T_i-77} = \left[xh_{CO} + (1-x)h_{CO_2} + \frac{x}{2}h_{O_2}\right]_{T_f-77}$$

In order to find the enthalpies of the product constituents, it is necessary to know T_f. Therefore the energy and equilibrium equations, practically speaking, cannot be solved simultaneously for x and T_f.

A convenient method for the solution of these equations is to assume values of T_f and calculate the corresponding values of x. A curve may

TABLE 14-3. LOGARITHMS OF EQUILIBRIUM CONSTANTS*

$$\log_{10} K_p = \log_{10} \frac{P_{A_3}{}^{a_3} \cdot P_{A_4}{}^{a_4}}{P_{A_1}{}^{a_1} \cdot P_{A_2}{}^{a_2}} \text{ for reaction } a_1A_1 + a_2A_2 = a_3A_3 + a_4A_4$$

P_{A_1} = partial pressure of A_1 constituent in equilibrium mixture, atm

Temp., °R	(1) $H_2 \rightarrow 2H$	(2) $O_2 \rightarrow 2O$	(3) $N_2 \rightarrow 2N$	(4) $N_2+O_2 \rightarrow 2NO$	(5) $H_2+O_2 \rightarrow 2OH$ (8)−(7)	(6) $2CO_2 \rightarrow 2CO+O_2$	(7) $2H_2O \rightarrow 2H_2+O_2$	(8) $2H_2O \rightarrow 2OH+H_2$	(9) $2H_2O+O_2 \rightarrow 4OH$ 2(5)+(7)	(10) $H_2+CO_2 \rightarrow H_2O+CO$ $\frac{(6)-(7)}{2}$	(11) $2H_2O+N_2 \rightarrow 2H_2+2NO$ (7)+(4)
3000	−7.89	−8.93	−15.68	−4.30	0.06	−8.68	−9.72	−9.66	−9.60	0.520	−14.02
3100	−7.44	−8.41	−14.97	−4.13	0.11	−8.12	−9.21	−9.10	−8.99	0.545	−13.34
3200	−7.01	−7.93	−14.28	−3.97	0.14	−7.58	−8.72	−8.58	−8.44	0.570	−12.69
3300	−6.61	−7.48	−13.63	−3.81	0.16	−7.08	−8.26	−8.10	−7.94	0.593	−12.07
3400	−6.23	−7.06	−13.01	−3.66	0.19	−6.60	−7.83	−7.64	−7.45	0.616	−11.49
3500	−5.87	−6.67	−12.43	−3.52	0.21	−6.15	−7.42	−7.21	−7.00	0.638	−10.94
3600	−5.53	−6.30	−11.89	−3.39	0.24	−5.72	−7.04	−6.80	−6.76	0.658	−10.43
3700	−5.21	−5.94	−11.37	−3.27	0.27	−5.32	−6.68	−6.41	−6.14	0.676	−9.95
3800	−4.91	−5.60	−10.88	−3.15	0.29	−4.95	−6.34	−6.05	−5.76	0.693	−9.49
3900	−4.62	−5.27	−10.41	−3.03	0.31	−4.59	−6.01	−5.70	−5.39	0.709	−9.04
4000	−4.34	−4.96	−9.97	−2.92	0.33	−4.25	−5.70	−5.37	−5.04	0.723	−8.62
4100	−4.08	−4.66	−9.55	−2.82	0.37	−3.93	−5.41	−5.04	−4.67	0.736	−8.23
4200	−3.83	−4.38	−9.16	−2.72	0.40	−3.63	−5.13	−4.73	−4.33	0.748	−7.85
4300	−3.60	−4.11	−8.79	−2.62	0.43	−3.35	−4.87	−4.44	−4.01	0.760	−7.49
4400	−3.38	−3.86	−8.44	−2.53	0.45	−3.08	−4.62	−4.17	−3.72	0.770	−7.15
4500	−3.17	−3.62	−8.10	−2.44	0.48	−2.83	−4.39	−3.91	−3.43	0.779	−6.83
4600	−2.97	−3.39	−7.77	−2.36	0.50	−2.59	−4.17	−3.67	−3.17	0.787	−6.53
4700	−2.77	−3.17	−7.45	−2.28	0.52	−2.36	−3.95	−3.43	−2.91	0.795	−6.23
4800	−2.58	−2.96	−7.15	−2.20	0.53	−2.12	−3.73	−3.20	−2.67	0.803	−5.93
4900	−2.40	−2.76	−6.86	−2.13	0.55	−1.90	−3.52	−2.97	−2.41	0.810	−5.65
5000	−2.22	−2.56	−6.68	−2.06	0.57	−1.70	−3.33	−2.76	−2.19	0.816	−5.39
5100	−2.05	−2.37	−6.31	−2.00	0.59	−1.51	−3.15	−2.56	−1.97	0.823	−5.15
5200	−1.88	−2.19	−6.05	−1.94	0.61	−1.32	−2.98	−2.37	−1.76	0.829	−4.92
5300	−1.72	−2.02	−5.80	−1.88	0.62	−1.13	−2.80	−2.18	−1.56	0.835	−4.68
5400	−1.58	−1.86	−5.56	−1.82	0.62	−0.94	−2.62	−2.00	−1.38	0.840	−4.44

* B. Lewis and G. von Elbe, Heat Capacities and Dissociation Equilibria of Gases, J. Am. Chem. Soc., Vol. 57, p. 612, 1935.

be obtained for values to T_f vs. x which satisfy the equilibrium equation. Values of K_p at various absolute temperatures are given in Table 14-3. Similarly a curve may be plotted for values of T_f vs. x obtained from the energy equation. The intersection of these two curves will give the values of T_f and x which satisfy both the equilibrium and energy equations.

Assume $T_f = 5000\ \text{R} = 4540\ \text{F}$ and, from Table 14-3,

$$K_P = \frac{(1 - x)^2(x + 2)}{6x^3} = 50$$

Simplifying,

$$299x^3 + 3x = 2$$

and

$$x = 0.17$$

Similarly other values of T_f are assumed and the corresponding values of x are calculated.

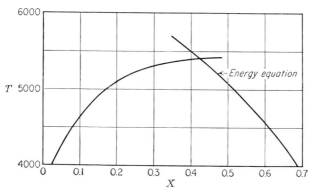

Fig. 14-3. Solution of T_f and x for combustion of CO.

Now the values of x and T_f which satisfy the energy equation are calculated and plotted in Fig. 14-3. Various values of T_f are assumed and the corresponding values of x are found as, for example, in the following equation. Assuming $T_f = 5000\ \text{R}$,

$$2(1 - x)(-\Delta H)_{\text{CO}_2} + (2h_{\text{CO}} + h_{\text{O}_2})_{537\ \text{R}} = [2xh_{\text{CO}}2(1 - x)h_{\text{CO}_2} + xh_{\text{O}_2}]_{5000\ \text{R}}$$

Taking values of the enthalpies from Table 14-2,

$$2(1 - x)(121{,}721) + (1078 + 539) = 74{,}524x + (1 - x)121{,}472 + 38{,}976$$

$$x = 0.52$$

The intersection of the equilibrium reaction and energy equations give the values of T_f and x which satisfy the two equations. From Fig. 14-3 it appears that $T_f = 5410\ \text{R}$ and $x = 0.42$.

THE MECHANICS OF COMBUSTION

14-13. Combustibles in Fuels. Gas-turbine plants operate primarily on liquid fuels although a number of stationary installations have been designed to use gaseous fuels. More recently coal has been successfully used in a gas-turbine locomotive on an experimental basis. In mobile installations it would appear desirable to use the denser liquid fuels to reduce fuel storage space. However, consideration of the economics of a given installation and the combustion difficulties encountered with certain of the denser liquid fuels will, to a large extent, influence the ultimate choice of fuel.

All the liquid fuels are complex mixtures of various hydrocarbons which may be classified broadly as aliphatic, aromatic, and alicyclic. The aliphatic hydrocarbons may be further classified as paraffins and olefins. The paraffin and olefin series conform to the formulas C_nH_{2n+2} and C_nH_{2n}, respectively. Some of the more common paraffins and olefins are listed below:

Paraffins:

CH_4, methane

C_2H_6, ethane

C_3H_8, propane

C_4H_{10}, butane

C_5H_{12}, pentane

C_4H_{14}, hexane

C_8H_{18}, octane (gasoline)

$C_{12}H_{26}$, dodecane (kerosene)

Olefins:

C_2H_4, ethylene

C_3H_6, propylene

C_4H_8, butylene

The aromatics and alicyclics do not obey any definite relationship between the numbers of atoms of hydrogen and carbon in the compounds. The better known members of the aromatics are benzene (C_6H_6), toluene (C_7H_8), xylene (C_8H_{10}), and naphthalene ($C_{10}H_8$). The alicyclics in unrefined petroleum are largely of the naphthene series and are of a very complex structure.

All the liquid fuels in general use in gas-turbine plants represent a complex mixture of the various hydrocarbons described. However, the most important are the paraffin series. Therefore the combustion reaction for liquid fuels for a stoichiometric mixture may be written

$$C_nH_{2n+2} + 0.5(3n + 1)O_2 + 1.88(3n + 1)N_2 \rightarrow n\ CO_2 + (n + 1)H_2O$$
$$+ 1.88(3n + 1)N_2 \quad (14\text{-}59)$$

The heat of reaction at constant pressure of pure hydrocarbons is given very closely by the following expression developed by Jessup:

$$-\Delta H_{77\ \mathrm{F}} = 111{,}490 + 279{,}000n + 111.24n^2 \ \mathrm{Btu/lb\ mole} \qquad (14\text{-}51)$$

where n = the number of carbon atoms in a molecule of the hydrocarbon. For hydrocarbon mixtures, very good correlation with experimentally determined heats of reaction at constant pressure is obtained from the following relationship developed by Cragoe:

$$-\Delta H_{77\ \mathrm{F}} = 19{,}960 + 1360(\mathrm{s.g.}) - 3780(\mathrm{s.g.})^2 \qquad (14\text{-}52)$$

where s.g. is the specific gravity of the liquid fuel.

14-14. Combustion Mechanism. The theory of the combustion mechanism is not fully developed and the whole phenomenon is not clearly understood. A rigorous discussion of this subject is considered to be beyond the scope of this book. Therefore an attempt will be made only to review briefly some of the current theory. For more detailed information, the reader is referred to the references listed at the end of this chapter.

There are three recognized postulations as to the combustion mechanism:

1. Carbon preferential burning, *i.e.*, carbon in the hydrocarbon burns before the hydrogen.

2. Hydrogen preferential burning.

3. Hydroxylation, which is the initial uniting of oxygen with the hydrocarbon to form a hydroxylated compound which, through chain reactions of molecules, atoms, and radicals, burns to CO, CO_2, and H_2O.

The hydroxylation theory, although not complete, has met with more general acceptance than the other two theories. This theory was first postulated by Bone and Wheeler but has more recently been extended by Lewis, von Elbe, Walsh, and others.

The modern theory finds its root in kinetic theory and the statistics of probability. From the kinetic theory of gases it is learned that the individual molecules are in motion at some average velocity but with a wide difference between the velocities of the slowest and fastest molecules. The molecules are continually colliding and if a collision occurs between molecules of high velocity, their kinetic energy may be converted into chemical energy, thus initiating a combustion reaction. The high-velocity molecules are comparatively few in number, however. Since temperature is a function of the molecular activity, raising the temperature increases the probability and intensity of the collision of high-velocity molecules and therefore increases the intensity of combustion. Now the ratio of the number of high-velocity collisions of molecules which may initiate combustion to the total number of collisions may be developed from the kinetic theory of gases as the expression $e^{-\Delta H_a/RT}$. The symbol ΔH_a is the energy of activation while R and T are the gas constant and the absolute temperature, respectively. It may be surmised from the foregoing that the speed or rate of reaction is some function of $e^{-\Delta H_a/RT}$, or

$$K_r = C\, e^{-\Delta H_a/RT} \qquad (14\text{-}53)$$

where C is a function dependent on temperature.

Once the initial combustion has begun, it proceeds by means of chain reactions. Acceleration of the reaction is brought about by chain branching and is retarded by chain breaking. Free atoms of H and O and the free radicals may act as the chain carriers. As the chain carriers increase in number, combustion proceeds rapidly; similarly, combustion speed is retarded by a decrease in the number of chain carriers. Chain carriers may be destroyed through a surface reaction. In normal combustion the relationship between chain branching and chain breaking is such that the reaction proceeds at a nearly steady rate. Should the chain branching be far in excess of the chain breaking, the conditions for an explosive reaction may exist. Similarly, if the chain breaking should dominate, combustion may fail.

A suggested example of a chain reaction is the combustion of methane:

$$OH + CH_4 \rightarrow H_2O + CH_3$$
$$CH_3 + O_2 \rightarrow HCHO + OH$$
$$OH + HCHO \rightarrow H_2O + CHO$$
$$CHO + O_2 \rightarrow CO + HO_2(HO_2 \xrightarrow{\text{surface}} \text{destruction})$$
$$CHO + O_2 \rightarrow CHO_3$$
$$CHO_3 + HCHO \rightarrow 2CO + H_2O + OH(OH \xrightarrow{\text{surface}} \text{destruction})$$
$$2CO + O_2 \rightarrow 2CO_2$$

14-15. Physical Characteristics of Combustion and Reactive Mixtures. The physical process of combustion may be divided into four important steps as follows:

1. Formation of the reactive mixture
2. Ignition
3. Flame propagation
4. Cooling of combustion products with air

Under ideal conditions each of these steps would be completed separately before proceeding to the next step. However, space restrictions under normal operating conditions do not permit the achievement of this ideal.

An essential prerequisite to complete combustion is the intimate and uniform mixing of fuel and air. The nearer this mixing approaches molecular dimensions, the more conducive the resulting reactive mixture is to complete combustion. A most satisfactory arrangement from the standpoint of mixing would be to provide for the vaporization of the fuel in a boiler prior to entering the combustor. However, this system does not lend itself to flexible operation and internal vaporization is generally used. That is to say, the fuel is atomized by means of a spray nozzle, thus providing for good distribution and large evaporative surface at the same time. Drop sizes average between 0.003 and 0.006 in., with minimum to maximum sizes ranging from 0.0004 to 0.0008 in.

Besides providing for vaporization and distribution of the fuel, it is necessary to maintain an optimum ratio of air to fuel in the mixture to ensure ignition and sufficiently fast combustion. Insufficient air (rich mixture) will result in cracking of the fuel with the formation of amorphous carbon which is difficult to burn and eventually becomes a troublesome deposit. Although insufficient air is a cause of carbon formation, the problem is intimately associated with improper mixing. On the other hand insufficient fuel (lean mixture) or poor mixing and atomization will lead to failure of combustion. In practice it is necessary to use air in excess of the stoichiometric mixture in order to satisfy this latter requirement, largely because atomization and distribution can never be

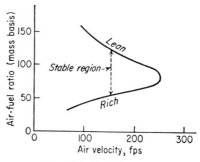

Fig. 14-4. Stability curve.

achieved on a molecular scale. The velocity at which air travels through the combustor limits the range of air-fuel ratios between the rich and lean mixtures. Operation outside this range results in unstable combustion manifested by pulsations or vibrations and combustion failure. Figure 14-4 shows a typical stability curve as a function of air-fuel ratio and mass rate of flow. The stable region lies between the rich and lean limits. It will be noticed that the stability range and air-fuel ratio range decrease as the air velocity is increased. Normally combustion chambers are designed with an inlet air velocity not exceeding 250 fps at design load.

In order to cool the products of combustion to a temperature suitable for use in the gas turbine, it is necessary to use a total air-fuel ratio far in excess of those permitting stable combustion. This difficulty is avoided by introducing a satisfactory amount of primary air to maintain stable combustion conditions. The products of combustion are then cooled with secondary air. The sum of the primary and secondary air is termed the total air-fuel ratio. This subject will be pursued further in connection with the cooling of combustion products.

For different fuels there are correspondingly different ranges of inflammability within which propagation of combustion will take place once the initial reaction is started. For a given fuel, this range is affected by limiting rich and lean mixtures beyond which a self-propagating combustion reaction cannot take place. The range of inflammability is variously affected by the pressure, temperature, and the thoroughness of mixing of fuel. The thoroughness of mixing, pressure, temperature, and strength of the mixture are intimately related in determining the ignition characteristics. Thus spontaneous combustion will occur in a reactive mixture if a certain limiting temperature is reached. At pressures below atmospheric, the ignition temperature is increased and this poses a particular problem in high-altitude aircraft.

Equation (14-53) shows that the reaction rate varies as an exponential function of the absolute temperature. Now the heat-transfer rate from the products of combustion formed in the initial reaction is a function of the temperature difference existing between the products and the surrounding unburned mixture. Hence it may be concluded that the reaction will become self-propagating only when the reaction rate exceeds the energy transfer to the surrounding unburned mixture. Time is required for the initial reaction to take place, and from the foregoing considerations it is clear that this time, called ignition lag, is dependent on the temperature of the mixture. If the fuel is heavy so that evaporation of the droplets is slow, the rate of chemical reaction will be slow also because of poor mixing, or the temperature of the mixture will be cooled to the extent that reaction is arrested. Normally, spark ignition is adequate to initiate combustion but where fuels with high ignition temperatures or where high convection heat-transfer rates are brought about by a high-velocity stream, a pilot flame may be necessary.

Consideration must be given to the rate of flame propagation, which is found to depend primarily on the range of inflammability, the temperature and pressure of the mixture, and the shape of the combustion chamber. To some extent the rate of flame propagation is affected by the expansion of hot gases behind the flame front. In a quiescent reactive mixture it is expected that the rate of reaction and the rate of flame propagation would increase. However, in the constant-pressure combustion process employed in the gas-turbine power plant it is found that after the initial acceleration the rate of flame propagation becomes steady at a value characteristic of the specified physical conditions enumerated above. This stability is brought about by the increased heat transfer from the flame front as it reaches the walls of the combustion chamber. Flame speeds in the constant-pressure combustion process are very slow, and therefore a region of low stream velocity must be provided in which the rate of flame propagation can become stabilized.

Turbulence is an important requirement in the process of mixing and has a marked effect on the speed of flame propagation. However, increased turbulence has a corresponding effect on the heat-transfer rate and it is reasonable to suppose there is an optimum condition of turbulence beyond which flame extinction would occur. When the flow velocity exceeds that of the flame, ignition may take place in a low-velocity region provided behind a grid, the turbulent wake aiding the propagation of the flame downstream from the grid.

The total air-fuel ratio for gas-turbine combustion may range from 50 to 120. Such a large total air-fuel ratio is necessary to produce combustion gases at a temperature feasible for use in the gas turbine. It is clear from the previous considerations that combustion at such a high air-fuel ratio is out of the question. A more reasonable air-fuel ratio for good combustion would be about 16. Therefore only part of the air is supplied with the fuel in the combustion chamber and the balance is mixed with the products of combustion to provide a suitable temperature before entering the turbine. This mixing is the last step in the combustion process. Although it is not as important a step as the mixing of fuel and air, nevertheless care must be taken not to chill the combustion products before combustion is actually completed. Sufficient turbulence must be introduced in order to cool the combustion products quickly and to avoid local regions of high temperature in the resulting combustion gas.

14-16. Pressure Losses. The pressure drop which occurs in the combustion process must be regarded as a parasitic loss and hence should be minimized. The pressure losses incurred are of two types, namely, pressure drop due to friction and that due to the accelerations accompanying heat addition.

The pressure drop due to friction may be obtained from Eq. (6-40) after determining the value of the friction parameter $4fl/D$, considering the combustor to be a round duct with no combustion taking place. The value of $4fl/D$ for a given combustor is obtained from test data using the relationships developed in Sec. 6-13.

The pressure drop due to heating, in the absence of friction, may be obtained from Eq. (6-70). The combined pressure loss due to both heating and friction is the sum of the pressure losses determined separately as being due to friction and heating.

THE COMBUSTOR

14-17. Requirements of the Combustor. The primary purpose of the combustor obviously is to provide for the chemical reaction of fuel and air, the air being supplied by the compressor and the products of combustion being delivered to the turbine. In carrying out this purpose, the combustor must fulfill the following important requirements:

1. Combustion must take place at a high efficiency because of the effect of combustion efficiency on the thermal efficiency of the gas-turbine cycle.

2. The pressure losses must be low.

3. The geometry and arrangement of the combustor must provide for stability of combustion over a wide range of air-fuel ratios.

4. Ignition must be reliable and accomplished with ease over a wide range of atmospheric conditions, especially in aircraft installations.

5. Thorough mixing of fuel and air, as well as combustion products and air, must be provided to effect complete combustion as well as uniform temperature distribution in the combustion gases supplied to the turbine.

6. Carbon deposits must not be formed under any expected conditions of service.

7. The volume and weight of the combustor must be kept within reasonable limits. In aircraft installations this is a major consideration. The satisfaction of all these requirements demands much of the ingenuity and intuitiveness of the designer. Although the fundamental theories offer guidance, the designer must be prepared to take considerable latitude in applying these theories to an actual situation.

14-18. Combustion Efficiency. It is difficult to determine the combustion efficiency from a chemical analysis of the combustion gases leaving the combustor. This difficulty arises from the fact that the combustion gases are dilute; hence the proportions of constituents in the whole sample are small, and thus the use of such apparatus as the Orsat impossible. Other complications arise when an attempt is made to obtain a representative sample from the high-velocity stream. Methods for determining the combustion efficiency by chemical means have been described by Lloyd. As a practical matter the combustion efficiency on an over-all basis is usually sufficient and is defined as follows:

$$\eta_b = \frac{\Delta h^\circ_{actual}}{\Delta h^\circ_{theoretical}} \qquad (14\text{-}54)$$

The theoretical stagnation enthalpy rise is obtained from the constant-pressure energy equation including kinetic energy and the heat of reaction. An efficiency of less than 95 per cent at the design load would be considered to be entirely unsatisfactory.

14-19. Fuel Injection and Atomization. Liquid fuels are the most widely used in gas turbines and a great body of experience with liquid-fuel injection acquired in connection with oil-fired furnaces is of direct value. The combustor is, of course, considerably smaller than the usual oil-fired furnace which, coupled with the fact the combustor is usually composed of a number of individual combustion cells arranged in parallel, requires the use of nozzles of small capacity. Consequently, comparatively finer atomization is achieved in the gas-turbine combustor.

Many types of fuel injection devices are available, in which mechanical atomization, air injection, steam injection, or what is known as a target jet are utilized. Typical arrangements of these fuel injection systems are illustrated in Fig. 14-5. Steam injection is favored for the heavier fuels when the unit is of such small capacity that the possibility of clogging the orifice might exist. The air atomizer has the advantage

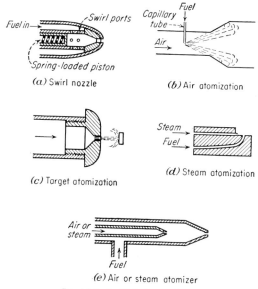

(a) Swirl nozzle

(b) Air atomization

(c) Target atomization

(d) Steam atomization

(e) Air or steam atomizer

Fig. 14-5. Fuel injection systems.

of operating on a low-pressure fuel system. Perhaps the most widely used fuel injection device is the mechanical atomizer.

When using such fuels as Bunker C, it is advisable to preheat the fuel as an aid to atomization and evaporation.

14-20. Combustion Chamber. The gas-turbine combustor is characterized by extremely high rates of heat release. The combustion chamber must provide sufficient volume and length for the complete combustion of the fuel. It would be, of course, disastrous for the flames to enter the turbine passages. The combustion chamber must also provide for the introduction of primary air in such a manner as not to chill the flame. This is usually accomplished by a series of inlet ports for the air or, in some cases, by means of a perforated liner. In any event air must be admitted in a manner which fosters turbulence. Finally, the secondary air must be admitted in such a way as not to arrest the combustion

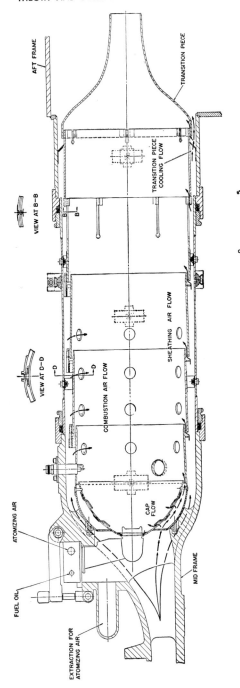

Fig. 14-6. Cross section of locomotive gas-turbine combustion chamber. (Courtesy of General Electric Company.)

process prematurely.   Here again a system encouraging turbulence must be employed.

Several combustion-chamber arrangements are in use, but only a few of the more common types will be treated here.   Figure 14-6 shows a straight-through type of combustion chamber used for the combustion of Bunker C fuel oil.   The air flow through the combustor is divided in four ways, as shown in the illustration.   It will be noticed that some of the air serves the dual purpose of cooling the liner as well as supporting combustion or cooling the combustion products.   It is also seen that the liner is sectionalized and arranged in such a way as to provide for expansion.

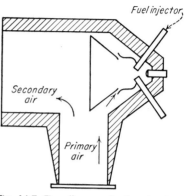

Fig. 14-7. The elbow combustion chamber.

Figure 14-7 shows a combustion chamber known as the elbow type. Here it will be noticed that the main air stream is turned through 90° to induce the formation of two vortices into which the fuel is injected. This type of chamber has a very high efficiency and is characterized by a small flame and efficient operation at part load.

Figure 14-8 illustrates a double-shell type of combustion chamber in which only combustion air enters the flame area.   A separate turbulent

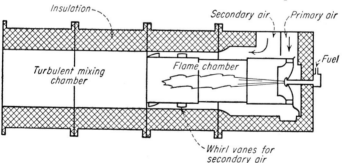

Fig. 14-8. Combustor with separate flame and mixing chambers.

mixing zone is provided for cooling the combustion products.   The secondary air on its way to the turbulent mixing zone is used to cool the inner shell.   This type of chamber has been used in marine applications of the gas turbine.

Figure 14-9 shows a reverse flow combustion chamber that was used in earlier aircraft gas-turbine installations.   It has the advantages of high turbulence and a long flow path but unfortunately also has the disadvantages of large pressure losses and a physical arrangement which requires the burners to surround the turbine, thus producing a large over-all engine diameter.

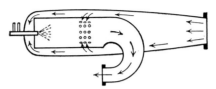

Fig. 14-9. Reverse-flow combustion chamber.

References

1. Bone, W. A., and D. T. Townend: "Flame and Combustion in Gases," Longmans, Green & Co., Inc., New York, 1927.
2. Bone, W. A., and R. V. Wheeler: *J. Chem. Soc.*, Vol. 85, 1904.
3. Campbell, A. S.: Thermodynamic Properties of Reactive Gas Mixtures, *J. Franklin Inst.*, 1951.
4. Cragoe, J.: *Natl. Bur. Standards (U.S.) Misc. Publ.* 97, 1937.
5. Hougen, O. A., and K. M. Watson: "Industrial Chemical Calculations," John Wiley & Sons, Inc., New York, 1936.
6. Jessup, R. S.: *J. Research Natl. Bur. Standards*, Vol. 18, 1937.
7. Lewis, B., and G. von Elbe: "Combustion, Flames and Explosions," Academic Press, New York, 1951.
8. Lichty, L. C.: "Internal Combustion Engines," 6th ed., McGraw-Hill Book Company, Inc., New York, 1951.
9. Lloyd, P.: Determination of Gas-turbine Combustion-chamber Efficiency by Chemical Means, *Trans. ASME*, 1948.
10. Mayers, M. A., and W. W. Carter: The Elbow Combustion Chamber, *Trans. ASME*, 1946.
11. Walsh, A. D.: *Trans. Faraday Soc.*, Vols. 42 and 43, 1946 and 1947.

Problems

14-1. Calculate the flame temperature of the products of combustion for the reaction

$$H_2 + \tfrac{1}{2}O_2 \to H_2O$$

if the process is at a constant pressure of 5 atm and is adiabatic. The reactants are at 200 F initially. (*a*) Neglect dissociation; (*b*) include dissociation.

14-2. Compute the heat of reaction at constant pressure for the reaction

$$CO + \tfrac{1}{2}O_2 \to CO_2$$

for the following temperatures: 0, 500, 1000, 1500, 2000, 4000, and 4500 F.

14-3. A mole of O_2 is at a pressure and temperature of 1 atm and 4500 F, respectively. If the mole of O_2 is in an insulated steel cylinder, find the equilibrium condition after dissociation, if (*a*) the cylinder is rigid and (*b*) the cylinder is equipped with a frictionless piston.

14-4. Compute the higher and lower heats of reaction at constant pressure and at 1200 F for the combustion of *n*-dodecane ($C_{12}H_{26}$) with 20 per cent excess air. The fuel is assumed to be in the vapor state.

CHAPTER 15

THE REGENERATOR

15-1. Introduction. The design of any component of the gas-turbine power plant is intimately related to the design of all the other components. While it is possible, for example, to conceive of the design of a boiler feed pump as being completely divorced from the design of the steam turbine in a steam power plant, a similar parallel does not exist in the gas-turbine power plant. The regenerator of the gas-turbine power plant is no exception to this observation, since the condition of the flow leaving the compressor and turbine influences the design of the regenerator. The amount of heat transfer accomplished in the regenerator, and the pressure drop incurred, have a direct influence on the performance of the whole plant. Just as plant performance is sensitive to the individual performances of the compressor, turbine, and combustor, so it is sensitive to the performance of the regenerator.

The purpose of this chapter is to examine some of the fundamental relationships upon which the design of the regenerator is based and to develop some working relationships for a design procedure.

15-2. Heat Transfer. The subject of heat transfer is too broad and complex, even as it relates to the gas-turbine heat exchanger alone, to be covered extensively in a book of this nature. Some of the basic aspects are reviewed in order to form a background for the material which is to follow.

Heat transfer takes place between two bodies because of a temperature difference and it is subject to the limitations of the second law of thermodynamics. The mechanisms by which heat transfer takes place are classified as conduction, convection, and radiation. All of these mechanisms may be in operation simultaneously. On the other hand only one or two of the mechanisms may be occurring to any significant extent.

Heat transfer by conduction is very slow and is defined as the transfer of heat from one molecule to another contiguous molecule, the molecules being fixed in position relative to each other. The rate of heat transfer by conduction is given by the following expression:

$$dq = -k \, dA \, \frac{dT}{x} \tag{15-1}$$

where q = rate of heat transfer, Btu per hr
   k = thermal conductivity, Btu/(hr)(sq ft)(°F)(ft)
   A = area normal to direction in which heat is transferred, sq ft
   dT = temperature differential, °F
   x = length of heat flow path, ft

If the heat transfer is steady, *i.e.*, there is no variation of temperature with time, and A is constant, Eq. (15-1) may be integrated to yield

$$q = - \frac{k}{x} A \, \Delta T \qquad (15\text{-}2)$$

Heat transfer by convection is more rapid than by conduction and is defined as the transfer of heat through the agency of a molecule which receives heat from a higher-temperature source and moves to the locality of a lower-temperature sink to reject heat. Convection is called free or natural if translation of the molecule is motivated by density changes attendant to temperature changes. If translation of the molecule is aided by mechanical means, such as pumping, the convection is said to be forced. It is apparent that the medium for convective heat transfer must be a fluid, or at least fluidized solids. The rate of heat transfer by convection is governed by the rate of heat transfer through the boundary layer, *i.e.*, the fluid film adjacent to the surface of a solid in contact with the fluid. The rate of heat transfer by convection is given by the following expression:

$$dq = h_c \, dA \, dT \qquad (15\text{-}3)$$

For steady-state heat transfer this equation is differentiated, with the result

$$q = h_c A \, \Delta T \qquad (15\text{-}4)$$

where q = rate of heat transfer, Btu per hr
   h_c = surface coefficient, Btu/(hr)(sq ft)(°F)
   A = area of surface of contact between fluid and solid, sq ft
   ΔT = temperature difference between the two sides of the boundary layer, °F

The surface coefficient h_c depends on the state and properties of the fluid, the geometry of the flow passage, and the fluid velocity. Some simplification is possible in the case of a gas-turbine regenerator since the fluid is in a single phase and forced convection is provided by a static pressure drop. The evaluation of h_c will be discussed in more detail in the succeeding section.

Radiant heat transfer is rapid and takes place by the transformation of thermal energy from a high-temperature source into an electromagnetic wave motion, the transmission of the wave motion through space, and the transformation of the wave motion into thermal energy which is absorbed by a low-temperature sink. The wave motion of radiant heat differs from radio waves, light waves, and x rays only in the matter of wavelength. The rate of radiant heat transfer is dependent on the fourth power of the temperatures of the emitting and receiving bodies, the surfaces and relative geometry of the two bodies, and the ability of the media separating the two bodies to absorb radiation. The general equation for the rate of radiant heat transfer is given by the following expression:

$$q = \sigma A \left[\left(\frac{T_1}{100} \right)^4 - \left(\frac{T_2}{100} \right)^4 \right] F_E F_A \qquad (15\text{-}5)$$

where q = radiant-heat-transfer rate, Btu per hr
σ = Stefan-Boltzmann constant = 0.174 Btu/(hr)(sq ft)(°R/100)⁴
A = area of body, sq ft
F_A = configuration factor to allow for relative geometry of the bodies
F_E = emissivity factor

Radiant heat transfer is not important in gas-turbine regenerators since neither the temperatures nor temperature differences are sufficiently high.

15-3. Heat Transfer by Conduction and Convection. Heat transfer in the regenerator occurs predominantly through the combined mechanisms of conduction and convection. It is convenient, therefore, to express the heat-transfer rate in terms of the combined mechanisms of convection and conduction.

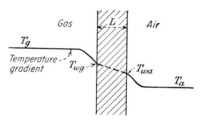

Fig. 15-1. Temperature gradient—heat transfer from gas to air through solid wall.

Figure 15-1 shows a temperature gradient for the transfer of heat from a gas through a solid wall to air. The heat transfer from the gas to the wall is by convection, and from Eq. (15-4),

$$q = h_{cg} A (T_g - T_{wg})$$

where h_{cg} is the film coefficient on the gas side. The heat transfer by conduction through the wall is given by Eq. (15-2):

$$q = \frac{k}{x} A (T_{wg} - T_{wa})$$

The heat transfer by convection from the wall to the air is

$$q = h_{ca} A (T_{wa} - T_a)$$

where h_{ca} is the film coefficient on the air side. Now for the condition of steady-state heat transfer the values of q in the three preceding equations must be all equal and may be expressed in terms of some over-all coefficient of heat transfer U, or

$$q = UA(T_g - T_a) \tag{15-6}$$

and

$$UA(T_g - T_a) = h_{cg}A(T_g - T_{wg})$$

$$UA(T_g - T_a) = \frac{k}{x}A(T_{wg} - T_{wa})$$

$$UA(T_g - T_a) = h_{ca}A(T_{wa} - T_a)$$

from which

$$\frac{U}{h_{cg}} = (T_g - T_a) = T_g - T_{wg}$$

$$\frac{Ux}{k}(T_g - T_a) = T_{wg} - T_{wa}$$

$$\frac{U}{h_{ca}}(T_g - T_a) = T_{wa} - T_a$$

When these equations are added, the result is

$$U\left(\frac{1}{h_{cg}} + \frac{x}{k} + \frac{1}{h_{ca}}\right) = 1$$

or

$$U = \frac{1}{(1/h_{cg}) + (x/k) + (1/h_{ca})} \tag{15-7}$$

It is evident from Eq. (15-7) that the reciprocals of the individual heat-transfer coefficients may be added as a series of resistances.

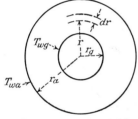

In the case of the flat wall just considered, the areas on both sides of the wall are equal and therefore disappear from the equations. If a round tube is considered, the area inside the tube will be less than the outside area and Eq. (15-7) must be modified to take this into account.

Fig. 15-2. Homogeneous tube wall.

Suppose, as shown in Fig. 15-2, that the gas flows inside the tube and the air outside. Then the heat transfer, which by conduction flows radially through the differential volume $2\pi r \, dr \, L$, where L is the length of tube, from Eq. (15-2), is

$$q = -2k\pi r L \frac{dT}{dr}$$

from which

$$dT = -\frac{q}{2\pi kL}\frac{dr}{r}$$

Integrating,

$$T = -\frac{q}{L}\ln r + C$$

The constant of integration C can be eliminated by noting that when $r = r_g$, $T = T_{wg}$ and when $r = r_a$, $T = T_{wa}$. Substituting in the preceding equation,

$$T_{wg} = - \frac{q}{2\pi kL} \ln r_g + C$$

$$T_{wa} = - \frac{q}{2\pi kL} \ln r_a + C$$

Subtracting,

$$T_{wg} - T_{wa} = - \frac{q}{2\pi kL} \ln \frac{r_g}{r_a}$$

Solving for q/L,

$$\frac{q}{L} = \frac{2\pi k(T_{wg} - T_{wa})}{\ln (r_a/r_g)}$$

Now if the over-all coefficient of heat transfer is related to the gas side area of the tube,

$$U_g 2\pi r_g L(T_g - T_a) = h_{cg} 2\pi r_g L(T_g - T_{wg})$$

$$U_g 2\pi r_g L(T_g - T_a) = k \frac{2\pi}{\ln (r_a/r_g)} L(T_{wg} - T_{wa})$$

$$U_g 2\pi r_g L(T_g - T_a) = h_{ca} 2\pi r_a L(T_{wa} - T_a)$$

and

$$\frac{U_g}{h_{cg}} (T_g - T_a) = T_g - T_{wg}$$

$$\frac{U_g}{k} r_g \ln \frac{r_a}{r_g} (T_g - T_a) = T_{wg} - T_{wa}$$

$$\frac{U_g}{h_{ca}} \frac{r_g}{r_a} (T_g - T_a) = T_{wa} - T_a$$

Adding these equations and solving for U_g,

$$U_g = \frac{1}{(r_g/h_{cg}r_a) + [r_g \ln (r_a/r_g)/k] + (1/h_{ca})} \tag{15-8}$$

Similarly the over-all heat-transfer coefficient for the air side is

$$U_a = \frac{1}{(r_a/h_{cg}r_g) + [r_g \ln (r_a/r_g)/k] + (1/h_{ca})} \tag{15-9}$$

15-4. Regenerator Types and Mean Temperature Difference.

Regenerators may be divided into three types, namely, parallel flow, counterflow, and crossflow. The relative flow directions and temperature gradients for parallel and counterflow regenerators are shown in Fig. 15-3. The letters A and B refer to the respective ends of the regenerators. The flow directions for a crossflow regenerator are shown in Fig. 15-4.

It is clear from Fig. 15-3 that ΔT is not constant along the flow path and therefore Eq. (15-6) is restricted to the instantaneous heat transfer.

To find the heat transfer over a finite length of flow path, Eq. (15-6) must be integrated,

$$\int dq = \int U \, dA \, \Delta T \tag{15-10}$$

The variation of U with temperature may be neglected in the case of

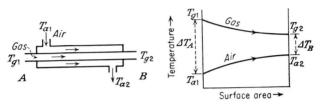

(a) Parallel flow regenerator

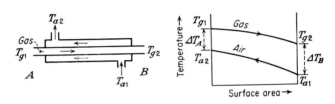

(b) Counterflow regenerator

Fig. 15-3. Temperature distribution in regenerators.

gas-air heat transfer and the change of area will be constant. If further kinetic energy changes are neglected and the regenerator is insulated, Eq. (15-10) may be integrated algebraically for the parallel and counterflow regenerator.

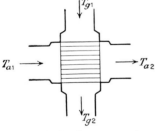

Fig. 15-4. Crossflow regenerator.

A balance of the energy interchange between the gas and air stream yields

$$dq = G_g C_{pg} \, \Delta T_g = G_a C_{pa} \, \Delta T_a$$

where the subscripts g and a refer, respectively, to gas and air as before, G is the mass rate of flow, and C_p is the specific heat at constant pressure. If the specific heats remain nearly constant, q may be regarded as linear with T and ΔT. Therefore the rate of change of ΔT with respect to q is

$$\frac{d(\Delta T)}{dq} = \frac{\Delta T_A - \Delta T_B}{q_A - q_B}$$

where the subscripts A and B refer to the respective ends of the regenerator as shown in Fig. 15-3. Substituting Eq. (15-10) in the preceding equation,

$$\frac{d(\Delta T)}{\Delta T} = \frac{U \, dA \, (\Delta T_A - \Delta T_{E})}{q_A - q_B}$$

and integrating between the limits A and B,

$$\ln \frac{\Delta T_A}{\Delta T_B} = \frac{UA \, (\Delta T_A - \Delta T_B)}{q_A - q_B}$$

from which

$$q_A - q_B = UA \frac{(\Delta T_A - \Delta T_B)}{\ln (\Delta T_A / \Delta T_B)} = UA \, \Delta T_m$$

and hence

$$\Delta T_m = \frac{\Delta T_A - \Delta T_B}{\ln (\Delta T_A / \Delta T_B)} \tag{15-11}$$

Equation (15-11) is an expression for the logarithmic mean temperature difference and is often expressed

$$\text{LMTD} = \frac{\Delta T_{\max} - \Delta T_{\min}}{\ln (\Delta T_{\max} / \Delta T_{\min})} \tag{15-12}$$

Equation (15-11) or Eq. (15-12) may be used for ΔT in Eq. (15-6) to find the over-all heat transfer in the regenerator.

It must be borne in mind that Eqs. (15-11) and (15-12) are appropriate for counterflow and parallel-flow regenerators under the conditions spec-

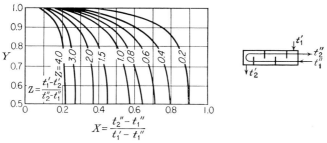

Fig. 15-5. LMTD correction factors for one-shell-pass counterflow regenerator with two (or a multiple of two) tube passes. (From Bowman, Mueller, and Nagle.[2])

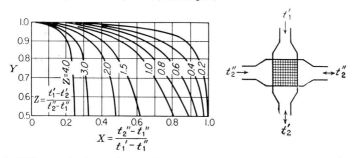

Fig. 15-6. LMTD correction factors for crossflow, air and gas unmixed, one-tube pass. (From Bowman, Mueller, and Nagle.[2])

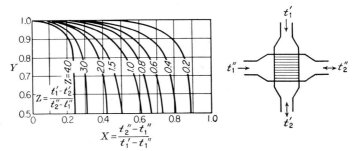

Fig. 15-7. LMTD correction factors for crossflow, gas mixed in shell, one-tube pass. (From Bowman, Mueller, and Nagle.[2])

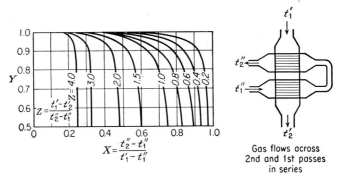

Gas flows across 2nd and 1st passes in series

Fig. 15-8. LMTD correction factors for crossflow, gas mixed in shell, two-tube passes. (From Bowman, Mueller, and Nagle.[2])

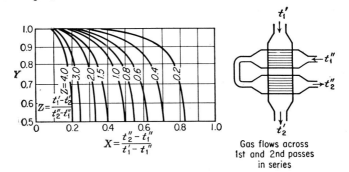

Gas flows across 1st and 2nd passes in series

Fig. 15-9. LMTD correction factors for crossflow, gas mixed in shell, two-tube passes. (From Bowman, Mueller, and Nagle.[2])

ified in the derivation of the equations. If a crossflow or multipass regenerator is under consideration, the expressions for the LMTD become quite involved. The usual procedure is to modify the simple LMTD by means of correction factors. Values of the correction factor Y may be obtained from Figs. 15-5 to 15-9 for different regenerator flow arrangements.

15-5. Film Coefficient. The heat-transfer rate by forced convection has been observed to be a function of the fluid velocity V, the specific mass rate of flow G/A or ρV, the specific heat and conductivity of the fluid, C_p and k, respectively, and the fluid viscosity μ. Related also is the inside diameter of the tube D. The thickness of the film is directly influenced by V, ρ, μ, and D.

To find the manner in which all of these variables are related, it is convenient to apply the principles of dimensional analysis. The dimensions selected will be H = heat, L = length, M = mass, T = temperature, and θ = time. The relationship between the variables affecting the film coefficient may be expressed

$$h_c = \phi(V^a \rho^b C_p{}^d D^c k^f \mu^g K_H{}^m) \tag{15-13}$$

where K_H is a dimensional constant introduced because the $HLMT\theta$ system is used and M and H are involved in the variables under consideration. Equation (15-13) is expressed dimensionally as follows:

$$\frac{H}{\theta L^2 T} = \phi \left(\frac{L}{\theta}\right)^a \left(\frac{M}{L^3}\right)^b \left(\frac{H}{MT}\right)^d L^c \left(\frac{H}{\theta LT}\right)^f \left(\frac{M}{L\theta}\right)^g \left(\frac{ML^2}{H\theta^2}\right)^m \tag{15-13a}$$

The summations of the exponents are

ΣH:
$$1 = d + f - m$$

ΣL:
$$-2 = a - 3b + c - f - g + 2m$$

ΣM:
$$0 = b - d - g - m$$

ΣT:
$$-1 = -d - f$$

$\Sigma\theta$:
$$-1 = -a - f - g - 2m$$

Solving these equations simultaneously in terms of a and f,

$$a = a$$
$$b = a$$
$$d = 1 - f$$
$$c = a - 1$$
$$f = f$$
$$g = 1 - f - a$$
$$m = 0$$

Substituting in Eq. (15-13),

$$h_c = \phi(V^a \rho C_p{}^a{}^{1-f} D^{a-1} k^f \mu^{1-f-a}) \tag{15-14}$$

and collecting terms,

$$\frac{h_c D}{k} = \phi \left(\frac{DV\rho}{\mu}\right)^a \left(\frac{\mu C_p}{k}\right)^{1-f} \tag{15-15}$$

The dimensionless groups $\dfrac{h_c D}{k}$, $\dfrac{DV\rho}{\mu}$, and $\dfrac{\mu C_p}{k}$ are called Nusselt, Reynolds, and Prandtl numbers after these earlier investigators in the fields of fluid flow and heat transfer. The values of the exponents a and $1 - f$ must be determined experimentally. According to McAdams a correlation of experimental results indicates that $a = 0.8$, $1 - f = 0.4$, and

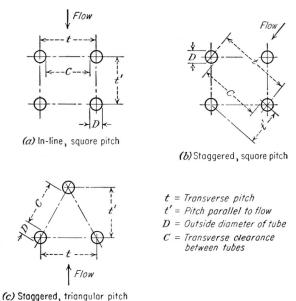

(a) In-line, square pitch

(b) Staggered, square pitch

t = Transverse pitch
t' = Pitch parallel to flow
D = Outside diameter of tube
C = Transverse clearance between tubes

(c) Staggered, triangular pitch

Fig. 15-10. Tube nest arrangements.

$\phi = 0.023$. If these values are substituted in Eq. (15-15) and an average value of $\mu C_p/k = 0.78$ is taken for turbine gases and air, the following expression for the film coefficient results:

$$h_c = 0.027 \frac{C_p(\rho V)^{0.8}\mu^{0.2}}{D^{0.2}} \tag{15-16}$$

This equation is a valid for turbulent flow, $\mathrm{Re} > 10{,}000$, which is the normal condition for which a regenerator is designed.

Equation (15-16) is appropriate for flow inside tubes, where D is the inside diameter. For longitudinal flow outside the tubes, it is necessary to substitute an equivalent diameter in Eq. (15-16). This equivalent diameter depends on the flow area presented by the particular tube arrangement under consideration. In general, the tube bundles or nests are arranged in line with square pitch or are staggered with triangular or square pitches. Figure 15-10 illustrates what is meant by the preceding terms.

Each tube may be regarded to be surrounded by a flow area similar in shape to the pitch arrangement. For the square-pitch tube bundle the flow area is evidently equal to $t^2 - (\pi D_o^2/4)$, where t is the pitch and D_o is the outside diameter of an individual tube. The hydraulic radius of an individual tube is $D_i/4 = r_h$, where D_i is the inside diameter.

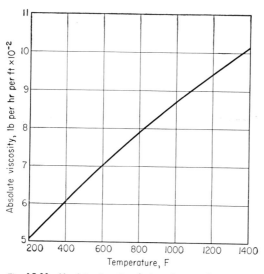

Fig. 15-11. Absolute viscosity of air and gas-turbine gases.

Therefore the equivalent of the tube inside diameter for substitution in Eq. (15-16) is four times the hydraulic radium of the flow area surrounding the tube, or

$$D_e = 4r_h = \frac{4A}{\text{wetted perimeter}} = \frac{4t^2 - D_o^2}{D_o}$$

$$D_e = 1.273 \frac{t^2}{D_o} - D_o \tag{15-17}$$

Similar expressions may be derived for the other tube arrangements.

For flow normal to a tube nest, it is not possible to develop expressions similar to Eqs. (15-15) and (15-16) because of the influence of the tube-nest geometry. Experimental investigations of convection heat transfer when flow occurs normal to a tube nest have been carried out by Pierson showing that the heat-transfer rate is a function of tube arrangement, but this function cannot be simply stated. Pierson reports his data in terms of three parameters for a given tube arrangement, that is

$$\text{Nusselt number} = \frac{h_c D}{k} \tag{15-18}$$

$$\text{Friction factor} = f' = \frac{30.1 \times 10^{-7} \, \Delta P}{N_D (G/A)^2 v_m} \tag{15-19}$$

$$\text{Reynolds number} = \text{Re} = \frac{\rho V D}{\mu} \tag{15-20}$$

where h_c = shell-side film coefficient, Btu/(hr)(sq ft)(°F)

     D = tube outside diameter, ft

     ΔP = pressure drop, shell side, psi

     G/A = specific mass rate of flow, lb per hr per sq ft of free flow area

     N_D = number of tubes in depth

     v = specific volume, cu ft per lb

     f' = friction factor for flow normal to a tube nest

     k = thermal conductivity of shell side gas, Btu/(hr)(sq ft)(°F)(ft)

     μ = absolute viscosity, lb per hr per ft

Figure 15-11 gives the absolute viscosity of air or gas-turbine gases at

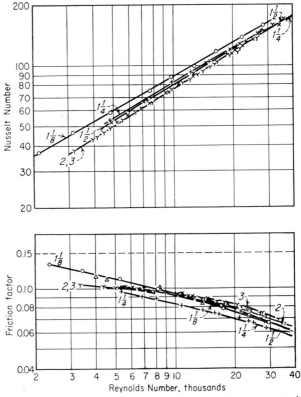

Fig. 15-12. Results for two-diameter transverse spacings, staggered arrangement. (From Pierson.[6])

various temperatures which permits the computation of Eq. (15-20), since the outside diameter of the tubes and the specific mass rate of flow normal to the tubes will be known. With the Reynolds number and the tube arrangement known, the values of $h_c D/k$ and f' may be obtained from Figs. 15-12 to 15-15, which have been reproduced from Pierson's original paper.

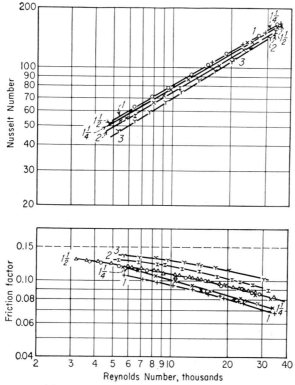

Fig. 15-13. Results for $1\frac{1}{2}$-diameter transverse spacings, staggered arrangement. (*From Pierson.*[6])

15-6. Pressure Losses. It is clear from Eq. (15-16) that high velocity and high turbulence are essential to a satisfactory heat-transfer rate. However, the high velocity can be achieved only with a correspondingly large static pressure drop. Now in order to provide for a large static pressure drop on the air side, the compressor must do more work if a predetermined static pressure is to be maintained at turbine inlet. Similarly for the gas side the turbine must exhaust at a higher static pressure and therefore the turbine work is reduced. The combined effect of the increased compressor work and the decreased turbine work on the cycle efficiency is obvious. It is vital then to the over-all performance of the plant that the static pressure drop in the regenerator be kept at a minimum consistent with an effective heat-transfer rate.

The static pressure drop in the regenerator tubes may be obtained from Eq. (6-40):

$$\Delta P = \left(\frac{G}{A}\right)^2 \frac{(v_2 - v_1)}{2g} + 4f_m \left(\frac{G}{A}\right)^2 \frac{Lv_m}{D2g} \tag{15-21}$$

where f_m = mean friction factor

v_m = mean specific volume, psf

The mean friction factor f_m may be taken as the mean of the values of f obtained from Fig. 15-16 for the inlet and exit of the tube. The mean density ρ_m is the mean value between tube inlet and outlet.

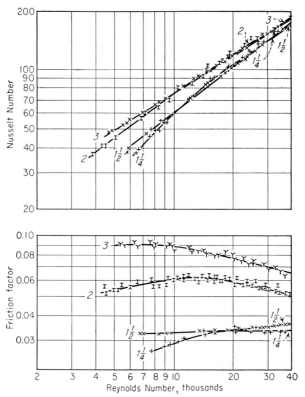

Fig. 15-14. Results for two-diameter transverse spacings, in-line arrangement. (From Pierson.[6])

In addition to the static pressure loss given by Eq. (15-18), other pressure losses are incurred at entrance because of sudden contraction and at exit because of sudden expansion. These losses are determined more or less empirically and depend on the geometry of the entrance and exit sections. Formulas for taking the end losses into account are given by

Boelter, Martinelli, Romie, and Morrin[1] (pages 121 and 122) or may be obtained from handbooks.

The pressure drop for flow normal to a tube nest may be obtained from Eq. (15-19) after finding the value of f' from Fig. 15-12, 15-13, 15-14, or 15-15.

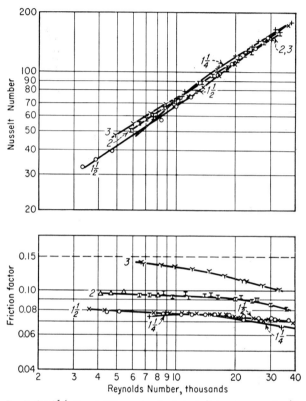

Fig. 15-15. Results for $1\frac{1}{2}$-diameter transverse spacings, in-line arrangement. (*From Pierson.*[6])

15-7. Regenerator Effectiveness. The regenerator effectiveness is sometimes referred to as the regenerator efficiency and is defined as follows:

$$e_r = \frac{\Delta h_{\text{air}}}{(1 + F)(\Delta h_{\text{gas}})_{\text{limit}}} \qquad (15\text{-}22)$$

where F represents the total fuel-air ratio. The limit on the change of enthalpy of the gas is imposed by the temperature of the gases leaving the turbine and the temperature of the air leaving the compressor. It is obvious from the second law of thermodynamics that even a perfect regenerator could not cool the gas to a temperature lower than the temperature of the air entering the regenerator.

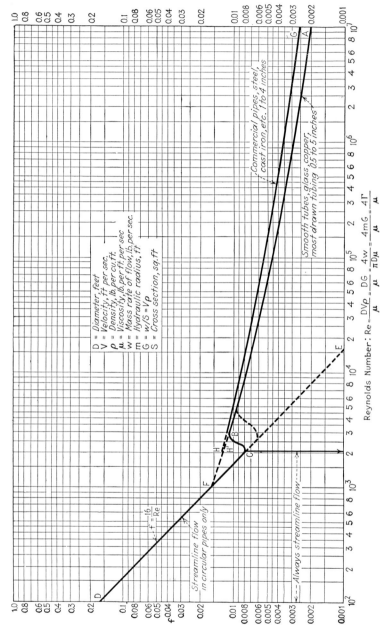

Fig. 15-16. Friction factors for isothermal flow in round pipes and tubes. (Reproduced with permission from "Principles of Chemical Engineering," by W. A. Walker, W. K. Lewis, W. H. McAdams, and E. R. Gilliland, McGraw-Hill Book Company, Inc., New York, 1937.)

If it is assumed that the differences between the specific heats and mass rates of flow of the air and gas are negligible, Eq. (15-22) may be simplified to

$$e_r = \frac{T_{a2} - T_{a1}}{T_{g1} - T_{a1}} \tag{15-23}$$

This expression also assumes that the specific heats are constant with temperature. Despite the assumptions, Eq. (15-23) is accurate enough for many applications and is considerably more convenient to use than Eq. (15-22).

15-8. Some Economic Aspects of Regenerator Design. Many factors must be considered in determining the optimum effectiveness for which a

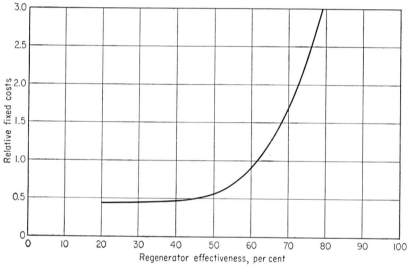

Fig. 15-17. Relationship of fixed costs to regenerator effectiveness.

regenerator is to be designed. The additional capital investment required for the regenerator must be always justified from the standpoint of operating savings. Although this is a simple enough principle, it is not always easy to apply to the gas-turbine regenerator. The materials, weight, size, flow arrangement, and heat-transfer surface are not only interrelated but are in turn related to the effectiveness and capital investment. The operating savings are affected by the pressure drop in the regenerator, the price of fuel, the size of the plant, and the effectiveness.

All the previously mentioned factors are so interdependent that it is impossible to arrive at a general expression for the optimum effectiveness which would be applicable to all cases. Therefore each design must be appraised in terms of its own requirements and the current prices for fuel and regenerators. Figure 15-17 shows that the fixed costs for regenerators increase very rapidly when the effectiveness exceeds 50 per cent. Beyond this point it becomes increasingly more difficult to justify the added investment costs by the savings in operating expenses. This is particularly true since the incremental increase in fuel savings in the usual plant begins to drop when an effectiveness of from 50 to 60 per cent is exceeded.

15-9. Regenerator Calculation

Example. A tubular regenerator is to be designed with two tube passes and one shell pass. The gases are to flow outside the tubes. The following data are given:

> Tubes: $\frac{5}{8}$ in. $-$ 18 BWG, steel
> Allowable pressure drop: 2.5 per cent (not including entrance and exit losses)
> Air pressure entering regenerator: 72 psia
> Gas pressure entering regenerator: 15.4 psia
> Effectiveness: 60 per cent
> Flow of air: 40,000 lb per hr
> Flow of gas: 40,700 lb per hr
> Air temperature entering regenerator: 300 F
> Gas temperature entering regenerator: 600 F

From Eq. (15-22),

$$e_r = 0.60 = \frac{(h_{a2} - h_{a1})40,000}{(h_{g1} - h_{a1})40,700}$$

Substituting from the gas tables, assuming the air and gases have the same properties,

$$h_{a2} = 0.60(255.8 - 182)\frac{40,700}{40,000} + 182$$

and

$$h_{a2} = 227 \text{ Btu per lb}$$
$$T_{a2} = 484 \text{ F}$$

The gas temperature leaving the regenerator is

$$(h_{a2} - h_{a1})40,000 = (h_{g1} - h_{g2})40,700$$
$$h_{g2} = 211.5 \text{ Btu per lb}$$
$$T_{g2} = 421 \text{ F}$$

Referring to Fig. 15-15, the values of Z and X are calculated and the LMTD correction factor is found from the curve:

$$Z = \frac{800 - 421}{484 - 300} = 2.06$$

$$X = \frac{484 - 300}{800 - 300} = 0.37$$

and

$$Y = 0.63$$

Then the corrected LMTD is

$$\text{LMTD} = Y \, \frac{(T_{g1} - T_{a1}) - (T_{a2} - T_{g2})}{\ln\left[(T_{g1} - T_{a1})/(T_{a2} - T_{g2})\right]}$$

TABLE 15-1. TUBE DATA

O.D., in.	Wall gauge, BWG stubs	Surface area		Cross-sectional area		Diameters	
		Outside surface per linear foot, sq ft	Inside surface per linear foot, sq ft	Outside, sq in.	Inside, sq in.	Outside, in.	Inside, in.
$\frac{1}{2}$	20	0.13090	0.11257	0.19635	0.14522	0.500	0.430
	19		0.10891		0.13592		0.416
$\frac{5}{8}$	18	0.16362	0.13797	0.30680	0.21813	0.625	0.527
	16		0.12959		0.19244		0.495
	14		0.12017		0.16547		0.459
$\frac{3}{4}$	18	0.19635	0.17069	0.44179	0.33388	0.750	0.652
	16		0.16232		0.30191		0.620
	14		0.15289		0.26787		0.584
$\frac{7}{8}$	18	0.22907	0.20342	0.60132	0.47417	0.875	0.777
	16		0.19504		0.43592		0.745
	14		0.18562		0.39481		0.709
1	18	0.26180	0.23614	0.78540	0.63900	1.000	0.902
	16		0.22777		0.59447		0.870
	14		0.21834		0.54629		0.834
$1\frac{1}{4}$	18	0.32725	0.30159	1.2272	0.04231	1.250	1.152
	16		0.29322		0.98520		1.120
	14		0.28379		0.92289		1.084
$1\frac{1}{2}$	16	0.39270	0.35867	1.7672	1.4741	1.500	1.370
	14		0.34924		1.3977		1.334
2	14	0.52360	0.48014	3.1416	2.6417	2.000	1.834
	12		0.46653		2.4941		1.782

$$\text{LMTD} = 0.63 \left(\frac{300 - 63}{\ln \left(300/63\right)} \right) = 100 \text{ F}$$

Conservation of energy requires that

$$q = UA \, \Delta T_m = G_g C_{pg} \, \Delta T_g$$

Assuming a heat-transfer rate of 16 Btu/(sq ft)(hr)(°F), the heat-transfer surface is

$$A = \frac{40,700 \times 0.241 \times 179}{16 \times 100} = 1096 \text{ sq ft}$$

From Table 15-1 the outside area per linear foot of one tube ($\frac{5}{8}$ in. − 18 BWG) is 0.1636 sq ft. The length of tube selected is influenced by the limitations imposed on the over-all length of the regenerator, the increased frictional loss with increased length, and the possible need for removing the tube nest periodically for cleaning and inspection. The cost per linear foot of tubes decreases with greater length of tube, and the lengths are more or less standardized at 8, 12, 16, and 20 ft. A nonstandard length may be procured at additional cost. Assume 10-ft tubes (20-ft tubes cut in two); then the number of tubes required is

$$\frac{1096}{0.1636 \times 10} = 670$$

or 335 tubes per tube pass. The cross-sectional area available for flow inside each tube is 0.218 sq in. from Table 15-1. The total flow area is

$$335 \times \frac{0.218}{144} = 0.507 \text{ sq ft}$$

The specific mass rate of flow $= \frac{G}{A} = \rho V = \frac{40,000}{0.507} = 78,000$ lb per hr per sq ft. The value of μ based on an air temperature of 300 F is found from Fig. 15-11 to be 0.056 lb per hr per ft. The inside diameter of the tube is 0.527 in. from Table 15-1. Substituting in the expression for Reynolds number,

$$\text{Re} = \frac{78,000 \times 0.527}{0.056 \times 12} = 61,200$$

From Fig. 15-16, $f = 0.005$. The specific volume of the air at entrance and exit may be assumed equal without significant error as far as Eq. (15-21) is concerned. The specific volume of the air at 300 F is

$$v = \frac{RT}{P} = \frac{53.34 \times 760}{72 \times 144} = 3.9 \text{ cu ft per lb}$$

From Eq. (15-21),

$$\Delta P = \frac{4 \times 0.005(78,000)^2 10 \times 2 \times 3.9 \times 12}{2 \times 32.2(3600)^2 0.527 \times 144}$$

$$\Delta P = 1.8 \text{ psi}$$

This checks with the allowable pressure drop of 2.5 per cent. It should be carefully noted that the losses incurred at entrance and exit of the tubes and the duct losses have not been included in the calculation. If the calculated pressure drop for the tubes had been exceeded, it would have been necessary to use shorter tubes, which would increase the number of tubes required. A larger diameter tube could also be adopted.

It is necessary now to consider the gas flow outside the tubes. Since the lower-pressure gas is outside the tubes, a rectangular shell can be adopted. If the high-pressure air had been on the outside of the tubes it would be advisable to use a shell of cylindrical form because of the greater strength this type of construction provides. A rectangular tube nest will be used with an in-line tube arrangement. Recommended practice

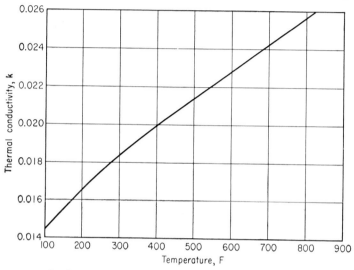

Fig. 15-18. Thermal conductivity of air and gas-turbine gases.

requires a minimum space between tubes of 0.25 in. or one-fourth of the outside tube diameter, whichever is larger. It will be assumed that the tube nest is 16 tubes wide and 42 tubes deep which makes a total of 672 tubes. The free area available for gas flow is

$$\frac{16 \times 0.25 \times 10}{12} = 3.33 \text{ sq ft}$$

and the specific mass rate of flow is

$$\rho V = \frac{G}{A} = \frac{40{,}700}{3.33} = 12{,}260 \text{ lb per sec per sq ft}$$

and

$$\text{Re} = \frac{12{,}260 \times 0.625}{0.07 \times 12} = 9150$$

The value of f'' is obtained from Fig. 15-15. Substituting in Eq. (15-19), noting $v = \dfrac{RT}{P} = \dfrac{53.34 \times 1060}{15.4 \times 144} = 26$ cu ft per lb,

$$\Delta P = \frac{0.077 \times 42(12{,}260)^2 26}{30.1 \times 10^{-7}} = 0.423 \text{ psi}$$

Also from Fig. 15-15 the Nusselt number, $h_c D/k = 66$, the value of k is obtained from Fig. 15-18 and

$$h_{cg} = \frac{66 \times 0.0229 \times 12}{0.625} = 28.3 \text{ Btu/(sq ft)(hr)(°F)}$$

The value of h_{ca} for the air side is obtained from Eq. (15-16).

$$h_{ca} = 0.027 \frac{0.24(78,000)^{0.8}(0.056)^{0.2}}{(0.527/12)^2}$$

$$h_{ca} = 53.4 \text{ Btu (sq ft)(hr)(°F)}$$

If the conductance of the tube material is neglected, the over-all coefficient of heat transfer is obtained from Eq. (15-7)

$$U = \frac{1}{(1/28.3) + (1/53.4)} = 18.4 \text{ Btu/(sq ft)(hr)(°F)}$$

This would be considered a satisfactory check with the assumed value of 16 Btu/(sq ft)(hr)(°F) and therefore the design is satisfactory.

References

1. Boelter, L. M. K., R. C. Martinelli, F. E. Romie, and E. H. Morrin: An Investigation of Aircraft Heaters, *NACA ARR* 5 A06.
2. Bowman, R. H., R. C. Mueller, and W. M. Nagle: Mean Temperature Difference in Design, *Trans. ASME*, 1940.
3. Jakob, M., and G. A. Hawkins: "Elements of Heat Transfer and Insulation," John Wiley & Sons, Inc., New York, 1950.
4. London, A. L., and W. M. Kays: The Gas Turbine Regenerator—The Use of Compact Heat Transfer Surfaces, *Trans. ASME*, 1950.
5. McAdams, W. H.: "Heat Transmission," 2d ed., McGraw-Hill Book Company, Inc., New York, 1942.
6. Pierson, O. L.: Experimental Investigation of the Influence of Tube Arrangement on Convection Heat Transfer and Flow Resistance in Cross Flow of Gases Over Tube Banks, *Trans. ASME*, 1937.

Problems

15-1. Determine the heat-transfer area for a regenerator with staggered tubes; the hot gases flow inside the tubes. The air flows normal to the tube bank. The following data are given:

Temperature of gas entering = 850 F
Temperature of air entering = 345 F
Air flow = 50 lb per sec
Air-fuel ratio = 45
$e_r = 0.5$
$\left(\dfrac{G}{A}\right)_{gas} = 6000$ lb per hr per sq ft
$\left(\dfrac{G}{A}\right)_{air} = 3000$ lb per hr per sq ft
Tubes = ¾ in. − 18 BWG steel

15-2. A regenerator is to be designed for two tube passes and one shell pass. Gases are to flow inside tubes. The following data are given:

Allowable pressure drop = 2 per cent
Air pressure entering regenerator = 60 psia
Gas pressure entering regenerator = 15 psia
e_r = 0.55
Air flow = 65,000 lb per hr
Air-fuel ratio = 50
Air temperature entering regenerator = 275 F
Gas temperature entering regenerator = 800 F
Tubes = ¾ in. − 18 BWG steel

15-3. Design the regenerator of Prob. 15-2 for air flow inside tubes.

15-4. Design the regenerator of Prob. 15-2 for three tube passes and ⅝ in.—18 BWG steel tubes.

CHAPTER 16

THE GAS-TURBINE POWER PLANT

16-1. Introduction. The performance of the gas-turbine power plant was evaluated in Chap. 5 in terms of thermodynamic considerations. The performance of the plant in terms of the operating characteristics of the components could not have been considered at that time. In the intervening chapters the design characteristics of the individual components were studied with some general references to their interdependence. It now remains to examine somewhat more critically the characteristics of the entire plant as a unit, the methods of control and governing, and the operation at other than design load.

To a large extent the desired performance characteristics of the gas-turbine power plant under conditions of service can be met by control of the design features of the components. Therefore design decisions for the components must be governed by what is best for the whole plant rather than what is necessarily best for the individual component. What is best for the whole plant is dictated by economic considerations, the purpose the plant is to serve, and such matters as weight and space restrictions.

16-2. Dimensionless Performance Parameters of the Stationary Plant. The dimensionless performance parameters for the compressor were derived by means of dimensional analysis in Sec. 12-9. A similar analysis for the turbine would provide the same parameters so that for both turbine and compressor the following dimensionless numbers are available besides the pressure ratio:

Flow:

$$\frac{G\sqrt{T}}{D^2P} \tag{16-1}$$

Speed:

$$\frac{ND}{\sqrt{T}} \tag{16-2}$$

By extension of the dimensional analysis the following dimensionless number is derived for the power developed or required for turbine or compressor:

456

Power:

$$\frac{\text{hp}}{P\sqrt{T}} \quad \text{or} \quad \frac{\text{hp}}{DNP} \tag{16-3}$$

Since the power developed in the turbine is some function of the fuel flow to the burner, this flow appears in dimensionless form as:

Fuel flow:

$$\frac{G_f}{P\sqrt{T}} \tag{16-4}$$

It will be recalled from Sec. 12-9 that the viscous effects are neglected since it has been demonstrated that Reynolds number is of little importance in high-speed turbomachinery. The efficiencies of the units are taken to be functions of Mach number and velocity ratio or flow coefficient.

In order to provide a convenient means of comparing the curves obtained from plots of dimensionless numbers, it is advantageous to refer data to some reference condition. The reference condition in most general use is 60 F and 14.7 psia designated as T_0 and P_0, respectively. Therefore applying the principles of dynamic and geometric similitude between the operating and standard conditions, the following relations are true. (Since the same machine is under consideration here, the geometry is unchanged and D = constant.)

$$\frac{G_0\sqrt{T_0}}{P_0} = \frac{G\sqrt{T}}{P} \tag{16-5}$$

from which
$$G_0 = \frac{G\sqrt{T/T_0}}{P/P_0} \tag{16-6}$$

Designating $T/T_0 = \theta$ and $P/P_0 = \delta$, the preceding equation becomes

$$G_0 = \frac{G\sqrt{\theta}}{\delta} \tag{16-7}$$

where G_0 is called the reduced or standardized mass rate of flow. Similarly the following relations may be derived for the reduced form of the other parameters:

$$N_0 = \frac{N}{\sqrt{\theta}} \tag{16-8}$$

$$\text{hp}_0 = \frac{\text{hp}}{\delta\sqrt{\theta}} \tag{16-9}$$

$$G_{f0} = \frac{G_f}{\delta\sqrt{\theta}} \tag{16-10}$$

Comparing Eqs. (16-1) to (16-4) with their counterparts Eqs. (16-7) to (16-10), it should be noted that only the scale of the curves obtained from a plot of these numbers has changed, and not the shape of the curves.

If units which are geometrically similar but of different size are to be compared, it is necessary to retain the diameters in the preceding expressions. Strictly speaking, Eqs. (16-7) to (16-10) are not dimensionless but are proportional to dimensionless numbers. If the diameters are retained, a diameter correction factor similar to δ and θ used for pressure and temperature may be used.

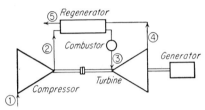

Fig. 16-1. Gas-turbine power plant.

Since stationary plants are being considered in this section, it is clear that the gross power developed by the turbine will exceed the power required by the air compressor. The following relations are held to be true (see Fig. 16-1).

$$N_{\text{turbine}} = N_{\text{compressor}} \quad \text{(direct-coupled)}$$
$$G_{\text{turbine}} = G_{\text{air}} + G_{\text{fuel}}$$
$$\text{hp}_{\text{turbine}} = \text{hp}_{\text{compressor}} + \text{hp}_{\text{net}}$$
$$P_3 = P_2 - (\Delta P_{\text{burner}} - \Delta P_{\text{regenerator}})$$

To find P_3 at various loads requires a knowledge of the variation of ΔP_{burner} and $\Delta P_{\text{regenerator}}$ with load. It is clear that the magnitude of these pressure losses will be a maximum at full load on the plant but no simple relationship exists for the variation of these pressure losses with load. Two types of approximations are used for the burner pressure losses:

1. The efficiency of the compressor is modified slightly to provide an over-all efficiency including the burner pressure loss.

2. The burner pressure loss is assumed to follow some law neglecting the temperature rise. Hence $\Delta P_{\text{burner}} = f(V^2/2gv)$, from Eq. (6-40), or $\Delta P_{\text{burner}}/P_2 = K(G\sqrt{T_2}/P_2)^2$ after substituting Gv/A for V and RT/P for v. The value of K is determined for one load and assumed constant for all other loads.

Approximations similar to those applied to the burner are used to determine the variation of pressure drop in the regenerator with load.

The flow through the turbine and compressor can often be regarded as being equal if the quantity of cooling air withdrawn is of the same order of magnitude as the fuel flow. Where this approximation cannot be made, the air-fuel ratios for the various loads on the plant must be obtained from a thermodynamic study of the cycle. A correction factor

$G_a/(G_a + G_f)$ is applied to the turbine flow in order to obtain an equivalent to the compressor flow.

Figure 16-2 shows in a qualitative way a typical performance map for a centrifugal compressor in terms of pressure ratio and reduced flow as coordinates with reduced speed, specific horsepower, and efficiency as

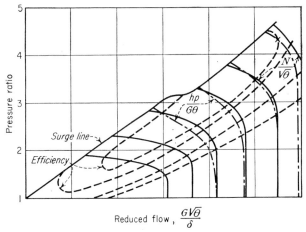

Fig. 16-2. Compressor performance map.

parameters. The specific horsepower is obtained by dividing Eq. (16-9) by Eq. (16-7), or

$$\frac{hp_0}{G_0} = \frac{hp}{G_0 \delta \sqrt{\theta}} = \frac{hp}{G\theta}$$

The pressure ratio has been corrected for combustor pressure losses. The predicted performance map for the compressor can be obtained by a tedious computation of the parameters for various load conditions.

Figure 16-3 is a similar performance map for the turbine with temperature ratio introduced as a parameter. Referring to Fig. 16-2, for a stated pressure ratio, speed, and mass rate of flow, the compressor specific horsepower is obtained. With the same pressure ratio, speed, and mass rate of flow the turbine horsepower is obtained from Fig. 16-3 along with the temperature ratio. It is now possible to determine the corresponding net horsepower as the difference between the turbine and compressor horsepowers. When this is done for a sufficient number of points, a performance map for the plant can be plotted as in Fig. 16-4 with the net specific horsepower, reduced speed, and temperature ratio as parameters.

An examination of Fig. 16-4 shows that the net power output of the plant may be varied by a corresponding variation, individually or in combination, of $\dfrac{G\sqrt{\theta}}{\delta}$, $\dfrac{T_3}{T_1}$, $\dfrac{N}{\sqrt{\theta}}$, and pressure ratio. For the case under

consideration, that is, constant speed, it appears that $\dfrac{G\sqrt{\theta}}{\delta}$ and $\dfrac{T_3}{T_1}$ are

the important control variables. It was demonstrated earlier that the cycle efficiency is sensitive to turbine inlet temperature which suggests

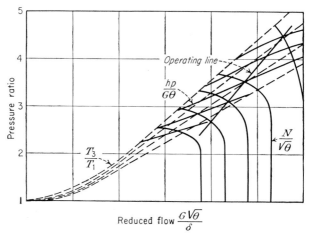

Fig. 16-3. Turbine performance map.

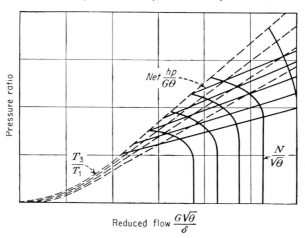

Fig. 16-4. Turbocompressor performance map.

that T_3/T_1 be maintained constant and output variation be controlled by throttling. Unfortunately, the pressure loss sustained by a throttling process cannot be tolerated since some of the work done to compress the air would then appear as unavailable energy. Actually for a plant consisting of direct-connected turbine and compressor about the only practical means of controlling output is to control the fuel rate, thereby controlling the turbine inlet temperature. Admittedly this method of output variation gives poor performance at part load but it is clear from Fig. 16-4 that such poor part-load performance is inherent in this plant arrangement. Further restrictions on the range of output variation are imposed by the compressor surge line of Fig. 16-2 and the maximum turbine inlet temperature which can be tolerated by the turbine materials.

The question might well be asked as to what effect the incorporation of a regenerator would have on the performance of the gas-turbine plant under consideration. It was shown earlier that the regenerator improves the over-all efficiency of the plant and this improvement would of course extend to part-load operation. However, there would be no essential change in the characteristics of the parameters of Fig. 16-4. To be sure, an additional pressure drop would be introduced by the regenerator and the rate of fuel consumption would be also reduced. In other words the relationship of part-load performance to design-load performance would be characteristically the same whether or not a regenerator were used, the over-all efficiency at all loads being higher.

16-3. Twin-shaft Plant. The twin-shaft plant was described in Chap. 2. The greater flexibility afforded by this arrangement now can be better appreciated in terms of the performance characteristics discussed in Sec. 16-2. Where the turbine, compressor, and generator are all direct-connected, it was observed that one degree of freedom, speed, is removed. If separate turbines are provided as prime movers for the compressor and generator, it is seen that the turbocompressor unit can operate at variable speed while the turbogenerator unit is maintained at constant speed. This permits variation of flow through the turbocompressor unit by control of its speed rather than by throttling (see Fig. 16-2). Of course the extent to which flow variation can be introduced is limited by the surging characteristics of the compressor. Flow variation permits operation with constant turbine inlet temperature and hence the part-load efficiency is greatly improved. Figure 16-5 shows characteristic performance curves for single-shaft and twin-shaft plants.

16-4. Dimensionless Performance Parameters of the Aircraft Plant. Two effects which were not present in the stationary plant must be considered in connection with the gas-turbine power plant for jet aircraft. First, there is the ram pressure developed in the diffuser by the deceleration of the incoming air from flight speed to the design velocity entering the compressor. Obviously, then, the static pressure of the air entering the compressor is some function of flight speed. The other effect to be considered is the thrust developed due to expansion of the turbine exhaust in the propelling jet. The thrust developed by a jet engine is obtained from the momentum changes experienced by the fluid passing through

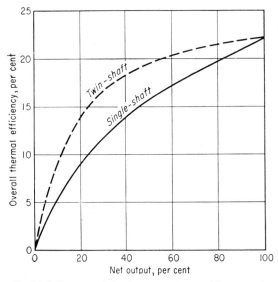

Fig. 16-5. Output variation by temperature and flow control.

the engine, or

$$F = \frac{G_a}{g}(V_j - V_0) + \frac{G_f}{g}V_j + P_jA_j - P_0A_0 \qquad (16\text{-}11)$$

where F = thrust, lb

G_a = mass rate of air flow, lb per sec

G_f = mass rate of fuel flow, lb per sec

V_j = velocity leaving jet relative to aircraft, fps

V_0 = velocity of atmospheric air relative to aircraft, fps

A_j = jet exit area, sq ft

A_0 = diffuser inlet area, sq ft

P_j = static pressure at jet exit, psf

P_0 = static pressure at diffuser inlet, psf

If the fuel flow is neglected and P_j is assumed equal to P_0, that is, expansion takes place entirely within the jet, Eq. (16-11) may be simplified as follows:

$$F = \frac{G_a}{g}(V_j - V_0) \qquad (16\text{-}12)$$

From Eqs. (16-11) and (16-12) it is seen that the thrust developed is some function of flight speed V_j and G_a. The mass rate of flow G_a was seen before to be a function of compressor rotational speed and compressor pressure ratio within the limits of choking flow which may be imposed by the turbine or jet (see Fig. 16-2). The velocity V_j is a function of turbine exhaust temperature and pressure for fixed values of P_0 and T_0.

In other words V_j is a function of the enthalpy drop through the jet. The turbine exhaust pressure and temperature are in turn functions of turbine inlet pressure and temperature. The parameters for the turbine can be linked to those of the compressor by the methods of Sec. 16-2. By means of dimensional analysis the reduced thrust is found to be related to rotational speed and flight speed for the specification of constancy of Mach number at each point in the engine at all load conditions and the further condition that the turbine and compressor are direct-connected.

$$\frac{F}{\delta} = f\left(\frac{N}{\sqrt{\theta}}, \frac{V_0}{\sqrt{\theta}}\right) \tag{16-13}$$

Similarly it can be shown that the reduced turbine inlet temperature and reduced mass rate of flow are also functions of the same reduced parameters given in Eq. (16-13):

$$\frac{T_3}{\theta} = f'\left(\frac{N}{\sqrt{\theta}}, \frac{V_0}{\sqrt{\theta}}\right) \tag{16-14}$$

$$\frac{G_a \sqrt{\theta}}{\delta} = f''\left(\frac{N}{\sqrt{\theta}}, \frac{V_0}{\sqrt{\theta}}\right) \tag{16-15}$$

The data for jet-aircraft engine performance usually call for the representation of T_3/θ as a function of reduced mass rate of fuel flow $G_f/\delta \sqrt{\theta}$.

If Figs. 16-2 and 16-3 are taken as representing the performance of the compressor and turbine, respectively, it is possible to match the compressor and turbine characteristics in the following manner. As before, the turbine mass rate of flow is corrected to correspond with compressor mass rate of flow. Also the compressor pressure ratio is corrected to include the combustor pressure losses. The turbine performance map can be superimposed on the compressor performance map. The lines of constant reduced flow, constant-pressure ratio, and constant reduced speed will coincide. Since the horsepower input to the compressor is equal to the horsepower output of the turbine, the intersection of the reduced horsepower lines will give the points of equilibrium operation. The locus of these points is the equilibrium operating line of the turbocompressor. The corresponding temperature-ratio lines for equilibrium operation pass through the intersections of the reduced horsepower lines (see Fig. 16-3). It will be noted that the equilibrium operating line diverges from the compressor surge line at lower mass rates of flow or lower speeds. The opposite is true at increased flow rates and speeds and care must be taken not to operate in the surging region of the compressor. Care must also be taken to avoid a situation where choking flow can occur in either the turbine or the propelling jet. This situation is not always evident from the performance map unless the occurrence of choking flow was anticipated in its preparation. The thrust developed by a jet engine can be controlled readily by governing the mass rate of fuel flow. If the fuel flow rate is reduced, the turbine inlet temperature is decreased and therefore the output of the turbine is reduced with a corresponding reduction in speed. For equilibrium operation, the compressor speed and horsepower are reduced with a corresponding reduction in mass rate of flow through the compressor. Because of reduced turbine inlet temperature, the temperature of the gases entering the propelling jet will be reduced. Also the pressure ratio will be altered so that the pressure of the gas entering the propelling jet is also reduced. It follows that the velocity generated in the jet will be lower, which, coupled with reduced mass rate of flow, brings about a reduction in thrust developed.

Often a variable-area jet is provided to avoid the condition of choking flow previously mentioned. At high altitudes the specific volume of the flow will be increased and may increase to a point where choking flow is brought about. This is readily seen from an examination of the continuity equation for a compressible fluid. The condition can be relieved, if choking flow occurs in the jet, by the expedient of increasing the jet area. A further advantage of the variable-area jet is the possibility of increasing the turbine-pressure ratio when starting by keeping the jet exit area in a wide-open position. This has the effect of reducing the jet load and therefore the turbine develops maximum torque to overcome the compressor load. The result is a quicker start. The introduction of the variable-area jet adds another factor to be controlled along with mass rate of fuel flow.

16-5. Torque Characteristics of the Gas-turbine Plant. The torque characteristics of the gas-turbine power plant constitute a very important consideration where the plant is to be used for traction purposes, as, for example, in locomotives, trucks, and automobiles. Consider the torque characteristics of the plant consisting of one turbine direct-connected to the compressor. For simplicity, let it be assumed that the turbine is also direct-connected to the load, or through a transmission of a fixed reduction ratio. When the load is applied, the turbine will slow down to provide the required torque. However, a reduction of turbine speed also calls for the same reduction of compressor speed. As a result, the compressor flow is reduced, the turbine power is reduced because of the reduction of flow, and the reduction of turbine power brings about a reduction in the torque developed. It may be concluded therefore that the torque characteristics of this type of plant make it totally unsuited for traction purposes. A possible modification which has been used with gas-turbine locomotives is to use a generator direct-connected to the turbocompressor, the load variations taking place at constant speed. The output of the generator is then used to energize traction motors.

The twin-shaft plant with its independent power turbine permits a reduction in the speed of the power turbine when higher torque is required. The speed of the turbocompressor unit is unaffected and therefore the mass rate of flow through the turbines is constant. The horsepower of the power turbine remains substantially constant and consequently a reduction of the speed of this turbine provides a higher torque. In a sense the power turbine itself becomes a torque converter.

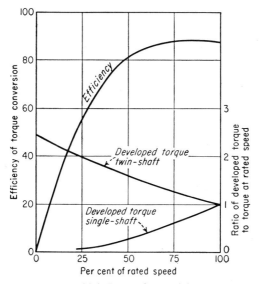

Fig. 16-6. Torque characteristics.

The efficiency of torque conversion will not be constant with speed for the reason that dynamic and geometric similarity are not maintained. The flow angles and geometric angles of the turbine blades will not correspond and therefore it is evident that the efficiency will decrease when the speed of the turbine differs from its design speed. Fortunately, the efficiency-vs.-speed curve is fairly flat until the speed is reduced about 50 per cent and the period of time the unit is operating below half speed is comparatively short. Figure 16-6 shows the torque characteristics for the single-shaft and twin-shaft arrangement as well as the efficiency of torque conversion for the twin-shaft plant at various percentages of rated speed.

16-6. Starting. The gas-turbine power plant is not self-starting. Therefore some provision must be made to bring the unit up to a speed at which the air flow is sufficient for combustion and for an adequate flow of combustion gases to the turbine for the independent operation of the plant. The starting power required is a function of the accelerating characteristics of the rotor, which depend chiefly on its aerodynamic characteristics rather than frictional resistance, and the time specified for the starting period.

The starting device may be an electric motor energized by batteries in an isolated plant or by electric energy supplied from the plant bus in

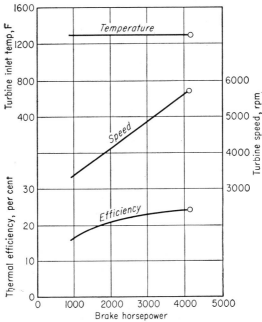

Fig. 16-7. Data for 4100-bhp gas-turbine-plant performance—speed control. (*Courtesy of Allis-Chalmers Manufacturing Company.*)

the case of a stationary plant. Other starting devices are small reciprocating internal-combustion engines or a very small gas turbine. The starting gas turbine itself may be started by hand cranking.

In stationary installations the starting period does not necessarily need to be short, so that the power developed by the starting device may be quite small in comparison to that of the plant itself. A turning gear is normally used during shutdown periods and is a contributing factor to faster starting.

In contrast to the stationary installation military aircraft require very quick starting. This requirement imposes the need for a starting device of considerable power (about 10 to 25 hp), which in turn creates a problem in view of weight limitations.

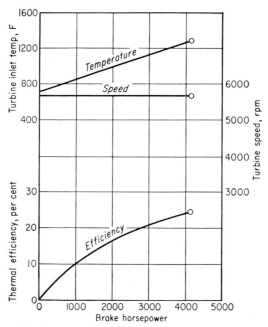

Fig. 16-8. Data for 4100-bhp gas-turbine-plant performance—temperature control. (*Courtesy of Allis-Chalmers Manufacturing Company.*)

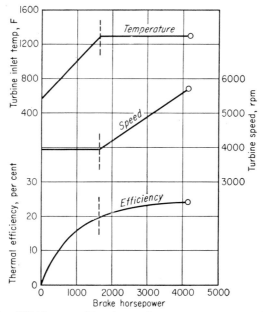

Fig. 16-9. Data for 4100-bhp gas-turbine-plant performance—combined speed and temperature control. (*Courtesy of Allis-Chalmers Manufacturing Company.*)

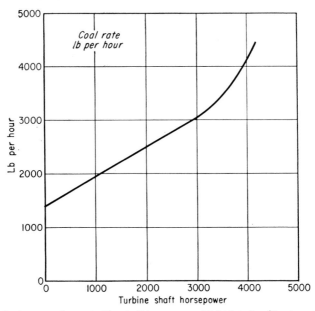

Fig. 16-10. Coal consumption vs. turbine shaft horsepower, 80 F inlet air.   (*Courtesy of J. I. Yellott and the Locomotive Development Committee.*)

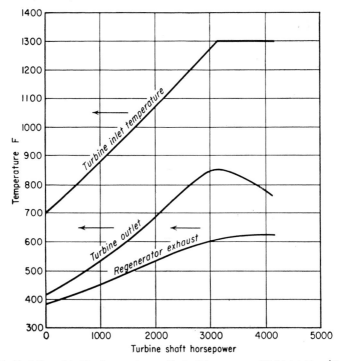

Fig. 16-11. Variation of turbine temperatures with shaft horsepower, 80 F inlet Air.   (*Courtesy of J. I. Yellott and the Locomotive Development Committee.*)

16-7. Performance of Gas-turbine Power Plants. The performance maps discussed in Secs. 16-2 and 16-4 offer a convenient and general representation of the performance parameters. These maps are of particular interest to the designer, since test data can be presented in such a way that it can be interpreted for whatever special conditions may be imposed in service. For example, an aircraft gas turbine may be tested at sea-level conditions but the reduced parameters permit calculation

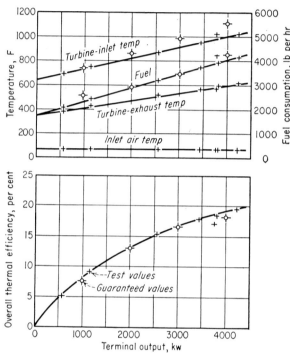

Fig. 16-12. Performance of a 4000-kw stationary gas-turbine power plant. (*Courtesy of Brown Boveri Corporation.*)

of performance data for actual conditions several thousand feet above sea level.

The user or purchaser of the gas turbine is generally more interested in specific information on performance under the conditions expected to be met in his plant. The elevation above sea level and the seasonal variations in ambient temperature will be known. In addition, the load characteristics and operating speeds will be known. Above all the purchaser of the gas turbine is interested in the over-all thermal efficiency of the plant at all loads.

Figures 16-7 to 16-9 show performance data at various loads on a 4100-bhp coal-burning gas-turbine power plant for locomotive use. The plant is of the single-shaft type and is provided with a regenerator. The data given in the curves are calculated for an ambient pressure and temperature of 14.7 psia and 70 F, respectively. The design turbine inlet temperature is 1300 F and the pressure ratio is 4.8. Figures 16-10 and 16-11 show the performance data obtained from test for ambient pressure and temperature of 14.7 psia and 80 F, respectively. The higher heating value of the coal used is 12,800 Btu per lb.

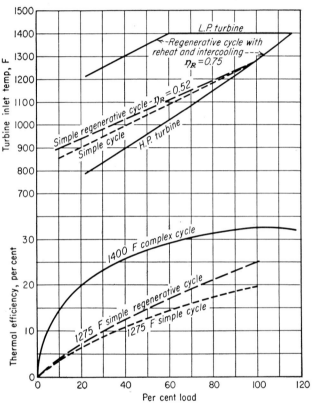

Fig. 16-13. Comparative performance of constant-speed gas-turbine power plants. (*Courtesy of Elliott Company.*)

Figure 16-12 shows a comparison of calculated and test performance data for a single-shaft 4000-kw stationary gas-turbine power plant without regenerator. Output is controlled by governing the fuel flow rate (turbine-inlet-temperature control) at constant speed of 3600 rpm. The fuel is a residual oil.

Figure 16-13 shows the comparative performance of a 4000-hp single-shaft locomotive gas turbine with and without regeneration, and a 3000-hp twin-shaft marine gas-turbine power plant with intercooling and reheat. The locomotive gas-turbine-performance data is for a speed of 5910 rpm using a centrifugal compressor. The marine gas-turbine-performance data is for a speed of 3580 rpm using a Lysholm compressor. The pressure ratios for the design load of the locomotive and marine

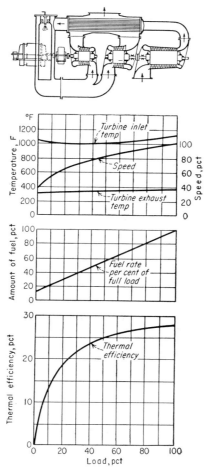

Fig. 16-14. Typical performance of two-shaft unit with one turbine driving the constant-speed generator, and another the compressor at variable speed. (*Courtesy of Brown Boveri Corporation.*)

plants are 3.5 and 5.75, respectively. The ambient temperature and pressure for both plants are 70 F and 14.7 psia, respectively.

Figure 16-14 gives the performance data for a stationary twin-shaft unit with regeneration. The ambient temperature and pressure are 60 F and 14.7 psia, respectively. The turbogenerator operates at constant speed, output variation being accomplished by turbine inlet-temperature control and control of turbocompressor speed.

References

1. Dennison, E. S.: Elliott Gas Turbine Developments Applicable to Power Generation, *Trans. AIEE*, 1949.
2. Godsey, A. W., Jr., and L. A. Young: "Gas Turbines for Aircraft," McGraw-Hill Book Company, Inc., New York, 1949.
3. Hall, R. S.: Aircraft Gas Turbines with Centrifugal Compressors, General Electric Company Aircraft Gas-turbine Conference, *GET*-1300, 1945.
4. Pfenninger, H.: Where Gas Turbines Will Fit in Future Power Fields, *Power*, November, 1946; January, 1947.
5. Sidler, P. R.: Performance of Commercial Gas Turbines, *ASME Paper* 48-S-7, 1948.
6. Tucker, W. B.: Construction of a Gas Turbine for Locomotive Power Plant, *Trans. ASME*, 1948.
7. Yellott, J. I.: L. D. C. Gas Turbine Runs on Coal, *Power Eng.*, May, 1952.

Problems

16-1. A propjet is tested at sea-level conditions of 14.7 psia and 60 F and the following data are obtained.

> Thrust: 600 lb
> Rotational speed (turbocompressor): 10,000 rpm
> Air flow: 30 lb per sec
> Power to propeller shaft: 1800 hp

The equivalent horsepower developed by the aircraft is the sum of the propeller horsepower plus the gross thrust times an aircraft speed of 375 mph. On this basis the specific fuel consumption is 0.83 lb per hr per equivalent horsepower.

(*a*) Determine the following data when the aircraft is at an altitude of 12,000 ft. (See Table 10 in the Appendix for temperature and pressure at this altitude.) Efficiency is constant.

> Rotational speed in rpm
> Propeller horsepower
> Thrust in pounds
> Air flow in pounds per second
> Specific fuel consumption (equivalent horsepower basis)

(*b*) Another propjet is designed to deliver the same propeller horsepower at an altitude of 6000 ft that the original propjet delivers at an altitude of 12,000 ft and at the same efficiency. Determine ratio of the geometric dimensions and the rotational speed of the new unit at an altitude of 12,000 ft.

APPENDIX

GAS TABLES

Tables 1 through 10 have been abstracted from "Gas Tables" by J. H. Keenan and J. Kaye with permission of the publishers, John Wiley & Sons, Inc.

Symbols and Units:

T = temperature, °R
h = enthalpy, Btu per lb
$\bar{h}$ = enthalpy, Btu per lb mole
P_r = relative pressure
u = internal energy, Btu per lb
$\bar{u}$ = internal energy, Btu per lb mole
v_r = relative volume

$$\phi = \int_{T_0}^{T} \frac{C_p}{T}\, dT,\ \text{Btu/(lb)(°R)}$$

$$\bar{\phi} = \int_{T_0}^{T} \frac{\bar{C}_p}{T}\, dT,\ \text{Btu/(lb mole)(°R)}$$

C_p = specific heat at constant pressure, Btu/(lb)(°R)
$\bar{C}_p$ = molal specific heat at constant pressure, Btu/(lb mole)(°R)
C_v = specific heat at constant volume, Btu/(lb)(°R)
$\bar{C}_v$ = molal specific heat at constant volume, Btu/(lb mole)(°R)

$$k = \frac{C_p}{C_v} = \frac{\bar{C}_p}{\bar{C}_v}$$

a = velocity of sound
M = Mach number
R = gas constant for air
A = cross-sectional area

Subscripts:

* refers to conditions where $M = 1$
° refers to isentropic stagnation conditions
x and y refer to conditions upstream and downstream of shock, respectively

Meaning of Relative Pressure and Relative Volume:

The ratio of the pressure P_a and P_b corresponding to the temperatures T_a and T_b, respectively, along a given isentropic is equal to the ratio of the relative pressure P_{ra} and P_{rb} as tabulated for T_a and T_b, respectively. Thus

$$\left(\frac{P_a}{P_b}\right)_{S=\text{const}} = \frac{P_{ra}}{P_{rb}}.\quad \text{Similarly,}\quad \left(\frac{v_a}{v_b}\right)_{S=\text{const}} = \frac{v_{ra}}{v_{rb}}$$

TABLE 1. THERMODYNAMIC PROPERTIES OF AIR

T	h	P_r	u	v_r	ϕ
400	95.53	0.4858	68.11	305.0	0.52890
410	97.93	0.5295	69.82	286.8	0.53481
420	100.32	0.5760	71.52	270.1	0.54058
430	102.71	0.6253	73.23	254.7	0.54621
440	105.11	0.6776	74.93	240.6	0.55172
450	107.5	0.7329	76.65	227.45	0.55710
460	109.90	0.7913	78.36	215.33	0.56235
470	112.30	0.8531	80.07	204.08	0.56751
480	114.69	0.9182	81.77	193.65	0.57255
490	117.08	0.9868	83.49	183.94	0.57749
500	119.48	1.0590	85.20	174.90	0.58233
510	121.87	1.1349	86.92	166.46	0.58707
520	124.27	1.2147	88.62	158.58	0.59173
530	126.66	1.2983	90.34	151.22	0.59630
540	129.06	1.3860	92.04	144.32	0.60078
550	131.46	1.4779	93.76	137.85	0.60518
560	133.86	1.5742	95.47	131.78	0.60950
570	136.26	1.6748	97.19	126.08	0.61376
580	138.66	1.7800	98.90	120.70	0.61793
590	141.06	1.8899	100.62	115.65	0.62204
600	143.47	2.005	102.34	110.88	0.62607
610	145.88	2.124	104.06	106.38	0.63005
620	148.28	2.249	105.78	102.12	0.63395
630	150.68	2.379	107.50	98.11	0.63781
640	153.09	2.514	109.21	94.30	0.64159
650	155.50	2.655	110.94	90.69	0.64533
660	157.92	2.801	112.67	87.27	0.64902
670	160.33	2.953	114.40	84.03	0.65263
680	162.73	3.111	116.12	80.96	0.65621
690	165.15	3.276	117.85	78.03	0.65973
700	167.56	3.446	119.58	75.25	0.66321
710	169.98	3.623	121.32	72.60	0.66664
720	172.39	3.806	123.04	70.07	0.67002
730	174.82	3.996	124.78	67.67	0.67335
740	177.23	4.193	126.51	65.38	0.67665
750	179.66	4.396	128.24	63.20	0.67991
760	182.08	4.607	129.99	61.10	0.68312
770	184.51	4.826	131.73	59.11	0.68629
780	186.94	5.051	133.47	57.20	0.68942
790	189.38	5.285	135.22	55.38	0.69251

TABLE 1. THERMODYNAMIC PROPERTIES OF AIR. *(Continued)*

T	h	P_r	u	v_r	ϕ
800	191.81	5.526	136.97	53.63	0.69558
810	194.25	5.775	138.72	51.96	0.69860
820	196.69	6.033	140.47	50.35	0.70160
830	199.12	6.299	142.22	48.81	0.70455
840	201.56	6.573	143.98	47.34	0.70747
850	204.01	6.856	145.74	45.92	0.71037
860	206.46	7.149	147.50	44.57	0.71323
870	208.90	7.450	149.27	43.26	0.71606
880	211.35	7.761	151.02	42.01	0.71886
890	213.80	8.081	152.80	40.80	0.72163
900	216.26	8.411	154.57	39.64	0.72438
910	218.72	8.752	156.34	38.52	0.72710
920	221.18	9.102	158.12	37.44	0.72979
930	223.64	9.463	159.89	36.41	0.73245
940	226.11	9.834	161.68	35.41	0.73509
950	228.58	10.216	163.46	34.45	0.73771
960	231.06	10.610	165.26	33.52	0.74030
970	233.53	11.014	167.05	32.63	0.74287
980	236.02	11.430	168.83	31.76	0.74540
990	238.50	11.858	170.63	30.92	0.74792
1000	240.98	12.298	172.43	30.12	0.75042
1010	243.48	12.751	174.24	29.34	0.75290
1020	245.97	13.215	176.04	28.59	0.75536
1030	248.45	13.692	177.84	27.87	0.75778
1040	250.95	14.182	179.66	27.17	0.76019
1050	253.45	14.686	181.47	26.48	0.76259
1060	255.96	15.203	183.29	25.82	0.76496
1070	258.47	15.734	185.10	25.19	0.76732
1080	260.97	16.278	186.93	24.58	0.76964
1090	263.48	16.838	188.75	23.98	0.77196
1100	265.99	17.413	190.58	23.40	0.77426
1110	268.52	18.000	192.41	22.84	0.77654
1120	271.03	18.604	194.25	22.30	0.77880
1130	273.56	19.223	196.09	21.78	0.78104
1140	276.08	19.858	197.94	21.27	0.78326
1150	278.61	20.51	199.78	20.771	0.78548
1160	281.14	21.18	201.63	20.293	0.78767
1170	283.68	21.86	203.49	19.828	0.78985
1180	286.21	22.56	205.33	19.344	0.79201
1190	288.76	23.28	207.19	18.940	0.79415

TABLE 1. THERMODYNAMIC PROPERTIES OF AIR. (*Continued*)

T	h	P_r	u	v_r	ϕ
1200	291.30	24.01	209.05	18.514	0.79628
1210	293.86	24.76	210.92	18.102	0.79840
1220	296.41	24.43	212.78	17.700	0.80050
1230	298.96	26.32	214.65	17.311	0.80258
1240	301.52	27.13	216.53	16.932	0.80466
1250	304.08	27.96	218.40	16.563	0.80672
1260	306.65	28.80	220.28	16.205	0.80876
1270	309.22	29.67	222.16	15.857	0.81079
1280	311.79	30.55	224.05	15.518	0.81280
1290	314.36	31.46	225.93	15.189	0.81481
1300	316.94	32.39	227.83	14.868	0.81680
1310	319.53	33.34	229.73	14.557	0.81878
1320	322.11	34.31	231.63	14.253	0.82075
1330	324.69	35.30	233.52	13.958	0.82270
1340	327.29	36.31	235.43	13.670	0.82464
1350	329.88	36.35	237.34	13.391	0.82658
1360	332.48	38.41	239.25	13.118	0.82848
1370	335.09	39.49	241.17	12.851	0.83039
1380	337.68	40.59	243.08	12.593	0.83229
1390	340.29	41.73	245.00	12.340	0.83417
1400	342.90	42.88	246.93	12.095	0.83604
1410	345.52	44.06	248.86	11.855	0.83790
1420	348.14	45.26	250.79	11.622	0.83975
1430	350.75	46.49	252.72	11.394	0.84158
1440	353.37	47.75	254.66	11.172	0.84341
1450	356.00	49.03	256.60	10.954	0.84523
1460	358.63	50.34	258.54	10.743	0.84704
1470	361.27	51.68	260.49	10.537	0.84884
1480	363.89	53.04	262.44	10.336	0.85062
1490	366.53	54.43	264.38	10.140	0.85239
1500	369.17	55.86	266.34	9.948	0.85416
1510	371.62	57.30	268.30	9.761	0.85591
1520	374.47	58.78	270.26	9.578	0.85767
1530	377.11	60.29	272.23	9.400	0.85940
1540	379.77	61.83	274.20	9.226	0.86113
1550	382.42	63.40	276.17	9.056	0.86285
1560	385.08	65.00	278.13	8.890	0.86456
1570	387.74	66.63	280.11	8.728	0.86626
1580	390.40	68.30	282.09	8.569	0.86794
1590	393.07	70.00	284.08	8.414	0.86962

TABLE 1. THERMODYNAMIC PROPERTIES OF AIR. (*Continued*)

T	h	P_r	u	v_r	φ
1600	395.74	71.73	286.06	8.263	0.87130
1610	398.42	73.49	288.05	8.115	0.87297
1620	401.09	75.29	290.04	7.971	0.97462
1630	403.77	77.12	292.03	7.829	0.87627
1640	406.45	78.99	294.03	7.691	0.87791
1650	409.13	80.89	296.03	7.556	0.87954
1660	411.82	82.83	298.02	7.424	0.88116
1670	414.51	84.80	300.03	7.295	0.88278
1680	417.20	86.82	302.04	7.168	0.88439
1690	419.89	88.87	304.04	7.045	0.88599
1700	422.59	90.95	306.06	6.924	0.88758
1710	425.29	93.08	308.07	6.805	0.88916
1720	428.00	95.24	310.09	6.690	0.89074
1730	430.69	97.45	312.10	6.576	0.89230
1740	433.41	99.69	314.13	6.465	0.89387
1750	436.12	101.98	316.16	7.367	0.89542
1760	438.83	104.30	318.18	6.251	0.89697
1770	441.55	106.67	320.22	6.147	0.89850
1780	444.26	109.08	322.24	6.045	0.90003
1790	446.99	111.54	324.29	5.945	0.90155
1800	449.71	114.03	326.32	5.847	0.90308
1810	452.44	116.57	328.37	5.752	0.90458
1820	455.17	119.16	330.40	5.658	0.90609
1830	457.90	121.79	332.45	5.566	0.90759
1840	460.63	124.47	334.50	5.476	0.90908
1850	463.37	127.18	336.55	5.388	0.91056
1860	466.12	129.95	338.61	5.302	0.91203
1870	468.86	132.77	340.66	5.217	0.91350
1880	471.60	135.64	342.73	5.134	0.91497
1890	474.35	138.55	344.78	5.053	0.91643
1900	477.09	141.51	346.85	4.974	0.91788
1910	479.85	144.53	348.91	4.896	0.91932
1920	482.60	147.59	350.98	4.819	0.92076
1930	485.36	150.70	353.05	4.744	0.92220
1940	488.12	153.87	355.12	4.670	0.92362
1950	490.88	157.10	357.20	4.598	0.92504
1960	493.64	160.37	359.28	4.527	0.92645
1970	496.40	163.69	361.36	4.458	0.92786
1980	499.17	167.07	363.43	4.390	0.92926
1990	501.94	170.50	365.53	4.323	0.93066

THEORY AND DESIGN OF STEAM AND GAS TURBINES

TABLE 1. THERMODYNAMIC PROPERTIES OF AIR. *(Continued)*

T	h	P_r	u	v_r	ϕ
2000	504.71	174.00	367.61	4.258	0.93205
2010	507.49	177.55	369.71	4.194	0.93343
2020	510.26	181.16	371.79	4.130	0.93481
2030	513.04	184.81	373.88	4.069	0.93618
2040	515.82	188.54	375.98	4.008	0.93756
2050	518.61	192.31	378.08	3.949	0.93891
2060	521.39	196.16	380.18	3.890	0.94026
2070	524.18	200.06	382.28	3.833	0.94161
2080	526.97	204.02	384.39	3.777	0.94296
2090	529.75	208.06	386.48	3.721	0.94430
2100	532.55	212.1	388.60	3.667	0.94564
2110	535.35	216.3	390.71	3.614	0.94696
2120	538.15	220.5	392.83	3.561	0.94829
2130	540.94	224.8	394.93	3.510	0.94960
2140	543.74	229.1	397.05	3.460	0.95092
2150	546.54	233.5	399.17	3.410	0.95222
2160	549.35	238.0	401.29	3.362	0.95352
2170	552.16	242.6	403.41	3.314	0.95482
2180	554.97	247.2	405.53	3.267	0.95611
2190	557.78	251.9	407.66	3.221	0.95740
2200	560.59	256.6	409.78	3.176	0.95868
2210	563.41	261.4	411.92	3.131	0.95996
2220	566.23	266.3	414.05	3.088	0.96123
2230	569.04	271.3	416.18	3.045	0.96250
2240	571.86	276.3	418.31	3.003	0.96376
2250	574.69	281.4	420.46	2.961	0.96501
2260	577.51	286.6	422.59	2.921	0.96626
2270	580.34	291.9	424.74	2.881	0.96751
2280	583.16	297.2	426.87	2.841	0.96876
2290	585.99	302.7	429.10	2.803	0.96999
2300	588.82	308.1	431.16	2.761	0.97123
2310	591.66	313.7	433.31	2.728	0.97246
2320	594.49	319.4	435.46	2.691	0.97369
2330	597.32	325.1	437.60	2.655	0.97489
2340	600.16	330.9	439.76	2.619	0.97611
2350	603.00	336.8	441.91	2.585	0.97732
2360	605.84	342.8	444.07	2.550	0.97853
2370	608.68	348.9	446.22	2.517	0.97973
2380	611.53	355.0	448.38	2.483	0.98092
2390	614.37	361.3	450.54	2.451	0.98212
2400	617.22	367.6	452.70	2.419	0.98331

TABLE 2. AIR AT LOW PRESSURES
(For one pound)

T	t	c_p	k	a
100	−360	0.2392	1.402	490.5
200	−260	0.2392	1.402	693.6
300	−160	0.2392	1.402	849.4
400	− 60	0.2393	1.402	980.9
500	40	0.2396	1.401	1096.4
600	140	0.2403	1.399	1200.3
700	240	0.2416	1.396	1295.1
800	340	0.2434	1.392	1382.5
900	440	0.2458	1.387	1463.6
1000	540	0.2486	1.381	1539.4
1200	740	0.2547	1.368	1678.6
1400	940	0.2611	1.356	1805.0
1600	1140	0.2671	1.345	1922.0
1800	1340	0.2725	1.336	2032
2000	1540	0.2773	1.328	2135
2200	1740	0.2813	1.322	2234
2400	1940	0.2848	1.317	2329
2600	2140	0.2878	1.313	2420
2800	2340	0.2905	1.309	2508
3000	2540	0.2929	1.306	2593
3200	2740	0.2950	1.303	2675
3400	2940	0.2969	1.300	2755
3600	3140	0.2986	1.298	2832
3800	3340	0.3001	1.296	2907
4000	3540	0.3015	1.294	2981
5000	4540	0.3072	1.287	3323
6000	5540	0.3114	1.282	3634

TABLE 3. $R \log_e N$ for Air, Btu/(lb)(°F abs)

N	$R \log_e N$	N	$R \log_e N$	N	$R \log_e N$	N	$R \log_e N$	N	$R \log_e N$
1.0	0.00000	2.0	0.04751	3.0	0.07531	4.0	0.09503	5.0	0.11033
1.1	0.00653	2.1	0.05086	3.1	0.07756	4.1	0.09672	5.5	0.11686
1.2	0.01250	2.2	0.05404	3.2	0.07973	4.2	0.09837	6.0	0.12282
1.3	0.01798	2.3	0.05709	3.3	0.08184	4.3	0.09999	6.5	0.12831
1.4	0.02306	2.4	0.06001	3.4	0.08389	4.4	0.10156	7.0	0.13339
1.5	0.02779	2.5	0.06281	3.5	0.08588	4.5	0.10310	7.5	0.13821
1.6	0.03222	2.6	0.06549	3.6	0.08781	4.6	0.10461	8.0	0.14254
1.7	0.03637	2.7	0.06808	3.7	0.08969	4.7	0.10608	8.5	0.14670
1.8	0.04029	2.8	0.07057	3.8	0.09151	4.8	0.10753	9.0	0.15062
1.9	0.04399	2.9	0.07298	3.9	0.09329	4.9	0.10894	9.5	0.15432

TABLE 4. PRODUCTS—400 PER CENT THEORETICAL AIR
(For 1 lb mole)

T	$\bar{h}$	P_r	$\bar{u}$	v_r	$\bar{\phi}$
300	2085.8	0.17264	1490.0	18648	42.238
400	2784.7	0.4754	1990.3	9030	44.249
500	3486.7	1.0457	2493.8	5131	45.815
600	4191.9	1.998	3000.4	3223	47.101
700	4901.7	3.467	3511.6	2167.0	48.195
800	5617.5	5.609	4028.8	1530.6	49.150
900	6340.3	8.611	4553.0	1121.6	50.002
1000	7072.1	12.694	5086.2	845.3	50.773
1100	7812.9	18.116	5628.4	651.6	51.479
1200	8563.4	25.17	6180.4	511.6	52.132
1300	9324.1	34.20	6742.5	407.9	52.741
1400	10095.0	45.60	7314.8	329.5	53.312
1500	10875.6	59.80	7896.8	269.2	53.851
1600	11665.6	77.30	8488.2	222.1	54.360
1700	12464.3	98.64	9088.3	184.93	54.844
1800	13271.7	124.45	9697.1	155.21	55.306
1900	14087.2	155.39	10314.1	131.22	55.747
2000	14910.3	192.21	10938.6	111.66	56.169
2100	15740.5	235.7	11570.2	95.61	56.574
2200	16577.1	286.7	12208.2	82.33	56.964
2300	17419.8	346.2	12852.3	71.28	57.338
2400	18268.0	415.3	13501.9	62.02	57.699
2500	19121.4	494.9	14156.8	54.20	58.048
2600	19979.7	586.4	14816.5	47.58	58.384
2700	20842.8	690.9	15481.0	41.94	58.710
2800	21709.8	809.9	16149.4	37.10	59.026
2900	22581.4	944.7	16822.4	32.94	59.331
3000	23456.6	1096.8	17499.0	29.35	59.628
3100	24335.5	1268.3	18179.3	26.23	59.916
3200	25217.8	1460.4	18863.1	23.51	60.196
3300	26102.9	1675.3	19549.5	21.14	60.469
3400	26991.4	1914.6	20239.6	19.06	60.734

TABLE 5. PRODUCTS—200 PER CENT THEORETICAL AIR
(For 1 lb mole)

T	$\bar{h}$	P_r	$\bar{u}$	v_r	$\bar{\phi}$
300	2096.7	0.16767	1500.9	19201	42.180
400	2801.4	0.4655	2007.0	9222	44.208
500	3511.2	1.0330	2518.3	5194	45.791
600	4226.3	1.992	3034.8	3233	47.094
700	4947.7	3.487	3557.6	2154.5	48.207
800	5676.3	5.690	4087.6	1508.7	49.179
900	6413.0	8.808	4625.7	1096.4	50.047
1000	7159.8	13.089	5173.9	819.8	50.833
1100	7916.4	18.822	5731.9	627.1	51.555
1200	8683.6	26.34	6300.6	488.9	52.222
1300	9461.7	36.05	6880.1	387.0	52.845
1400	10250.7	48.38	7470.5	310.5	53.430
1500	11050.2	63.88	8071.4	252.0	53.981
1600	11859.6	83.10	8682.2	206.63	54.504
1700	12678.6	106.70	9302.6	170.97	55.000
1800	13507.0	135.43	9932.4	142.63	55.473
1900	14344.1	170.09	10571.0	119.87	55.926
2000	15189.3	211.6	11217.6	101.43	56.360
2100	16042.4	260.9	11872.1	86.36	56.777
2200	16902.5	319.2	12533.6	73.96	57.177
2300	17769.3	387.5	13201.8	63.68	57.562
2400	18642.1	467.4	13876.0	55.12	57.933
2500	19520.7	559.8	14556.0	47.91	58.292
2600	20404.6	666.6	15241.3	41.85	58.639
2700	21293.8	789.4	15932.0	36.71	58.974
2800	22187.5	929.8	16627.1	32.31	59.300
2900	23086.0	1089.8	17327.0	28.56	59.615
3000	23988.5	1271.1	18030.9	25.321	59.921
3100	24895.3	1476.8	18739.1	22.528	60.218
3200	25805.6	1708.2	19450.8	20.103	60.507
3300	26719.2	1968.3	20165.8	17.992	60.789
3400	27636.4	2259.1	20884.4	16.152	61.063
3500	28556.8	2584	21606.2	14.535	61.329
3600	29479.9	2946	22330.8	13.114	61.590
3700	30406.0	3347	23058.3	11.862	61.843
3800	31334.8	3792	23788.5	10.754	62.091
3900	32266.2	4284	24521.3	9.770	62.333

TABLE 6. ONE-DIMENSIONAL ISENTROPIC COMPRESSIBLE FLOW FUNCTIONS FOR A
PERFECT GAS WITH CONSTANT SPECIFIC HEAT
$(k = 1.4)$

M	M_*	$\dfrac{A}{A_*}$	$\dfrac{p}{p_0}$	$\dfrac{\rho}{\rho_0}$	$\dfrac{T}{T_0}$	$\dfrac{F}{F_*}$	$\left(\dfrac{A}{A_*}\right)\left(\dfrac{p}{p_0}\right)$
0.05	0.05476	11.592	0.99825	0.99875	0.99950	9.1584	11.571
0.10	0.10943	5.8218	0.99303	0.99502	0.99800	4.6236	5.7812
0.15	0.16395	3.9103	0.98441	0.98884	0.99552	3.1317	3.8493
0.20	0.21922	2.9635	0.97250	0.98027	0.99206	2.4004	2.8820
0.25	0.27216	2.4027	0.95745	0.96942	0.98765	1.9732	2.3005
0.30	0.32572	2.0351	0.93947	0.95638	0.98232	1.6979	1.9119
0.35	0.37879	1.7780	0.91877	0.94128	0.97608	1.5094	1.6336
0.40	0.43133	1.5901	0.89562	0.92428	0.96899	1.3749	1.4241
0.45	0.49326	1.4487	0.87027	0.90552	0.96108	1.2763	1.2607
0.50	0.53452	1.3398	0.84302	0.88517	0.95238	1.2027	1.12951
0.55	0.58506	1.2550	0.81416	0.86342	0.94295	1.1472	1.02174
0.60	0.63480	1.1882	0.78400	0.84045	0.93284	1.10504	0.93155
0.65	0.68374	1.1356	0.75283	0.81644	0.92208	1.07314	0.85493
0.70	0.73179	1.09437	0.72092	0.79158	0.91075	1.04915	0.78896
0.75	0.77893	1.06242	0.68857	0.76603	0.89888	1.03137	0.73155
0.80	0.82514	1.03823	0.65602	0.74000	0.88652	1.01853	0.69110
0.85	0.87037	1.02067	0.62351	0.71361	0.87374	1.00966	0.63640
0.90	0.91460	1.00886	0.59126	0.68704	0.86058	1.00399	0.59650
0.95	0.95781	1.00214	0.55946	0.66044	0.84710	1.00093	0.56066
1.0	1	1	0.52828	0.63394	0.83333	1	0.52828
1.1	1.08124	1.00793	0.46835	0.58169	0.80515	1.00305	0.47206
1.2	1.1583	1.03044	0.41238	0.53114	0.77640	1.01082	0.42493
1.3	1.2311	1.06631	0.36092	0.48291	0.74738	1.02170	0.38484
1.4	1.2999	1.1149	0.31424	0.43742	0.71839	1.03458	0.35036
1.5	1.3646	1.1762	0.27240	0.39498	0.68965	1.04870	0.32039
1.6	1.4254	1.2502	0.23527	0.35573	0.66138	1.06348	0.29414
1.7	1.4825	1.3376	0.20259	0.31969	0.63372	1.07851	0.27099
1.8	1.5360	1.4390	0.17404	0.28682	0.60680	1.09352	0.25044
1.9	1.5861	1.5552	0.14924	0.25699	0.58072	1.1083	0.23211
2.0	1.6330	1.6875	0.12780	0.23005	0.55556	1.1227	0.21567
2.2	1.7179	2.0050	0.09352	0.18405	0.50813	1.1500	0.18751
2.4	1.7922	2.4031	0.06840	0.14720	0.46468	1.1751	0.16437
2.6	1.8572	2.8960	0.05012	0.11787	0.42517	1.1978	0.14513
2.8	1.9140	3.5001	0.03685	0.09462	0.38941	1.2182	0.12897
3.0	1.9640	4.2346	0.02722	0.07623	0.35714	1.2366	0.11528
3.2	2.0079	5.1210	0.02023	0.06165	0.32808	1.2530	0.10359
3.4	2.0466	6.1837	0.01512	0.05009	0.30193	1.2676	0.09353
3.6	2.0808	7.4501	0.01138	0.04089	0.27840	1.2807	0.08482
3.8	2.111	8.9506	0.00863	0.03355	0.25720	1.2924	0.07723
4.0	2.1381	10.719	0.00658	0.02766	0.23810	1.3029	0.07059
4.2	2.1622	12.792	0.00506	0.02292	0.22085	1.3123	0.06475
4.4	2.1837	15.210	0.00392	0.01909	0.20525	1.3208	0.05959
4.6	2.2030	18.018	0.00305	0.01597	0.19113	1.3284	0.05500
4.8	2.2204	21.264	0.00240	0.01343	0.17832	1.3354	0.05091
∞	2.4495	∞	0	0	0	1.4289	0

TABLE 7. RAYLEIGH LINE

(k = 1.4, subsonic branch only)

M	$\dfrac{T_0}{T_{0*}}$	$\dfrac{T}{T_*}$	$\dfrac{p}{p_*}$	$\dfrac{p_0}{p_{0*}}$	$\dfrac{V}{V_*}$
0	0	0	2.4000	1.2679	0
0.05	0.01192	0.01430	2.3916	1.2657	0.00598
0.10	0.04678	0.05602	2.3669	1.2591	0.02367
0.15	0.10196	0.12181	2.3267	1.2486	0.05235
0.20	0.17355	0.20661	2.2727	1.2346	0.09091
0.25	0.25684	0.30440	2.2069	1.2177	0.13793
0.30	0.34686	0.40887	2.1314	1.1985	0.19183
0.35	0.43894	0.51413	2.0487	1.1779	0.25096
0.40	0.52903	0.61515	1.9608	1.1566	0.31372
0.45	0.61393	0.70803	1.8699	1.1351	0.37865
0.50	0.69136	0.79012	1.7778	1.1140	0.44445
0.55	0.75991	0.85987	1.6860	1.09397	0.51001
0.60	0.81892	0.91670	1.5957	1.07525	0.57447
0.65	0.86833	0.96081	1.5080	1.05820	0.63713
0.70	0.90850	0.99289	1.4235	1.04310	0.69751
0.75	0.94009	1.01403	1.3427	1.03010	0.75525
0.80	0.96394	1.02548	1.2658	1.01934	0.81012
0.85	0.98097	1.02854	1.1931	1.01091	0.86204
0.90	0.99207	1.02451	1.1246	1.00485	0.91097
0.95	0.99814	1.01463	1.0603	1.00121	0.95692
1.00	1	1	1	1	1

TABLE 8. FANNO LINE
($k = 1.4$, subsonic branch only)

M	$\dfrac{T}{T_*}$	$\dfrac{p}{p_*}$	$\dfrac{p_0}{p_{0*}}$	$\dfrac{V}{V_*}$	$\dfrac{F}{F_*}$	$4\dfrac{fL_{max}}{D}$
0	1.2000	∞	∞	0	∞	∞
0.05	1.1994	21.903	11.5914	0.05476	9.1584	280.02
0.10	1.1976	10.9435	5.8218	0.10943	4.6236	66.922
0.15	1.1946	7.2866	3.9103	0.16395	3.1317	27.932
0.20	1.1905	5.4555	2.9635	0.21822	2.4004	14.533
0.25	1.1852	4.3546	2.4027	0.27217	1.9732	8.4834
0.30	1.1788	3.6190	2.0351	0.32572	1.6979	5.2992
0.35	1.1713	3.0922	1.7780	0.37880	1.5094	3.4525
0.40	1.1628	2.6958	1.5901	0.43133	1.3749	2.3085
0.45	1.1533	2.3865	1.4486	0.48326	1.2763	1.5663
0.50	1.1429	2.1381	1.3399	0.53453	1.2027	1.06908
0.55	1.1315	1.9341	1.2549	0.58506	1.1472	0.72805
0.60	1.1194	1.7634	1.1882	0.63481	1.10504	0.49081
0.65	1.10650	1.6183	1.1356	0.68374	1.07314	0.32460
0.70	1.09290	1.4934	1.09436	0.73179	1.04915	0.20814
0.75	1.07865	1.3848	1.06242	0.77893	1.03137	0.12728
0.80	1.06383	1.2892	1.03823	0.82514	1.01853	0.07229
0.85	1.04849	1.2047	1.02067	0.87037	1.00966	0.03632
0.90	1.03270	1.12913	1.00887	0.91459	1.00399	0.014513
0.95	1.01652	1.06129	1.00215	0.95782	1.00093	0.003280
1.00	1	1	1	1	1	0

TABLE 9. ONE-DIMENSIONAL NORMAL SHOCK FUNCTIONS
$(k = 1.4)$

M_x	M_x	$\dfrac{p_v}{p_x}$	$\dfrac{\rho_y}{\rho_x}$	$\dfrac{T_y}{T_x}$	$\dfrac{p_{oy}}{p_{ox}}$	$\dfrac{p_{oy}}{p_x}$
1.0	1.00000	1.00000	1.00000	1.00000	1.00000	1.8929
1.1	0.9117	1.2450	1.1691	1.06494	0.99892	2.1328
1.2	0.84217	1.5133	1.3416	1.1280	0.99280	2.4075
1.3	0.78596	1.8050	1.5157	1.1909	0.97935	2.7135
1.4	0.73971	2.1200	1.6896	1.2547	0.95819	3.0493
1.5	0.70109	2.4583	1.8621	1.2302	0.92978	3.4133
1.6	0.66844	2.8201	2.0317	1.3880	0.89520	3.8049
1.7	0.64055	3.2050	2.1977	1.4583	0.85573	4.2238
1.8	0.61650	3.6133	2.3592	1.5316	0.81268	4.6695
1.9	0.59562	4.0450	2.5157	1.6079	0.76735	5.1417
2.0	0.57735	4.5000	2.6666	1.6875	0.72088	5.6405
2.1	0.56128	4.9784	2.8119	1.7704	0.67422	6.1655
2.2	0.54706	5.4800	2.9512	1.8569	0.62812	6.7163
2.3	0.53441	6.0050	3.0846	1.9468	0.58331	7.2937
2.4	0.52312	6.5533	3.2119	2.0403	0.54015	7.8969
2.5	0.51299	7.1250	3.3333	2.1375	0.49902	8.5262
2.6	0.50387	7.7200	3.4489	2.2383	0.46012	9.1813
2.7	0.49563	8.3383	3.5590	2.3429	0.42359	0.98625
2.8	0.48817	8.9800	3.6635	2.4512	0.38946	10.569
2.9	0.48138	9.6450	3.7629	2.5632	0.35773	11.302
3.0	0.47519	10.333	3.8571	2.6790	0.32834	12.061
4.0	0.43496	18.500	4.5714	4.0469	0.13876	21.068
5.0	0.41523	29.000	5.0000	5.8000	0.06172	32.654
∞	0.37796	∞	6.0000	∞	0	∞

TABLE 10. STANDARD ATMOSPHERE

Altitude, ft.	t	T	p	ρ
0	59.0	518.7	14.696	0.07651
1,000	55.4	515.1	14.175	0.07430
2,000	51.9	511.6	13.664	0.07213
3,000	48.3	508.0	13.168	0.07001
4,000	44.7	504.4	12.692	0.06794
5,000	41.2	500.9	12.225	0.06592
6,000	37.6	497.3	11.778	0.06395
7,000	34.0	493.7	11.341	0.06202
8,000	30.5	490.2	10.914	0.06013
9,000	26.9	486.6	10.501	0.05829
10,000	23.3	483.0	10.108	0.05649
12,000	16.2	475.9	9.347	0.05303
14,000	9.1	486.8	8.630	0.04973
16,000	1.9	461.6	7.962	0.04658
18,000	− 5.2	454.5	7.338	0.04359
20,000	−12.3	447.4	6.753	0.04075
22,000	−19.5	440.2	6.203	0.03806
24,000	−26.6	433.1	5.693	0.03550
26,000	−33.7	426.0	5.216	0.03308
28,000	−40.9	418.8	4.774	0.03078
30,000	−48.0	411.7	4.362	0.02861
32,000	−55.1	404.6	3.978	0.02656
34,000	−62.2	397.5	3.625	0.02463
36,000	−67.0	392.7	3.296	0.02265
38,000	−67.0	392.7	2.996	0.02059
40,000	......	.....	2.721	0.01872
42,000	......	.....	2.475	0.01701
44,000	......	.....	2.250	0.01546
46,000	......	.....	2.043	0.01405
48,000	......	.....	1.857	0.01277
50,000	......	.....	1.690	0.01161
52,000	......	.....	1.532	0.01055
54,000	......	.....	1.395	0.00959
56,000	......	.....	1.267	0.00872
58,000	......	.....	1.154	0.00792
60,000	......	.....	1.046	0.00720
62,000	......	.....	0.953	0.00655
64,000	......	.....	0.864	0.00595

TABLE 11. DRY SATURATED STEAM: PRESSURE TABLE*

Abs Press., Lb Sq In. p	Temp., °F t	Specific Volume		Enthalpy			Entropy			Internal Energy		Abs Press., Lb Sq In. p
		Sat. Liquid v_f	Sat. Vapor v_g	Sat. Liquid h_f	Evap h_{fg}	Sat. Vapor h_g	Sat. Liquid s_f	Evap s_{fg}	Sat. Vapor s_g	Sat. Liquid u_f	Sat. Vapor u_g	
0.491	79.03	0.01608	652.3	47.05	1049.2	1096.3	0.0914	1.9473	2.0387	47.05	1037.0	0.491
0.736	91.72	0.01611	444.9	59.71	1042.0	1101.7	0.1147	1.8894	2.0041	59.71	1041.1	0.736
0.982	101.14	0.01614	339.2	69.10	1036.6	1105.7	0.1316	1.8481	1.9797	69.10	1044.0	0.982
1.227	108.71	0.01616	274.9	76.65	1032.3	1108.9	0.1449	1.8160	1.9609	76.65	1046.4	1.227
1.473	115.06	0.01618	231.6	82.99	1028.6	1111.6	0.1560	1.7896	1.9456	82.99	1048.5	1.473
1.964	125.43	0.01622	176.7	93.34	1022.7	1116.0	0.1738	1.7476	1.9214	93.33	1051.8	1.964
2.455	133.76	0.01626	143.25	101.66	1017.0	1119.4	0.1879	1.7150	1.9028	101.65	1054.3	2.455
5	162.24	0.01640	73.52	130.13	1001.0	1131.1	0.2347	1.6094	1.8441	130.12	1063.1	5
10	193.21	0.01659	38.42	161.17	982.1	1143.3	0.2835	1.5041	1.7876	161.14	1072.2	10
14.696	212.0	0.01672	26.80	180.07	970.3	1150.4	0.3120	1.4446	1.7566	180.02	1077.5	14.696
15	213.03	0.01672	26.29	181.11	969.7	1150.8	0.3135	1.4415	1.7549	181.06	1077.7	15
16	216.32	0.01674	24.75	184.42	967.6	1152.0	0.3184	1.4313	1.7497	184.37	1078.7	16
18	222.41	0.01679	22.17	190.56	963.6	1154.2	0.3275	1.4128	1.7403	190.50	1080.4	18
20	227.96	0.01683	20.089	196.16	960.1	1156.3	0.3356	1.3962	1.7319	196.10	1081.9	20
25	240.07	0.01692	16.303	208.42	952.1	1160.6	0.3533	1.3606	1.7139	208.34	1085.1	25
30	250.33	0.01701	13.746	218.82	945.3	1164.1	0.3680	1.3313	1.6993	218.73	1087.8	30
35	259.28	0.01708	11.898	227.91	939.2	1167.1	0.3807	1.3063	1.6870	227.80	1090.1	35
40	267.25	0.01715	10.498	236.03	933.7	1169.7	0.3919	1.2844	1.6763	235.90	1092.0	40
45	274.44	0.01721	9.401	243.36	928.6	1172.0	0.4019	1.2650	1.6669	243.22	1093.7	45
50	281.01	0.01727	8.515	250.09	924.0	1174.1	0.4110	1.2474	1.6585	249.93	1095.3	50
55	287.07	0.01732	7.787	256.30	919.6	1175.9	0.4193	1.2316	1.6509	256.12	1096.7	55
60	292.71	0.01738	7.175	262.09	915.5	1177.6	0.4270	1.2168	1.6438	261.90	1097.9	60
65	297.97	0.01743	6.655	267.50	911.6	1179.1	0.4342	1.2032	1.6374	267.28	1099.1	65
70	302.92	0.01748	6.206	272.61	907.9	1180.6	0.4409	1.1906	1.6315	272.38	1100.2	70
75	307.60	0.01753	5.816	277.43	904.5	1181.9	0.4472	1.1787	1.6259	277.19	1101.2	75
80	312.03	0.01757	5.472	282.02	901.1	1183.1	0.4531	1.1676	1.6207	281.76	1102.1	80
85	316.25	0.01761	5.168	286.39	897.8	1184.2	0.4587	1.1571	1.6158	286.11	1102.9	85
90	320.27	0.01766	4.896	290.56	894.7	1185.3	0.4641	1.1471	1.6112	290.27	1103.7	90
100	327.81	0.01774	4.432	298.40	888.8	1187.2	0.4740	1.1286	1.6026	298.08	1105.3	100
110	334.77	0.01782	4.049	305.66	883.2	1188.9	0.4832	1.1117	1.5948	305.30	1106.5	110

p	t	v_f	v_g	h_f	h_{fg}	h_g	s_f	s_{fg}	s_g	u_f	u_g
120	341.25	0.01789	3.728	312.44	877.9	1190.4	0.4916	1.0962	1.5878	312.05	1107.6
130	347.32	0.01796	3.455	318.81	872.9	1191.7	0.4995	1.0817	1.5812	318.38	1108.6
140	353.02	0.01802	3.220	324.82	868.2	1193.0	0.5069	1.0682	1.5751	324.35	1109.6
150	358.42	0.01809	3.015	330.51	863.6	1194.1	0.5138	1.0556	1.5694	330.01	1110.5
160	363.53	0.01815	2.834	335.93	859.2	1195.1	0.5204	1.0436	1.5640	335.39	1111.2
170	368.41	0.01822	2.675	341.09	854.9	1196.0	0.5266	1.0324	1.5590	340.52	1111.9
180	373.06	0.01827	2.532	346.03	850.8	1196.9	0.5325	1.0217	1.5542	345.42	1112.5
190	377.51	0.01833	2.404	350.79	846.8	1197.6	0.5381	1.0116	1.5497	350.15	1113.1
200	381.79	0.01839	2.288	355.36	843.0	1198.4	0.5435	1.0018	1.5453	354.68	1113.7
250	400.95	0.01865	1.8438	376.00	825.1	1201.1	0.5675	0.9588	1.5263	375.14	1115.8
300	417.33	0.01890	1.5433	393.84	809.0	1202.8	0.5879	0.9225	1.5104	392.79	1117.1
350	431.72	0.01913	1.3260	409.69	794.2	1203.9	0.6056	0.8910	1.4966	408.45	1118.0
400	444.59	0.0193	1.1613	424.0	780.5	1204.5	0.6214	0.8630	1.4844	422.6	1118.5
450	456.28	0.0195	1.0320	437.2	767.4	1204.6	0.6356	0.8378	1.4734	435.5	1118.7
500	467.01	0.0197	0.9278	449.4	755.0	1204.4	0.6487	0.8147	1.4634	447.6	1118.6
550	476.94	0.0199	0.8424	460.8	743.1	1203.9	0.6608	0.7934	1.4542	458.8	1118.2
600	486.21	0.0201	0.7698	471.6	731.6	1203.2	0.6720	0.7734	1.4454	469.4	1117.7
650	494.90	0.0203	0.7083	481.8	720.5	1202.3	0.6826	0.7548	1.4374	479.4	1117.1
700	503.10	0.0205	0.6554	491.5	709.7	1201.2	0.6925	0.7371	1.4296	488.8	1116.3
750	510.86	0.0207	0.6092	500.8	699.2	1200.0	0.7019	0.7204	1.4223	498.0	1115.4
800	518.23	0.0209	0.5687	509.7	688.9	1198.6	0.7108	0.7045	1.4153	506.6	1114.4
850	525.26	0.0210	0.5327	518.3	678.8	1197.1	0.7194	0.6891	1.4085	515.0	1113.3
900	531.98	0.0212	0.5006	526.6	668.8	1195.4	0.7275	0.6744	1.4020	523.1	1112.1
950	538.43	0.0214	0.4717	534.6	658.5	1193.1	0.7355	0.6602	1.3957	530.9	1110.8
1000	544.61	0.0216	0.4456	542.4	649.4	1191.8	0.7430	0.6467	1.3897	538.4	1109.4
1100	556.31	0.0220	0.4001	557.4	630.4	1187.8	0.7575	0.6205	1.3780	552.9	1106.4
1200	567.22	0.0223	0.3619	571.7	611.7	1183.4	0.7711	0.5956	1.3667	566.7	1103.0
1300	577.46	0.0227	0.3293	585.4	593.2	1178.6	0.7840	0.5719	1.3559	580.0	1099.4
1400	587.10	0.0231	0.3012	598.7	574.7	1173.4	0.7963	0.5491	1.3454	592.7	1095.4
1500	596.23	0.0235	0.2765	611.6	556.3	1167.9	0.8082	0.5269	1.3351	605.1	1091.2
2000	635.82	0.0257	0.1878	671.7	463.4	1135.1	0.8619	0.4230	1.2849	662.2	1065.6
2500	668.13	0.0287	0.1307	730.6	360.5	1091.1	0.9126	0.3197	1.2322	717.3	1030.6
3000	695.36	0.0346	0.0858	802.5	217.8	1020.3	0.9731	0.1885	1.1615	783.4	972.7
3206.2	705.40	0.0503	0.0503	902.7	0	902.7	1.0580	0	1.0580	872.9	872.9

TABLE 12. DRY SATURATED STEAM: TEMPERATURE TABLE*

Temp. F, t	Abs Press., Lb Sq In. p	Specific Volume Sat. Liquid v_f	Specific Volume Evap. v_fg	Specific Volume Sat. Vapor v_g	Enthalpy Sat. Liquid h_f	Enthalpy Evap. h_fg	Enthalpy Sat. Vapor h_g	Entropy Sat. Liquid s_f	Entropy Evap. s_fg	Entropy Sat. Vapor s_g	Temp. F, t
32	0.08854	0.01602	3306	3306	0.00	1075.8	1075.8	0.0000	2.1877	2.1877	32
35	0.09995	0.01602	2947	2947	3.02	1074.1	1077.1	0.0061	2.1709	2.1770	35
40	0.12170	0.01602	2444	2444	8.05	1071.3	1079.3	0.0162	2.1435	2.1597	40
45	0.14752	0.01602	2036.4	2036.4	13.06	1068.4	1081.5	0.0262	2.1167	2.1429	45
50	0.17811	0.01603	1703.2	1703.2	18.07	1065.6	1083.7	0.0361	2.0903	2.1264	50
60	0.2563	0.01604	1206.6	1206.7	28.06	1059.9	1088.0	0.0555	2.0393	2.0948	60
70	0.3631	0.01606	867.8	867.9	38.04	1054.3	1092.3	0.0745	1.9902	2.0647	70
80	0.5069	0.01608	633.1	633.1	48.02	1048.6	1096.6	0.0932	1.9428	2.0360	80
90	0.6982	0.01610	468.0	468.0	57.99	1042.9	1100.9	0.1115	1.8972	2.0087	90
100	0.9492	0.01613	350.3	350.4	67.97	1037.2	1105.2	0.1295	1.8531	1.9826	100
110	1.2748	0.01617	265.3	265.4	77.94	1031.6	1109.5	0.1471	1.8106	1.9577	110
120	1.6924	0.01620	203.25	203.27	87.92	1025.8	1113.7	0.1645	1.7694	1.9339	120
130	2.2225	0.01625	157.32	157.34	97.90	1020.0	1117.9	0.1816	1.7296	1.9112	130
140	2.8886	0.01629	122.99	123.01	107.89	1014.1	1122.0	0.1984	1.6910	1.8894	140
150	3.718	0.01634	97.06	97.07	117.89	1008.2	1126.1	0.2149	1.6537	1.8685	150
160	4.741	0.01639	77.27	77.29	127.89	1002.3	1130.2	0.2311	1.6174	1.8485	160
170	5.992	0.01645	62.04	62.06	137.90	996.3	1134.2	0.2472	1.5822	1.8293	170
180	7.510	0.01651	50.21	50.23	147.92	990.2	1138.1	0.2630	1.5480	1.8109	180
190	9.339	0.01657	40.94	40.96	157.95	984.1	1142.0	0.2785	1.5147	1.7932	190
200	11.526	0.01663	33.62	33.64	167.99	977.9	1145.9	0.2938	1.4824	1.7762	200
210	14.123	0.01670	27.80	27.82	178.05	971.6	1149.7	0.3090	1.4508	1.7598	210
212	14.696	0.01672	26.78	26.80	180.07	970.3	1150.4	0.3120	1.4446	1.7566	212
220	17.186	0.01677	23.13	23.15	188.13	965.2	1153.4	0.3239	1.4201	1.7440	220
230	20.780	0.01684	19.365	19.382	198.23	958.8	1157.0	0.3387	1.3901	1.7288	230
240	24.969	0.01692	16.306	16.323	208.34	952.2	1160.5	0.3531	1.3609	1.7140	240
250	29.825	0.01700	13.804	13.821	218.48	945.5	1164.0	0.3675	1.3323	1.6998	250
260	35.429	0.01709	11.746	11.763	228.64	938.7	1167.3	0.3817	1.3043	1.6860	260
270	41.858	0.01717	10.044	10.061	238.84	931.8	1170.6	0.3958	1.2769	1.6727	270
280	49.203	0.01726	8.628	8.645	249.06	924.7	1173.8	0.4096	1.2501	1.6597	280
290	57.556	0.01735	7.444	7.461	259.31	917.5	1176.8	0.4234	1.2238	1.6472	290

Temp	p	vf	vfg	vg	hf	hfg	hg	sf	sfg	sg	Temp
300	67.013	0.01745	6.449	6.466	269.59	910.1	1179.7	0.4369	1.1980	1.6350	300
310	77.68	0.01755	5.609	5.626	279.92	902.6	1182.5	0.4504	1.1727	1.6231	310
320	89.66	0.01765	4.896	4.914	290.28	894.9	1185.2	0.4637	1.1478	1.6115	320
330	103.06	0.01776	4.289	4.307	300.68	887.0	1187.7	0.4769	1.1233	1.6002	330
340	118.01	0.01787	3.770	3.788	311.13	879.0	1190.1	0.4900	1.0992	1.5581	340
350	134.63	0.01799	3.324	3.342	321.63	870.7	1192.3	0.5029	1.0754	1.5783	350
360	153.04	0.01811	2.939	2.957	332.18	862.2	1194.4	0.5158	1.0519	1.5677	360
370	173.37	0.01823	2.606	2.625	342.79	853.5	1196.3	0.5286	1.0287	1.5573	370
380	195.77	0.01836	2.317	2.335	353.45	844.6	1198.1	0.5413	1.0059	1.5471	380
390	220.37	0.01850	2.0651	2.0836	364.17	835.4	1199.6	0.5539	0.9832	1.5371	390
400	247.31	0.01864	1.8447	1.8633	374.97	826.0	1201.0	0.5664	0.9608	1.5272	400
410	276.75	0.01878	1.6512	1.6700	385.83	816.3	1202.1	0.5788	0.9386	1.5174	410
420	308.83	0.01894	1.4811	1.5000	396.77	806.3	1203.1	0.5912	0.9166	1.5078	420
430	343.72	0.01910	1.3308	1.3499	407.79	796.0	1203.8	0.6035	0.8947	1.4982	430
440	381.59	0.01926	1.1979	1.2171	418.90	785.4	1204.3	0.6158	0.8730	1.4887	440
450	422.6	0.0194	1.0799	1.0993	430.1	774.5	1204.6	0.6280	0.8513	1.4793	450
460	466.9	0.0196	0.9748	0.9944	441.4	763.2	1204.6	0.6402	0.8298	1.4700	460
470	514.7	0.0198	0.8811	0.9009	452.8	751.5	1204.3	0.6523	0.8083	1.4606	470
480	566.1	0.0200	0.7972	0.8172	464.4	739.4	1203.7	0.6645	0.7868	1.4513	480
490	621.4	0.0202	0.7221	0.7423	476.0	726.8	1202.8	0.6766	0.7653	1.4419	490
500	680.8	0.0204	0.6545	0.6749	487.8	713.9	1201.7	0.6887	0.7438	1.4325	500
520	812.4	0.0209	0.5385	0.5594	511.9	686.4	1198.2	0.7130	0.7006	1.4136	520
540	962.5	0.0215	0.4434	0.4649	536.6	656.6	1193.2	0.7374	0.6568	1.3942	540
560	1133.1	0.0221	0.3647	0.3868	562.2	624.2	1186.4	0.7621	0.6121	1.3742	560
580	1325.8	0.0228	0.2989	0.3217	588.9	588.4	1177.3	0.7872	0.5659	1.3532	580
600	1542.9	0.0236	0.2432	0.2668	617.0	548.5	1165.5	0.8131	0.5176	1.3307	600
620	1786.6	0.0247	0.1955	0.2201	646.7	503.6	1150.3	0.8398	0.4664	1.3062	620
640	2059.7	0.0260	0.1538	0.1798	678.6	452.0	1130.5	0.8679	0.4110	1.2789	640
660	2365.4	0.0278	0.1165	0.1442	714.2	390.2	1104.4	0.8987	0.3485	1.2472	660
680	2708.1	0.0305	0.0810	0.1115	757.3	309.9	1067.2	0.9351	0.2719	1.2071	680
700	3093.7	0.0369	0.0392	0.0761	823.3	172.1	995.4	0.9905	0.1484	1.1389	700
705.4	3206.2	0.0503	0	0.0503	902.7	0	902.7	1.0580	0	1.0580	705.4

TABLE 13. PROPERTIES OF SUPERHEATED STEAM*

Abs Press., Lb Sq In. (Sat. Temp.)		Temperature—Degrees Fahrenheit												
		200	220	300	350	400	450	500	550	600	700	800	900	1000
1 (101.74)	v	392.6	404.5	452.3	482.2	512.0	541.8	571.6	601.4	631.2	690.8	750.4	809.9	869.5
	h	1150.4	1159.5	1195.8	1218.7	1241.7	1264.9	1288.3	1312.0	1335.7	1383.8	1432.8	1482.7	1533.5
	s	2.0512	2.0647	2.1153	2.1444	2.1720	2.1983	2.2233	2.2468	2.2702	2.3137	2.3542	2.3923	2.4283
5 (162.24)	v	78.16	80.59	90.25	96.26	102.26	108.24	114.22	120.19	126.16	138.10	150.03	161.95	173.87
	h	1148.8	1158.1	1195.0	1218.1	1241.2	1264.5	1288.0	1311.7	1335.4	1383.6	1432.7	1482.6	1533.4
	s	1.8718	1.8857	1.9370	1.9664	1.9942	2.0205	2.0456	2.0692	2.0927	2.1361	2.1767	2.2148	2.2509
10 (193.21)	v	38.85	40.09	45.00	48.03	51.04	54.05	57.05	60.04	63.03	69.01	74.98	80.95	86.92
	h	1146.6	1156.2	1193.9	1217.2	1240.6	1264.0	1287.5	1311.3	1335.1	1383.4	1432.5	1482.4	1533.2
	s	1.7927	1.8071	1.8595	1.8882	1.9172	1.9436	1.9689	1.9924	2.0160	2.0596	2.1002	2.1383	2.1744
14.696 (212.00)	v		27.15	30.53	32.62	34.68	36.73	38.78	40.82	42.86	46.94	51.00	55.07	59.13
	h		1154.4	1192.8	1216.4	1239.9	1263.5	1287.1	1310.9	1334.8	1383.2	1432.3	1482.3	1533.1
	s		1.7624	1.8160	1.8460	1.8743	1.9008	1.9261	1.9498	1.9734	2.0170	2.0576	2.0958	2.1319
20 (227.96)	v			22.36	23.91	25.43	26.95	28.46	29.97	31.47	34.47	37.46	40.45	43.44
	h			1191.6	1215.6	1239.2	1262.9	1286.6	1310.5	1334.4	1382.9	1432.1	1482.1	1533.0
	s			1.7808	1.8112	1.8396	1.8664	1.8918	1.9160	1.9392	1.9829	2.0235	2.0618	2.0978
40 (267.25)	v			11.040	11.843	12.628	13.401	14.168	14.93	15.688	17.198	18.702	20.20	21.70
	h			1186.8	1211.9	1236.5	1260.7	1284.8	1308.9	1333.1	1381.9	1431.3	1481.4	1532.4
	s			1.6994	1.7314	1.7608	1.7881	1.8140	1.8384	1.8619	1.9058	1.9467	1.9850	2.0214
60 (292.71)	v			7.259	7.818	8.357	8.884	9.403	9.916	10.427	11.441	12.449	13.452	14.454
	h			1181.6	1208.2	1233.6	1258.5	1283.0	1307.4	1331.8	1380.9	1430.5	1480.8	1531.9
	s			1.6492	1.6830	1.7135	1.7416	1.7678	1.7926	1.8162	1.8605	1.9015	1.9400	1.9762
80 (312.03)	v				5.803	6.22	6.624	7.020	7.410	7.797	8.562	9.322	10.077	10.830
	h				1204.3	1230.7	1256.1	1281.1	1305.8	1330.5	1379.9	1429.7	1480.1	1531.3
	s				1.6475	1.6791	1.7078	1.7346	1.7598	1.7836	1.8281	1.8694	1.9079	1.9442
100 (327.81)	v				4.592	4.937	5.268	5.589	5.905	6.218	6.835	7.446	8.052	8.656
	h				1200.1	1227.6	1253.7	1279.1	1304.2	1329.1	1378.9	1428.9	1479.5	1530.8
	s				1.6188	1.6518	1.6813	1.7085	1.7339	1.7581	1.8029	1.8443	1.8829	1.9193
120 (341.25)	v				3.783	4.081	4.363	4.636	4.902	5.165	5.683	6.195	6.702	7.207
	h				1195.7	1224.4	1251.3	1277.2	1302.5	1327.7	1377.8	1428.1	1478.8	1530.2
	s				1.5944	1.6287	1.6591	1.6869	1.7127	1.7370	1.7822	1.8237	1.8625	1.8990

Pressure (Sat. Temp)										
140 (353.02)	v	3.468	3.715	3.954	4.186	4.413	4.861	5.301	5.738	6.172
	h	1221.1	1248.7	1275.2	1300.9	1326.4	1376.8	1427.3	1478.2	1529.7
	s	1.6087	1.6515	1.6683	1.6945	1.7190	1.7645	1.8063	1.8451	1.8817
160 (363.53)	v	3.008	3.230	3.443	3.648	3.849	4.244	4.631	5.015	5.396
	h	1217.6	1246.1	1273.1	1299.3	1325.0	1375.7	1426.4	1477.5	1529.1
	s	1.5908	1.6230	1.6519	1.6785	1.7033	1.7491	1.7911	1.8301	1.8667
180 (373.06)	v	2.649	2.852	3.044	3.229	3.411	3.764	4.110	4.452	4.792
	h	1214.0	1248.5	1271.0	1297.6	1323.5	1374.7	1425.6	1476.8	1528.6
	s	1.5745	1.6077	1.6373	1.6642	1.6894	1.7355	1.7776	1.8167	1.8534
200 (381.79)	v	2.361	2.549	2.726	2.895	3.060	3.380	3.693	4.002	4.309
	h	1210.3	1240.7	1268.9	1295.8	1322.1	1373.6	1424.8	1476.2	1528.0
	s	1.5594	1.5937	1.6240	1.6513	1.6767	1.7232	1.7655	1.8048	1.8415
220 (389.86)	v	2.125	2.301	2.465	2.621	2.772	3.066	3.352	3.634	3.913
	h	1206.5	1237.9	1266.7	1294.1	1320.7	1372.6	1424.0	1475.5	1527.5
	s	1.5453	1.5808	1.6117	1.6395	1.6652	1.7120	1.7545	1.7939	1.8308
240 (397.37)	v	1.9276	2.1120	2.247	2.393	2.533	2.804	3.068	3.327	3.584
	h	1202.5	1234.9	1264.5	1292.4	1319.2	1371.5	1423.2	1474.8	1526.9
	s	1.5319	1.5686	1.6003	1.6286	1.6546	1.7017	1.7444	1.7839	1.8209
260 (404.42)	v		1.9183	2.063	2.199	2.330	2.582	2.827	3.067	3.305
	h		1232.0	1262.3	1290.5	1317.7	1370.4	1422.3	1474.2	1526.3
	s		1.5573	1.5897	1.6184	1.6447	1.6922	1.7352	1.7748	1.8118
280 (411.05)	v		1.7674	1.9047	2.033	2.156	2.392	2.621	2.845	3.066
	h		1228.9	1260.0	1288.7	1316.2	1369.4	1421.5	1473.5	1525.8
	s		1.5464	1.5796	1.6087	1.6354	1.6834	1.7265	1.7662	1.8033
300 (417.33)	v		1.6364	1.7675	1.8891	2.005	2.227	2.442	2.652	2.859
	h		1225.8	1257.6	1286.8	1314.7	1368.3	1420.6	1472.8	1525.2
	s		1.5360	1.5701	1.5998	1.6268	1.6751	1.7184	1.7582	1.7954
350 (431.72)	v		1.3734	1.4923	1.6010	1.7036	1.8980	2.084	2.266	2.445
	h		1217.7	1251.5	1282.1	1310.9	1365.5	1418.5	1471.1	1523.8
	s		1.5119	1.5481	1.5792	1.6070	1.6563	1.7002	1.7403	1.7777
400 (444.59)	v		1.1744	1.2851	1.3843	1.4770	1.6508	1.8161	1.9767	2.134
	h		1208.8	1245.1	1277.2	1306.9	1362.7	1416.4	1469.4	1522.4
	s		1.4892	1.5281	1.5607	1.5894	1.6398	1.6842	1.7247	1.7623

* Abridged from "Thermodynamic Properties of Steam," by Joseph H. Keenan and Frederick G. Keyes. Copyright, 1937, by Joseph H. Keenan and Frederick G. Keyes. Published by John Wiley & Sons, Inc., New York.

TABLE 13. PROPERTIES OF SUPERHEATED STEAM.* (Continued)

Abs Press. Lb Sq In. (Sat. Temp.)		Temperature—Degrees Fahrenheit													
		500	550	600	620	640	660	680	700	800	900	1000	1200	1400	1600
450 (456.28)	v	1.1231	1.2155	1.3005	1.3332	1.3652	1.3967	1.4278	1.4584	1.6074	1.7516	1.8928	2.170	2.443	2.714
	h	1238.4	1272.0	1302.8	1314.6	1326.2	1337.5	1348.8	1359.9	1414.3	1467.7	1521.0	1628.6	1738.7	1851.9
	s	1.5095	1.5437	1.5735	1.5845	1.5951	1.6054	1.6153	1.6250	1.6699	1.7108	1.7486	1.8177	1.8803	1.9381
500 (467.01)	v	0.9927	1.0800	1.1591	1.1893	1.2188	1.2478	1.2763	1.3044	1.4405	1.5715	1.6996	1.9504	2.197	2.442
	h	1231.3	1266.8	1298.6	1310.7	1322.6	1334.2	1345.7	1357.0	1412.1	1466.0	1519.6	1627.6	1737.9	1851.3
	s	1.4919	1.5280	1.5588	1.5701	1.5810	1.5915	1.6016	1.6115	1.6571	1.6982	1.7363	1.8056	1.8683	1.9262
550 (476.94)	v	0.8852	0.9686	1.0431	1.0714	1.0989	1.1259	1.1523	1.1783	1.3038	1.4241	1.5414	1.7706	1.9957	2.219
	h	1223.7	1261.2	1294.3	1306.8	1318.9	1330.8	1342.5	1354.0	1409.9	1464.3	1518.2	1626.6	1737.1	1850.6
	s	1.4751	1.5131	1.5451	1.5568	1.5680	1.5787	1.5890	1.5991	1.6452	1.6868	1.7250	1.7946	1.8575	1.9155
600 (486.21)	v	0.7947	0.8753	0.9463	0.9729	0.9988	1.0241	1.0489	1.0732	1.1899	1.3013	1.4096	1.6208	1.8279	2.033
	h	1215.7	1255.5	1289.9	1302.7	1315.2	1327.4	1339.3	1351.1	1407.7	1462.5	1516.7	1625.5	1736.3	1850.0
	s	1.4586	1.4990	1.5323	1.5443	1.5558	1.5667	1.5773	1.5875	1.6343	1.6762	1.7147	1.7846	1.8476	1.9056
700 (503.10)	v		0.7277	0.7934	0.8177	0.8411	0.8639	0.8860	0.9077	1.0108	1.1082	1.2024	1.3853	1.5641	1.7405
	h		1243.2	1280.6	1294.3	1307.5	1320.3	1332.8	1345.0	1403.2	1459.0	1513.3	1623.3	1734.8	1848.8
	s		1.4722	1.5084	1.5212	1.5333	1.5449	1.5559	1.5665	1.6147	1.6573	1.6963	1.7666	1.8299	1.8881
800 (518.23)	v		0.6154	0.6779	0.7006	0.7223	0.7433	0.7635	0.7833	0.8763	0.9633	1.0470	1.2088	1.3662	1.5214
	h		1229.8	1270.7	1285.4	1299.4	1312.9	1325.9	1338.6	1398.6	1455.4	1511.0	1621.4	1733.2	1847.5
	s		1.4467	1.4863	1.5000	1.5129	1.5250	1.5366	1.5476	1.5972	1.6407	1.6801	1.7510	1.8146	1.8729
900 (531.98)	v		0.5264	0.5873	0.6089	0.6294	0.6491	0.6680	0.6863	0.7716	0.8506	0.9262	1.0714	1.2124	1.3509
	h		1215.0	1260.1	1275.9	1290.9	1305.1	1318.8	1332.1	1393.9	1451.8	1508.1	1619.3	1731.6	1846.3
	s		1.4216	1.4653	1.4800	1.4938	1.5066	1.5187	1.5303	1.5814	1.6257	1.6656	1.7371	1.8009	1.8595
1000 (544.61)	v		0.4533	0.5140	0.5350	0.5546	0.5733	0.5912	0.6084	0.6878	0.7604	0.8294	0.9615	1.0893	1.2146
	h		1198.3	1248.8	1265.9	1281.9	1297.0	1311.4	1325.3	1389.2	1448.2	1505.1	1617.3	1730.0	1845.0
	s		1.3961	1.4450	1.4610	1.4757	1.4893	1.5021	1.5141	1.5670	1.6121	1.6525	1.7245	1.7886	1.8474
1100 (556.31)	v			0.4532	0.4738	0.4929	0.5110	0.5281	0.5445	0.6191	0.6866	0.7503	0.8716	0.9885	1.1031
	h			1236.7	1255.3	1272.4	1288.5	1303.7	1318.3	1384.3	1444.5	1502.2	1615.2	1728.4	1843.8
	s			1.4251	1.4425	1.4583	1.4728	1.4862	1.4989	1.5535	1.5995	1.6405	1.7130	1.7775	1.8363
1200 (567.22)	v			0.4016	0.4222	0.4410	0.4586	0.4752	0.4909	0.5617	0.6250	0.6843	0.7967	0.9046	1.0101
	h			1223.5	1243.9	1262.4	1279.6	1295.7	1311.0	1379.3	1440.7	1499.2	1613.1	1726.9	1842.5
	s			1.4052	1.4243	1.4413	1.4568	1.4710	1.4843	1.5409	1.5879	1.6293	1.7025	1.7672	1.8263

Pressure (sat. temp)													
1400 (587.10)	v	0.8640	0.7727	0.6789	0.5805	0.5281	0.4714	0.4062	0.3912	0.3753	0.3580	0.3390	0.3174
	h	1840.0	1723.7	1608.9	1493.2	1433.1	1369.1	1295.5	1278.5	1260.3	1240.4	1218.4	1193.0
	s	1.8083	1.7489	1.6836	1.6093	1.5666	1.5177	1.4567	1.4419	1.4258	1.4079	1.3877	1.3639
1600 (604.90)	v	0.7545	0.6738	0.5906	0.5027	0.4553	0.4034	0.3417	0.3271	0.3112	0.2936	0.2733	.....
	h	1837.5	1720.5	1604.6	1487.0	1425.3	1358.4	1278.7	1259.6	1238.7	1215.2	1187.8	....
	s	1.7926	1.7328	1.6669	1.5914	1.5476	1.4964	1.4303	1.4137	1.3952	1.3741	1.3489	....
1800 (621.03)	v	0.6693	0.5968	0.5218	0.4421	0.3986	0.3502	0.2907	0.2760	0.2597	0.2407	.....	.....
	h	1835.0	1717.3	1600.4	1480.8	1417.4	1347.2	1260.3	1238.5	1214.0	1185.1	....	....
	s	1.7786	1.7185	1.6520	1.5752	1.5301	1.4765	1.4044	1.3855	1.3638	1.3377	....	....
2000 (635.82)	v	0.6011	0.5352	0.4668	0.3935	0.3532	0.3074	0.2489	0.2337	0.2161	0.1936	.....	.....
	h	1832.5	1714.1	1596.1	1474.5	1409.2	1335.5	1240.0	1214.8	1184.9	1145.6	....	....
	s	1.7660	1.7055	1.6384	1.5603	1.5139	1.4576	1.3783	1.3564	1.3300	1.2945	....	....
2500 (668.13)	v	0.4784	0.4244	0.3678	0.3061	0.2710	0.2294	0.1686	0.1484	.....	.....	.....	.....
	h	1826.2	1706.1	1585.3	1458.4	1387.8	1303.6	1176.8	1132.3	....	....	....	....
	s	1.7389	1.6775	1.6088	1.5273	1.4772	1.4127	1.3073	1.2687	....	....	....	....
3000 (695.36)	v	0.3966	0.3505	0.3018	0.2476	0.2159	0.1760	0.0984	.....	.....	.....	.....	.....
	h	1819.9	1698.0	1574.3	1441.8	1365.0	1267.2	1060.7	....	....	....	....	....
	s	1.7163	1.6540	1.5837	1.4984	1.4439	1.3690	1.1966	....	....	....	....	....
3206.2 (705.40)	v	0.3703	0.3267	0.2806	0.2288	0.1981	0.1583	.....	.....	.....	.....	.....	.....
	h	1817.2	1694.6	1569.8	1434.7	1355.2	1250.5	....	....	....	....	....	....
	s	1.7080	1.6452	1.5742	1.4874	1.4309	1.3508	....	....	....	....	....	....
3500	v	0.3381	0.2977	0.2546	0.2058	0.1762	0.1364	0.0306	.....	.....	.....	.....	.....
	h	1813.6	1689.8	1563.3	1424.5	1340.7	1224.9	780.5	....	....	....	....	....
	s	1.6968	1.6336	1.5615	1.4723	1.4127	1.3241	0.9515	....	....	....	....	....
4000	v	0.2943	0.2581	0.2192	0.1743	0.1462	0.1052	0.0287	.....	.....	.....	.....	.....
	h	1807.2	1681.2	1552.1	1406.8	1314.4	1174.8	763.8	....	....	....	....	....
	s	1.6795	1.6154	1.5417	1.4482	1.3827	1.2757	0.9347	....	....	....	....	....
4500	v	0.2602	0.2273	0.1917	0.1500	0.1226	0.0798	0.0276	.....	.....	.....	.....	.....
	h	1800.9	1673.5	1540.8	1388.4	1286.5	1113.9	753.5	....	....	....	....	....
	s	1.6640	1.5990	1.5235	1.4253	1.3529	1.2204	0.9235	....	....	....	....	....
5000	v	0.2329	0.2027	0.1696	0.1303	0.1036	0.0593	0.0268	.....	.....	.....	.....	.....
	h	1794.5	1665.3	1529.5	1369.5	1256.5	1047.1	746.4	....	....	....	....	....
	s	1.6499	1.5839	1.5066	1.4034	1.3231	1.1622	0.9152	....	....	....	....	....
5500	v	0.2106	0.1825	0.1516	0.1143	0.0880	0.0463	0.0262	.....	.....	.....	.....	.....
	h	1788.1	1657.0	1518.2	1349.3	1224.1	985.0	741.3	....	....	....	....	....
	s	1.6369	1.5699	1.4908	1.3821	1.2930	1.1093	0.9090	....	....	....	....	....

* Abridged from "Thermodynamic Properties of Steam," by Joseph H. Keenan and Frederick G. Keyes, Copyright, 1937, by Joseph H. Keenan and Frederick G. Keyes.

Published by John Wiley & Sons, Inc., New York.

INDEX

Absolute temperature, 70
Adiabatic process, 61, 62
Advantages, of gas turbines, 48–50
of steam turbines, 1, 2
Aircraft gas turbines, 33–35
Airfoil, 154–158
angle of attack, 157
camber, camber line, and camber angle, 244
characteristics, 157, 245
drag and drag coefficient, 158
elements of, 243–245
lift and lift coefficient, 157, 158, 247
AIEE-ASME preferred standard steam turbine, 345–348
Angular momentum, 184
Applications, of gas turbine, 31–33, 36, 37
of steam turbine, 2
Armengaud and Lemale, 29, 30
Aspect ratio, 248
Axial-flow compressors, 371–399
axial velocity distribution, 391
blade angles, 388, 389
blade loading, 382–385
as function, of exit angle, 385
of pressure coefficient, 384
of work coefficient, 384
blading efficiency, 376–380
comparison with reaction turbine, 371
degree of reaction, 377, 378
drag coefficient, 387
effect of Mach and Reynolds numbers on efficiency, 389
energy transfers, 204, 205
flow coefficient, 377, 378
incidence angle, 386, 387
lift coefficient, 385–388
nonsymmetric stage, 373, 374
performance characteristics, 393
pressure coefficient, 381
solidity, 385, 386
stage characteristics, 372–376
stagnation-pressure rise, 379
stagnation-temperature rise, 205
stalling, 387

Axial-flow compressors, static-pressure rise, 379
supersonic, 392
symmetric stage, 373, 374
three-dimensional considerations, 390
vortex stage, 375
work coefficient, 381, 382

Back-pressure turbine, 11
Barber, J., 29
Bearings, 4, 5
losses in, 282
Beattie-Bridgeman equation of state, 53
constants for, 54
Berry, C. H., 415
Blades for turbines, 3
aspect ratio, 248
cooling, 297–298
efficiency, 189, 190, 200, 210
fastenings, 293–296
bulb and shank, 293, 294
Christmas-tree, 295, 296
straddle, 295
straddle-T, 294
T-shaped, 295
friction factor, 192
section orientation, 268
stresses, 284–290
bending, 285–288
centrifugal, 284, 285
vibration, 288–291
velocity, 188, 189
work, 189, 190
(See also Impulse-turbine blades; Reaction blades)
Boundary of a system, 51, 56
Boundary-layer separation, 159, 160
Boyle's law, 53
Brayton cycle, 94–102
ideal, 94–96
compared with Carnot cycle, 96
with regeneration, 99
irreversible, 96–102
inlet temperature, 98
with regeneration, 100–102

Brayton cycle, irreversible, thermal efficiency, 97, 99
Buckets, 3, 6
(*See also* Blades for turbines)
Buckingham's π theorem, 359
Bulk modulus, 119

Callendar equation of state, 55
Camber, 244
Camber angle, 244
Camber line, 244
Carnot cycle, 66–70, 83, 93
Carry-over loss coefficient, 231, 233
Carry-over velocity, 216–219
Cascade principle, 250
Casing, gas-turbine, 306
  joints, 306, 307
  steam-turbine, 3, 304–306
Centrifugal compressors, 349–370
  adiabatic efficiency, 354
  diffuser, 351, 356, 357
    effect of off-design, 357
  effect of compressibility, 354–356
  energy transfers, 352, 353
  losses, 353, 354
  Mach number, 354–356, 365–369
  operation, 350–352
  performance, 358–361
  pressure coefficient, 361, 362
  prewhirl, 357, 358
  slip factor, 362, 366
  surging, 360, 362, 363
  velocity diagrams, 351, 352
Ceramic blades, 303, 304
Characteristics, method of, 129
Charles' law, 53
Choking of flow, 146
Circulation, 156, 185
  for blades, 247
  relation of momentum, 185, 186
Circulatory flow, 153, 154
Classification, of gas turbines, 32–48
  of steam turbines, 7, 9, 10, 14, 19–27
Clausius equation of state, 55
Clausius-Clapeyron equation, 80, 81
Closed-cycle gas turbines, 41, 43, 44
  advantages and disadvantages, 112, 113
  semiclosed cycle, 111
Coefficient of lift, 157, 158, 247, 385–388
Combustion, 401–432
  air-fuel ratio, 425, 427
  carbon-preferential burning, 423

Combustion, chain reactions, 424
  chemical equilibrium, 405
  combustibles in fuels, 422
  dissociation, 418
  enthalpy and internal-energy tables, 414
  entropy of ideal-gas mixtures, 404
  equations, 401–403
  equilibrium constants, 420
  excess air, 427
  flame propagation, 426
  fuels, 422–423
  Gibbs theorem, 405
  heat of, 411
  heat of reaction, 408, 409, 411, 412
  hydrogen-preferential burning, 423
  hydroxylation, 423
  inflammability range, 426
  laws of gas mixtures, 403, 404
  Le Châtelier principle, 410
  mechanism of, 423, 424
  mole fraction, 424
  physical characteristics of reactive mixtures, 424
  pressure losses, 427
  reaction, rate of, 426
  reactions involving solids and liquids, 411
  stability, 425
  third law, 411
  turbulence, 426
  (*See also* Combustor)
Combustor, 427–432
  combustion chamber, 429–432
  efficiency, 428
  fuel injection, 428,
  mixing chamber, 431
  primary air, 429, 431
  requirements, 427, 428
  secondary air, 429, 431
  (*See also* Combustion)
Compressibility burble, 160
Compressor, Elliott-Lysholm, 39, 41
  (*See also* Axial-flow compressors; Centrifugal compressors)
Condition line, 211
Conductivity of air and gas-turbine gases, 453
Continuity equation, 117
Corrosion, 301
Creep, 299, 300
Critical pressure ratio, 164–166

Curtis, C. G., 1
Curtis stage, description, 7, 8
Cycle, Brayton (see Brayton cycle)
Carnot, 66–70, 83, 93
Joule (see Brayton cycle)
Rankine, 84, 85
regenerative steam, 86
reheat steam, 86
reversible, 66
Stirling, 102–104
Cycle efficiency, effect of temperature
and pressure on, 87

Damping, 301
De Laval stage, description, 7, 8
Diaphragm, 4
Diesel engine, 1, 50
Dieterici equation of state, 55
Dimensional analysis, 358–361, 393–394,
441–442, 463
Disc friction, 271, 272
Disc stresses, 291–293
Discharge coefficient, 174, 175
Dissociation, 418
Drag, 158
coefficient of, 158
induced, 158
Ductility, 300
Dumbell, J., 29

Efflux angle, 222–229
Egli, A., 275, 276, 307
Elliott-Lysholm compressor, 39, 41
Emergency trip, 6
Endurance, 300, 301
Energy changes in a fluid, 186
Energy equation for isentropic compressible flow, 118
Energy transfers, in axial-flow compressors, 204, 205
in centrifugal compressors, 352, 353
Engine efficiency, 91
Enthalpy, 64
Entropy, 70
Equation of state, Beattie-Bridgeman, 53, 54
Callendar, 55
Clausius, 55
Dieterici, 55
van der Waals', 54
Ericsson cycle, ideal, 104–105
for closed-cycle plant, 111

Ericsson cycle, ideal, compared with Carnot cycle, 105
thermal efficiency, 105
Euler equation, 185

Fanning friction factor, 142, 143
Fanno equation, 124, 144
Fanno line, 145, 146
First law, 57
Flow, choking of, 146
circulatory, 153, 154
compressible, heat transfer in, 147–151
with friction, 140–147
isentropic, in passages of nonuniform
cross section, 136–139
in nozzles, 151–153
critical pressure ratio, 152
critical velocity ratio, 152
deflection of, at exit, 229
energy equation, 151
maximum mass rate of, 153
of supersaturated steam in, 169
supersonic, 130, 131
Forced vortex, 154, 239
Free piston, 46–48
Free vortex, 154, 238–239
Frequency factors, 290

Gas tables, 473–487
Gases, air and gas-turbine, conductivity
of, 453
viscosity of, 443
enthalpy and internal-energy tables,
414
thermodynamic properties of, 76
Gay-Lussac law, 53
Gear, turning, 4
Generator, 344, 345
Gibbs function, 73
Gibbs theorem, 405
Goudie, W. J., 212n., 268
Governing of steam turbines, 4, 311–330
centrifugal, 314, 315
direct-acting, 312, 313
emergency, 327–330
hydraulic, 321
nozzle, 318
pressure-responsive, 321–324
principles, 311, 312
servomotors, 316, 318
speed regulation, 314, 315, 324–329
speed-responsive, 312–321

Guides, 3
  (*See also* Blades for turbines)

Heat exchanger (*see* Regenerators)
Heat rate, 90
Heat transfer, 433–447
  in compressible flow, 147–151
  conduction, 433, 435, 436
  conductivity of air and gas-turbine
    gases, 453
  convection, 434–436
  film coefficient, 441, 442
  friction factor, 444
  mean temperature difference, 438, 439
  Nusselt number, 444
  radiation, 434
  Reynolds number, 444, 448
Helmholtz function, 73
Holzwarth, H., 31

Impulse force defined, 187
Impulse stage, 195–197
  maximum efficiency, 194, 195
  work and efficiency, 192–195
Impulse-turbine blades, construction, 230
  effect of off-design operation on angles,
    226
  entrance and exit angles, 225–227
  height, 221–225
  losses in, 230–234
  pitch and width, 219, 220
  profiles, 219
  (*See also* Blades for turbines)
Incidence loss coefficient, 231, 232
Induced drag, 158
Intercooling, 105–109
  actual, 107–109
  advantages and disadvantages, 108
  effect on thermal efficiency, 108
  optimum pressures, 107
Isentropic flow in passages of nonuniform
    cross section, 136–139

Joule cycle (*see* Brayton cycle)
Joule's law, 60
Joule-Thomson experiment, 63

Kutta-Joukowsky equation, 156

Lacing wires, 297
Leakage, 273, 274
Leakage efficiency, 280, 281

Leakage losses, 275, 276
Leaving loss, 218
Le Châtelier principle, 410
Lees equation of state, 55
Lift, 157, 158, 247
  for blade, 247
  coefficient of, 157, 158, 247, 385–388
Locomotive gas turbine, 38, 39
Loss coefficient, incidence, 231, 232
Losses, in bearings, 282
  in impulse-turbine blades, 230–234
  leakage, 275, 276
  leaving, 218
  pressure, in combustion, 427
    in regenerators, 445
  radiation, in turbines, 283
  reaction-blade, 238
  secondary flow, 251
  supersaturation, 171
  windage, 272, 273

Mach angle, 122
Mach number, 121
Mach waves, 121
Marine gas turbines, 39, 40
Matching turbine and compressor char-
    acteristics, 463
Maxwell equations, 74
Mean effective temperature, 85n.
Mechanical efficiency, 91
Metallurgy, 298–304
  powder, 303
Metals, properties of, 298, 299, 302, 303
  workability of, 303
Mixed staging in turbines, 198, 199
Momentum, angular, 184
  moment of, 182
Momentum equations, 181, 182
Moyer, J. A., 273

Newton's law, 117
Nozzle and blade efficiency, combined,
    195, 201
Nozzles, 2, 161–180
  calculations, 175–179
  characteristics, 163
  critical pressure ratio, 164–166
  discharge coefficient, 174, 175
  efficiency, 168
  flow in (*see* Flow, in nozzles)
  function of, 2
  shock waves in, 172–174

Nozzles, types, 161–165
  underexpansion and overexpansion, 173, 174
  velocity coefficient, 166, 168

Opening coefficient, 228
Overexpansion in nozzles, 173, 174

Parsons, C. A., 1, 29
Parsons number, 337–339
Parsons staging, description, 8
Performance, of gas turbines, 456–472
  aircraft plants, 461–464
  coal-burning plants, 468–470
  dimensionless parameters, 456–458, 463
  marine plants, 470
  matching turbine and compressor characteristics, 463
  starting, 465–466
  stationary power plants, 456, 469–471
  torque characteristics, 464, 465
  turbocompressor performance map, 460
  twin-shaft plant, 461, 470–471
  of steam turbines, 330–348
  automatic extraction, 339–343
  effect on, of initial pressure and temperature, 332–335
  of nozzle governing, 333, 336, 337
  of throttle governing, 330–332
  mixed pressure, 343, 344
  preferred standard, 345–348
Powder metallurgy, 303
Prandtl-Meyer equation, 128, 129
Pressure ratio, critical, 164–166
Profile loss coefficient, 231, 232
Properties of metals, 298, 299, 302, 303
Propjet, 32, 34

Quality factor, 337–339

Radial equilibrium, 239
Radial-flow turbine, 17, 27
Radiation losses in turbines, 283
Rankine cycle, 84, 85
  with superheat, 85
Rarefaction, 123
Rateau staging, description, 8, 9
Rayleigh line, 150
Reaction blades, angles, 235

Reaction blades, gauging, 235
  height, 236, 237
  losses, 238
  pitch, 235
  profiles, 234
  width, 235
  (See also Blades for turbines)
Reaction force defined, 187
Reaction turbine, rotor arrangements, 237
Reaction-turbine stages, characteristics, 6, 199
  maximum efficiency, 202
  velocity diagrams, 199, 200
  velocity ratio, 202
  work and efficiency, 200–202
Regenerative steam cycle, 86
Regenerators, 433–455
  counterflow, 438
  economic aspects, 449
  effectiveness, 447
  LMTD correction factors, 439, 440
  parallel flow, 437
  pressure losses, 445
  tube data, 451
  tube nest arrangements, 442
  types, 437
Reheat factor, definition, 211
  for gas, 214
  relation of, to stage and internal efficiency, 216
    to velocity ratio, 215, 216
  for steam, 215
Reheat gas turbines, 109, 110
  advantages, 110
  effect on thermal efficiency, 110
  optimum pressures, 110
Reheat steam cycle, 86
Relative velocity defined, 188
Rettaliata, J. T., 166, 179
Reversible cycle, 66
Reversible process, 56
Reynolds number defined, 139
Robinson, E. L., 215, 269

Seals, 274–280
  carbon-ring, 277, 278
  end-tightening, 280
  labyrinth, 274, 275
  tip profiling, 280
  water, steam, and air, 278
Second law, 65

Secondary flow losses, 251
Shock, change in state properties through, 125
plane normal, 123–125
Shock polar, 131
transformed, 133
Shock waves, attached and detached, 132, 133
in converging passage, 126
in diverging passage, 126
inclined, 125–134
in nozzles, 172–174
oblique, 125–134
strong, 130–134
Shrouding, 296, 297
Single-airfoil principle, 245–249
limitations of, 250
Solidity factor, 247
Sonic velocity, derivation, 119–121
Stage efficiency, turbine, 209, 210, 283
Stage output, turbine, 283
Staging, Curtis, 8
Parsons, 8
Rateau, 8
simple impulse, 7
Stagnation properties, 134–135
Steady-flow energy equation, 65
Steam rate, 91
Steam tables, 488–495
Stirling cycle, 102–104
with regeneration, 103
thermal efficiency, 103
Stodola, A., 271
Stoltze, F., 30
Streamline theory, 182, 183
Supersaturated steam, 169
Supersaturation losses, 171
Supersonic flow, around inside corners, 130
around outside corners, 131
Supervisory instruments for steam turbines, 309–311

Tangential-flow turbine, 18–20
Taper factors, 286
Temperature, absolute, 70
mean effective, 85n.
Thermal choking, 149
Thermal efficiency of steam cycles, 88–90
Third law, 411
Thrust, 462
Torque, 184

Torque characteristics of gas turbines, 464, 465
Trailing vortices, 159
Transfer of heat (see Heat transfer)
Transverse vibrations, 289
Turbine stages compared for energy-absorbing ability, 202, 203
Turning gear, 4

Underexpansion in nozzles, 173, 174

Valve, throttle, or stop, 4
van der Waals' equation of state, constants for, 54
Velocity, carry-over, 216–219
sonic, derivation, 119–121
Velocity coefficient, 166, 168
Velocity diagrams, axial-flow compressor, 203, 204, 373–376
construction of, 264
50-per cent reaction turbine, 243
free-vortex turbine, 242
impulse-turbine stage, 190–192
nonsymmetric-compressor stage, 373, 374
radial equilibrium, 240–243
reaction-turbine stage, 202
symmetric-compressor stage, 373, 374
vortex-compressor stage, 375
Velocity ratio, definition, 189
isentropic, 208, 209
for optimum efficiency, 197, 198, 202
relationships for, 252–256
Vibrations, 288–291
damping, 301
frequency, 288, 290
modes, 289
transverse, 289
Viscosity of air and gas-turbine gases, 443
Vortex, forced, 154, 239
free, 154, 238–239
Vortices, trailing, 159
Vorticity defined, 153

Waves, Mach, 121
shock (see Shock waves)
Willan's line, 331, 332
Wilson line, 170
Windage losses, 272, 273
Work coefficient, 381, 382
Workability of metals, 303

Yellott, J. I., 38, 39